Contents

Foreword by Zamzam Ibrahim   iv

Introduction   iv

Grant-making charities – their processes
and effectiveness   iv

About this guide   v

How to use this guide   vii

How to identify sources of help – a quick
reference flowchart   viii

How to make an application   ix

Using the application form template for
financial assistance   x

Application form template   xi

About the Directory of Social Change   xiii

General educational needs   3

Local charities   109

Statutory grants and student support   281

Types of school in the UK and their funding   283

Alternative routes to employment:
apprenticeships   287

Company sponsorships   289

Funding for gap-years and overseas
voluntary work   291

Contacts and sources of further information   293

Index   297

Foreword

At the beginning of a new decade, society faces many challenges and uncertainties. Whether we think about the climate emergency, technological change and automation in the workplace, the rising need for social care or our new relationship with the European Union, there will be difficult choices and significant change ahead.

It'll come as no surprise that the National President of NUS believes in the importance of education, but I also passionately believe that expanding and maintaining access to education is essential if we are to understand and adapt to social change and if we are to find the right solutions to the challenges we're facing.

However, it remains the case that further and higher education is out of reach for too many individuals. The barriers to participation in education are many and varied, but a perennial issue is cost. Too often student support is inadequate or simply unavailable, while the cost of accommodation, books and equipment continues to rise.

As National President of NUS, my focus has been on transforming our tertiary education system to ensure it is fully funded, lifelong and accessible to all. No student, whatever their level or mode of study, should feel they cannot afford to take up the opportunity that education represents. I know that such a transformation will take many years and, therefore, while we build public and political support and develop new approaches, it's crucial that students today are aware of the less obvious sources of funding than can unlock education for them.

This is why *The Guide to Educational Grants* is such an important publication. This comprehensive guide enables students, teachers, advisers and anyone else helping those who seek education to understand the enormous range of charitable funding available towards further and higher education in the UK, helping you to get a good idea of what is offered, who is eligible and how to apply. For so many students this funding could make all the difference to them accessing or succeeding in education and, by doing so, move us all one step forward as a society.

One day, I hope the generosity of these funders is no longer necessary, but in the meantime NUS is proud to support DSC in its efforts to bring information to those who need it.

Zamzam Ibrahim,
NUS National President 2019/20

Introduction

Welcome to the sixteenth edition of *The Guide to Educational Grants*. The main objective of this guide is to provide information on grant-making charities that offer financial support for individuals who are in education or training. This guide contains over 800 grant-making charities with a total of £47.2 million available in grants, and has over 100 grant-makers new to this edition. Many of the organisations included also give grants to individuals in need for welfare purposes. These are also featured in the sister guide to this book, *The Guide to Grants for Individuals in Need*, also published in 2020 by the Directory of Social Change (DSC).

This edition of *The Guide to Educational Grants* has a greater emphasis on further education. We have therefore included more sources of scholarships and postgraduate funding. Grants for school uniforms and equipment can now be found in the latest edition of *The Guide to Grants for Individuals in Need*.

Acknowledgements

We would like to offer a special thank you to Zamzam Ibrahim for her contribution to this introduction.

We are extremely grateful to many people, including charity trustees, staff, volunteers and others, who have helped compile this guide. To name them all individually would be impossible.

How to give feedback to us

The research for this guide was undertaken as carefully and thoroughly as we were able, but there will still be relevant charities that we have missed and some of the information may be incomplete or will become out of date. If you come across omissions or mistakes in this guide, please let us know so we can rectify them. An email to DSC's Research Department (research@dsc.org.uk) is all that is needed. We are also always looking for ways to improve our guides and would appreciate any comments, positive or negative, about this guide. We welcome suggestions on what other information would be useful for inclusion when we research for the next edition.

Grant-making charities: their processes and effectiveness

DSC has a vision of an independent voluntary sector at the heart of social change. Based upon this vision and our experience of researching this publication for over 25 years, we would like to suggest some ways in which charities that give grants to individuals could seek to encourage greater fairness and more effective practices in grant-making. We suggest that they do the following:

▷ Seek to collaborate with others that have similar objectives. By sharing knowledge and best practice,

2020/21

THE GUIDE TO

EDUCATIONAL GRANTS

16th edition

Ian Pembridge

Additional research by:
Mairéad Bailie, Rebecca Eddington,
María Alejandra Puerta Reyes,
Lauren Shaw, Jessica Threlfall
and Judith Turner.

dsc
directory of social change

Published by the Directory of Social Change (Registered Charity no. 800517 in England and Wales)

Head office: Resource for London, 352 Holloway Road, London N7 6PA

Northern office: Suite 103, 1 Old Hall Street, Liverpool L3 9HG

Tel: 020 7697 4200

Visit www.dsc.org.uk to find out more about our books, subscription funding websites and training events. You can also sign up for e-newsletters so that you're always the first to hear about what's new.

The publisher welcomes suggestions and comments that will help to inform and improve future versions of this and all of our titles. Please give us your feedback by emailing publications@dsc.org.uk.

First published 1988
Second edition 1992
Third edition 1994
Fourth edition 1996
Fifth edition 1998
Sixth edition 2000
Seventh edition 2002
Eighth edition 2004
Ninth edition 2006
Tenth edition 2009
Eleventh edition 2011
Twelfth edition 2013
Thirteenth edition 2014
Fourteenth edition 2016
Fifteenth edition 2018
Sixteenth edition 2020

ISBN 978–1–78482–063–3

British Library Cataloguing in Publication Data
A catalogue record for this book is available from the British Library

Cover and text design by Kate Griffith
Typeset by Marlinzo Services, Frome
Printed and bound in the UK by Page Bros, Norwich

organisations can contribute towards improving the wider grant-making landscape.

▸ Do as much as possible to decrease the amount of ineligible applications they receive. This is a joint responsibility with applicants, who should make sure that they read criteria carefully and should not apply to charities for funding for which they are not eligible. However, grant-makers should facilitate this by ensuring that eligibility criteria and application guidelines are transparent and easily available. Our research suggests that a growing number of charities choose to move towards electronic application forms and also sometimes consider a two-stage application process. Many willingly offer help and guidance with filling in the application form.

▸ Ensure, where they are local, that they are very well known within their area of benefit by writing to local Citizens Advice, local authorities, schools and other educational establishments and community centres. As made clear by the comments of the charity trustees during our research, an effective measure of raising the organisation's profile remains word of mouth, particularly with smaller charities. Ideally charities should aim to ensure that needs can be met as rapidly as possible, for example by empowering the clerk or a small number of trustees to make small emergency grants. If trustees can only meet twice a year to consider applications, these should cover the following peak times: in May to June when people are running out of money at the end of the academic year, or looking ahead to funding courses beginning in September; and November to December when people who have started their courses have a much clearer picture of how much money they need.

▸ Form clear policies on whom they can support and what they can provide, targeting those most in need.

About this guide

What charities are included?

We have included in this guide grant-making charities that give or have the potential to give:

▸ At least £500 a year in educational grants (most give considerably more)

▸ Funding for post-16 education, including postgraduate level. Some of the funders included may also give for primary school and preschool education ('education' is defined in its loosest sense, and therefore includes all types of vocational education and training, extracurricular activities and personal or professional development)

▸ Grants to students of more than one educational establishment

Almost 20% of the charities in this guide also give grants to individuals in need for the relief of poverty and hardship (these, along with many others, are included in the guide's sister publication *The Guide to Grants for*

Individuals in Need). The charities in this guide often additionally support educational charities, youth organisations, community groups and educational establishments. However, the information given relates only to that which is relevant for individuals. *The Directory of Grant Making Trusts*, also published by DSC, contains funding sources for organisations.

How charities are ordered

The grant-making charities in this guide are listed in five sections. The majority of grant-makers featured in the first four sections operate nationally, with criteria defined by something other than the geographical area of the applicant, although there are a few exceptions.

The five sections are:

▸ General educational charities (for example, general educational needs, further and higher education, overseas students and study abroad/placements, personal development, vocational training and apprenticeships)

▸ National charities classified by subject

▸ National charities classified by type of beneficiary

▸ National charities classified by occupation or parent/guardian occupation

▸ Local charities (grant-makers which support individuals living in specific geographical areas – see page 109 for details about how to use this section)

What are grants given for?

Generally, the charities in this guide offer one-off grants for a specific purpose or recurrent support for the duration of the individual's course or project. In some instances support may be given for a specific number of years or, in some rare instances, throughout the individual's education. The majority of the support given is intended to be supplementary and applicants will often need to secure money from different sources. However, small costs of necessities or sometimes even bigger projects may be covered in full. A handful of the grant-makers listed may offer low-interest or interest-free loans as well.

Grant-makers in this guide can give supplementary help with, mostly, small grants for:

▸ Books, training materials, equipment, tools and specialist instruments

▸ Small-scale fees associated with the course or training, such as exam, registration or workshop fees

▸ Living expenses and maintenance costs or accommodation

▸ Travel costs both in the UK and overseas, including for overseas study, educational trips, voluntary and gap-year experience, field studies or research purposes

▸ Course, school or training fees, particularly those for professional, technical or vocational courses and qualifications

▸ Extracurricular activities aimed at the physical and social development of the individual, including sports, outdoor activities, music (including the purchase or the loan of musical instruments) and arts

- Specialist equipment related to disability that cannot be funded from statutory sources
- Childcare costs, particularly for mature students
- Expenses associated with apprenticeships or entering a trade or profession (this can sometimes include business start-up costs)

Supporting information and advice

This guide also contains supporting information and advice on:

- Statutory grants and student support (see page 281)
- Types of school in the UK and their funding (see page 283)
- Alternative routes to employment: apprenticeships (see page 287)
- Company sponsorships (see page 289)
- Funding for gap-years and overseas voluntary work (see page 291)
- Contacts and sources of further information (see page 293)

How to use this guide

Below is a typical charity record, showing the format we have used to present the information on each of the charities.

On the following page is a flowchart. We recommend that you follow the order indicated in the flowchart to look at each section of the guide and find charities that are relevant to you. You can also use the information in the sections 'About this guide' and 'How to make an application' to help inform your applications.

The Fictitious Charity

£ £24,000 (2017/18)

Correspondent: Ms I. M. Helpful, Charity Administrator, 7 Pleasant Road, London SN0 0ZZ (tel: 020 7123 4567; email: admin@fictitious.org.uk)

 www.fictitious.org.uk

CC number: 112234

Eligibility
Children or young people up to the age of 25 who are in need. Preference is given to children from single-parent families and/or those who come from a disadvantaged family background.

Types of grant
Small one-off grants of up to £250 for a wide range of needs, including books, equipment and educational trips in the UK and abroad. Grants are also available for childcare costs.

Exclusions
No grants are given for private school or university fees.

Applications
Applications can be made using a form available from the correspondent. They can be submitted directly by the individual, or by the parent or guardian for those under 18. Applications are considered in January, April, July and October.

Financial information
Year end	05/04/2018
Income	£521,000
Total expenditure	£574,000

Further financial information
The charity made grants to 251 individuals during 2017/18.

Other information
The charity also gives relief-in-need grants to individuals and supports charities working with children and young people in need.

Sources of information
Accounts; annual report; Charity Commission record; funder's website.

Grant total
This shows the total (or estimated) amount given in grants during the financial year in question.

Correspondent
This shows the name and contact details of the charity's correspondent. In many cases, this correspondent is the same contact listed on the Charity Commission's online register. However, in cases where we could find a more appropriate correspondent on the charity's website, their name has been included here instead.

Charity Commission number
This is the number given to a charity upon registration with the Charity Commission for England and Wales, Charity Commission for Northern Ireland or the Office of the Scottish Charity Regulator. A small number of the grant-makers detailed in this guide are not registered charities and so do not have a Charity Commission number.

Eligibility
This states who is eligible to apply for a grant. For example, criteria can be based on place of residence, age, subject studied or occupation.

Types of grant
This section specifies whether the charity gives one-off or recurrent grants, the size of grants given and for which items or costs grants are actually given. This section will also indicate if the charity runs various schemes.

Exclusions
This field gives information, where available, on what the charity will not fund.

Applications
This section includes information on how to apply, who should make the application (i.e. the individual or a third party) and when to submit your request.

Financial information
This section includes the charity's financial year end and annual income and expenditure.

Further financial information
This field provides additional information that may be of interest, such as the number of grants made each year.

Other information
This section contains other helpful or interesting information about the charity.

Sources of information
This details sources where we found the information used in the record.

How to identify sources of help – a quick reference flowchart

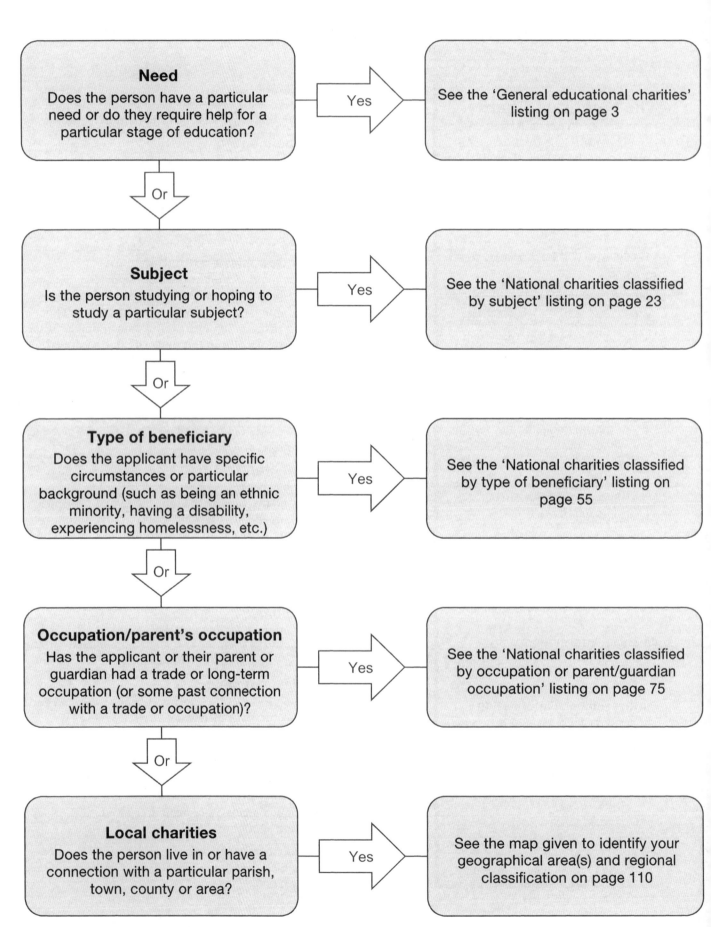

Need
Does the person have a particular need or do they require help for a particular stage of education?

Yes → See the 'General educational charities' listing on page 3

Or

Subject
Is the person studying or hoping to study a particular subject?

Yes → See the 'National charities classified by subject' listing on page 23

Or

Type of beneficiary
Does the applicant have specific circumstances or particular background (such as being an ethnic minority, having a disability, experiencing homelessness, etc.)

Yes → See the 'National charities classified by type of beneficiary' listing on page 55

Or

Occupation/parent's occupation
Has the applicant or their parent or guardian had a trade or long-term occupation (or some past connection with a trade or occupation)?

Yes → See the 'National charities classified by occupation or parent/guardian occupation' listing on page 75

Or

Local charities
Does the person live in or have a connection with a particular parish, town, county or area?

Yes → See the map given to identify your geographical area(s) and regional classification on page 110

How to make an application

This section gives you some information on how to make an application, with additional tips from funders' perspectives.

1. Exhaust other sources of funds

All sources of statutory funding should have been applied for and/or received before applying to a charity. Applications, therefore, should include details of these sources and any refusals. Where statutory funding has been received but is inadequate, an explanation that this is the case should be made. A supporting reference from a relevant agency may also be helpful.

If the applicant attends an educational establishment, it should also have been approached to see if there are any funds that may give financial support or if a reduction in fees is available.

'The best way to get help for individual funding is to start by helping yourself – try every avenue to raise as much of the money yourself before and while you approach others for a contribution to your cause. If they can see how determined you are and how hard you've worked already, they'll naturally feel motivated to help you find the remainder.'

BBC Performing Arts Fund

Other possible sources of funding and advice are listed on page 293.

2. Check eligibility criteria

Submitting ineligible applications is the biggest mistake that applicants make. A charity cannot fund you if you are not eligible and you merely waste both your own and the charity's time and resources by applying. If you are in any doubt, contact the grant-maker for clarification. Please remember that many charities are run by volunteers and their time is particularly valuable.

'Always read carefully a charity's criteria for eligibility. We, for example, are only allowed to help the children of actors, but three quarters of the applications we receive do not match this basic requirement. You are wasting your time and hopes by applying to a trust which clearly is not allowed to help you.'

The Actors' Children's Trust

3. Follow the application procedures precisely

Wherever they are available, we have included application procedures in the records; applicants should take great care to follow these. If there is an application form, use it! Please read any guidelines thoroughly and take note of deadlines. Some charities can consider applications throughout the year whereas others may meet monthly, quarterly or just once a year. Very urgent applications can sometimes be considered between the main meetings. Make sure that the appropriate person submits the application – this could be the individual, their parent or guardian or a professional such as a social worker.

Evidence from our research shows that the majority of organisations welcome initial contact before a full application is made, so if you are unsure about anything, get in touch with them.

4. Give details of any extenuating or unforeseen circumstances

Potential applicants should think carefully about any circumstances which put them at a disadvantage from other families or students, such as coming from a low-income background, being in receipt of state benefits, being a single parent, having a health problem or disability and so on. Where relevant, try to show how the circumstances you are now in could not have been foreseen (for example, illness, family difficulties, loss of job and so on). Charities are often more willing to help if financial difficulties are a result of unforeseen circumstances rather than a lack of forward planning. The funding in this guide is aimed at those facing the largest number of barriers to education or training.

5. Give clear, honest details about your circumstances, including any savings, capital or compensation

Most trustees will consider the applicant's savings when they are awarding a grant, although sometimes this does not need to affect the trustees' calculations. In circumstances where you are certain that your savings are not relevant to grant calculations, you should explain this in the application.

'Be open and honest about your circumstances. We have to ensure that we have all the information we need to put your case forward. If essential details emerge at a later date, this can affect your application. Be honest about how much you want to apply for and don't ask for the most expensive item. If you show that you've done your research, then that helps us too.'

Fashion and Textile Children's Trust

6. Tailor the application to suit the particular charity

For example, if an application is being made to a trade charity on behalf of a child whose parent had lengthy service in that particular trade, then a detailed description (and, where possible, supporting documentation) of the parent's service would be highly relevant.

7. Ask for a suitable amount

Ask for an amount that the organisation is able to give. If a charity only makes small grants, try asking for help with books, travel, childcare expenses and similar costs, and apply for fees elsewhere.

8. Mention applications to other charities

Explain that other charities are being approached, when this is the case, and state that any surplus money raised will be returned.

9. Offer to supply references

For example, from a teacher, college tutor, support worker and/or another independent person. If the individual has relevant disabilities or medical needs, then a report from a GP would be necessary.

10. Be honest and realistic, not moralising and emotional

Some applicants try to morally bribe trustees into supporting the application, or launch into tirades against the current political regime. It is best to confine your application to clear and simple statements of fact.

11. Be clear, concise and provide sufficient detail

Give as much relevant information as possible, in the most precise way. For example, 'Place of birth' on an application form is sometimes answered with 'Great Britain', but if the charity only gives grants in Liverpool, 'Great Britain' is not a detailed enough answer and the application will be delayed pending further information. Make sure that you write clearly and do not use jargon so that your application is easily understood.

12. Say thank you

Charitable organisations generally like to be kept informed of how their grants have made a difference. It is also important to keep in touch if you are in need of recurrent funding. Feedback also helps charities in their future grant-giving.

> 'Don't consider the moment the grant appears in your bank account as the end of your relationship with the grant-maker – try to provide updates on the work the grant has helped you to undertake, including photos, videos and other resources.'

Royal Geographical Society

Remember to thank grant-makers for their support and let them know how their funding has helped.

Using the application form template for financial assistance

Following on from this is a general purpose application form. It has been compiled with the help of the Gaddum Centre. It can be photocopied and used whenever convenient and should enable applicants (and agencies or people applying on behalf of individuals) to state clearly the basic information required by most grant-makers.

Alternatively, applicants can use it as a checklist of points to include in the letter. Applicants using this form should note the following things in particular:

1   It is worth sending a short letter setting out the request in brief, even when using this application form.

2   Because this form is designed to be useful to a wide range of people in need, not all the information asked for in the form will be relevant to every application. For example, not all applicants are in receipt of state benefits, nor do all applicants have hire purchase commitments. In such cases, applicants should write N/A (not applicable) in the box or on the line in question.

3   Similarly, if you do not have answers for all the questions at the time of applying (for example, if you have applied to other charities and are still waiting for a reply), you should write 'Pending' under the question: 'Have you written to any other charities? What was the outcome of the application?'

4   The first page is relevant to all applicants, but the second page is only relevant to people applying for school or college fees. If you are applying for clothing or books for a schoolchild, then it may be worth filling in only the first page of the form and submitting a covering letter outlining the reasons for the application.

5   Filling out the weekly income and expenditure parts of the form can be worrying or even distressing. Expenditure when itemised in this way is usually far higher than people expect. It is probably worth filling out this form with the help of a professional.

6   You should always keep a copy of the completed form in case the trust has a specific query.

7   This form should not be used where the trust has its own form, which must be completed.

Application form template

Purpose for which grant is sought	Amount sought from this application £
Applicant (name)	Occupation/School
Address	
Telephone no.	
Date of birth	Age	Place of birth
Nationality	Religion (if any)

☐ Single ☐ Married ☐ Divorced ☐ Partnered ☐ Separated ☐ Widow/er

Family details: Name	Age	Occupation/School
Parents/ Partner	. . . .	. . . .
Brothers/Sisters/ Children	. . . . . .	. . . .
. . . .	. . . . . .	. . . .
. . . .	. . . . . .	. . . .
Others (specify)	. . . . . .	. . . .

Income (weekly)	£	p	Expenditure (weekly – *excluding course fees*)	£	p
Father's/husband's wage	. . . . . .		Rent/mortgage	. . . . . .	
Mother's/wife's wage	. . . . . .		Council tax	. . . . . .	
Partner's wage	. . . . . .		Water rate	. . . . . .	
Income Support	. . . . . .		Electricity	. . . . . .	
Jobseeker's Allowance	. . . . . .		Gas	. . . . . .	
Employment and Support Allowance	. . . . . .		Other fuel	. . . . . .	
Pension Credit	. . . . . .		Insurance	. . . . . .	
Working Tax Credit	. . . . . .		Fares/travel	. . . . . .	
Child Tax Credit	. . . . . .		Household expenses (food, laundry, etc.)	. . . . . .	
Child Benefit	. . . . . .		Clothing	. . . . . .	
Housing Benefit	. . . . . .		School dinners	. . . . . .	
Attendance Allowance	. . . . . .		Childcare fees	. . . . . .	
Disability Living Allowance	. . . . . .		Hire purchase commitments	. . . . . .	
Universal Credit	. . . . . .		Telephone	. . . . . .	
Personal Independence Payments	. . . . . .		TV rental	. . . . . .	
Maintenance payments	. . . . . .		TV licence	. . . . . .	
Pensions	. . . . . .		Other expenditure (specify)	. . . . . .	
Other income (specify)	. . . . . .		. . . .	. . . . . .	
. . . .	. . . . . .		. . . .	. . . . . .	
. . . .	. . . . . .		. . . .	. . . . . .	
. . . .	. . . . . .		. . . .	. . . . . .	

Total weekly income £ [   ]   **Total weekly expenditure** £ [   ]

Name of school/college/university:

Address

Course:

Is the course ☐ full-time? ☐ part-time?

Date of starting course: | Date of finishing course:

Name of local education authority:

Have you applied for a grant? ☐ YES ☐ NO

What was the outcome of the application?

Give details of any other grants or scholarships awarded:

Have you applied to your school/college/university for help? ☐ YES ☐ NO

What was the outcome of the application?

Have you applied to any other charities? ☐ YES ☐ NO

What was the outcome of the application?

Have you applied for any loans? ☐ YES ☐ NO

What was the outcome of the application?

How much are your school/college fees?

£

Have they been paid in full? ☐ YES ☐ NO

If NO, please give details:

Other costs (e.g. books, clothing, equipment, travel, etc.):

How much money do you need to complete the course? £

Examinations passed and other qualifications

Previous employment (with dates)

Any other relevant information (please continue on separate sheet if necessary)

Signature: | **Date:**

About the Directory of Social Change

At the Directory of Social Change (DSC), we believe that the world is made better by people coming together to serve their communities and each other. For us, an independent voluntary sector is at the heart of that social change and we exist to support charities, voluntary organisations and community groups in the work they do. Our role is to:

- **Provide practical information** on a range of topics from fundraising to project management in both our printed publications and e-books
- **Offer training** through public courses, events and in-house services
- **Research funders** and maintain a subscription database, *Funds Online*, with details on funding from grant-making charities, companies and government sources
- **Offer bespoke research** to voluntary sector organisations in order to evaluate projects, identify new opportunities and help make sense of existing data
- **Stimulate debate and campaign** on key issues that affect the voluntary sector, particularly to champion the concerns of smaller charities

We are a registered charity ourselves but we self-fund most of our work. We charge for services, but cross-subsidise those which charities particularly need and cannot easily afford.

Visit our website **www.dsc.org.uk** to see how we can help you to help others and have a look at **www.fundsonline.org.uk** to see how DSC could improve your fundraising. Alternatively, call our friendly team at **020 7697 4200** to chat about your needs or drop us a line at **cs@dsc.org.uk**.

National and general sources of help

There are a number of grant-makers which do not fall into any specific category; these appear in the first group under 'General educational charities'. The other records in this section are arranged into three groups: 1) classified by subject, 2) classified by beneficiary, and 3) classified by occupation of applicant or parent/guardian. Charities appear in full in the section that is most relevant (usually the section which occurs first) and are then cross-referenced.

This breakdown is designed to be the easiest way to identify charities which might be of relevance and as such we have attempted to make the terms as specific as possible. However, there is some crossover between sections and a number of categories might be relevant depending on personal circumstances.

Charities are arranged alphabetically within each category. We always caution against using these lists alone as a guide to sources of money. Read each main record carefully as there will usually be other criteria that must be met. See the advice in the 'How to make an application' section on page ix for more information on how to apply.

General educational charities

Further and higher education 3

Further education 5

Higher education 6

General educational needs 9

Overseas students 14

Personal development/extracurricular activities 15

Postgraduate study 16

Study abroad/placements 19

Vocational training and apprenticeships (both) 20

Classification by subject

Formal sciences 23

Humanities 24

   Arts 25

   History 30

   Languages 30

Law 31

Natural sciences 32

   Biology 32

   Physics 33

Professional and applied sciences 33

   Architecture and design 33

   Business and finance 34

   Education 35

   Engineering 35

   Environment and agriculture 38

   Heritage and conservation 41

   Hospitality 42

   Media, journalism and communication 43

   Medicine 44

   Social work 48

Religion 48

Skilled crafts 50

Social sciences 51

   Cultural studies 53

   Geography 53

Classification by type of beneficiary

Asylum seekers and refugees 55

Children and young people 56

Ethnic minorities in the UK 59

Gender 62

Homelessness 64

Illness and disability 65

Miscellaneous 68

Offenders and ex-offenders 69

Older people 71

Religion 71

   Christianity 71

   Islam 71

   Judaism 72

Specific circumstances 73

Classification by occupation of applicant or parent/guardian

Armed forces 75

Arts and heritage 79

Construction 82

Education and training 83

Engineering 84

Environment 85

Financial services 86

Hospitality 88

Manufacturing 88

1

NATIONAL AND GENERAL SOURCES OF HELP

Maritime 89

Marketing and PR 91

Media 91

Medicine and health 92

Mining and quarrying 96

Other specific industries 97

Public sector 98

Religious occupations 99

Retail 101

Science 102

Service industry 103

Skilled crafts and trades 103

Sports 104

Transport and travel 106

Voluntary sector 106

General educational charities

Further and higher education

Family Action

£123,000 (2017/18)

Correspondent: The Grants Service, 34 Wharf Road, London N1 7GR (tel: 020 7254 6251; email: grants. enquiry@family-action.org.uk)

 www.family-action.org.uk

CC number: 264713

Eligibility

The charity's website states:

Family Action distributes grants to individuals over the age of 14, looking to unlock their educational potential by participating in further education.

Many individuals face challenges during their time at college which may mean they're unable to complete their studies and pursue their future career goals. For others, their life situation may change meaning they need to re-train to gain employment that suits their family life.

Family Action's Educational Grants Programme helps individuals to begin their studies as well as supporting existing students to continue and complete their studies.

Applicants must:

- Be studying at an organisation affiliated to Family Action's Educational Grants Service
- Be studying on a further education course, including pre-access and access
- Be living on a low income (primarily in receipt of benefits), includes low waged

- Have right of residency in the UK or be an asylum seeker (overseas students are ineligible for grants from Family Action)
- Be 14 years or older

Types of grant

Grants can be awarded for the additional costs associated with studying such as clothing, books, travel, examination costs and laptops. The average grant is likely to be in the region of £200 to £300.

Exclusions

Grants are not available for:

- Course fees
- Costs already incurred
- Items provided by the college for the course
- Childcare
- Study outside the UK
- Higher education costs
- Postgraduate study
- Personal expenditure not directly associated with study, such as food, clothing and household bills

Applications

To apply for welfare grants create an account on the Family Action website. Usually responses will take three working days.

To apply for educational grants all applications must be submitted by authorised members of college staff from affiliated organisations.

Family Action do not accept postal applications.

Financial information

Year end	31/03/2018
Income	£23,389,000
Total expenditure	£22,080,000

Other information

Family Action provides a range of advice and support services across the country – see the 'Find us' facility on the charity's website to find the applicant's local office. Support is given to help in the areas of some of the most complex issues, including financial hardship, mental health problems, social isolation, learning disabilities, domestic abuse, or substance misuse and alcohol problems. It aims to improve the lives of children and families, help through the early years of child development and ensure adult mental health and wellbeing.

Sources of information

Accounts; annual report; Charity Commission record; funder's website; guidelines for applicants.

The Fire Service Research and Training Trust

Correspondent: J. B. Lancaster, Secretary, c/o Fire Protection Association, London Road, Morton in Marsh GL56 0RH (tel: 01608 812511; email: info@firetrust.info)

 https://www.firetrust.info

CC number: 234873

Eligibility

People looking for study and/or research opportunities in the following areas:

- Research into the prevention of, protection from, or response to fire and rescue service-related risks posed to businesses or communities
- Securing improvements in appliances of value to the fire and rescue service
- Securing the general efficiency and effectiveness of the UK fire and rescue service as a whole

Fire and rescue service personnel are eligible for funding, particularly for the development of training programmes. For full eligibility criteria, see the trust's website.

Types of grant

Scholarship Award scheme: grants of up to 100% of tuition fees (with a maximum value of £2,500) for any study programme related to the objects of the trust.

Small Project Grant scheme: grants of between £1,000 and £30,000 are awarded for services or training programmes designed for the benefit of the UK fire and rescue service. This grant can be paid to individuals or a suitable host organisation.

Research Fellowship Award scheme: grants of up to 100% of the cost of a postgraduate course (with a maximum value of £20,000) with a research focus into matters that relate to the objects of the trust. Grants are tenable for up to three years or up to six years for part-time study.

Applications

Application forms and guidance notes are available to download from the charity's website.

Financial information

Year end	30/09/2018
Income	£163,000
Total expenditure	£210,400

Further financial information

We could not determine the grant total as grants are paid to universities on an individual's behalf.

Other information

The charity's Research Project Grant scheme is aimed at recognised research organisations for research projects that align with the objects of the trust. The minimum award given is £10,000, up to a maximum of £150,000 over a period four years.

Sources of information

Accounts; annual report; Charity Commission record; funder's website.

Helena Kennedy Foundation

£ £113,100 (2017/18)

Correspondent: Shahida Aslam, Operations Manager, South and City College Birmingham (SCCB), Handsworth Campus, Council House, Soho Road, Birmingham B21 9DP (tel: 0121 644 2406; email: shahida@hkf.org.uk)

 www.hkf.org.uk

CC number: 1074025

Eligibility

Socially, economically or otherwise disadvantaged students attending a publicly funded adult or further education institution in the UK who are progressing to university education may be eligible to apply. Applicants must be intending to undertake a higher diploma or undergraduate degree for the first time. Students taking a gap-year will also be considered, as will students studying part-time or for distance learning degrees. The foundation's Article 26 scheme supports people who have fled persecution and sought asylum in the UK and who wish to study in higher education. The foundation's DISCOVER bursary scheme supports students in college in their first year of a two-year level three study programme at certain further education institutions.

Types of grant

The foundation's main bursary scheme provides a bursary of £2,250 paid by instalments during the student's time in higher education. The foundation also provides successful applicants with: a named contact at the foundation to provide support and advice; access to free training sessions on a range of skills; work-shadowing opportunities; volunteering opportunities.

The Article 26 scheme aims to promote and improve access to higher education for students who have fled persecution and sought asylum in the UK. Bursaries are available through a number of higher education institutions, which are listed on the foundation's website. There are a range of undergraduate and postgraduate opportunities and each university has its own eligibility criteria.

DISCOVER bursaries of £1,000 each are provided to students in the first year of a two-year level three study programme at specific further education institutions, also listed on the foundation's website.

Exclusions

Funding is not available to:

- People who have already undertaken a higher education course
- Postgraduate students
- Students at private institutions
- Previous bursary recipients
- Students at international institutions

Applications

Applications can be made using the form on the foundation's website, where further guidance is also provided. Applications generally open in January and close in April, with successful applicants being notified at the end of July, for awards to be made in September. Applicants will need to demonstrate severe financial hardship and barriers to accessing higher education and all applications must be supported by the applicant's educational institution.

Financial information

Year end	31/05/2018
Income	£217,700
Total expenditure	£213,300

Other information

The foundation also provides mentoring, information, one to one advice, specialist and practical support, skills training and work experience opportunities.

Sources of information

Accounts; annual report; Charity Commission record; funder's website.

The Praebendo Charitable Foundation

£ £3,100 (2017/18)

Correspondent: The Trustees, 22 St Mary's Street, Stamford, Lincolnshire PE9 2DG

CC number: 1137426

Eligibility

Educational grants are awarded to young people under the age of 30 in England, Scotland and Wales who are in higher or further education. Those preparing for entry into a trade of profession upon leaving education are also eligible for support.

Types of grant

Educational grants are made in the form of scholarships and maintenance allowances.

Applications

Apply in writing to the correspondent.

Financial information

Year end	30/09/2018
Income	£294,500
Total expenditure	£12,400

Further financial information

Note: the grant total has been estimated.

Other information

The charity recently purchased a residential home, which is being leased by another charity for the purpose of providing support for people who are currently homeless. The charity also makes grants to organisations and provides recreational facilities and facilities for learning, particularly in music and the arts. Grants are also awarded to individuals for welfare purposes.

Sources of information

Accounts; annual report; Charity Commission record.

Scottish Power Foundation

Correspondent: The Trustees, 320 St Vincent Street, Glasgow G2 5AD

 https://www.scottishpower.com/pages/scottishpower_masters_scholarships.aspx

OSCR number: SC043862

Eligibility

Postgraduates studying for a master's in the following areas:

- Electrical/mechanical/civil/naval engineering
- Renewable/sustainable energy
- Onshore/offshore renewable engineering
- Environmental sciences/climate change
- Computer Science and IT/software engineering/telecoms

A list of all eligible universities can be found on the foundation's website. Those applicants with two GCSEs at grades A to C (4 to 9) in Maths, English and/or a STEM related subject, or with two National 5s in the same subjects, are eligible for the Engineering Pre-Apprenticeship Programme.

Types of grant

Scholarships: monthly allowances of £1,200 are awarded for maintenance costs. The foundation will also cover university enrolment fees. **Engineering Pre-Apprenticeship Programme:** monthly allowances of £200 are given as a contribution towards travel to and from college.

Applications

Applications for master's studies typically open in February. See the foundation's website for further information. Applications for the Pre-Apprenticeship Programme should be submitted via the applicant's local participating college, details of which can be found on the website. If applicants wish to apply to more than one college, contact the Programme Coordinator on 0141 614 2120 or by email susan.ireland@ScottishPower.com.

Financial information

Year end	31/12/2018
Income	£1,170,000
Total expenditure	£1,090,000

Further financial information

Note: we were unable to determine the grant total for 2018. In the previous financial year, a total of £582,000 was awarded in the form of scholarships.

Other information

The foundation runs a variety of apprenticeships, summer placements and graduate programmes. For full details on each scheme, see its website.

Sources of information

Accounts; annual report; funder's website; OSCR record.

Further education

The NFL Trust

 £83,000 (2017/18)

Correspondent: Margot Chaundler, The Administrator, 9 Muncaster Road, London SW11 6NY (tel: 020 7223 7133; email: nfltrust@mail.com)

 www.nfltrust.org.uk

CC number: 1112422

Eligibility

Girls between the ages of 11 and 18 who are attending schools and colleges in the UK, in particular, fee-paying schools are eligible to apply. Priority may be given to students embarking on a course of public examinations in school years 10 and 11, or 12 and 13. Grants are open to girls of all faiths.

Types of grant

Grants are awarded towards the cost of education at fee-paying schools and colleges, including to assist with A-levels. The trust also administers the 'Diana Matthews Trust Fund' which is used towards educational extras, usually from girls who have already received a bursary from the trust. A recent example includes support towards an A-level drama trip.

Exclusions

The trust will not usually provide support towards the cost of boarding.

Applications

Application forms and further details can be requested from the correspondent. Applications should be made in the summer around 18 months ahead of the academic year in which the bursary is needed.

Financial information

Year end	31/08/2018
Income	£81,300
Total expenditure	£190,100

Further financial information

In 2017/18 a total of £165,900 was awarded in bursaries to 45 students. One grant totalling £230 was awarded to one individual through the Diana Matthews Trust Fund towards the cost of a school trip. We estimate that of that total, £83,000 was awarded to pupils for welfare purposes and £83,000 was awarded for educational purposes for students undertaking post-16 education.

Sources of information

Accounts; annual report; Charity Commission record; funder's website.

Thornton-Smith and Plevins Trust

£ £193,100 (2017/18)

Correspondent: Heather Cox, Grants Secretary, 298 Icknield Way, Luton, Bedfordshire LU23 2JS (tel: 01582 611675; email: thornton.smithypt@ntlworld.com)

educational-grants.org/find-charity/thornton-smith-plevins

CC number: 1137196

Eligibility

Support may be given to people over the age of 25 and to individuals of the professional or business classes who have fallen into poverty and are unable to make adequate provision for their retirement or old age.

Currently the trust's primary object is to support sixth form students aged 16 to 19 who are in independent education.

Types of grant

One-off and recurrent grants are awarded according to need.

Grants and loans are given towards school fees and in some cases other educational expenses for pupils studying for A-levels. Scholarships are also given towards educational travel abroad. The family of the young person will be expected to make a contribution towards the school fees.

Applications

Contact the correspondent to request an application form. All applications will be subject to a financial assessment to ensure that there is a need for the trust's support.

Financial information

Year end	31/07/2018
Income	£870,000
Total expenditure	£401,700

Further financial information

In 2017/18 individual grants and loans to assist with school fees and expenses totalled £190,600 and scholarships for educational travel abroad totalled £2,500. Grants were given to 76 individuals and the average grant was £2,500. Note the grant total may include loans. A total of £8,000 was continued for existing elderly beneficiaries.

Other information

This trust was formerly the Thornton-Smith Young People's Trust which, for efficiency, has been combined with the Wilfred Maurice Plevin's Trust, Thornton-Smith Plevins Common Investment Fund and The Thornton-Smith Trust. To be assisted by The Wilfred Maurice Plevins Fund, beneficiaries must also be aged ten or over and be the children of a professional. Beneficiaries older than 25 may only receive assistance from The Thornton-Smith Fund.

Sources of information

Accounts; annual report; Charity Commission record; funder's website.

Higher education

Ameobi Hardship Fund for International Students (AHFIS)

 £4,900 (2017/18)

Correspondent: The Trustees, c/o The Apolstolic Church, 6 Callerton Place, Newcastle upon Tyne NE4 5NQ (email: admin@ahfis.org.uk)

https://www.ahfis.org.uk

CC number: 1138926

Eligibility

International students who are studying or conducting research at an institution of higher education in the UK and whose funding has ceased due to circumstances out of their control are eligible to apply.

Types of grant

Grants up to £1,000 to help students who are near to completing their studies and/or research. The fund's website notes: 'The AHFIS grant is meant to help the beneficiary towards the tuition fees and NOT for personal upkeep.'

Applications

Application forms are available to download from the fund's website and can be submitted by email or post. The trustees meet four times a year to consider applications.

Financial information

Year end	31/03/2018
Income	£5,800
Total expenditure	£5,400

Further financial information

Full accounts were not available to view on the Charity Commission's website due to the charity's low income. We have therefore estimated the grant total based on the charity's total expenditure.

Sources of information

Charity Commission record; funder's website.

The Carnegie Trust for the Universities of Scotland

 £2,680,000 (2017/18)

Correspondent: Prof. Andy Walker, Secretary and Treasurer, Andrew Carnegie House, Pittencrief Street, Dunfermline, Fife KY12 8AW (tel: 01383 724990)

www.carnegie-trust.org

OSCR number: SC015600

Eligibility

The trust supports undergraduate or postgraduate students and academic staff at the 15 Scottish universities (Aberdeen, Abertay, Dundee, Edinburgh, Edinburgh Napier, Glasgow, Glasgow Caledonian, Heriot-Watt, Queen Margaret, Robert Gordon, St Andrews, Stirling, Strathclyde, UHI and West of Scotland). More specific eligibility requirements apply to different categories (very detailed guidelines are available on the trust's website).

Types of grant

The trust offers support through the following awards:

- Undergraduate Tuition Fee Grants – aimed at students required to pay tuition fees themselves due to prior study (usually having dropped out due to ill-health, financial problems or personal circumstance or students who are seeking asylum. Up to £1,820 can be awarded and additional hardship grants are also available
- Vacation Scholarships – undergraduate degree students at a Scottish university demonstrating exceptional merit to undertake a specific programme of independent research over the summer vacation. A stipend is paid at the equivalent of the current Scottish Living Wage rate, per week for 2–12 weeks
- Carnegie-Caledonian PhD Scholarships – a first-class honours undergraduate degree is a pre-requisite. A stipend is paid for living expenses, tuition fees and research allowance
- St Andrew's Society of New York Scholarships – awarded by the St Andrew's Society for the State of New York. Awards are given to two Scottish students each year towards a year of study in the USA, up to $35,000. A stipend is paid for living expenses, tuition fees and research allowance
- Research Incentive Grants – from £1,500 to £15,000 for early career researchers to undertake a short research project at a Scottish university
- Carnegie Research Workshops – of up to £50,000 for a joint research project (researchers from more than one Scottish university) which aims to advance new research ideas

For more detailed information on each grant, including eligibility, visit the trust's website.

Applications

Some applications may be made online on the trust's website, some may need an academic referral or nomination. For specific details of each of the awards and their opening and closing dates see the trust's website. A preliminary telephone call may be helpful.

Financial information

Year end	30/09/2018
Income	£3,560,000
Total expenditure	£3,130,000

Further financial information

Grants to 480 individuals were made as follows:

PhD Scholarships	£1,080,000
Research Incentive Grants	£1,020,000
Undergraduate Fees	£292,900
Vacation Scholarships	£234,500
Hardship Grants (undergraduate)	£55,600

Sources of information

Accounts; annual report; funder's website; OSCR record.

Gilchrist Educational Trust

 £30,000 (2018/19)

Correspondent: Valerie Considine, Secretary, 43 Fern Road, Storrington, Pulborough, West Sussex RH20 4LW (tel: 01903 746723; email: valconsidine7@gmail.com)

www.gilchristgrants.org.uk

CC number: 313877

Eligibility

Full-time students at a UK university who fit one of the following categories: nearing the end of a self-funded degree or higher education course but are facing unexpected financial difficulty; or those who are required to spend a period studying in another country as part of their university course.

Types of grant

Travel grants are available towards the cost of essential travel associated with the course (average £531). Adult Study

Grants are awarded to help individuals to complete a degree or higher education course when faced with unexpected financial hardship (average £528).

Exclusions

Support is not given to the following:
- Part-time students
- Foundation degrees until they have been converted to an honours degree
- People seeking funding to allow them to take up a place on a course
- Students who are seeking assistance to meet the cost of maintaining dependants
- Students who are required to spend all or most of their academic year studying in another country
- Those wishing to go abroad for independent travel, exploratory or educational projects

Applications

Those wishing to apply should contact the grants officer by email at gilchrist.et@gmail.com or by post to: 4 St Michaels Gate, Shrewsbury SY1 2HL. Other enquiries should be made to the correspondent. Applications can be submitted at any time of year and must be sent by post. Applications sent by email will not be accepted.

Financial information

Year end	28/02/2019
Income	£93,900
Total expenditure	£93,700

Further financial information

In 2018/19 a total of £30,000 was awarded to individuals. This is broken down as follows: 34 Travel Study grants totalling £17,000 and 20 Adult Study grants totalling £13,000.

Other information

The trust also supports organisations, university expeditions and offers a biennial Gilchrist Fieldwork Award of £15,000. This competitive award is offered in even-numbered years and is open to small teams of qualified academics or scientists in established posts in university departments or research establishments in the UK, wishing to undertake a field season of over six weeks. Throughout 2018/19 the trust supported 15 organisations and 12 expeditions.

Sources of information

Accounts; annual report; Charity Commission record; funder's website.

Lloyds Scholars

Correspondent: The Administrator, (email: lloydsscholars@lloydsbanking.com)

 https://www.lloyds-scholars.com

Eligibility

Students who have a confirmed offer for a three-year undergraduate honours degree at one of the following universities: University College London; University of Bath; University of Birmingham; University of Birmingham; University of Bristol; University of Edinburgh; University of Oxford; University of Warwick; University of Sheffield; Queen's University Belfast. Applicants must have a UK fees status and a residual household income (i.e. before tax and national insurance deductions) of under £25,000. Applicants must also commit to 100 hours of volunteer work. Preference is given to applicants who:
- Live in a postcode area which has a high level of financial, social or economic deprivation
- Attended a school with lower than average performance
- Attended a state school
- Come from a home where neither parent attended university

Types of grant

Bursaries of up to £1,500 per annum to help with living costs and study materials. Beneficiaries are also guaranteed at least one paid internship (with a pro-rata salary of approximately £18,000) and will be partnered with a dedicated mentor, who can provide general support and advice throughout the experience.

Exclusions

Applicants on courses involving a placement year (for example, year in industry) will not receive their bursary or any other financial awards during placement. International students (excluding EU residents living in the UK) are not eligible to apply. All offers for a place on the programme relate only to an applicant's first choice university hence, applicants who fail to gain a place at their first choice university will not be eligible.

Applications

Information on the application process will be published on the charity's website nearer to the time applications open. Any enquiries about the programme can be sent to the team by email.

Other information

The organisation also makes excellence awards of up to £3,000 to 'top' scholars at the end of their course.

Sources of information

Funder's website.

Lloyd's Tercentenary Research Foundation

 £145,600 (2017/18)

Correspondent: Michaele Hawkins, Secretary, One Lime Street, London EC3M 7HA (tel: 020 7327 5484; email: responsiblebusiness@lloyds.com)

https://www.lloyds.com/about-lloyds/responsible-business/community-involvement/lloyds-tercentenary-research-foundation

CC number: 298482

Eligibility

British academics who wish to undertake risk-related research in the USA. A list of suggested research topics/areas can be found on the Fulbright Commission website: http://www.fulbright.org.uk/going-to-the-usa/academic-and-professional/fulbright-scholar-awards/awards-available/lloyds-of-london. Applicants are expected to have attained (at least) a 2:1 in their undergraduate degree. Those with a 2:2 overall result may be considered, although exceptionally.

Types of grant

Grants of $5,000 per month are made for research projects (lasting 3–12 months) in the USA to cover fees, accommodation and maintenance costs. The Fulbright Lloyd's Postgraduate Award, with a value of $45,000, is awarded to eligible people towards first-year master's degree fees and maintenance costs.

Applications

Details on the application process can be found on the Fulbright Commission website. Applications typically open in August.

Financial information

Year end	30/09/2018
Income	£186,300
Total expenditure	£323,100

Further financial information

During 2017/18, the charity awarded grants to three beneficiaries.

Sources of information

Accounts; annual report; Charity Commission record; Fulbright Commission website; funder's website.

The Sidney Perry Foundation

 £195,400 (2018)

Correspondent: Lauriann Owens, Secretary, PO Box 889, Oxford, Oxfordshire OX1 9PT (tel: 07858 940665)

www.the-sidney-perry-foundation. co.uk

CC number: 313758

Eligibility

The foundation primarily supports people undertaking their first degree at a UK university. Applicants must be no more than the age of 35 at the time the course begins. Further information on eligibility can be found on the foundation's website.

Types of grant

Grants of up to £1,500 are given towards the cost of education. Applications with a shortfall of more than £3,000 will not be considered. The foundation's website states that grants are intended to be supplementary and that the majority of funding required should be sourced from other places.

Exclusions

According to its website, the foundation is unable to assist:
- Medical students during their first year if medicine is their second degree
- Medical students during elective periods and intercalated courses
- Second degree courses where the grade in the first is lower than a 2:1, save in exceptional circumstances
- Second degree courses/other postgraduate study unrelated to the first unless they are a necessary part of professional training (e.g. medicine or dentistry)
- Overseas study or expeditions, emergency funding or clearance of existing debts
- Students over the age of 35 when their course of study commences, save in exceptional circumstances
- A-level and GCSE examinations. Except in exceptional circumstances students on Access, ESOL, HNC, HND, GNVQ and NVQ levels 1–4.
- Students on access, ESOL, HNC, HND, BTEC, GNVQ and NVQ levels 1–4 and foundation courses
- Open University, apart from Engineering which is supported.

Distance learning, correspondence, part-time and short-term courses may only be considered in some circumstances.

Applications

Application forms can be downloaded from the foundation's website. Completed forms should be submitted along with proof of a college/university offer, a personal statement, details of two referees including a signed academic reference (on official paper) and an sae. Applicants will be notified of the outcome by post and no further correspondence will be undertaken following a refusal.

Financial information

Year end	31/12/2018
Income	£219,100
Total expenditure	£222,800

Further financial information

In 2018 a total of £195,400 was awarded as grants. This was distributed as follows: £147,600 was awarded to 139 individuals (out of 180 applicants) towards educational courses; seven String and Wind Fellowships totalling £25,000 were awarded through the Philharmonia Orchestra/Martin Musical Scholarship Fund; vocal scholarships totalling £20,000 were awarded to four students at the Guildhall School of Music; and one grant totalling £2,800 was given to one Open University student working towards professional engineer status.

Sources of information

Accounts; annual report; Charity Commission record; funder's website.

Reuben Foundation

 £700,200 (2018)

Correspondent: The Trustees, 4th Floor, Millbank Tower, 21–24 Millbank, London SW1P 4QP (tel: 020 7802 5014; email: contact@reubenfoundation.com)

 www.reubenfoundation.com

CC number: 1094130

Eligibility

Current or prospective students at Oxford or Cambridge University from 'less advantaged backgrounds'.

Types of grant

Grants are made towards living costs and academic fees.

Applications

Initial enquiries should be made by contacting either Oxford or Cambridge University directly, not the charity.

Financial information

Year end	31/12/2018
Income	£5,570,000
Total expenditure	£4,010,000

Other information

The foundation also awards grants to organisations.

Sources of information

Accounts; annual report; Charity Commission record; funder's website.

The Sir Richard Stapley Educational Trust

 £156,000 (2018)

Correspondent: The Clerk, PO Box 76132, London E8 9HE (email: admin@ stapleytrust.org)

https://www.stapleytrust.org

CC number: 313812

Eligibility

Students over the age of 24 who are studying (or planning on studying) a second degree in medicine, dentistry or veterinary studies, or a master's or doctorate in any discipline at a UK university. Applicants must be UK residents or must remain resident in the UK for the duration of their course. Those applying for postgraduate courses must hold a first or high 2:1 (at least 65%) honours degree from a UK institution, or a master's degree from a UK institution, or equivalent from non-UK institutions. A list of overseas degree equivalencies can be found on the trust's website. Awards are competitive and decisions are based on academic merit and a calculation of financial need.

Types of grant

Grants usually ranging from £500 to £1,500 are awarded to cover the shortfall incurred by educational and subsistence expenses upon payment of tuition fees.

Exclusions

Grants are not awarded for/to:
- Electives
- Student placements
- Diploma courses
- PGCE courses
- Professional training courses
- Students who have already been supported by the trust for a postgraduate degree in another field
- Students currently holding a major award from another source (i.e. a grant intended to cover fees and maintenance)
- Full-time PhD students beyond their third year of study
- Part-time PhD students beyond their sixth year of study

Applications

Download the application pack from the trust's website ('Applications' page). Applications typically open in January and close in February/early March, or whenever 300 applications have been received. Students with disabilities may be allowed more time to complete their application. Applicant's should contact the Clerk as soon as possible if they require an extension.

Financial information

Year end	31/12/2018
Income	£171,500
Total expenditure	£183,500

Further financial information

During 2018, the charity awarded grants to 133 beneficiaries.

Sources of information

Accounts; annual report; Charity Commission record; funder's website.

UK Electronics Skills Foundation

 £116,400 (2018/19)

Correspondent: Stew Edmondson, Chief Executive, North End House, North End, Ashton Keynes, Wiltshire SN6 6QR (tel: 07894 899544; email: info@ukesf. org)

www.ukesf.org

OSCR number: SC043940

Eligibility

Electronics/electronic engineering students at a UKESF partner university. For all eligible universities, and for each grant scheme's eligibility criteria, see the foundation's website.

Types of grant

Scholarship scheme: scholars are awarded an annual bursary of £1,000, a pre-loaded Blackwell's gift card to the value of £200 in their first year of scholarship and a paid-for place at a residential UKESF Scholar Workshop. Scholars will also be given a paid summer work placement for each year of their study (eight weeks minimum).

Dialog Award for Female Undergraduates: female students due to start their first degree in an electronics-related course are eligible for a one-off bursary of £1,500, a paid-for student membership of the Women's Engineering Society for the duration of their degree and a paid summer work placement (six weeks minimum) at the end of their first year of study.

Internship programme: interns are given a minimum of £300 per week, a paid summer placement of at least six weeks after their first academic year and work experience at an electronics company.

Applications

For details on how to apply for your chosen scheme, see the foundation's website. Advice on how to maximise your chance of success when applying for funding can also be found on the website.

Financial information

Year end	30/06/2019
Income	£402,400
Total expenditure	£384,700

Further financial information

During 2018/19, the charity awarded 69 Scholarships as well as Internships and Dialog Awards. Note: the grant total has been estimated.

Other information

The UKESF offers a variety of prizes to students in their partner universities, in fields such as automotive electronics, embedded systems and radio frequency engineering. Winners receive £1,000, with one or two runners-up receiving £500. For further information contact competitions@ukesf.org. The foundation also supports a range of educational electronics-focused activities for students of school age through to university. Recently, the foundation developed a ten-week engineering challenge called Go4SET aimed at schoolchildren aged between 12 and 14.

Sources of information

Accounts; annual report; funder's website; OSCR record.

General educational needs

The Michael Barnard Charitable Trust

 £17,900 (2017/18)

Correspondent: The Trustees, Brown Heath Park, Gregory Lane, Durley, Southampton, Hampshire SO32 2BS (tel: 07977 403704)

CC number: 1157878

Eligibility

People living in the UK who are in need due to their social or economic circumstances, natural disasters or because of crime, injustice or violence.

Types of grant

Grants are awarded for a wide range of purposes including to support the education of people in need. Previous examples of support include help towards course fees, accommodation costs and living expenses.

Applications

Apply in writing to the correspondent.

Financial information

Year end	31/03/2018
Income	£52,400
Total expenditure	£368,900

Further financial information

A total £35,800 was awarded to individuals in 2017/18. We estimate that £17,900 was awarded for welfare purposes and £17,900 was awarded for educational purposes.

Other information

Grants are also given to organisations.

Sources of information

Accounts; annual report; Charity Commission record.

The Book Trade Charity

£28,100 (2018)

Correspondent: David Hicks, Chief Executive/Company Secretary, The Foyle Centre, The Retreat, Abbots Road, Kings Langley, Hertfordshire WD4 8LT (tel: 01923 263128; email: info@btbs.org)

https://www.btbs.org

CC number: 1128129

Eligibility

People who have worked in the UK book trade for at least one year (normally publishing/distribution/book-selling) and are in need. Support is also extended to the dependants of such people.

Types of grant

Educational grants of up to £2,000 awarded to interns to help cover travel costs, rent and general living costs incurred when undertaking an internship. Grants are also available to those studying a training/postgraduate course and are awarded according to need.

Applications

Application forms are available to download from the charity's website. If a request is urgent, applicants are advised to contact the charity by telephone.

Financial information

Year end	31/12/2018
Income	£689,200
Total expenditure	£910,500

Further financial information

During 2018, the charity awarded educational grants to 83 beneficiaries.

Other information

The charity operates two subsidised housing facilities in Kings Langely and Whetstone, which are available to all who have worked, or are currently working in the book trade, including new entrants to the trade. Application forms for housing are available to download from the charity's website. Applicants must be earning less than £25,000 per annum and must be in their first or second job, or undertaking an internship.

Sources of information
Accounts; annual report; Charity Commission record; funder's website.

The Brenley Trust

£ £23,700 (2017/18)

Correspondent: Patrick Riley, 17 Princes Drive, Oxshott, Leatherhead, Surrey KT22 0UL (tel: 01372 841801; email: patrick.riley@btinternet.com)

CC number: 1151128

Eligibility
People in financial hardship.

Types of grant
Grants are awarded for general educational purposes; the 2017/18 annual report states 'The trust does not adopt a rigid approach in...grant making. Grants are awarded as the trustees see fit'.

Applications
Apply in writing to the correspondent.

Financial information

Year end	31/01/2018
Income	£503,700
Total expenditure	£345,700

Other information
The trust also provides grants to organisations and to individuals for welfare purposes. The trust operates in the UK and in South Africa.

Sources of information
Accounts; annual report; Charity Commission record.

The Alan Brentnall Charitable Trust

Correspondent: Roger Lander, Cathkin, Nelson Road, Forres, Moray IV36 1DR (tel: 07713 878448)

CC number: 1153950

Eligibility
People who need the provision of education or relief from hardship. The trust imposes no geographical restrictions.

Types of grant
Grants are made to help individuals with their education.

Applications
Applications may be made in writing to the correspondent.

Financial information

Year end	31/03/2018
Income	£352,700
Total expenditure	£81,000

Further financial information
In 2017/18 no grants were awarded for educational purposes, however grants have been made in previous years.

Sources of information
Accounts; annual report; Charity Commission record.

The British Council

Correspondent: The Trustees, 10 Spring Gardens, London SW1A 2BN (tel: 0161 957 7755; email: trustees@britishcouncil.org)

 www.britishcouncil.org

CC number: 209131

Eligibility
The eligibility criteria is different for each programme. Refer to the charity's website for details.

Types of grant
One-off and recurrent grants according to need.

Applications
Applications are made online through the British Council website.

Financial information

Year end	31/03/2019
Income	£1,250,000,000
Total expenditure	£1,220,000,000

Further financial information
We were unable to determine a grant total for 2018/19.

Other information
The British Council is the UK's international organisation cultural relations and educational opportunities. It works with over 100 countries in the fields of arts and culture, the English language, education and civil society. It offers educational opportunities to: learn the English language; study and work abroad for UK-based students and graduates (the Erasmus+ schemes); study in the UK for non-UK students; train as a language assistant for non-UK nationals.

Sources of information
Accounts; annual report; Charity Commission record; funder's website.

Churchill University Scholarships Trust for Scotland

£ £22,500 (2017/18)

Correspondent: The Trustees, Ferguson Whyte Solicitors, 185 Byres Road, Glasgow G12 8TS

OSCR number: SC013492

Eligibility
Students in Scotland.

Types of grant
One-off grants according to need.

Applications
Apply in writing to the correspondent.

Financial information

Year end	05/04/2018
Income	£23,300
Total expenditure	£25,000

Further financial information
Full accounts were not available to view on the Charity Commission's website due to the charity's low income. We have therefore estimated the grant total based on the charity's total expenditure.

Sources of information
OSCR record.

The Community Foundation in Wales

Correspondent: Grants Team, St Andrew's House, 24 St Andrew's Crescent, Cardiff CF10 3DD (tel: 029 2037 9580; email: info@communityfoundationwales.org.uk)

 www.cfiw.org.uk

CC number: 1074655

Eligibility
Individuals living in Wales. Each fund has their own specific eligibility criteria – see the community foundation's website for details.

Types of grant
Grants range in size and are given towards the costs of education including higher and further education, travel costs, course fees, equipment, travel and so on.

Grants are awarded for a range of purposes including counselling, clothing for job interviews, driving lessons, furniture, gym membership, assistance with education for schoolchildren and so on. Visit the foundation's website for further information on current grants.

Applications

Application details for different schemes are available on the foundation's website.

Financial information

Year end	31/03/2019
Income	£2,870,000
Total expenditure	£3,030,000

Further financial information

Grants totalling £50,800 were awarded to individuals in 2018/19. We were unable to determine the split between educational grants and social welfare grants.

Other information

This is one of the 46 community foundations, which distribute funding for a wide range of purposes. Grant schemes tend to change frequently; therefore, consult the foundation s website for details of current programmes and upcoming deadlines.

Sources of information

Accounts; annual report; Charity Commission record; funder's website.

Family Action

See record on page 3

The Fort Foundation

£1,900 (2017/18)

Correspondent: Edward Fort, Trustee, c/o Fort Vale Engineering Ltd, Calder Vale Park, Simonstone Lane, Simonstone, Burnley BB12 7ND (tel: 01282 440000; email: info@fortvale.com)

CC number: 1028639

Eligibility

According to the trustees' annual report, the foundation operates throughout England and Wales and gives grants to individuals and organisations for general charitable purposes.

Types of grant

One-off and recurring grants according to need.

Applications

Apply in writing to the correspondent.

Financial information

Year end	28/02/2018
Income	£465,200
Total expenditure	£402,300

Further financial information

Grants for welfare were broken down as follows:

Amateur sport	£23,300
Citizenship and community welfare	£3,500
Environmental protection and improvement	£1,000

Sources of information

Accounts; annual report; Charity Commission record.

The Carol Hayes Foundation

£7,000 (2017/18)

Correspondent: The Trustees, Carol Hayes Management, 5–6 Underhill Street, London NW1 7HS (tel: 020 7482 1555; email: carol@carolhayesmanagement.co.uk)

CC number: 1153269

Eligibility

Young people, usually from a disadvantaged background.

Types of grant

Financial support and the provision of specialist equipment for those is need which will enable them to pursue a trade, career apprenticeship or similar vocational training and allow them to participate in society.

Applications

Apply in writing to the correspondent.

Financial information

Year end	31/03/2018
Income	£15,000
Total expenditure	£7,800

Further financial information

Full accounts were not available to view on the Charity Commission's website due to the charity's low income. We have therefore estimated the grant total based on the charity's total expenditure.

Sources of information

Charity Commission record.

George Heim Memorial Trust

£1,800 (2017/18)

Correspondent: Paul Heim, Trustee, Wearne Wyche, Picts Hill, Langport, Somerset TA10 9AA (tel: 01458 252097)

CC number: 1069659

Eligibility

People under the age of 30 who are in education or training.

Types of grant

Grants are awarded to encourage education.

Applications

Apply in writing to the correspondent.

Financial information

Year end	02/04/2018
Income	£4,700
Total expenditure	£2,000

Further financial information

Full accounts were not available to view on the Charity Commission's website due to the charity's low income. We have therefore estimated the grant total based on the charity's total expenditure.

Sources of information

Charity Commission record.

Johnson Matthey Public Limited Company Educational Trust

£27,600 (2017/18)

Correspondent: The Trustees, Johnson Matthey plc, 25 Farringdon Street, London EC4A 4AB (tel: 020 7269 8400; email: group.hr@matthey.com)

CC number: 313576

Eligibility

UK students who have a parent or grandparent who is associated with the precious metals industry. Preference may be given to those studying a scientific or technical subject.

Types of grant

Financial assistance is given towards the cost of education and training.

Applications

Apply in writing to the correspondent.

Financial information

Year end	31/03/2018
Income	£5,800
Total expenditure	£30,600

Further financial information

Full accounts were not available to view on the Charity Commission's website due to the charity's low income. We have therefore estimated the grant total based on the charity's total expenditure.

Other information

The trust also works to establish professorships, lectureships and other teaching posts and promotes research into any scientific or academic subject.

Sources of information

Charity Commission record.

The NFL Trust
See record on page 5

Paradigm Foundation

 £6,300 (2017/18)

Correspondent: Jane Harrison, Secretary, Paradigm Housing Group, Glory Park Avenue, Wooburn Green, High Wycombe, Buckinghamshire HP10 ODF (tel: 01628 811829; email: enquiries@paradigmfoundation.org.uk)

 www.paradigmfoundation.org.uk

CC number: 1156204

Eligibility
Paradigm residents who are in need.

Types of grant
Educational grants, ranging between £100 and £1,500, are awarded to help people access training and/or education to facilitate employment.

Applications
Application forms are available to download from the charity's website. Completed forms can be sent to the charity at their postal address, or by email with the subject line 'Paradigm Foundation application'. The charity may take up to ten weeks to make a decision on a grant application. Once a grant is awarded, the charity may arrange a follow-up visit.

Financial information
Year end	31/03/2018
Income	£350,000
Total expenditure	£264,800

Further financial information
Note: the grant total has been estimated.

Other information
This charity also makes grants to organisations, such as St Albans and Hertsmere Women's Refuge, Aylesbury Child Contact Centre, Buckinghamshire Mind and others.

Sources of information
Accounts; annual report; Charity Commission record; funder's website.

The Praebendo Charitable Foundation
See record on page 4

Professionals Aid Council

 £19,400 (2018)

Correspondent: D. Trevers, Company Secretary, 10 St Christopher's Place, London W1U 1HZ (tel: 020 7935 0641; email: admin@professionalsaid.org.uk)

www.professionalsaid.org.uk

CC number: 207292

Eligibility
Educational grants are available to people over the age of 18, living in the UK, who have a degree level qualification or equivalent (level 6 on the education framework) and who are in need of assistance with further education costs. Applicants must have already completed at least one term on the course for which they are applying for funding. Applicants must have savings of less than £6,000 if below pensionable age, and £10,000 if over pensionable age.

Types of grant
Educational grants are awarded towards the cost of course fees, course-related expenses (equipment, books, etc.), travel expenses and general living expenses.

Exclusions
Educational grants cannot be given for:
- Student sponsorships
- Study abroad
- Ordination courses
- Conversion courses
- Intercalated years or medical elective periods
- The International English Language Testing System (IELTS) for university entrants
- The Overseas Registration Exam (ORE) for dental practitioners
- The Professional and Linguistic Assessments Board (PLAB) tests for oversees doctors

The charity cannot help individuals who do not already have some funding in place for their studies. The charity will only consider applications *without* funding if planned funding has broken down due to circumstances beyond the individual's control.

Applications
Application forms are available to download from the charity's website. Completed forms should be sent by post to the charity. The charity aims to review applications within eight to twelve weeks.

Financial information
Year end	31/12/2018
Income	£183,200
Total expenditure	£411,500

Further financial information
The charity awarded grants to 146 beneficiaries, with 25 grants made to 25 higher/further education students.

Sources of information
Accounts; annual report; Charity Commission record; funder's website.

The Rotary Foundation Scholarships

Correspondent: A. Watkin, Secretary, Rotary International in Great Britain and Ireland, Kinwarton Road, Alcester, Warwickshire B49 6PB (tel: 01789 765411; email: rfuk@rotarygbi.org)

https://www.rotary.org/en/our-programs/scholarships

CC number: 1002059

Eligibility
Scholarships to further international understanding for secondary school students, graduates and undergraduates.

Types of grant
Scholarships are available from local rotary clubs. The foundation's website can be used to find and contact local clubs for eligibility guidance. Postgraduate funding is also available from local clubs in one of Rotary's six main causes which are: promoting peace; fighting disease; providing clean water, sanitation and hygiene; saving mothers and children; supporting education; growing local economies. Clubs and districts create their own scholarships funded through district grants. In addition to these grants the foundation also offers a Peace Fellowship which provides scholarships for graduates and professionals to study peace and conflict resolution at one of its six partner universities. For eligibility requirements see the foundation's website.

Exclusions
Scholarships are not available for members and their families.

Applications
Applications can only be made through a rotary club in the district where the applicant lives, studies or works. To find out more about the application process contact a local rotary club. Applications for the Peace Fellowship can be made to a local district through the online application form although applicants are advised to contact the local district first to request an interview. Further guidance notes can be found on the foundation's website.

Financial information

Year end	30/06/2018
Income	£3,500,000
Total expenditure	£3,500,000

Further financial information

We were unable to determine the grant total.

Sources of information

Accounts; annual report; Charity Commission record; funder's website.

Scarr-Hall Memorial Trust

 £5,000 (2017/18)

Correspondent: Donna Thorley, Administrator, Baker Tilly, Festival Way, Festival Park, Stoke-on-Trent, Staffordshire ST1 5BB (tel: 01859 560200; email: donna.thorey@bakertilly.co.uk)

CC number: 328105

Eligibility

Students in education and training throughout the UK.

Types of grant

Grants ranging between £100 and £500 to assist students in financial hardship.

Applications

Apply in writing to the correspondent providing an sae and stating the individual's relevant circumstances, reasons why the grant is needed and how much is required.

Financial information

Year end	31/03/2018
Income	£26,500
Total expenditure	£7,700

Other information

Grants may also be made to organisations.

Sources of information

Accounts; annual report; Charity Commission record; Lead Scotland website.

The School Fees Charitable Trust

 £16,100 (2017/18)

Correspondent: The Trust Secretary, Unit 21, Dean House Farm, Church Road, Newdigate, Surrey RH5 5DL (tel: 01306 746300; email: customerservices@sfs-group.co.uk or sfct@sfs-group.co.uk)

https://www.sfs-group.co.uk/charitable-trust

CC number: 1011711

Eligibility

Children in independent schools whose parents are unable to pay their school fees because of a sudden and unforeseen change in finances over the previous year. Children must be in the final year of GCSEs, A-levels (A2) or equivalent, such as the International Baccalaureate, Standards and Higher. In exceptional circumstances, children in their final year of preparatory school may be eligible for support.

Types of grant

Grants of 25% of net school fees (after the deduction of any other awards from the school or other charitable trusts) for the final year of study. The charity may make grants for a longer period, although exceptionally.

Exclusions

The charity can only consider applications where the school and the parent(s) make a contribution to fees. The charity does not normally support parents with children in state-funded boarding schools. Grants cannot be made to cover any arrears of fees incurred prior to making an application. If there are arrears, the charity will require assurance from the school that any grant made will not be used to reduce debts.

Applications

Apply in writing to the Trust Secretary explaining your circumstances.

Financial information

Year end	31/08/2018
Income	£112,400
Total expenditure	£41,700

Sources of information

Accounts; annual report; Charity Commission record; funder's website.

South Yorkshire Community Foundation

 £1,600 (2017/18)

Correspondent: Grants Team, Unit 9–12 Jessops Riverside, 800 Brightside Lane, Sheffield, South Yorkshire S9 2RX (tel: 0114 242 4294; email: grants@sycf.org.uk)

www.sycf.org.uk

CC number: 1140947

Eligibility

The Sir Samuel Osborn's Deed of Gift Relief Fund supports former employees of the Samuel Osborn Company, or one of its subsidiaries, and their direct descendants (e.g. son/daughter, grandson, etc.). Consult the foundation's website for further information on eligibility criteria.

Types of grant

The Sir Samuel Osborn's Deed of Gift Relief Fund awards grants of up to £1,000 towards the costs of education and training, including books, equipment and living costs.

Applications

Application forms and further guidelines can be found on the foundation's website.

Financial information

Year end	30/09/2018
Income	£1,580,000
Total expenditure	£1,300,000

Other information

This is one of the 46 community foundations, which distribute funding for a wide range of purposes. Grant schemes tend to change frequently; therefore, consult the foundation's website for details of current programmes and upcoming deadlines.

Sources of information

Accounts; annual report; Charity Commission record; funder's website.

The Talisman Charitable Trust

£27,000 (2017/18)

Correspondent: Philip Denman, Chief Executive, Lower Ground Floor Office, 354 Kennington Road, London SE11 4LD (tel: 020 7820 0254)

www.talismancharity.org

CC number: 207173

Eligibility

People in the UK living in poverty, as defined by the Charity Commission.

Types of grant

One-off and recurring grants according to need.

Exclusions

The trust cannot accept applications made by recorded delivery or 'signed-for' services.

Applications

Applications should be made on behalf of an individual by a local authority, charitable organisation or a social or professional worker and should be completed on letter-headed stationery. The trust's website provides a detailed list of all the information needed to process the application. The applicant may need to provide further medical documentation, appropriate quotes for work or services and information on other assistance being received. The trust will only respond to successful applications and does not discuss applications before a decision has been made.

Financial information

Year end	05/04/2018
Income	£230,800
Total expenditure	£266,300

Further financial information

In 2017/18 the trust received 1,296 applications of which 328 were successful. Of the successful applications, 30 grants were awarded for educational purposes. A further 292 grants were awarded to individuals for welfare purposes (such as housing, disability, health and child poverty) and totalled £181,900. The remaining six grants went to organisations and totalled £27,000.

Other information

Occasionally grants are made to organisations with similar aims.

Sources of information

Accounts; annual report; Charity Commission record; funder's website.

Overseas students

The Australian Music Foundation in London

 £17,900 (2017)

Correspondent: The Trustees, 51 Musgrove Road, London SE14 5PP (tel: 020 7635 1680; email: info@australianmusicfoundation.org)

australianmusicfoundation.org

CC number: 270784

Eligibility

Instrumentalists up to the age of 26 and singers, conductors, accompanists, repetiteurs and composers under the age of 30. Candidates must be Australian citizens. Candidates who have been offered a place of postgraduate study, or are part-way through postgraduate study will be considered. Candidates who are part-way through undergraduate study can be supported. Candidates must be studying at an institution in the UK, the USA, or Europe.

Types of grant

Awards are made to contribute towards:
- Tuition fees for both full-time and part-time study at an institution with an outstanding international reputation
- Maintenance costs during full-time study at an overseas institution with outstanding international reputation
- Private tuition

- Language courses
- Purchase of musical instruments
- Travel costs

Applicants are required to produce evidence that the award has been used for the purpose for which it was given. Funds are paid in Australian dollars into an Australian bank account.

Exclusions

Candidates who have not yet started their undergraduate course or who are in their first year of undergraduate study are not eligible.

Applications

Applications are completed in two stages:
- Candidates must first complete the application form (available to download from the foundation's website) and submit it online together with audition videos. There is a £10 administration fee for this submission. Applications must be sent by early May
- Successful candidates will be invited to perform at the live finals in London in early October. Candidates who are unable to attend the finals will be considered based on the strength of their new and original video material

Candidates should also have two referees, who are required to be distinguished members of the music profession.

Financial information

Year end	31/12/2017
Income	£20,400
Total expenditure	£19,000

Further financial information

Full accounts were not available to view on the Charity Commission's website due to the charity's low income. We have therefore estimated the grant total based on the charity's total expenditure.

Sources of information

Charity Commission record; funder's website.

The Charles Wallace India Trust

 £290,900 (2017/18)

Correspondent: Shreela Ghosh, Secretary, 36 Lancaster Avenue, London SE27 9DZ (tel: 020 8670 2825; email: cwit@in.britishcouncil.org)

www.wallace-trusts.org.uk

CC number: 283338

Eligibility

Students, scholars and professionals of Indian nationality and citizenship (generally between the ages of 25 and 38) studying in the UK in the field of arts, heritage, conservation or humanities. Applicants should normally be resident in India and intend to return there at the end of their study. Certain short-term awards are available for people aged between 25 and 45.

Types of grant

Grants and scholarships towards educational courses, research or professional development in the fields of the visual and performing arts, heritage, conservation and humanities. Most awards are given at a postgraduate level to supplement other sources of funding or constitute completion of study awards for those whose scholarships have run out. A limited number of postdoctoral or post-professional research grants are awarded. Support includes fully-funded awards, visiting fellowships in agreed subjects at specific institutions, grants for research and professional visits, grants for doctoral study and grants to attend the Scottish Universities Summer School or specialist training.

Exclusions

Studies relating to economic development or leading to professional legal, business or administrative qualifications are not normally considered.

Applications

Apply in writing to the correspondent. Applications can be found on the British Council website (www.britishcouncil.in/study-uk/scholarships/charles-wallace-india-trust-scholarships) together with respective deadlines. Applicants are required to identify what benefit an award will bring not only to them personally but also to the people of India.

Financial information

Year end	05/04/2018
Income	£297,100
Total expenditure	£328,400

Other information

There are separate, smaller Charles Wallace Trusts for Bangladesh, Burma and Pakistan. All of the trusts are registered charities in the UK with separate and independent boards of trustees. Note: the British Council facilitates and advises on the visas but the cost must be borne by the applicant. Further enquiries can also be addressed to the British Council in New Delhi at: cwit@in.britishcouncil.org.

Sources of information

Accounts; annual report; Charity Commission record.

Personal development/extra-curricular activities

The John Maurice Aitken Trust

 £9,000 (2017/18)

Correspondent: The Trustees, c/o Nevis Capital LLP, 221 West George Street, Glasgow G2 2ND (email: info@jmatrust.com)

jmatrust.com

OSCR number: SC045343

Eligibility
Young people aged 15 to 25 who are in need and live in Scotland.

Types of grant
Bursaries are made to students attending university or college for courses in mathematics or a statistics-related degree. Grants are also given more generally to students in university or college who are experiencing financial hardship.

Applications
Contact the charity for information on how to apply.

Financial information
Year end	31/03/2018
Income	£97,100
Total expenditure	£149,200

Further financial information
During 2017/18, the charity awarded seven welfare grants and 21 educational grants. Note: the grant total has been estimated.

Other information
This charity also makes grants to organisations, particularly to other charitable organisations whose work supports current and former cancer patients, and to sporting organisations whose work promotes public participation at a non-professional level.

Sources of information
Accounts; annual report; funder's website; OSCR record.

Creative Scotland

Correspondent: The Administrator, Waverley Gate, 2–4 Waterloo Place, Edinburgh EH1 3EG (tel: 0845 603 6000; email: enquiries@creativescotland.com)

 www.creativescotland.com

Eligibility
People resident in, or based in, Scotland who are involved in the arts. Note: eligibility criteria varies between grant schemes. See the organisation's website to confirm your eligibility.

Types of grant
There are many funding programmes available, each tailored to a different field of the arts. Current schemes for individuals include:
- **Open Project Fund:** grants are made to artists and creative practitioners (such as musicians, dancers, producers, etc.) for projects that 'develop the artistic and creative practice and skills of those based in Scotland.'
- **Screen Professional Development Fund:** grants ranging from £250 to £5,000 are awarded to freelance screenwriters for training, mentoring and other professional development opportunities
- **Made in Scotland Showcase:** grants are made towards the cost of presenting work at the Edinburgh Fringe Festival

For more information, see the organisation's website.

Exclusions
Funding is not usually awarded to students.

Applications
Application forms, guidelines and deadlines for all funding programmes are available on Creative Scotland's website.

Further financial information
The organisation's website states that in 2018/19, it awarded £419,000 in Open Project funding to 55 individuals. Financial information is unavailable for other funding programmes.

Other information
Creative Scotland supports creative organisations through its regular funding programme, through which grants are made to help with ongoing running costs and to enable organisations to change/develop their future plans. Creative organisations are also supported through various grant schemes for film and screen, theatre, dance and music, information for which can be found on the organisation's website.

Sources of information
Funder's website.

England Golf Trust

 £16,400 (2017/18)

Correspondent: Di Horsley, Chair, c/o England Golf, The National Golf Centre, Woodhall Spa, Lincolnshire LN10 6PU (tel: 01526 354500; email: admin@englandgolftrust.org)

https://www.englandgolftrust.org

CC number: 1160992

Eligibility
Young people under the age of 21 in full-time education, and attending some form of golf coaching or already involved with golf.

Types of grant
There are three bursaries for educational purposes such as tuition fees, books and accommodation that young golfers can apply for. These are:
- Angela Uzielli Bursary – between £1,250 and £2,000 per annum for up to three years awarded to girls in further or higher education with financial need, studying a non-golf related subject and wanting to develop their golfing skills
- Bellamy Bursary – between £1,000 and £1,5000 per annum for three years were awarded in 2017/18 to young women who are studying a golf related subject in further or higher education
- England Golf Bursary – up to £1,500 per annum for up to three years awarded to anyone studying a golf related subject at a higher or further education institution

For more information on the bursaries, visit the trust's website.

Applications
Application and sponsor forms are available to download from the trust's website or by contacting the offices via telephone. Sponsors should be people who know the applicant, including one who can support their golf (i.e. a coach or club organiser). Check the website for the closing dates.

Financial information
Year end	30/09/2018
Income	£26,200
Total expenditure	£37,200

Further financial information
Grants were awarded to 56 children and young people for welfare and educational purposes.

Sources of information
Accounts; annual report; Charity Commission record; funder's website.

The Brian Johnston Memorial Trust

 £9,000 (2017/18)

Correspondent: The Trustees, c/o The Lord's Taverners, Brian Johnston Memorial Trust, 90 Chancery Lane, London WC2A 1EU (tel: 020 7025 0000; email: tim.berg@lordstaverners.org)

www.lordstaverners.org

CC number: 1045946

Eligibility

Young promising cricketers who are in need of financial assistance to further their personal and cricketing development.

Types of grant

Scholarships are available for young cricketers at county academy and university level, towards travel, equipment and coaching.

Applications

Apply in writing to the correspondent.

Financial information

Year end	30/09/2018
Income	£114,100
Total expenditure	£74,800

Other information

The trust is also known as The Johnners Trust and is administered by The Lord's Taverners' charity (Charity Commission no.306054). As well as awarding individual scholarships, the trust runs the BJMT/ECB Elite Spin Bowling Programme and provides grants to cricket associations to assist the participation of people who are visually impaired and blind.

Sources of information

Accounts; annual report; Charity Commission record; funder's website.

Virgin Atlantic Be the Change Volunteer Trip Scholarship

Correspondent: The Trustees, 14 Bowden Street, London SE11 4DS (tel: 020 8266 1616; email: ukyouth@we.org)

https://www.we.org/en-GB/our-work/we-schools/virgin-atlantic-volunteer-trip

CC number: 1138645

Eligibility

Young people aged between 12 and 18 (as of the application deadline) who have 'demonstrated a commitment to global issues or community

volunteerism'. The charity's website states that the ideal candidate is someone who is 'already working to improve their local or global community and who will use this experience to motivate and inspire others'.

Types of grant

Each year 30 scholarships are awarded to travel to Rajasthan in India to experience the culture, volunteer in the community and participate in interactive workshops about global issues.

Exclusions

It is the beneficiary's responsibility to cover the cost of a passport, visa, vaccinations, insurance, travelling costs to a London airport and spending money.

Applications

For details on how to apply for the next trip, see the charity's website. Once applications are open, students can nominate themselves or can be nominated by a third party such as a teacher, family member or someone from their local community.

Financial information

Year end	31/03/2018
Income	£51,600
Total expenditure	£19,300

Further financial information

We were unable to determine a grant total from the 2017/18 accounts.

Other information

Scholarships are provided by the Virgin Atlantic Foundation in partnership with Free The Children UK, which is also known as WE Charity (Charity Commmission no. 1138645).

Sources of information

Accounts; annual report; Charity Commission record; funder's website.

Miss E. B. Wrightson's Charitable Settlement

 £11,500 (2017/18)

Correspondent: Trust Administrator, Swangles Farm, Cold Christmas Lane, Thundridge, Ware, Hertfordshire SG12 7SP (email: info@wrightsontrust.co.uk)

wrightsontrust.co.uk

CC number: 1002147

Eligibility

Young musicians, usually between the ages of 11 and 18, who are in need.

Types of grant

One-off and recurrent grants ranging from £100 to £800 can be given towards music college fees, choir/orchestra tour

fees and so on. An individual may receive a maximum of three grants from the trust.

Exclusions

Assistance cannot be given towards school fees.

Applications

Application forms can be downloaded from the charity's website. Completed forms should be submitted by email using the child's name as the subject line. Applications must be submitted along with a brief music CV, two letters of support from teachers/tutors, details reasons for applying, any other supporting documents and a list of other grant-giving bodies applied to. Alternatively, applications may be returned by post, sending three copies of the form, two copies of the CV and details of references.

Financial information

Year end	05/04/2018
Income	£21,700
Total expenditure	£93,500

Further financial information

Full accounts were not available to view on the Charity Commission's website due to the charity's low income. We have therefore estimated the grant total based on the charity's total expenditure.

Other information

The charity also supports organisations.

Sources of information

Charity Commission record; funder's website.

Post-graduate study

Fulbright Postgraduate Scholarships

Correspondent: The US-UK Fulbright Commission, Unit 302, 3rd Floor Camelford House, 89 Albert Embankment, London SE1 7TP (tel: 020 7498 4010; email: contact form on the website)

www.fulbright.org.uk/going-to-the-usa/postgraduate/fulbright-postgraduate-scholarships

Eligibility

UK citizens wanting to study a postgraduate course at a university in the USA. Applicants must hold, or expect to obtain, an undergraduate degree with at least a 2:1 overall result.

Candidates with a 2:2 overall result may be considered, although exceptionally. Preference is given to those who do not have extensive experience (i.e. six months or longer) in the US.

Types of grant

There are many scholarships available in various disciplines (such as journalism, film, law, business, data analytics, etc.), as well as scholarships for study in any discipline at specific universities such as Harvard University, Brown University, The New School and others. The Fulbright All Discipline Scholarship covers postgraduate study in any subject at any accredited US university. Scholarships range in value from $12,000 to $60,000, with some awards covering the cost of tuition fees in full. For more information on specific scholarships, see the organisation's website.

Exclusions

Dual USA-UK citizens, USA Green Card holders or those who are resident in the USA at the time of application are ineligible to apply.

Applications

Applications can be made on the organisation's website using an online form. Applications open in August. Applicants must provide contact details for three referees. Photocopies of your CV, passport photo page and official final and/or interim transcripts must be attached to all applications. If successful after shortlisting, applicants will be invited to attend an interview in February in London, Cardiff, Edinburgh or Belfast. Interviews cannot be rescheduled. Applicants will be notified of the final outcome of their application in March.

Sources of information

Funder's website.

The Great Britain-China Educational Trust

 £53,500 (2017/18)

Correspondent: The Trustees, Great Britain China Centre, 15–15 Belgrave Square, London SW1X 8PS (tel: 020 7235 6696; email: trust@gbcc.org.uk)

 www.gbcc.org.uk

CC number: 269944

Eligibility

Students who have Chinese nationality and are studying in the UK or British students who are studying the Chinese language as a taught element of their degree or for training which is not part of their degree but would aid their research.

Types of grant

There are two different types of grants:

- **Chinese Student Awards** – awards up to £3,000, but usually between £1,500 and £2,000, for students who are of Chinese nationality and are studying for a PhD in any subject at a UK university. Students must have started their third year in their undergraduate degree before they can submit an application. They may apply twice but the applications must be a year apart
- **Chinese Language Awards** – awards up to £2,000 for British nationality postgraduate students who are normally resident in the UK. Applicants must be seeking funding for the study of the Chinese language (spoken or written) as a taught element of their degree or for Chinese language training which is not built into their degree but which would aid their research e.g. PhD courses. Applicants whose principle degree course does not include language training as integral to the course (usually PhD courses) must also provide proof of enrolment on to a language course. No previous knowledge of Chinese is required to be eligible

See the trust's website for more detailed information on eligibility for each of the awards.

Exclusions

For the Chinese Student Awards the trustees will not consider applications:

- From undergraduates, or postgraduates enrolled on a taught course e.g. MA and MSc, or students requiring funding for the first two years of a PhD
- From Chinese nationals attending or giving papers at conferences, conducting fieldwork or taking research trips
- For funding intended for research materials (e.g. books, lab equipment, software). The awards are meant to contribute towards applicants' university tuition fees, and living expenses

For the Chinese Language Awards trustees will not consider applications from:

- Undergraduates, post-doctorates, or those without British nationality
- Those undertaking private tuition or informal language swap arrangements
- Applicants with an undergraduate honours degree (single or combined) that included Chinese language as a major component of the degree

Applications

Application forms, along with application instructions can be downloaded from the trust's website. There are separate forms for each award.

The trustees meet twice a year to review applications.

Financial information

Year end	31/03/2018
Income	£60,800
Total expenditure	£61,400

Other information

The trust's website also provides information on the Universities' China Committee in London who provide grants for Chinese scholars who seek to make research visits to the UK and for British-based scholars who seek to make research visits to China.

Sources of information

Accounts; annual report; Charity Commission record; funder's website.

The Leverhulme Trust

 £110,500,000 (2018)

Correspondent: Gordon Marshall, Director, 1 Pemberton Row, London EC4A 3BG (tel: 020 7042 9888; email: grants@leverhulme.ac.uk)

www.leverhulme.ac.uk

CC number: 1159154

Eligibility

Researchers at every career stage. The trust prioritises 'work of outstanding scholarship', focusing on the following criteria: originality; importance; significance; merit. Further detail is given on the trust's website.

Types of grant

The trust has 13 grant schemes which include:

- Research assistance on projects (including leadership awards, fellowships and project grants)
- International travel scholarships
- Research leave to pursue projects
- Postdoctoral research (including awards, early career fellowships and study abroad)
- Emeritus fellowships
- Arts scholarships
- Visiting professorships
- Major research initiatives

Information about each of the trust's grant schemes, including eligibility and what the grant can be used for, is given on its website.

Exclusions

According to its website, the trust does not fund the following kinds of research:

- Studies of disease, illness and disabilities in humans and animals, or research that is intended to inform clinical practice or the development of medical applications

- Policy-driven research where the principal objective is to assemble an evidence base for immediate policy initiatives
- Research where advocacy is an explicit component
- Research aimed principally at an immediate commercial application
- Proposals in which the balance between assembling a data bank or database and the related subsequent research is heavily inclined to the former

Refer to the trust's website for exclusions from each specific grant scheme.

Applications

Information about each of the grant schemes, including how to apply and deadlines, is given on the trust's website. The website also lists the contact details of the relevant individuals to contact for information on particular schemes.

Financial information

Year end	31/12/2018
Income	£109,630,000
Total expenditure	£113,460,000

Further financial information

The number of applications received for consideration for all schemes amounted to 3,748 in 2018. The number of grants which were subsequently made amounted to 670.

Other information

Although the trust does not provide funding for postgraduate and undergraduate study, its sister charity, Leverhulme Trade Charities Trust (Charity Commission no. 1159171), does offer support for individuals whose parent or spouse is a commercial traveller, grocer or chemist.

Sources of information

Accounts; annual report; Charity Commission record; funder's website.

McGlashan Charitable Trust

 £44,300 (2018/19)

Correspondent: The Trustees, 66 Octavia Terrace, Greenock, Renfrewshire PA16 7PY (email: info@mcglashantrust.org)

https://mcglashantrust.org

OSCR number: SC020930

Eligibility

Grants are made in a very wide range of subjects to postgraduate students who are aged under 30 and were either born in Scotland or were born elsewhere and are studying in Scotland.

Types of grant

Grants tend to be in the range of £500 to £1,000.

Applications

Application forms are available to download from the trust's website and should be submitted by email by the end of May. Applicants will be notified in July about their grant decision. The trustees require a report on the progress of study at the end term of a grant.

Financial information

Year end	05/04/2019
Income	£86,000
Total expenditure	£110,800

Other information

A few substantial grants are made to major Scottish charities, mainly those active in the arts.

Sources of information

Accounts; annual report; Charity Commission record; funder's website.

The James Pantyfedwen Foundation (Ymddiriedolaeth James Pantyfedwen)

 £278,500 (2017/18)

Correspondent: Gwenan Creunant, Executive Secretary, Pantyfedwen, 9 Market Street, Aberystwyth, Ceredigion SY23 1DL (tel: 01970 612806; email: post@jamespantyfedwen.cymru)

www.jamespantyfedwen.cymru

CC number: 1069598

Eligibility

People who have had a permanent address in Wales at any point during the three years immediately preceding the application (excluding those with only term-time addresses as a college/university student in Wales). Applicants must also be either: born in Wales; have a parent/parents who were born in Wales; or have attended any educational institution in Wales for at least seven years. Only applications for postgraduate study will be considered.

Types of grant

Grants of up to £7,000 to support postgraduate studies, including master's or PhDs. Grants are awarded for tuition fees only. All subject areas are considered.

Exclusions

Support is not given to supplement awards provided by the local authorities and research councils. In addition, the foundation does not support the following:

- Undergraduate courses (including intercalated degree courses in medical science or four-year undergraduate courses)
- Undergraduate courses (including intercalated degree courses in medical science or four-year undergraduate courses)
- Higher degrees where students already have a postgraduate qualification (this does not exclude progress from a master's degree to a PhD)
- Accounting training courses
- Private tuition (e.g. for music students)
- PGCE courses
- Postgraduate training courses in social work
- CPE course in law (but Legal Practice Courses are permitted)
- Master's courses that is more than one year's duration. Where a student is pursuing a two years' master's degree course on a full-time basis the foundation is prepared to consider assistance for the second and final year of study

Applications

Application forms and detailed guidelines can be downloaded from the foundation's website. Applications can be submitted after 1 April each year for courses beginning the following academic year. The deadline for applications is usually the end of June. Applicants who are awaiting examination results may apply before the outcome is known; however, the foundation must be informed of the outcome at a later date.

Financial information

Year end	31/03/2018
Income	£766,200
Total expenditure	£700,500

Further financial information

In 2017/18 a total of £278,500 was awarded to 54 postgraduate students.

Other information

The foundation also makes grants to organisations, mainly supporting Eisteddfodau and religious buildings.

Sources of information

Accounts; annual reports; Charity Commission record; funder's website.

Study abroad/ placements

The Winston Churchill Memorial Trust

 £980,600 (2017/18)

Correspondent: The Trustees, 29 Great Smith Street, London SW1P 3BL (tel: 020 7999 1660; email: office@wcmt. org.uk)

 www.wcmt.org.uk

CC number: 313952

Eligibility
British citizens resident in the UK who are over the age of 18.

Types of grant
Grants are made to people for a specific project which involves travelling overseas (normally for four to eight weeks) in order to bring back knowledge and best practice for the benefit of others in their professions, communities and the UK as a whole. Support covers return travel, daily living, insurance, travel within the countries being visited and occasionally assistance with home expenses. The categories which projects are drawn from change year on year so check the trust's website for up-to-date information.

Exclusions
Awards are not made for attendance of courses, academic studies, student grants, gap-year projects, electives, degree placements, internships and postgraduate studies (unless real and wider benefits to others in the UK can be clearly demonstrated). Projects involving less than four weeks of travel are not eligible. Existing fellows may not reapply.

Applications
Applications can be made online on the trust's website. Applications open in May of each year and should be submitted by the end of September for projects the following year. Shortlisted candidates will be asked to attend an interview in January or early February.

Financial information
Year end	30/09/2018
Income	£2,105,000
Total expenditure	£2,090,000

Further financial information
Fellowships were awarded to 150 people in 2017/18. Bursaries totalling £37,000 were also awarded to students in Churchill College but this amount was not included in the grant total.

Other information
The charity also awards bursaries to students at Churchill College, Cambridge. The charity's financial reports state this makes up about 5% of its charitable expenditure.

CoScan Trust Fund

Correspondent: Tony Bray, 14 Ridge Avenue, Marple, Cheshire SK6 7HJ (tel: 07778 648082; email: tony.bray@ coscan.org.uk)

 www.coscan.org.uk/travel-award

Eligibility
British people aged between 15 and 25 who are 'planning to undertake a worthwhile project of a broadly educational nature'.

Types of grant
One-off grants, typically in the region of £100 to £200, to travel to a Scandinavian country for vocational experience, summer camps/courses, etc.

Applications
Application forms are available to download from the CoScan website. Applications typically close in March. If successful, beneficiaries are required to submit a short report and photographs of their experience.

Further financial information
Financial information was unavailable.

Sources of information
Funder's website.

The Worshipful Company of Cutlers General Charitable Fund – Captain F. G. Boot Scholarships

 £5,500 (2017/18)

Correspondent: Rupert Meacher, The Worshipful Company of Cutlers, Cutlers' Hall, 4 Warwick Lane, London EC4M 7BR (tel: 020 7248 1866; email: clerk@cutlerslondon.co.uk)

www.cutlerslondon.co.uk

CC number: 283096

Eligibility
Students between the ages of 17 and 25 travelling abroad for at least six months to develop a second language and learn about other cultures. Applicants should either be awaiting entry to further education or be studying abroad as a part of their university degree.

Types of grant
At least five scholarships are awarded each year. Grants can range between £500 and £1,200 depending on the individual's circumstances.

Applications
Application forms can be downloaded from the charity's website. Application forms, completed in handwriting, should be accompanied by two references and posted to the charity before 12 June. Shortlisted applicants will be invited for an interview.

Financial information
Year end	30/06/2018
Income	£121,600
Total expenditure	£150,000

Further financial information
Grants were awarded to five individuals during 2017/18.

Other information
The charity also provides a number of specific awards to students at nominated universities/schools/colleges; gives recurrent grants to charitable organisations; offers an annual Surgical Prize to a scientist developing the design or application of surgical instruments or surgical techniques.

Sources of information
Accounts; annual report; Charity Commission record; funder's website.

Gilchrist Educational Trust
See record on page 6

The Kennedy Memorial Trust

 £576,300 (2018/19)

Correspondent: Dr Emily Charnock, 3 Birdcage Walk, Westminster, London SW1H 9JJ (tel: 020 7222 1151 (Monday to Thursday); email: emily@ kennedytrust.org.uk)

https://www.kennedytrust.org.uk

CC number: 234715

Eligibility
British citizens who are ordinarily resident in the UK wanting to study at Harvard University or the Massachusetts Institute of Technology (MIT). Applicants must have been wholly or mainly educated in the UK. Graduates must have spent at least two of the

previous seven years studying as an undergraduate at a British university, graduating from their first degree no earlier than 2015.

Types of grant

Scholarships are made to cover full tuition fees and health insurance. Scholarships also include a means-tested bursary (of up to $27,250) for living expenses. Scholars are expected to spend part of their summer vacation in the USA at the end of the academic year and may also apply for an additional grant of $2,500 for vacation travel.

Exclusions

Applications cannot be accepted from those already in the USA. Scholarships will not be made to postdoctoral candidates wishing to pursue further research in their own field. There is no additional funding available for dependants.

Applications

Applicants should first make an admission application directly to their chosen programme at Harvard and/or MIT. Applications for Kennedy Scholarships can then be made using an online form on the trust's website. Applicants must submit an essay of no more than 1,000 words along with their application, outlining their academic pursuits, intellectual interests, reasons for their chosen course/university and plans for the future. Applications must also include two references. At least one referee must be academic. If successful after shortlisting, applicants will be invited to attend an interview in London in January.

Financial information

Year end	30/04/2019
Income	£417,300
Total expenditure	£724,500

Further financial information

During 2018/19, the trust awarded 11 scholarships. Two additional awards were made to existing students at Harvard and MIT to enable them to complete their degrees.

Other information

Summer research scholarships are awarded to British citizens enrolled on doctoral programmes at Harvard or MIT in support of particular research projects. These scholarships are advertised internally.

Sources of information

Accounts; annual report; Charity Commission record; funder's website.

Frank Knox Fellowships

Correspondent: Annie Thomas, 3 Birdcage Walk, Westminster, London SW1H 9JJ (tel: 020 7222 1151 (Monday to Friday); email: annie@ frankknoxfellowships.org.uk)

 https://www.frankknoxfellowships. org.uk

Eligibility

Students who are British citizens/ normally resident in the UK looking to study at Harvard University. Applicants must:

▶ Be studying for a first or higher degree in their final year of study
▶ Be studying for a PhD in the UK hoping for an additional year as a Visiting Fellow
▶ Hold a first or higher degree having graduated no earlier than 2015

Types of grant

Fellowships of at least $32,000 per academic year to cover tuition fees, health insurance and general living expenses.

Exclusions

Except in cases of severe hardship, travel costs are not usually covered. Fellowships are not awarded for postdoctoral or undergraduate study, nor for part-time study, online programmes or the Executive Education programme.

Applications

Applicants must first file an admissions application directly with the graduate school of their choice at Harvard University. Fellowships cannot be awarded until an applicant has been admitted to a school. Once completed, applicants can apply for a fellowship using an online form on the organisation's website. Candidates applying for multiple schools will have to make this clear in their application to Frank Knox. Applicants are asked to write a short essay (not exceeding 1,000 words) giving an account of their academic pursuits, intellectual interests plus reasons for wanting to study in the USA and future plans beyond university. Applications must also include the names and professional email addresses of two referees. At least one reference must be academic. If successful after shortlisting, applicants will be invited to attend an interview in London in January.

Sources of information

Funder's website.

Vocational training and apprentice-ships (both)

The City and Guilds of London Institute

💷 £216,000 (2017/18)

Correspondent: David Miller, City and Guilds of London Institute, 1 Giltspur Street, London EC1A 9DD (tel: 020 7294 2591; email: bursaries@cityandguilds. com)

 https://www.cityandguildsgroup. com/about-us/our-social-purpose/community-investments/ bursaries

CC number: 312832

Eligibility

To be eligible, applicants must:
▶ Be aged 16 or over
▶ Be currently studying, or wanting to study, a City and Guilds or ILM qualification
▶ Be a resident in the UK
▶ Have genuine financial need

Types of grant

Educational bursaries up to £10,000 are available for course and exam fees, living costs, books/equipment, travel costs, childcare and other needs. Around 100 awards are made each year.

Exclusions

Retrospective payments, grants for career development or deferred loans taken out with a college or bank are not covered.

Applications

Applications can be made online on the website. Shortlisted applicants will be required to attend an interview. See the charity's website for a full guide to the bursary applications.

Financial information

Year end	31/08/2018
Income	£143,600,000
Total expenditure	£155,000,000

Further financial information

Bursaries were awarded to 72 people in 2017/18.

Other information

The institute primarily exist to provide qualifications, awards, assessments and support across a range of occupations in industry, commerce and the public services.

The Thomas Wall Trust

 £50,100 (2017/18)

Correspondent: Chief Accountant, Skinners' Hall, 8 Dowgate Hill, London EC4R 2SP (tel: 020 7236 5629; email: information@thomaswalltrust.org.uk)

www.thomaswalltrust.org.uk

CC number: 206121

Eligibility
People aged 18 and over. Preference is given to those with little or no work experience, lack of school qualifications, applications that demonstrate a realistic plan to seek employment and courses that provide support for gaining employment. Applicants must be:

- Experiencing financial and other challenges (major trauma or a life event, mental health issues, disability, etc.)
- Unemployed (for at least six months over the last two years)
- From a low-income household*
- Legal to work and study in the UK
- Resident in the UK for at least three years

*Factors such as relationship status and number of dependants influence the definition of a low-income household. For full eligibility criteria, see the funder's website.

Types of grant
Grants of up to £1,500 for accredited vocational training up to level 3 and/or costs associated with study such as childcare, travel expenses and accessible study materials.

Exclusions
Grants are not awarded towards the following:

- Courses that are not accredited
- Courses leading to self-employment (such as those in health and beauty, personal fitness, etc.)
- Business start-up costs
- GCSEs, A-levels or equivalent qualifications
- Undergraduate or postgraduate degrees
- Travel, study or work abroad
- Private dance, drama or performing arts courses

Those who already have a degree are not eligible to apply. Courses that are eligible for a 19+ Advanced Learner Loan are not prioritised by the charity.

Applications
Applications can be made online using a form on the funder's website. The grants programme is normally open all year round, although funding is awarded on a first come first served basis. All applications must include a reference from a professional who is known to the applicant (support workers, tutors, probation officers, etc.) References are not accepted from relatives. The trust aims to process applications within eight weeks.

Financial information

Year end	31/07/2018
Income	£184,400
Total expenditure	£143,900

Further financial information
The trust made grants to 71 individuals.

Other information
This charity also makes grants to small organisations that are 'active in serving the social and/or educational needs of their communities'.

National charities classified by subject

Formal sciences

The British Computer Society (BCS)

 £116,000 (2017/18)

Correspondent: The Trustees, The Chartered Institute for IT, First Floor, Block D, North Star House, North Star Avenue, Swindon SN2 1FA (tel: 01793 417417; email: registrar@bcs.uk)

https://www.bcs.org

CC number: 292786

Eligibility
People with a qualification at least equivalent to a 2:2 grade in a bachelor's degree in computer science or a related field (e.g. mathematics, engineering, technology) who are applying for their Initial Teacher Training (ITT) year to become computer science teachers. The charity's website says: 'Anyone with a passion for computing or teaching can apply (no previous teaching experience necessary).' Applicants must be an EU national and have been resident in the EU for the past three years.

Types of grant
Scholarships of £28,000 a year are available to support unsalaried trainee secondary school teachers. As well as the grant, support will be offered along the way, through accessing resources, free continuing professional development (CPD) webinars, a coaching programme and workshops and also a free, two-year associate membership of the BCS.

Exclusions
- The BCS Scholarship is not available for trainees who want to train to become a post-16 (further education) teacher with QTLS (Qualified Teacher Learning and Skills) status
- The BCS Scholarship does not cover tuition fees, but tuition fee loans are available for eligible students
- Unsuccessful applicants to the BCS Scholarship can still apply for a government bursary of £26,000 (but can't receive both)

Applications
There is an initial online application form and if the application is successful applicants are invited to a BCS Scholarship assessment day. Visit the society's website for further detailed information as to what to include on the application form and what happens on the assessment day.

Financial information

Year end	31/08/2018
Income	£19,507,000
Total expenditure	£23,780,000

Other information
The society carries out a wide range of charitable activities to raise standards of competence and conduct across the IT industry. The activities are built on BSC's five strategic pillars: supporting careers, sharing expertise, improving education, influencing practice, driving standards.

Sources of information
Accounts; annual report; Charity Commission record; funder's website.

Google Scholarship for Students with Disabilities

 £60,000

Correspondent: (email: googlescholarship@employ-ability.org.uk)

https://buildyourfuture.withgoogle.com/scholarships/google-students-with-disabilities-scholarship

CC number: GSSD

Eligibility
Students in Europe, over the age of 18, who have a disability and are studying computer science, computer engineering, informatics or a closely related technical field full-time at university. Students at bachelor's, master's and PhD level are all supported. Applicants must be able to display an outstanding academic record and exemplify leadership and a passion for computer science and technology.

Types of grant
Scholarships of €7,000 are awarded to be used for tuition, books, supplies and equipment required for the course.

Exclusions
Google employees cannot apply for the scholarship.

Applications
Applications are made online using the form on the Google Scholarship website. Applicants must also submit electronic versions of their CV, response to an essay question, transcripts and a name and email for a reference. Applications open in autumn and close on 5 December yearly for the following academic year.

Further financial information

Each year Google Students awards €7,000 to ten students in Europe.

Other information

Other programmes and resources, conferences, internships and job opportunities are offered to those looking for a tech-based career.

Sources of information

Funder's website.

Humanities

The British Institute of Archaeology at Ankara (British Institute at Ankara)

£ £281,000 (2017/18)

Correspondent: Laura Paterson, London Manager, 10 Carlton House Terrace, London SW1Y 5AH (tel: 020 7969 5204; email: biaa@britac.ac.uk)

 www.biaa.ac.uk

CC number: 313940

Eligibility

The institute supports research focused on the Turkish and Black Sea littoral in academic disciplines within the arts, humanities and social sciences, particularly the archaeology of Turkey. A range of research grants are available for undergraduates, postgraduates, PHD students and postdoctoral study. Each grant has separate eligibility criteria, visit the institute's website for more information.

Types of grant

The range of grants available includes those towards research projects, fellowships, postdoctoral research and overseas study. Visit the institute's website for further details of the specific grants.

Applications

Further details and information about how to apply for each grant can be found on the institute's website when applications open.

Financial information

Year end	31/03/2018
Income	£926,600
Total expenditure	£914,200

Other information

The institute also awards grants to educational organisations for research in Turkey and the Black Sea region in a wide range of fields.

Sources of information

Accounts; annual report; Charity Commission record; funder's website.

The Broncel Trust

£ £12,400 (2017/18)

Correspondent: The Trustees, 371 Uxbridge Road, London W3 9RH (tel: 020 8992 9997; email: info@akpp.co.uk)

CC number: 1103737

Eligibility

People involved with Polish history, literature, art or social sciences.

Types of grant

The trust awards scholarships, financial assistance for research and grants for publishing Polish works of literature.

Applications

Apply in writing to the correspondent.

Financial information

Year end	30/04/2018
Income	£880
Total expenditure	£27,400

Further financial information

Full accounts were not available to view on the Charity Commission's website due to the charity's low income. We have therefore estimated the grant total based on the charity's total expenditure.

Other information

Grants are made to both organisations and individuals. Occasional financial support can be provided for libraries, museums and exhibitions.

Sources of information

Charity Commission record.

Catherine Mackichan Trust

£ £1,700 (2017/18)

Correspondent: David Mackichan, Secretary, 2 Hutton Avenue, Houston, Renfrewshire PA6 7JS (email: david.mackichan@sky.com)

 www.mackichantrust.co.uk

OSCR number: SC020459

Eligibility

Grants are available to students of history, particularly (but not exclusively) Celtic and/or West Highland history or medieval history. People who are researching various aspects of Scottish history and the border counties of the north of England, including archaeology, genealogy and language studies are equally eligible.

Types of grant

Grants range from £200 to £500 but in exceptional circumstances greater amounts can be awarded. Support can be given for specific costs of research e.g. the costs of travel for site visits, excavations, access to specialist services such as radiocarbon dating, and documentation or publication. Assistance is available to postgraduate students, individuals without formal attachment to any institute of education and amateur historians.

Exclusions

Support is not provided for university undergraduate or postgraduate fees or living expenses while studying for a degree.

Applications

Application forms can be requested from the correspondent at the email address shown. They should be submitted between January and mid-April.

Financial information

Year end	05/04/2018
Income	£3,200
Total expenditure	£3,700

Further financial information

Full accounts were not available to view on the Charity Commission's website due to the charity's low income. We have therefore estimated the grant total based on the charity's total expenditure.

Other information

Grants are also given to schools, groups and local history societies for local history and archaeological purposes.

Sources of information

Charity Commission record; funder's website.

Society of Antiquaries of London

£ £1,900 (2017/18)

Correspondent: John Lewis, General Secretary, Burlington House, Piccadilly, London W1J 0BE (tel: 020 7479 7080; email: admin@sal.org.uk)

 www.sal.org.uk/grants

CC number: 207237

Eligibility

People in higher education (including postgraduates), early career researchers and scholars studying archaeological, antiquarian, architectural subjects, art history, documentary and other research projects focusing on material cultural heritage.

Types of grant

The society offers travel grants to assist undergraduate or first-year postgraduate students studying archaeology at a UK university to gain archaeological fieldwork experience in addition to their degree studies, away from their home base and ideally abroad. Grants are made towards travel and travel-related expenses.

Exclusions

Some of the awards are not available to students. See the charity's website for the exclusions of each programme.

Applications

Applications can be made online or downloaded from the society's website. Applications should not exceed four A4 pages and, together with a reference, should be submitted by 15 January for consideration in March. Applicants will be notified of a decision by 31 March.

Financial information

Year end	31/03/2018
Income	£2,260,000
Total expenditure	£2,050,000

Other information

The society also administers the William and Jane Morris Fund (Church Conservation Grant Awards), awarding grants to churches, chapels and other places of worship in the UK.

Sources of information

Accounts; annual report; Charity Commission record; funder's website.

Arts

The Artistic Endeavours Trust

 £18,000 (2017)

Correspondent: The Trustees, MHA Macintyre Hudson LLP, 30–34 New Bridge Street, London EC4V 6BJ (tel: 020 7240 4100; email: james.midgley@mhLLP.co.uk)

CC number: 1044926

Eligibility

Students undertaking education in the arts and other creative subjects, or entering artistic professions.

Types of grant

Grants are awarded to graduate and undergraduate arts students for tuition fees, equipment, books, clothing, educational travel and anything that will assist their education in the arts.

Applications

Apply in writing to the correspondent.

Financial information

Year end	31/12/2017
Income	£10,000
Total expenditure	£39,900

Further financial information

Full accounts were not available to view on the Charity Commission's website due to the charity's low income. We have therefore estimated the grant total based on the charity's total expenditure.

Other information

The trust may also support organisations.

Sources of information

Charity Commission record.

The William Barry Trust

See record on page 42

The Lionel Bart Foundation

 £36,000 (2017/18)

Correspondent: John Cohen, Trustee, Clintons, 55 Drury Lane, London WC2B 5SQ (tel: 020 7379 6080; email: jc@clintons.co.uk)

CC number: 1086343

Eligibility

Undergraduate and postgraduate students who are aiming to become actors, composers, lyricists, book writers, playwrights, designers, choreographers, directors and anyone who wishes to have a career in theatre but cannot afford the necessary fees in order to achieve this.

Types of grant

Around 12 grants between £1,000 and £3,000 are awarded each year towards tuition fees.

Applications

Applications should be made in writing to the correspondent. Applications must demonstrate financial need and commitment to the course and should also explain how the funds will be used. Eligible students at certain schools may be contacted directly.

Financial information

Year end	05/04/2018
Income	£24,900
Total expenditure	£40,000

Further financial information

Full accounts were not available to view on the Charity Commission's website due to the charity's low income. We have therefore estimated the grant total based on the charity's total expenditure.

Sources of information

Charity Commission record; Uni Grants website.

The Philip Bates Trust

 £3,000 (2018)

Correspondent: The Trustees, 24 Elmfield Road, Castle Bromwich, Solihull, West Midlands B36 0HL (tel: 0121 747 5705; email: info@philipbatestrust.org.uk)

www.philipbatestrust.org.uk

CC number: 1094937

Eligibility

People under the age of 25 who are wishing to pursue creative and artistic achievement.

Types of grant

Grants can be given towards the cost of music lessons, courses and so on.

Applications

Apply in writing to the correspondent including a summary of activities and requirements. All applications for assistance will be considered at the trustees next meeting.

Financial information

Year end	31/12/2018
Income	£11,500
Total expenditure	£13,500

Further financial information

Full accounts were not available to view on the Charity Commission's website due to the charity's low income. We have therefore estimated the grant total based on the charity's total expenditure.

Other information

Grants are also made to charitable organisations in support of projects or workshops which aim to develop creative and artistic interests and skills in young people.

Sources of information

Charity Commission record.

Benney Arts Foundation

 £2,100 (2017/18)

Correspondent: Paul Benney, Trustee, Somerset House, Strand, London WC2R 1LA (tel: 07973 373220; email: info@benneyartsfoundation.org)

www.benneyartsfoundation.org

CC number: 1154043

Eligibility

Young artists over the age of 18 who have financial difficulties and who do not have sufficient funds to continue their education as an apprentice with an established artist.

Types of grant

Applicants are paired with an established artist to apprentice under, and can be awarded bursaries of up to £15,000 dependent on financial means and the period of apprenticeship.

Applications

Application forms are available to download from the foundation's website. Applications must include images of the artist's work, copies of educational transcripts, financial information, and a reference. Use the correspondence address which is given on the application form.

Financial information

Year end	31/08/2018
Income	£2,500
Total expenditure	£2,300

Further financial information

Full accounts were not available to view on the Charity Commission's website due to the charity's low income. We have therefore estimated the grant total based on the charity's total expenditure.

Sources of information

Charity Commission record; funder's website.

The Busenhart Morgan-Evans Foundation

£850 (2018/19)

Correspondent: The Trustees, 455 Woodham Lane, Woodham, Addlestone, Surrey KT15 3QQ (tel: 01932 344806; email: maria@mercurybookkeeping.co.uk)

CC number: 1062453

Eligibility

Young musicians at the start of their professional career.

Types of grant

One-off and recurrent grants are awarded towards the cost of equipment, instruments and course fees.

Applications

Applications should be made through the individual's college and submitted to the correspondent.

Financial information

Year end	31/03/2019
Income	£13,400
Total expenditure	£3,800

Further financial information

Full accounts were not available to view on the Charity Commission's website due to the charity's low income. We

have therefore estimated the grant total based on the charity's total expenditure.

Other information

Organisations are also supported for music, health and local community causes.

Sources of information

Charity Commission record; Uni Grants website.

The Coats Foundation Trust

See record on page 88

The Company of Arts Scholars Charitable Trust

£3,500 (2017/18)

Correspondent: Hon. Secretary, 13 Roehampton House, Vitali Close, London SW15 5FH (tel: 020 3894 5642; email: clerk@artsscholars.org)

 www.artsscholars.org

CC number: 1121954

Eligibility

Applicants for the Arts Scholar Research Award should be sixth form students wishing to undertake placement at a heritage site and be attendees of one of the following schools:
- City of London Academy (Southwark)
- Beckett School (Nottingham)
- William Morris Sixth Form (Hammersmith)
- The Charter School (Southwark)
- Bacon's College (Southwark)

Awards and scholarships are also available to university students in the UK, studying art or architecture.

Types of grant

Various grants are available for research internships, to support university students in their studies or to gain experience of the environment of the work in major institutions. For detailed information on the different awards available visit the trust's website.

Applications

The awards have different correspondents, see the trust's website for contact details. Any general enquiries should be directed to the correspondent.

Financial information

Year end	31/03/2018
Income	£142,300
Total expenditure	£89,400

Further financial information

The grant total was broken down as follows:

Other grants and awards	£2,000
Art scholars research awards	£1,000
Geoffrey Bond travel award	£500

Other information

Grants are also awarded to organisations.

Sources of information

Accounts; annual report; Charity Commission record; funder's website.

Felicity Belfield Scholarship

£3,300 (2017/18)

Correspondent: The Trustees, 3 French Mill Rise, Shaftesbury, Dorset SP7 8HS (tel: 01747 853250)

CC number: 313095

Eligibility

Ballet students who are studying at vocational schools and colleges in the UK.

Types of grant

Grants are awarded towards training fees.

Applications

Apply in writing to the correspondent.

Financial information

Year end	05/04/2018
Income	£7,400
Total expenditure	£3,700

Further financial information

Full accounts were not available to view on the Charity Commission's website due to the charity's low income. We have therefore estimated the grant total based on the charity's total expenditure.

Sources of information

Charity Commission record.

The Kathleen Trust

£135,200 (2017/18)

Correspondent: The Trustees, Currey & Co., 21 Buckingham Gate, London SW1E 6LS (tel: 020 7828 4091; email: kathleentrust@curreyandco.co.uk)

CC number: 1064516

Eligibility

Young musicians who are in need.

Types of grant

Grants can be given towards course fees. According to previous research the trust may offer loans in the form of musical instruments.

Applications

Apply in writing to the correspondent.

Financial information

Year end	05/04/2018
Income	£22,300
Total expenditure	£150,200

Further financial information

Full accounts were not available to view on the Charity Commission's website due to the charity's low income. We have therefore estimated the grant total based on the charity's total expenditure.

Sources of information

Charity Commission record; Uni Grants website.

Paul Mellon Centre

 £461,600 (2017/18)

Correspondent: The Trustees, 16 Bedford Square, London WC1B 3JA (tel: 020 7580 0311; email: info@ paul-mellon-centre.ac.uk)

https://www.paul-mellon-centre.ac. uk

CC number: 313838

Eligibility

People wishing to undertake research in British art and architectural history from the medieval period to the present.

Types of grant

Research support grants: up to £2,000 is awarded towards expenses incurred when visiting collections, libraries, archives or historic sites within the UK or abroad for research purposes.

Andrew Wyld research support grants: up to £2,000 is awarded to help with travel and subsistence when undertaking research in the field of 18th and 19th century British works of art on paper, including watercolour, prints and drawings.

Terra-PMC fellowship: £9,500 is awarded for a four-month, full-time research project into an aspect of British-American artistic exchange from any period up to 1980. Funding can be taken as either replacement teaching of staff costs (which is paid directly to the applicant's university or institution) or as a lump-sum grant if the applicant is an independent scholar.

Junior and senior research fellowships: awards of £40,000 are awarded for nine-month, full-time projects leading to the completion of a book, publication, catalogue or an exhibition. Funding can be taken as either replacement teaching of staff costs (which is paid directly to the applicant's university or institution) or as a lump-sum grant if the applicant is an independent scholar. See the

charity's website to confirm your eligibility for a junior or senior fellowship.

Postdoctoral fellowships: awards of £10,000 are given to fellows for support when undertaking doctoral-level research. Funding can be taken as either replacement teaching of staff costs (which is paid directly to the applicant's university or institution) or as a lump-sum grant if the applicant is an independent scholar.

Rome fellowship: funding covers three months of residential accommodation and meals at the British School in Rome when undertaking research on a topic of British-Italian art history. Fellowships also include a stipend ranging from £3,000 to £7,000 depending on the candidate's circumstances.

Research collections fellowship: funding of £10,000 over a period of a year is awarded directly to the fellow for research into the development of art history as a discipline in the UK in the 20th century. Fellows will be required to use the archives and library collections at the Paul Mellon Centre when conducting research. Funding covers accommodation costs and subsistence, although an additional travel bursary will be made to applicants based abroad or far from London for international flights/trains to London.

Applications

Applications must be made online. See the charity's website for opening/closing dates for specific schemes.

Financial information

Year end	30/06/2018
Income	£4,520,000
Total expenditure	£4,240,000

Further financial information

During 2017/18, the charity awarded grants and fellowships to 61 beneficiaries.

Other information

Funding is also awarded to organisations for research, events, publications and digital projects all pertaining to the field of British art and architectural history. For more information, see the charity's website.

Sources of information

Accounts; annual report; Charity Commission record; funder's website.

Worshipful Company of Musicians Charitable Fund

See record on page 82

National Youth Arts Trust (NYAT)

 £12,700 (2018/19)

Correspondent: Ruth O'Brien, Director of Operations, c/o The Furniture Practice, 31 Pear Tree Street, London EC1V 3AG (tel: 07891 835589; email: admin@nationalyouthartstrust.org.uk)

www.nationalyouthartstrust.com

CC number: 1152367

Eligibility

UK citizens between the ages of 12 and 25 who cannot afford access to opportunities in the arts. Applicants must be either: enrolled in full or part-time education and eligible for Pupil Premium and/or free school meals; or if not in education, employment or training, or applying from Scotland, must be able to provide evidence of any state benefits the applicant/applicant's family receives. Applicants must be able to demonstrate talent and dedication to improving skills in their chosen art.

Types of grant

The trust offers bursaries of up to £1,000 in the fields of dance, music and drama.

- **Dance bursaries** are given to fund dance classes taught by an Imperial Society of Teachers of Dance (ISTD) teacher, or taken at a Council for Dance Education and Training (CDET) School or an Arts Council funded dance company. Funding can also be used to cover the cost of specialist dance clothing and travel expenses
- **Music bursaries** are given to fund music lessons (instrumental and singing) taught by teachers who will enter the pupils into the Associated Board of the Royal Schools of Music examinations. Funding can also be used to cover the costs of musical instrument hire, music ensemble membership and travel expenses. Beginner applications are only accepted from secondary school age individuals for singing. All other music bursary applicants must have started lessons by the age of 12

The trust provides 'access bursaries' of up to £1,000 to help with the cost of drama school audition recalls, tuition fees, books, educational materials or part-time drama classes. Drama schools must be one of the following: a former Drama UK accredited school; a Conservatoires for Dance and Drama accredited school; a Conservatoires UK school; or a drama school that is part of the Federation of Drama Schools.

Applications

Application forms can be completed online on the trust's website or requested from the correspondent. Applications must include the following:
- A reference, signed, stamped, and on school letterhead paper or other
- A letter from the applicant's school confirming they receive Pupil Premium or free school meals (if applicable), otherwise the applicant must provide evidence that they are in receipt of benefits
- A copy of a utility bill or council tax letter as a proof of address
- A copy of the applicant's passport
- A copy of a letter of enrolment to a dance, drama or music school
- A copy of a letter of invitation to audition at an accredited drama school or conservatoire (if applicable)
- A copy of an academic transcript, CV, certificates or qualifications in the art form
- A YouTube or other online video, no more than five minutes long of individual's performing arts practice (optional)

Financial information

Year end	31/03/2019
Income	£99,900
Total expenditure	£98,100

Further financial information

In 2018/19 grants of £12,700 were awarded to individuals. A total of £4,000 was given to seven individuals for music bursaries, we estimate that dance bursaries given to two individuals totalled £1,100. Access grants were given to 13 individuals totalling £7,600.

Other information

The trust also funds a number of youth theatre projects.

Sources of information

Accounts; annual report; funder's website.

The Royal Scottish Academy (RSA)

£ £29,000 (2017/18)

Correspondent: The Trustees, Royal Scottish Academy, The Mound, Edinburgh EH2 2EL (tel: 0131 225 6671; email: opportunities@ royalscottishacademy.org)

 www.royalscottishacademy.org

OSCR number: SC004198

Eligibility

Professional artists and art students in Scotland.

Types of grant

The academy offers various awards and scholarships:
- **The RSA William Littlejohn Award** – an award of £2,000 funded by The William Littlejohn Bequest for excellence and innovation in water-based media
- **The Barns-Graham Travel Award** - a sum of £2,000 funded by the Barns-Graham Charitable Trust for a travel and research opportunity for graduating and postgraduate students. The award consists of funding for the research, production and development of a body of work and exhibition of the work at the RSA Annual Exhibition
- **The RSA John Kinross Scholarships** – ten awards of £2,500 each are for final year and postgraduate artists (at art schools in Aberdeen, Dundee, Edinburgh, Glasgow, and Moray) and architects (RIBA Part 2 students in their final year, or currently attending a master's programme, at one of the six Scottish Schools of Architecture) to spend 6–12 weeks in Florence to research and develop their practice. Initially £2,300 is given for travel, accommodation, subsistence and entrance to galleries/museums or any study visits to the surrounding areas, and the remaining £200 is made on the satisfactory completion of the scholarship
- **The Morton Award for Lens Based Work** – an award of £5,000 funded by The Morton Charitable Trust for artists working in a lens-based media
- **The David Michie Travel Award** an award of £2,500 for a travel and research opportunity for graduating and postgraduate drawing and painting students

Applications

Application forms together with detailed guidelines for the scholarships and awards are available on the RSA website. Further information on other awards can be also be obtained from the academy website.

Financial information

Year end	31/03/2018
Income	£1,394,600
Total expenditure	£938,000

Other information

The Royal Scottish Academy is an independent membership-led organisation who run a programme of exhibitions, artist opportunities, educational talks and events to support artists at all stages of their careers.

Sources of information

Accounts; annual report; funder's website; OSCR record.

The RVW Trust

£ £20,000 (2017)

Correspondent: Rosie Johnson, Secretary, 13 Calico Row, Plantation Wharf, London SW11 3YH (tel: 020 7223 3385; email: info@rvwtrust.org.uk)

 www.rvwtrust.org.uk

CC number: 1066977

Eligibility

Students who have been accepted onto a taught master's course in composition at a British university or conservatoire.

Types of grant

The trusts offers 'Vaughan Williams Bursaries' of £4,000 to up to five postgraduate students studying composition each year.

Exclusions

The trust does not make grants for:
- Courses in TV/ film composition
- Courses teaching only electro-acoustic composition
- Performance courses
- PhDs and research degrees focusing on musicology and analysis
- Courses outside the UK

Applications

Application forms will be made available from the trust's website as soon as submissions open, usually in autumn.

Financial information

Year end	31/12/2017
Income	£455,300
Total expenditure	£274,800

Further financial information

In 2017 the a total of £20,000 was awarded to five individuals for postgraduate study.

Other information

The trust also assists organisations in order to promote public knowledge and appreciation of 20th and 21st century British music. It also provides assistance for the recording of music, concerts, performances and other events.

Sources of information

Accounts; annual report; Charity Commission record; funder's website.

The South Square Trust

 £34,600 (2017/18)

Correspondent: The Trustees, PO Box 69, Wadebridge, Cornwall PL27 9BZ (tel: 07951 822916)

www.southsquaretrust.org.uk

CC number: 278960

Eligibility

Students over the age of 18 who are studying full-time practical degree courses in the fine and applied arts (especially those related to gold, silver and metalwork), also music, drama and dance. Preference is given to students who have been educated mainly in the UK, those in their third year of an undergraduate level or postgraduate students.

Types of grant

The trust assists students directly and also provides scholarships and bursaries to a number of schools/colleges. Individual awards can be given towards fees or for living expenses.

Applications

Application forms are available on the trust's website.

Financial information

Year end	31/07/2018
Income	£887,200
Total expenditure	£274,400

Further financial information

During 2017/18, 27 grants were awarded to individuals.

Other information

In 2017/18 bursaries and scholarships to 18 schools and colleges totalled £119,200.

Sources of information

Accounts; annual report; Charity Commission record.

Split Infinitive Trust

 £31,100 (2017/18)

Correspondent: The Administrator, PO Box 409, Scarborough, North Yorkshire YO11 9AJ (email: splitinfin@ haydonning.co.uk)

www.splitinfinitivetrust.co.uk

CC number: 1110380

Eligibility

People involved in live and performance arts, in general or in education. Applications with a Yorkshire/regional focus and performance arts courses (such as music, dance or drama) will be favoured. The trust may consider other

arts areas and potential applicants should contact the trust to see if their course is eligible.

Types of grant

Grants are awarded for specific projects and towards educational costs such as course fees, travel fees, study materials and living expenses. Average grants are between £250 and £750.

Exclusions

The trust will not award grants for general running costs, projects outside the UK or to charities seeking funds in order to offer their own grants.

Applications

Application forms are available to download from the trust's website. They should be submitted along with a covering letter and an acceptance form for the course of study (for students) or evidence of the project/commission and/ or a CV (for non-students). The trustees meet four times a year, usually in March, June, September and December, but this can vary. Previous recipients are welcome to apply; however, repeat grants are rare.

Financial information

Year end	31/03/2018
Income	£50,200
Total expenditure	£43,700

Further financial information

In 2017/18 a total of £32,900 was awarded to individuals and can be broken down as follows: £28,500 was awarded for training, £2,600 to education and the remaining £1,700 went towards productions and social costs.

Other information

The trust also supports organisations.

Sources of information

Accounts; annual report; Charity Commission record; funder's website.

The Talbot House Trust

 £11,200 (2018/19)

Correspondent: The Trustees, The Trust Partnership LLP, 6 Trull Farm Buildings, Trull, Tetbury, Gloucestershire GL8 8SQ (tel: 01285 841900; email: talbothousetrust@thetrustpartnership. com)

CC number: 1010214

Eligibility

UK residents who are studying performing arts courses (i.e. drama, dance and music).

Types of grant

One-off grants are awarded to students in further/higher education towards the

costs of course fees. In some cases, support will be given for maintenance, equipment or travel. Applications will only be considered for one year of study.

Exclusions

Postgraduate study is not supported by the trust.

Applications

Application forms are available from the correspondent and should usually be received by March for consideration in May. Applicants should include details of financial hardship and any other reason why special consideration should be given to their application.

Financial information

Year end	05/04/2019
Income	£9,000
Total expenditure	£12,500

Further financial information

Full accounts were not available to view on the Charity Commission's website due to the charity's low income. We have therefore estimated the grant total based on the charity's total expenditure.

Sources of information

Charity Commission record; Uni Grants website.

Universal Music UK Sound Foundation

 £116,800 (2017/18)

Correspondent: Janie Orr, Chief Executive, 4 Pancras Square, London N1C 4AG (tel: 020 3932 6101; email: emimusicsoundfoundation@umusic. com)

www.emimusicsoundfoundation. com

CC number: 1104027

Eligibility

Young people in the UK who are undertaking music education. Applicants must have been resident in the UK for a minimum of three years and: be a British citizen; be a national of a member state of the European Economic Area; have been granted leave to enter or remain in the UK for an indefinite period; or hold a certificate of right of abode in the UK. Note: individuals resident in the UK solely for the purpose of education or attending a course of study are not eligible.

Types of grant

Grants, usually of up to £1,500, towards the purchase of instruments and music equipment in tertiary education. The foundation also operates a bursary scheme where grants of £5,000 are awarded to selected musical colleges and institutes for distribution to their students. These are: Birmingham Conservatoire; Brighton and Bristol Institute of Modern Music (BIMM); Centre for Young Musicians; English National Opera (ENO); International World Music Centre, Limerick; National Children's Orchestra; Royal Academy of Music, London; Royal Conservatoire of Scotland; Royal Welsh College of Music and Drama; and Tech Music Schools, London. Each college/institution has specific criteria, see their websites for eligibility and information on the application process.

Exclusions

Grants are not provided to/for:

- Applicants based outside the UK and Ireland
- Applications for tuition fees and living expenses (other than through the bursary scheme)
- Applications over £2,000
- Private instrumental lessons

Applications

Application forms for instrument/ equipment grants can be downloaded from the foundation's website or requested from the correspondent. They should be submitted by individuals or their school via post, together with all the relevant documentation and references a month before the trustees' meeting. The meetings are held twice a year, normally in October and March (for exact dates consult the foundation's website). Candidates are invited to approach the foundation with queries prior to application. Applications for bursaries should be made through the individual's educational establishment.

Financial information

Year end	31/07/2018
Income	£414,900
Total expenditure	£826,700

Further financial information

In 2017/18, an estimated £51,800 was awarded to individuals in secondary and tertiary education and £65,000 was awarded to educational organisations to award bursaries to their students.

Other information

The foundation also gives grants to a number of secondary schools to fund music education.

Sources of information

Accounts; annual report; Charity Commission record; funder's website.

Miss E. B. Wrightson's Charitable Settlement
See record on page 16

History

The Alice McCosh Trust

 £1,800 (2017/18)

Correspondent: Grace Carswell, Trust Secretary, 49 Cluny Street, Lewes, East Sussex BN7 1LN (email: info@ thealicemccoshtrust.org.uk)

www.thealicemccoshtrust.org.uk

OSCR number: SC035938

Eligibility

People of any age undertaking work or study related to natural history and/or the environment. The trust's website states: 'Applications are invited from individuals attached to institutions and those following a programme of study or qualification, as well as people engaged in private/personal study related to natural history and/or the environment.' Preference will be given to individuals from (or work relating to) Scotland, England, Turkey and Uganda.

Types of grant

One-off grants in the region of £1,000, to cover, for example, the cost of a field trip or project, an expedition as part of a research project or the development of new teaching materials for schools or institutes of higher education.

Applications

Applications can be made on a form available from the trust's website along with guidelines. They should be emailed to the correspondent between 1 October and 30 November each year. Applications received at other times, or sent by post, will not be considered. Applications should be concise and include two referee statements. On completion of the project the trust requires a report to be published on its website.

Financial information

Year end	05/04/2018
Income	£1,900
Total expenditure	£2,000

Further financial information

Full accounts were not available to view on the Charity Commission's website due to the charity's low income. We have therefore estimated the grant total based on the charity's total expenditure.

Sources of information

Funder's website; OSCR record.

Languages

Interdoceo

 £846,500 (2017/18)

Correspondent: Thomas Dawid, Director, 1 Princeton Mews, 167–169 London Road, Kingston upon Thames, Surrey KT2 6PT (email: info@ interdoceo.org)

www.interdoceo.org

CC number: 1163436

Eligibility

Young people interested in learning and teaching a foreign language. The charity's website states:

- Young individuals aged over 18 with less than two years of professional experience in teaching their own language
- Having English, French or German as a first language, or having completed secondary education in any of these languages
- When an undergraduate degree is required to join one of the programs, it must have been obtained in the four years previous to the start of the grant
- The minimum stay in Spain will be 5 months

Types of grant

Grants are awarded to further training to become a foreign language teacher. There are three different programmes to apply for:

- Postgraduate – aimed at graduates who have a degree related to teaching either in their own or a foreign language
- Graduate – aimed at graduates from any degree
- Speakers – aimed at young people ages between 18 and 24. A-levels or equivalent qualifications are required

Applications

Contact the charity using the form on its website.

Financial information

Year end	31/07/2018
Income	£852,300
Total expenditure	£854,200

Sources of information

Accounts; annual report; Charity Commission record; funder's website.

John Speak Foundation Foreign Languages Scholarships Trust Fund (John Speak Trust)

 £10,700 (2017/18)

Correspondent: The Trustees, West and North Yorkshire Chamber, Devere House, Vicar Lane, Little Germany, Bradford BD1 5AH (tel: 01274 230090; email: john.speak@wnychamber.co.uk)

 www.johnspeaktrust.co.uk

CC number: 529115

Eligibility

British-born citizens over the age of 18 who wish to improve their knowledge of a foreign language while living overseas. Applicants should be intending to have a career in British trade and services abroad. A basic knowledge of the foreign language to be studied (at least GCSE or equivalent) is essential. Applicants must either be studying at a recognised college/university or obtain suitable voluntary employment.

Types of grant

Funding is available for overseas travel to study a language, including compulsory travel required for a university course. Average grants of £1,900 are paid in monthly instalments for the duration of the stay and can be used towards living expenses and in some cases travel costs. Scholarships can last 3–12 months and are tailored to the individual. Successful applicants are required to live in accommodation within the local community rather than with English speakers during their stay and must provide the foundation with monthly reports of no less than 250 words.

Applications

Applications can be made online using a form available on the trust's website. A letter of recommendation from the applicant's head of department/language tutor (if at university or college) or employer must be submitted along with the form. Potential applicants are invited for an interview with the trustees (either in person or electronically) and must be able to demonstrate sufficient competence in their chosen language. Consult the trust's website for current deadlines and further guidelines.

Financial information

Year end	31/03/2018
Income	£16,500
Total expenditure	£11,900

Further financial information

Full accounts were not available to view on the Charity Commission's website due to the charity's low income. We have therefore estimated the grant total based on the charity's total expenditure.

Sources of information

Charity Commission record; funder's website.

Law

The Clark Foundation for Legal Education

Correspondent: The Administrator, (email: clarkfoundation@lindsays.co.uk)

 www.clarkfoundation.org.uk

OSCR number: SC018520

Eligibility

Law students researching Scots law.

Types of grant

Grants are made to cover undergraduate and postgraduate course fees and living expenses incurred while undertaking researching areas in Scots law. Previously funded projects include e-commerce and distribution agreements under EU Competition Law, advancing the understanding of online sexual extortion in Scotland and so on. A full list past research projects can be found on the foundation's website.

Exclusions

The foundation does not support students studying for LLB/Diploma in Professional Legal Practice, other than in cases of exceptional hardship.

Applications

Application forms are available to download from the foundation's website when applications open, typically at the end of January. Completed forms should be returned by email.

Other information

A list of additional prizes and awards (awarded mainly to organisations) can be found on the foundation's website.

Sources of information

Funder's website.

Gray's Inn Scholarships

Correspondent: The Administrator, 8 South Square, London WC1R 5ET (tel: 020 7458 7800 (Monday to Friday 8:30am until 6pm); email: contact form on the website)

https://www.graysinn.org.uk/ scholarships

Eligibility

Law students/graduates who intend to pursue a career at the Bar of England and Wales. Applicants do not need to be a member of the Inn to apply, except in the case of Pupillage Scholarships.

Types of grant

There are many different funding programmes available. Current schemes include:

- **GDL Scholarships:** grants of at least £10,000 are awarded to those studying a Graduate Diploma in Law
- **BPTC Scholarships:** grants of up to £30,000 are made to those studying a Bar Professional Training Course
- **BPTC Residential Scholarships:** grants of this type are awarded in conjunction with the BPTC Scholarship, for those in need of accommodation while studying for a BPTC
- **Senior Scholarships for Pupillage:** grants of £5,000 are given to those who have passed the BPTC examinations unconditionally and are about to undertake barrister training
- **The Hebe Plunkett Scholarship:** grants are made to students with disabilities to help with any additional costs incurred while undertaking the GDL, the BPTC or pupillage

For more information, see the funder's website.

Exclusions

GDL and BPTC scholarships can only be awarded once.

Applications

Applications can be made online on the Gray's Inn website. Deadlines for each scholarship can also be found on the funder's website. All applications must include two references from academics (lecturers, teachers, barristers, etc.) who they have known for at least one year. If successful at the shortlisting stage, applicants will be required to attend an interview. Note: applicants can only apply to one Inn.

Other information

Prizes ranging from £500 to £1,500 are awarded for essays on Administrative Law and Common or Statute Law. For details on how to enter, see the website.

Sources of information

Funder's website.

Natural Sciences

Biology

Botanical Society of Britain and Ireland

 £8,600 (2018/19)

Correspondent: Dr A.I. Denholm, Chair of the Trustees, 29 West Farm Court, Broompark, Durham DH7 7RN (tel: 07725 862957; email: enquiries@bsbi.org)

https://bsbi.org

CC number: 1152954

Eligibility

People studying or have an interest in studying botany.

Types of grant

Training grants – Grants of up to £250 are given to aspiring botanists wishing to go on short training courses. The charity's website states that applicants typically include recent graduates who are 'looking to start a career in botany or take part in interest-led botanical recording.' Preference is given to members when awarding grants.

Plant study grants – Grants of up to £1,000 per year are awarded to undergraduate and postgraduate botany students.

Research grants – Small grants are awarded for botanical publications in Britain and Ireland which enhance the knowledge of flora. These grants are designed for PhD students, academic researchers and amateur researchers.

Conference bursaries – Students can apply for bursaries to help with the costs of conferences.

Applications

See the charity's website for application information including the dates when applications are accepted.

Financial information

Year end	31/03/2019
Income	£474,900
Total expenditure	£478,600

Further financial information

In 2018/19 grants were made as follows: 22 training grants; 12 plant study grants; and four science and research grants.

Other information

The society is one of the world's largest contributors of biological records which are used to inform scientific research and underpin evidence-based conservation. Its website also details other organisations that award grants for plant study.

Sources of information

Accounts; annual report; Charity Commission record; funder's website.

The British Ornithologists' Union

 £17,300 (2017)

Correspondent: Grants Committee, 3 Crowtree Cottages, Straight Drove, Farcet, Peterborough, Cambridgeshire PE7 3DL (tel: 01733 844820; email: bou@bou.org.uk)

www.bou.org.uk

CC number: 249877

Eligibility

Small Research Grant eligibility
- Applicants must be a British Ornithology Union member
- Applicants must be the principal investigator
- The research must be of high scientific quality, interesting, innovative, and have a potentially high impact
- The project must have a clearly justified budget, and be feasible in terms of time and resources allocated
- The amount applied for must make up all or a substantial amount of the funds allocated

Career Development Bursary eligibility
- Applicants must be a British Ornithology Union Early Career Researcher (BOUECR)
- Applicants must have completed a first or higher degree within the last two years
- The work must not be funded already; however, it may be linked to existing programmes
- The work must take place in a third-party institute and be supervised by someone from that institute
- The work must be carried out away from your home institute

John and Pat Warham Studentship
- Applicants must be a British Ornithology Union Early Career Researcher (BOUECR)
- Applicants must be a postgraduate researching any aspect of the biology or ecology of Sphenisciformes and Procellariiformes
- Applicants must have an academic position during, and beyond, the duration of the studentship in the research institution that will administer the grant

Types of grant

There are three types of funding available:
- **Small Research Grants:** awards of up to £2,000 are available to support small projects outright, or to part-fund medium-sized projects. The closing date for applications is usually the end of November and the award is made in March the following year. Check the charity's website before applying as these dates may change
- **Career Development Bursary:** awards of up to £2,500 are available to support short-term research positions for early career ornithologists, usually between a first and higher degree programme, or immediately after completion of a higher degree programme
- **John and Pat Warham Studentship:** awards for 3.5 year studentships to provide training to PhD level in research on any aspect of the biology or ecology of Sphenisciformes and Procellariiformes

Exclusions

A full list of exclusions for each programme can be found on the charity's website.

Applications

Application guidelines and forms for each grant programme can be found on the charity's website.

Financial information

Year end	31/12/2017
Income	£205,200
Total expenditure	£199,600

Further financial information

Grants were awarded to ten individuals during 2017.

Other information

The union's main activities are: IBIS international journal of avian science; conferences; grants and bursaries; promoting ornithology; supporting young researchers; publications; The British List. The majority of the organisation's charitable expenditure went towards conference and publication costs.

Sources of information

Accounts; annual report; Charity Commission record; funder's website.

The Genetics Society

 £222,100 (2018)

Correspondent: The Trustees, 1 Naoroji Street, London WC1X 0GB (tel: 020 3925 3672; email: theteam@genetics.org. uk)

 www.genetics.org.uk

CC number: 261062

Eligibility
Students and early stage researchers who are members of The Genetics Society. Although most grants are open to undergraduate students, postgraduate students, junior postdocs and P/I's the grants do have different eligibility criteria; see the helpful chart on the society's website.

Types of grant
The society offers different grant schemes; the main ones are listed below. For more detailed information on each grant visit the society's website.

- **Genes and Development Summer Studentship** – for undergraduate students to gain research experience in any area of genetics. Up to £750 to cover justifiable expenses incurred by the host laboratory and a stipend to cover eight weeks' subsistence will be paid directly to the student
- **Junior Scientist Conference Grant** – to support attendance at conferences on research in genetics
- **One-off Meeting Sponsorship** – sponsorship of genetic themed meetings not organised directly by The Genetics Society
- **Training Grants** – up to £1,000 to support attendance at short training courses in the area of genetics research
- **Heredity Fieldwork Grant** – up to £1,500 to support field-based genetic research

Applications
Application forms are available to download from the society's website. Each grant has a different application process, visit the website for detailed guidelines and submission dates.

Financial information
Year end	31/12/2018
Income	£665,200
Total expenditure	£588,900

Further financial information
The grant total is broken down as follows:

Summer Studentships	£79,400
Junior Scientist Travel Grants	£74,700
Sponsorship of Meetings	£20,000
Genetics Society Training Grants	£17,700
Miscellaneous Grants	£17,200
Heredity Fieldwork Grants	£13,100

Other information
The society holds meetings and lectures, and publishes newsletters and journals, as well as awarding grants. Membership prices: £25 or £15 for postgraduates and £5 for undergraduates.

Sources of information
Accounts; annual report; Charity Commission record; funder's website.

Physics

The Institute of Physics

Correspondent: The Trustees, 37 Caledonian Road, London N1 9BU (tel: 020 7470 4800; email: education@ iop.org)

 www.iop.org/education/index.html

CC number: 293851

Eligibility
To be eligible for a Teacher Training Scholarship individuals must either have: a physics or related degree with a proven or predicted grade of at least a 2:1; obtained a relevant PhD or master's degree; or completed a Subject Knowledge Enhancement course in physics. Those who obtained a 2.2 degree will still be considered if significant physics related experience and knowledge can be demonstrated. Scholarships are also available to PhD students from groups that are under-represented in physics. Further information on eligibility can be found on the charity's website.

Types of grant
Scholarships of £28,000 are awarded to assist with physics teacher training. After completing the qualification, eligible physics teachers will receive an additional £6,000 on top of their salaries for the first four years of work. The Bell Burnell Graduate Scholarship Fund provides support to full-time or part-time students for up to four years (or equivalent if part-time study). Funding can be used towards course fees, living costs and support accessibility, including support for carer responsibilities.

Applications
Application forms for the Teacher Training Scholarship can be completed on the charity's website. Application forms for the Bell Burnell Graduate Scholarship Fund and further information can be found at: https://beta.iop.org/bellburnellfund. Check the website for current deadlines.

Financial information
Year end	31/12/2018
Income	£73,310,000
Total expenditure	£65,020,000

Further financial information
In 2018, 132 teaching scholarships were awarded. We were unable to determine the grant total.

Other information
Successful teacher training scholars will also have access to workshops and masterclasses and receive free IOP membership for their training year. The institute also administers a range of awards designed to recognise contributions to physics.

Sources of information
Accounts; annual report; Charity Commission record; funder's website.

Professional and applied sciences

Architecture and design

The Nicholas Boas Charitable Trust
See record on page 80

Design History Society

 £19,700 (2017/18)

Correspondent: The Trustees, Design History Society, 70 Cowcross Street, London EC1M 6EJ (tel: 020 7490 4712; email: designhistorysociety@gmail.com)

https://www.designhistorysociety.org

CC number: 1155117

Eligibility
People engaged with the subject of design history.

Types of grant
A variety of grants, awards and prizes are available to support students, researchers, educators, designers, critics, curators and others involved with design history. There are four annual research grants available and student grants for research-related travel and to attend the society's conference. Grants are also available for events and symposiums. See the society's website for full details of the types of funding available.

Applications

Application forms, along with guidance notes and full eligibility information, are available from the society's website.

Financial information

Year end	30/06/2018
Income	£74,200
Total expenditure	£97,762

Further financial information

The grant total was estimated from the 2017/18 accounts.

Other information

As well as providing grants there are a number of prizes offered by the society to compete for.

Sources of information

Accounts; annual report; Charity Commission record; funder's website.

The Gane Charitable Trust
See record on page 82

Business and finance

The Company of Actuaries Charitable Trust Fund

 £18,300 (2017/18)

Correspondent: Patrick O'Keeffe, Broomyhurst, Shobley, Ringwood, Hampshire BH24 3HT (tel: 01425 472810; email: almoner@ actuariescompany.co.uk)

www.actuariescompany.co.uk

CC number: 280702

Eligibility

Further and higher education students progressing towards actuarial qualifications.

Types of grant

Bursaries are available to those in their final year of an Actuarial Science degree at a UK university to help with course and exam fees.

Applications

Application forms are available on the charity's website or from the correspondent. Applications are mainly considered in October, but also in January, April and July. Applicants must provide details of their financial situation, demonstrate serious intentions of joining the Institute and Faculty of

Actuaries, and be making good progress on their course and in their examinations.

Financial information

Year end	31/07/2018
Income	£179,600
Total expenditure	£161,400

Other information

The trust also gives prizes to university and Institute and Faculty of Actuaries students, as well as donations to organisations and other charities.

Sources of information

Accounts; annual report; Charity Commission record; funder's website.

The London Institute of Banking and Finance

Correspondent: The Trustees, 4–9 Burgate Lane, Canterbury CT1 2XJ (tel: 01227 818609; email: customerservices@libf.ac.uk)

 https://www.libf.ac.uk

CC number: 297107

Eligibility

Students undertaking (or planning to undertake) the London Institute of Banking and Finance's degree programmes. For full-time students, their annual household income must not exceed £40,000. For part-time students, household income must not exceed £25,000 per annum. Applicants must also be in receipt of Universal Credit or other state benefits i.e. housing benefit, council tax benefit, income-based employment and support allowance and income-based jobseeker's allowance. Eligibility varies between grant schemes. See policy notes (available to download from the charity's website) to confirm your eligibility.

Types of grant

Scholarships of between £500 and £1,500 are awarded for those in full-time study on an undergraduate degree. Those studying a part-time undergraduate degree are eligible for a scholarship of up to £1,000 in the form of course fee subsidies. Postgraduate scholarships ranging from £500 to £2,000 are awarded to students in either part-time or full-time study. The amount awarded in every case (except for part-time undergraduates) is dependent on the candidate. Means-tested bursaries for both part-time and undergraduate study are also available. The organisation makes an additional two bursaries (worth a maximum of three years tuition fees) to support asylum seekers wishing to pursue a career in finance.

Exclusions

International, European, Channel Islands and Isle of Man students are not eligible to apply. Bursaries cannot be awarded retrospectively. Students in receipt of a bursary must meet the minimum attendance requirement of 85% in lectures and seminars, or payment will be revoked. Three late arrivals will be classed as one non-attendance.

Applications

Full-time students should first apply to Student Finance England for a maintenance loan and grant. When applying to Student Finance England, the student will be asked to give consent (on behalf of themselves and their family) for family income data to be shared with the London Institute of Banking and Finance. Once this information has been received, the organisation will then determine whether the applicant is eligible for funding. Part-time students can download an application form from the charity's website. Completed forms should be returned by email or by post.

Financial information

Year end	31/07/2018
Income	£16,140,000
Total expenditure	£16,590,000

Further financial information

We were unable to determine the grant total for 2017/18.

Other information

The charity also awards prizes of £500 to the highest scores in modules and projects, as well as for other achievements. For more information, see the policy notes available to download from the charity's website.

Sources of information

Accounts; annual report; Charity Commission record; funder's website.

UK Business School Bursary

 £1,000

Correspondent: The Administrator, (email: contact form on the website)

https://corporatefinanceinstitute. com/resources/support/ scholarship/uk-business-school-bursary

Eligibility

Those who are studying an undergraduate or master's degree, or a doctorate, and who are passionate about finance. In each case, there must be an evident financial need. Applicants must also demonstrate their determination to improve the lives of others through their career.

Types of grant
Scholarships of £500 are awarded to two students each year.

Applications
Applications can be made on the funder's website using an online form.

Sources of information
Funder's website.

Education

The All Saints Educational Trust

 £74,500 (2017/18)

Correspondent: Mr K. Mitchell, The Clerk, Knightrider House, 2 Knightrider Court, London EC4V 5AR (tel: 020 7248 8380; email: aset@aset.org.uk)

www.aset.org.uk

CC number: 312934

Eligibility
People Over the age of 18, studying a course at an accredited higher education institution in the UK. Courses must be either: teaching training courses (to either acquire Qualified Teacher Status, register with the General Teaching Council for Scotland or Northern Ireland, or to become better qualified teachers), or courses focused on religious education or home economics. Overseas students must have already acquired a first degree (or equivalent) at least two years prior to starting the postgraduate course that the scholarship is intended to fund. For further information on eligibility criteria, consult the trust's website.

Types of grant
Scholarships are available for up to three years towards tuition fees, related expenses and maintenance costs.

Exclusions
Scholarships are not currently awarded for further education (up to the standard of GCE Advanced Level, Scottish Highers, NVQ Level 3 or equivalent) or to cover the school fees of an applicant's children. Courses lasting less than a year are not normally considered and those who already have sufficient funds to sustain themselves while studying will not be supported. Scholarships cannot be an alternative to a student loan or government grant.

The trust's website states that the following are examples of purposes that will not be supported:

- 'Undergraduate courses in subjects other than education, even if the applicant proposes subsequently to acquire a teaching qualification in that subject'
- 'Courses in social work, special needs, youth work, or welfare'
- 'Courses in hospitality or catering (unless specifically focused on nutrition)'
- 'Initial training for church ministry, or courses designed to equip the applicant to deliver such training'
- 'Conference fees or associated costs'

Applications
Applicants should first complete an enquiry form to check their eligibility, this can be found on the trust's website or can be requested from the correspondent by post (include an sae). Once the trust has confirmed eligibility it will provide a full application form and pack. Three references will be required to support the application. Current deadlines for each stage of the application can be found on the trust's website. Applicants will be informed of the decision as soon as possible.

Financial information
Year end	30/06/2018
Income	£735,800
Total expenditure	£287,600

Further financial information
In 2017/18 a total of £74,500 was awarded as scholarships, grants and bursaries to individuals. The trust supported 19 scholars during the year, this included 11 new home scholars and two overseas scholars.

Other information
The trust also provides corporate awards and the All Saxsons Fellowship award which funds specific research projects as well as providing chaplaincy for students and staff at Middlesex Polytechnic.

Sources of information
Accounts; annual report; Charity Commission record; funder's website.

Engineering

The Coachmakers and Coach Harness Makers Charitable Trust 1977

 £30,800 (2017/18)

Correspondent: Comm. Mark Leaning, The Old Barn, Church Lane, Glentham, Market Rasen, Lincolnshire LN8 2EL (email: clerk@coachmakers.co.uk)

www.coachmakers.co.uk

CC number: 286521

Eligibility
People studying/working in the aerospace, automotive and coach-making or associated industries.

Types of grant
Grants are available to individuals in technical education and training, including apprenticeships. Awards are usually given towards general educational needs, research, study/travel overseas and maintenance expenses. There are various different awards, check the trust's website for detailed information.

Exclusions
The trust's website states that 'awards are as substantial as possible, but bursaries are allocated on an annual basis and, because funds cannot always be guaranteed, the Livery cannot accept commitments to individuals for long-term educational courses'.

Applications
Online application forms for the various awards and scholarships can be found on the trust's website.

Financial information
Year end	31/08/2018
Income	£208,700
Total expenditure	£227,600

Other information
The charity also makes awards to organisations.

Sources of information
Accounts; annual report; Charity Commission record; funder's website.

The Worshipful Company of Engineers Charitable Trust Fund
See record on page 84

The Hickman Education Foundation

 £18,300 (2017/18)

Correspondent: The Trustees, 15–17 Church Street, Stourbridge, West Midlands DY8 1LU (tel: 01384 376964; email: enquiries@fwca.co.uk)

https://hickmanfoundation.co.uk

CC number: 1164149

Eligibility
Young people interested in a career in engineering. Preference is given to individuals from deprived backgrounds.

Types of grant

The foundation advances the education and training of young people through:

- Wholly or partly funded apprenticeships
- Scholarships, maintenance allowances or grants tenable at any British university college or institution of higher or further education
- Business start-up grants

Applications

To apply for support contact the correspondent or enquire through the foundation's online form.

Financial information

Year end	31/03/2018
Income	£31,250
Total expenditure	£18,300

Further financial information

In 2017/18, £15,300 was awarded to sponsor apprenticeships and £3,000 was awarded to sponsor undergraduates.

Other information

The foundation also provides a mentoring service.

Sources of information

Accounts; annual report; Charity Commission record; funder's website.

ICE Benevolent Fund

 £134,300 (2018)

Correspondent: K. L. Barnett, Company Secretary, 5 Mill Hill Close, Haywards Heath, West Sussex RH16 1NY (tel: 01444 417979 (Monday to Friday, 8:45am to 5pm) or 0800 587 3428 (free 24-hour helpline); email: info@ icebenfund.com)

www.icebenfund.com

CC number: 1126595

Eligibility

Support is available to students on an ICE accredited civil engineering degree course, studying in the UK. Students must have reached the second year of their course.

Types of grant

Grants of up to £1,000 per term are awarded to students towards the cost of travel, equipment/course materials and general living expenses.

Applications

Prospective applicants should first complete the eligibility questionnaire on the funder's website. If eligible, applicants should then set up an online application account.

Financial information

Year end	31/12/2018
Income	£1,620,000
Total expenditure	£1,230,000

Further financial information

Grants were made to four students to help fund their studies. Note: the grant total has been estimated.

Other information

The charity runs a 24-hour helpline (0800 587 3428) which offers support and advice on personal and/or work-related issues. This service is free and strictly confidential. Face-to-face and specialist counselling (delivered by Anxiety UK) is available to those who need help with managing stress, anxiety and depression. The charity also offers subsidised housing in West Sussex through 33 rental properties. The charity's Back to Work initiative involves services such as personal career advice (with up to six coaching sessions), CV development, interview preparation and access to job vacancies through a partner company's exclusive job portal. The charity also offers debt management services for those in need of financial advice.

Sources of information

Accounts; annual report; Charity Commission record; funder's website.

The Institution of Engineering and Technology (IET)
See record on page 84

The Institution of Mechanical Engineers (IMechE)

Correspondent: Prizes and Awards Team, 1 Birdcage Walk, IMechE Prizes and Awards Department, Northgate Avenue, Westminster, London SW1H 9JJ (tel: 01284 717887; email: awards@ imeche.org)

 www.imeche.org/About-Us/ scholarships-and-awards

CC number: 206882

Eligibility

People undertaking education or training to begin or progress in a career in mechanical engineering. The institution offers a range of scholarships and grants for undergraduate students, apprentices, cadets, postgraduates and members of the institution. See the charity's website for eligibility criteria specific to each scheme.

Types of grant

The institution offers various grants, awards and scholarships which range in size and include both one-off and recurrent payments.

Applications

Details on how to apply for each scheme along with further information can be found on the charity's website.

Financial information

Year end	31/12/2018
Income	£23,510,000
Total expenditure	£26,120,000

Further financial information

In 2018 a total of £674,000 was awarded in prizes, awards and scholarships. We were unable to determine the total amount awarded to individuals for educational purposes.

Sources of information

Accounts; annual report; Charity Commission record; funder's website.

The Leathersellers' Company Charitable Fund

 £198,000 (2017/18)

Correspondent: David Santa-Olalla, Clerk, The Leathersellers' Company, 7 St Helen's Place, London EC3A 6AB (tel: 020 7330 1444; email: enquiries@ leathersellers.co.uk)

www.leathersellers.co.uk

CC number: 278072

Eligibility

Higher education students on a full-time degree course at any UK university. Applicants must have an unconditional offer for, or be enrolled on, a full-time course. Preference may be given to students from the Greater London area and to those studying engineering or subjects related to the leather trade, including fashion students working with leather.

Types of grant

Grants of up to £5,000 a year, for up to four years, are given to support higher education. According to the charity's website, the trustees may 'also consider full- or part-time courses that are not degrees but lead to nationally recognised qualifications. However, you will need to show how gaining this qualification would significantly improve your future employability/career prospects'.

Applications

Applications should be made using the online form on the Leathersellers' Company website. Guidance on what to include, deadlines for applications (usually around July for the next academic year) and other information is given on the charity's website.

Financial information

Year end	31/07/2018
Income	£1,940,000
Total expenditure	£3,250,000

Further financial information

Grants were awarded to 97 individuals during 2017/18.

Other information

The fund also gives grants to organisations for both education and a wide range of welfare causes. Both successful and unsuccessful applicants are informed in due course and the fund requests not to be contacted with queries regarding the outcome of the application, unless your contact address has changed.

Sources of information

Accounts; annual report; Charity Commission record; funder's website.

The Royal Academy of Engineering

Correspondent: Jacqueline Clay, 3–4 Carlton House Terrace, London SW1Y 5DG (tel: 020 7766 0648; email: els@raeng.org.uk)

 https://www.raeng.org.uk

CC number: 293074

Eligibility

Students studying an undergraduate degree at a UK Higher Education Institution who have completed at least one year of their degree and have two years left to complete before graduating.

Types of grant

Engineering Leaders Scholarships – provides support for undergraduates who have the potential to become leaders in engineering. Recipients will have the opportunity to acquire the skills needed to fulfil their potential by receiving £5,000 over their three years at university towards career personal development activities.

Sir Ralph Robins Scholarships – applicants for the Engineering Leaders Scholarship may also apply for this scholarship if they were eligible for free school meals, are the first generation from their immediate family to attend university or have been in local authority care. This is an additional £5,000 towards tuition fees and an optional paid internship at Rolls-Royce.

Applications

The application is a two stage process. A written application first needs to be submitted online then successful applicants will be invited to a selection event. There are detailed guidance notes available on the charity's website which should be read before applying. The application deadline is in January, see the charity's website for up-to-date details.

Financial information

Year end	31/03/2019
Income	£36,749,000
Total expenditure	£37,720,000

Further financial information

We were unable to determine a grant total for 2018/2019. In that year, the academy supported 108 students through the Engineering Leaders Scholarship scheme and three students through the Sir Ralph Robins Scholarship fund.

Other information

The academy also provides Sainsbury Management Fellowships for engineers with four to ten years of professional experience post-degree, wanting to undertake an MBA course at a major international business school. It also offers the Graduate Engineering Engagement Programme to increase the transition of diverse engineering graduates from diverse backgrounds into employment.

Sources of information

Accounts; annual report; Charity Commission record; funder's website.

Royal Commission for the Exhibition of 1851

 £2,690,000 (2018)

Correspondent: Nigel Williams, Secretary, 453 Sherfield Building, Imperial College, London SW7 2AZ (tel: 020 7594 8790; email: royalcom1851@imperial.ac.uk)

https://www.royalcommission1851.org

CC number: 206123

Eligibility

Early career scientists and engineers. Eligibility criteria varies between grant schemes. See guidance notes/terms and conditions on the charity's website to confirm your eligibility.

Types of grant

Research fellowships: for research into any of the physical or biological sciences i.e. in mathematics, applied science or in any branch of engineering.

Industrial fellowships: grants vary depending on the candidate. Grants can be made towards university fees or as a supplement to salary. In all cases, beneficiaries will receive up to £3,500 per annum for travel costs.

Design fellowships: up to £50,000 per annum is awarded for research projects. Grants have been made for projects on the future of business in design, the link between technology and productive industry, 3D printing, etc. A full list of previous projects can be found on the charity's website. Entries can be accepted by individuals and from formal or informal partnerships.

Industrial design studentships: grants are made for tuition fees (up to the normal UK course level) and some travel expenses. Grants include a stipend of £12,000 per annum (plus a £3,000 London weighting where applicable) and an annual allowance of £850 for materials.

Built Environment Fellowship: up to £50,000 per annum is awarded for research projects. Grants have been made for research into transport and the built environment, cycling and the built environment, housing for the 21st century, etc. A full list of previous projects can be found on the charity's website. Entries can be accepted by individuals and from formal or informal partnerships.

RAEng 1851 Enterprise Fellowship: up to £60,000 in funding (broken down as £45,000 in salary support and £15,000 for other support costs) is awarded to postdoctoral researchers or recent graduates with an innovation or technology they wish to develop.

Great Exhibition Scholarships: grants are awarded through the Institution of Engineering and Technology to those who have achieved three A grades at A-level or equivalent and are about to start an IET accredited undergraduate degree. Scholars receive an annual stipend.

Exclusions

Refer to guidance notes/terms and conditions for exclusions.

Applications

Applications for most schemes can be made online using a portal featured on the charity's website. If this is not possible for your chosen grant scheme, contact the correspondent for information on how to apply.

Financial information

Year end	31/12/2018
Income	£3,190,000
Total expenditure	£4,770,000

Further financial information

Grants are broken down as follows:

Research fellowships	9	£1,130,000
Industrial fellowships	12	£718,600
Industrial design studentships	11	£496,300
Enterprise fellowships	3	£187,500
Design fellowships	1	£100,000
Great Exhibition fellowships	10	£57,000

Other information

Special Awards are made to organisations pursuing specific projects (and to individuals for travel and study) for STEM education and outreach. Note: Special Awards cannot be awarded to individuals for university courses or postgraduate research. For more information, and for details of previous projects that have received funding, see the charity's website.

Sources of information

Accounts; annual report; Charity Commission record; funder's website.

South Wales Institute of Engineers Educational Trust

£ £2,000 (2017/18)

Correspondent: Megan Hardy, Administrative officer, Floor 2, Cambrian Buildings, Mount Stuart Square, Cardiff Bay, Cardiff CF10 5FL (tel: 029 2063 0561; email: megan. hardy@swieet2007.org.uk)

 swieet2007.org

CC number: 1013538

Eligibility

Students and apprentices undertaking a recognised engineering course in Wales.

Types of grant

Grants are awarded to undergraduates, students and apprentices to support their studies.

Applications

Applicants should contact the correspondent by email for further details, indicating their interest and level of study (e.g. undergraduate). Applicants may be invited for an interview.

Financial information

Year end	30/09/2018
Income	£23,500
Total expenditure	£62,900

Further financial information

Full accounts were not available to view on the Charity Commission's website due to the charity's low income. We have therefore estimated the grant total based on the charity's total expenditure.

Other information

The trust also gives support to organisations, engineering graduates in their first years of work and school age children who are deciding on their career path. It also administers the William Norman Thomas Travel Award which provides grants to members of institutes to travel abroad to complete a research project related to their work. The trust also administers the David Douglas award which offers grants to professional engineers and postgraduate students to produce a research paper to be published on the trust's website.

Sources of information

Charity Commission record; funder's website.

Women's Engineering Society

Correspondent: Sally Sudworth, Honorary Secretary, Michael Faraday House, Six Hills Way, Stevenage SG1 2AY (tel: 01438 765506; email: info@wes.org.uk)

 https://www.wes.org.uk

CC number: 1008913

Eligibility

Women beginning a recognised first engineering degree or HND course at a British university or college who, without funding, would be unable to take up their place on the course due to inadequate funding or would suffer undue hardship in doing so. Applicants should:

- Have a conditional or unconditional offer at a UK university or college
- Intend to work as an engineer in the UK upon completion of their course
- Take out a student loan to support themselves at university (if applicable)

Full eligibility criteria can be found on the charity's website.

Types of grant

Grants of between £500 and £1,000 are made to help with costs incurred when undertaking study.

Exclusions

Access courses and free-standing foundation years are not supported.

Applications

Contact the charity for information on how to apply.

Financial information

Year end	31/03/2019
Income	£389,400
Total expenditure	£379,500

Further financial information

No grants were made during 2018/19.

Other information

Awards are also made to female engineers who have made outstanding contributions to the field.

Sources of information

Accounts; annual report; Charity Commission record; funder's website.

Environment and agriculture

The Douglas Bomford Trust

£ £16,100 (2017/18)

Correspondent: Alan Plom, Secretary, Bullock Building, University Way, Cranfield, Bedford MK45 3QH (tel: 01234 750876; email: enquiries@dbt. org.uk)

 www.dbt.org.uk

CC number: 1121785

Eligibility

People involved in the education, research and practice of agricultural engineering and mechanisation who are aiming to become professional engineers or scientists and intend to work applying their expertise to agricultural and land-related problems. Priority is given to individuals who work in areas of particular national or technical importance and those who can receive part of the costs from other sources. Some connection with the UK is required, either through nationality, residency, or place of learning/ registration.

Types of grant

The trust can offer: travel scholarships for educational tours overseas, conferences and for presenting papers at international conferences; scholarships to undergraduate students; support towards postgraduate study and research; discretionary awards in cases of hardship; and various prizes to students showing high academic achievements or to the authors of papers published in allied journals.

Applications

There are different grant schemes for travel awards, undergraduate students, postgraduate research and other awards. Application forms and details for each of them can be found on the trust's website.

Financial information

Year end	31/03/2018
Income	£156,200
Total expenditure	£181,700

Further financial information

The grant total was broken down as follows:

Studentships	£7,600
Discretionary awards	£3,500
Travel grants	£2,600
Other awards	£1,350
Research programme	£1,000

Other information

The trust also awards grants to organisations, mainly to institutes of higher education for research.

Sources of information

Accounts; annual report; Charity Commission record; funder's website.

Chadacre Agricultural Trust

 £91,600 (2018/19)

Correspondent: The Governors, The Willows, Bury Road, Lackford, Bury St Edmunds, Suffolk IP28 6HT (tel: 01284 728316; email: estate.office@elveden.com)

 www.chadacre-trust.org.uk

CC number: 310496

Eligibility

The trust offers a number of different grants:

- **Student grants:** people living Suffolk, Norfolk, Essex or Cambridgeshire who have been accepted for training or study in agriculture or a related subject
- **Farming education grants:** Farmers and other people working within agriculture who wish to acquire new skills. Applicants must be based or have links with, Suffolk, Norfolk, Essex or Cambridgeshire
- **Research grants:** Postgraduate students undertaking research that will be of definable benefit to farming in the eastern counties. Students must be under the supervision of a senior research leader at an appropriate centre within the UK

Types of grant

Grants are awarded for a range of purposes:

- **Student grants:** grants are awarded to enable individuals to study the theory of practice of agriculture, farming and related subjects on a relevant diploma, certificate, degree or higher degree course
- **Farming education grants:** grants are awarded to enable individuals to acquire new skills
- **Research grants:** grants are awarded to promote research in to all aspects of agriculture and farming, ecology and nature conservation when it is likely to have a practical outcome for farming

Exclusions

The trust will not provide support to those who are eligible to receive funding from the state.

Applications

To request an application form, contact the trust using the form on its website.

Financial information

Year end	31/03/2019
Income	£269,100
Total expenditure	£237,700

Further financial information

In 2017/18 a total of £42,300 was awarded to 29 students and was distributed as follows:

Agriculture students	19
Veterinary students	6
Farriery apprenticeships	4

A further £49,300 was awarded as grant aid to 11 research projects.

Other information

Grants are also given to projects with the aims of educating the public on farming.

Sources of information

Accounts; annual report; Charity Commission record; funder's website.

Forest Industries Education and Provident Fund
See record on page 85

Gardeners' Royal Benevolent Society (Perennial)
See record on page 86

The Dick Harrison Trust

 £720 (2017/18)

Correspondent: Mr T. Parsons, Secretary, H&H Land and Property Ltd, Borderway, Montgomery Way, Rosehill Industrial Estate, Carlisle, Cumbria CA1 2RS (tel: 01228 406260; email: tim.parsons@hhland.co.uk)

www.dickharrisontrust.org.uk

CC number: 702365

Eligibility

Students undertaking further education courses/training in rural estate management or livestock auctioneering who were born, reside in or have parents residing in Scotland, Cumbria or Northumberland.

Types of grant

Grants are awarded towards fees, books, equipment, maintenance/living expenses and study or travel in the UK and abroad.

Applications

Application forms can be downloaded from the trust's website. Applicants are required to provide two references and attend an interview.

Financial information

Year end	31/10/2018
Income	£1,200
Total expenditure	£800

Further financial information

Full accounts were not available to view on the Charity Commission's website due to the charity's low income. We have therefore estimated the grant total based on the charity's total expenditure.

Sources of information

Charity Commission record; funder's website.

The Institute of Chartered Foresters

Correspondent: The Trustees, Educational and Scientific Trust, Institute of Chartered Foresters, 59 George Street, Edinburgh EH2 2JG (tel: 0131 240 1425; email: icf@charteredforesters.org)

www.charteredforesters.org

Eligibility

Students of forestry and related disciplines.

Types of grant

Grants are available for students and others at an early stage in their career in forestry. There is a travel bursary of £500, professional development awards, and events bursaries of £100 for students to attend the ICF National Conference or Study Tour. There are also several awards programmes for journal articles, work placement exchanges with Canada and honorary fellowships.

Applications

The institute's website lists all the awards available and how to apply. It also provides full eligibility criteria and examples of past award winners.

Sources of information

Funder's website.

The Alice McCosh Trust
See record on page 30

Perry Foundation

 £115,100 (2017/18)

Correspondent: Gordon Bennett, Secretary, 16 Sandgate Lane, London SW18 3JP (tel: 0208 874 1460 or 07722 332858; email: perry.gbennett@gmail.com)

https://www.perryfoundation.co.uk

CC number: 310885

Eligibility
People studying a PhD in an agriculture-related discipline, including veterinary disciplines.

Types of grant
Study Awards: grants of up to £12,000 for each year of a PhD project, normally for around three or four years.

Arnold Hitchcock Travel Awards: grants totalling £1,000 in each year (with a limit of £500 available for each of the two review periods) for travel and accommodation costs to enable Perry Foundation students to attend meetings, seminars or symposia relevant to their PhD project.

Exclusions
Retrospective applications for travel grants will not be considered.

Applications
Application forms for Study Awards are available to download from the charity's website. Completed forms, plus a CV and cover letter, should be returned by email to the correspondent. Applications typically close at the end of October. Shortlisted applicants will be invited to attend an interview in the following January. Applications for Travel Awards can be made at any time of the year, by writing an email to the Secretary. Applications should include:
- Full details of the reasons for the travel and estimates of costs
- Details of any joint funding
- Endorsement from the applicant's university

Financial information
Year end	30/09/2018
Income	£145,700
Total expenditure	£158,300

Further financial information
During 2017/18, the charity awarded £114,100 in PhD scholarships and £1,000 in travel grants.

Sources of information
Accounts; annual report; Charity Commission record; funder's website.

The Henry Plumb Foundation

 £12,200 (2018)

Correspondent: The Trustees, Bat's Loft, The Sheep Centre, Malvern, Worcestershire WR13 6PH (tel: 01684 899255; email: info@thehenryplumbfoundation.org.uk)

www.thehenryplumbfoundation.org.uk

CC number: 1151449

Eligibility
Young people aged 18 to 35 with interests, business ideas or study plans that will lead to a careers in the agricultural or food industry.

Types of grant
Funding of between £500 and £3,000 is given towards travel expenses for overseas exchanges, courses and events (not including conferences), management courses and internships.

Applications
Application forms and further guidelines are available to download from the foundation's website.

Financial information
Year end	31/12/2018
Income	£64,200
Total expenditure	£36,600

Further financial information
In 2018 a total of £24,400 was awarded to individuals. We estimate that £12,200 was awarded towards business start-ups with the remaining £12,200 given for education. Nine new scholars and two existing ones received help from the foundation during the year.

Other information
In 2018 the foundation received 15 applications for help, ten of these were invited to interview and nine were successful.

Sources of information
Accounts; annual report; Charity Commission record; funder's website.

Studley College Trust

 £98,200 (2017/18)

Correspondent: Christine Copeman, Trust Secretary, Kernow House, Lower Boddington, Daventry, Northamptonshire NN11 6YB (tel: 01327 260165; email: studleyct@btinternet.com)

www.studleytrust.co.uk

CC number: 528787

Eligibility
British or Irish nationals aged 18 to 30 (except cases of genuine career change) who are enrolled or intending to enrol on a college/university course connected with UK land-based activities (agriculture, horticulture, forestry, fish farming, food technology, agricultural or horticultural marketing, arboriculture, agricultural engineering, game keeping and estate skills) whose progress is obstructed by lack of funds. Practical experience and/or a strong rural background are required. The trust is looking to support students in their early qualifications.

Types of grant
Grants of up to £2,000 per academic year towards accommodation costs, transport, food, books and study materials, specialist clothing, external tests/examination fees and educational trips (between £500 and £2,000). The trust also provides scholarships through the Professional Gardeners' Guild, Nuffield Farming Scholarships Trust and Tresco Abbey Gardens, as well as bursaries for studying at certain colleges – refer to the charity's website for more information.

Exclusions
Grants are not usually awarded for:
- Master's degree courses or PhDs
- Courses in the following subjects: veterinary science; animal behaviour; food science; farriery; floristry; animal care; environmental studies; countryside and land management; equine management; landscape architecture
- Hire purchase payments
- Support for dependants
- Overdraft and loan repayments
- Long-term housing costs
- Students on industrial placements more than six weeks in length

Applications
Apply in writing to the correspondent. Applications will be considered in July and October each year, deadlines are usually 1 June and 1 October. Those wishing to apply to one of the trust's partner colleges should apply directly to the preferred college via their student support team (details are listed on the trust's website). Applicants should refer any queries to the correspondent.

Financial information
Year end	30/06/2018
Income	£151,900
Total expenditure	£123,700

Further financial information
A total of £98,200 was paid in 105 grants and bursaries to support the education of students of agriculture, horticulture and other land-based activities.

Sources of information

Accounts; annual report; Charity Commission record; funder's website.

Heritage and conservation

The Zibby Garnett Travelling Fellowship

 £8,800 (2017/18)

Correspondent: Julia Foster, Administrator, Upper Morgans, Shortbridge Road, Piltdown, Uckfield, East Sussex TN22 3XA (tel: 01923 245431; email: info@zibbygarnett.org)

www.zibbygarnett.org

CC number: 1081403

Eligibility

People who are studying (or have recently been studying) for a recognised degree/diploma at university or college and those who are in the formative years of their career such as trade apprentices, trainee architects and landscape architects who wish to travel to widen their knowledge of conservation. Applicants must be UK residents and hold a UK bank account (however, they do not need to be British).

Types of grant

Grants of between £300 and £2,000 are awarded to enable individuals to travel overseas to study a subject in one of the following fields: historic buildings; historical designed landscapes and historic gardens; allied trades, techniques, skills and crafts; or artefacts and decorative arts. Applicants must choose their own subject and arrange their placement before applying, non-British applicants should avoid choosing their home country as the destination. Imaginative and unusual ideas that will broaden the applicant's understanding of the subject are encouraged. Grants can contribute to and in some cases, meet almost all of the cost of a study placement.

Exclusions

Grants are not given retrospectively, for placements in the UK, for conferences/formal courses or holidays. Support is intended for practical work in conservation, not new work.

Applications

Application forms can be downloaded from the charity's website. Applications should be submitted along with a CV, small photograph, confirmation of overseas placement and a letter of support from a current UK tutor/employer. Shortlisted applicants will be invited to an interview usually in London. Check the charity's website for further information and current deadlines.

Financial information

Year end	31/03/2018
Income	£10,900
Total expenditure	£19,200

Further financial information

Full accounts were not available to view on the Charity Commission's website due to the charity's low income. We have therefore estimated the grant total based on the charity's total expenditure.

Other information

Successful applicants will be expected to produce a written report and presentation to the trustees.

Sources of information

Charity Commission record; funder's website.

The Hellenic Foundation

 £1,100 (2018)

Correspondent: The Trustees, 4th Floor, 24–26 Baltic Street West, London EC1Y 0RP (tel: 020 7251 5100)

hfc-worldwide.org

CC number: 326301

Eligibility

Students studying the culture, tradition and heritage of Greece, particularly in subjects involving education, research, music, theatre productions, exhibitions and concerts.

Types of grant

One-off grants for projects involving education, research, music and dance for books and university symposia.

Applications

Apply in writing to the correspondent.

Financial information

Year end	31/12/2018
Income	£15,100
Total expenditure	£2,500

Further financial information

Full accounts were not available to view on the Charity Commission's website due to the charity's low income. We have therefore estimated the grant total based on the charity's total expenditure.

Sources of information

Charity Commission record.

Anna Plowden Trust

 £58,800 (2017/18)

Correspondent: Francis Plowden, Secretary, 4 Highbury Road, London SW19 7PR (tel: 020 8879 9841; email: info@annaplowdentrust.org.uk)

www.annaplowdentrust.org.uk

CC number: 1072236

Eligibility

People who wish to pursue a qualification in heritage conservation and practicing conservators in the UK who are looking to develop their skills in conservation.

Types of grant

Scholarships are available for individuals (usually graduates) towards the cost of studying for qualifications in order to enter the conservation profession. Refer to the trust's website for details of all current grant programmes.

Exclusions

Conservation students, PhD students and interns are not eligible to apply for a continuing professional development (CPD) grant. Grants are not given to conservators working outside the UK. Grants will not cover living costs or courses focused on the conservation of non-moveable heritage (e.g. building or natural environment conservation).

Applications

Application forms, further guidelines and current deadlines for each type of grant are available from the trust's website. Applications should be submitted sufficiently ahead of the relevant deadline as the trust may take up to four weeks to consider applications. Applications for funding are also invited through advertisements in national conservation journals.

Financial information

Year end	30/11/2018
Income	£225,100
Total expenditure	£107,700

Further financial information

In 2017/18 grants totalling £83,800 were awarded to individuals and can be broken down as follows: A total of 44 continuing professional development (CPD) grants were awarded totalling around £25,000; we have estimated that scholarships awarded to 29 students totalled around £58,800.

Sources of information

Accounts; annual report; Charity Commission record; funder's website.

Hospitality

The William Barry Trust

 £28,000 (2017/18)

Correspondent: The Trustees, c/o HTS Management Holdings, Church Road, Lane End, Buckinghamshire HP14 3HH. (email: williambarrytrust@gmail.com)

 www.williambarrytrust.org.uk

CC number: 272551

Eligibility

People over the age of 16 in vocational studies and training, such as hospitality, hotel management, technical crafts, or artistic occupations (singing, dancing, acting, etc.).

Types of grant

Grants are available on a one-off and recurrent basis, to assist with education and training fees for courses, workshops, exhibitions, lectures, seminars, and other educational activities.

Exclusions

Grants are not available for career development or postgraduate degrees.

Applications

Candidates are required to include an introductory letter explaining:

- Why they are applying for your particular course
- What they hope to achieve, and how the trust might help them with this
- How they intend to fund any remaining costs

Financial information

Year end	30/04/2018
Income	£26,600
Total expenditure	£50,500

Other information

The trust also supports organisations.

Sources of information

Accounts; annual report; Charity Commission record; funder's website.

HIT Scotland

 £192,400 (2018)

Correspondent: The Trustees, PO Box 14598, Milnathort, Kinross KY13 9WS (tel: 01577 865231; email: info@hitscotland.co.uk)

 https://hitscotland.co.uk

OSCR number: SC047053

Eligibility

People over the age of 16 (although, some schemes require applicants to be over the age of 18) working in, or studying towards, a career in the Scottish hospitality industry.

Types of grant

The charity offers a wide variety of scholarships which are split into three categories:

- **Business empowerment:** scholarships of this type are designed to enhance a scholar's business skills. Scholarships are available in areas such as management, leadership and executive leadership
- **Operational empowerment:** these scholarships aim to help enhance and grow key skills required for various hospitality roles. Scholarships are available in areas such as sales, digital marketing, customer experience, etc.
- **Inspirational empowerment:** scholarships are designed to inspire personal growth both in and outside the workplace. Scholarships in green tourism, future leadership and others are available

For more information on specific schemes, see the charity's website.

Exclusions

If a scholar moves from Scotland, or leaves the hospitality industry, their scholarship will be revoked. Previous scholarship winners cannot reapply for at least two years.

Applications

Application forms are available on the charity's website when applications open. Applications usually open in September and close in November. If successful after shortlisting, applicants will be invited to attend an interview in January. Scholarship winners are announced in February.

Financial information

Year end	31/12/2018
Income	£685,700
Total expenditure	£758,200

Other information

The charity also holds events, conferences and awards ceremonies.

Sources of information

Accounts; annual report; OSCR record; funder's website.

The Mitchells & Butlers Charitable Trusts

 £9,100 (2017/18)

Correspondent: The Trustees, Mitchells & Butlers, 73–77 Euston Road, London NW1 2QS (tel: 0121 498 6514; email: charitable.trusts@mbplc.com)

 www.mbtrusts.org.uk

CC number: 528922

Eligibility

The following people are eligible to apply for a grant:

- **The Mitchell Fund** – employees and former employees of Mitchells & Butlers, Six Continents and Bass Companies who are experiencing hardship
- **The Welfare Fund** – people over the age of 16 who are resident in Birmingham or Smethwick and are studying at secondary school or are undertaking higher/further education in the UK. Internal applications can be made by employees, ex-employees and children of employees of Mitchells & Butlers and 'successors in business' of the company
- **The Scholarship Fund** – students studying courses relating to brewing, catering, hotel management or hospitality management

Further eligibility guidelines are available on the charity's website.

Types of grant

The charity administers a number of different funds to be distributed for educational purposes:

- **The Welfare Fund:** grants are available to assist students attending school, university and other places of higher education. Financial assistance can be used towards course fees, books, equipment, uniform, travel and other educational costs and necessities
- **The Scholarship Fund:** grants to assist with course fees, books, equipment and other necessities for the course

Exclusions

Support is not given towards master's degree courses.

Applications

Application forms for the Welfare Fund and application deadlines can be found on the trust's website. Application forms for the Scholarship Fund can be obtained by emailing the correspondent.

Applications for the Mitchell Fund can be made through the Licensed Trade Charities website, details of which can be found on the Mitchells & Butlers Charitable Trust's website.

Financial information

Year end	05/04/2018
Income	£118,600
Total expenditure	£78,300

Further financial information

In 2017/18 the charity awarded 21 grants to individuals for education and welfare purposes totalling £11,300. The distribution of grants is broken down as follows:

The Welfare Fund	19	£9,000
The Scholarship Fund	1	£130
The Mitchell Fund	1	£2,200

Other information
The charity administers four funds (The Welfare Fund, The Scholarship Fund, The Mitchell Fund and The Common Investment Fund) which are all administered under the same Charity Commission number. The Welfare Fund and Scholarship Fund also support organisations. The Mitchell Fund has established links with the Licensed Trade Charity and funds all grants the charity gives to employees and ex-employees of Mitchell and Butler.

Sources of information
Accounts; annual report; Charity Commission record; funder's website.

Media, journalism and communication

The Journalism Diversity Fund

Correspondent: The Trustees, National Council for the Training of Journalists, New Granary, Station Road, Newport, Saffron Walden, Essex CB11 3PL (tel: 01799 544014; email: journalismdiversityfund@nctj.com)

 https://www.journalismdiversity fund.com

CC number: 1026685

Eligibility
The fund wishes to support people from socially and ethnically diverse backgrounds who wish to train in journalism. Applicants must meet all of the following criteria:
- Have secured a place on a National Council for the Training of Journalists (NCTJ) accredited course
- Be a British citizen residing in the UK
- Be able to demonstrate a genuine commitment and potential to be a successful journalist through a range of journalism-related work experience (due to the high standard of applicants, experience on a student newspaper is not sufficient)
- Not be in receipt of any other bursary award

Types of grant
Bursaries to assist people in need who wish to undertake a NCTJ-accredited journalism courses. Grants can be used towards the cost of course fees and living expenses. Successful applicants will also be paired with a working journalist to

mentor and support them through their studies.

Applications
Application forms and guidelines can be found on the fund's website. Consult the website for current deadlines. Shortlisted applicants will be required to attend an interview.

Financial information

Year end	30/06/2018
Income	£241,300
Total expenditure	£244,300

Further financial information
In 2017/18 a total of £244,300 was awarded to 40 individuals. However, we were unable to determine how much was given in educational grants.

Other information
The fund is administered by the National Council For The Training of Journalists. In 2017/18 the fund received 80 applications, 45 applicants were invited to interview and 40 applicants were successful.

Sources of information
Accounts; annual report; Charity Commission record; funder's website.

Royal Television Society

Correspondent: The Trustees, Kildare House, 3 Dorset Rise, London EC4Y 8EN (tel: 020 7822 2810; email: bursaries@rts.org.uk)

 https://rts.org.uk/education-training/rts-bursaries

CC number: 313728

Eligibility
Students from lower income backgrounds studying TV production and journalism or related subjects such as physics, maths and computer science. Both current first years and those about to begin a degree/HND level 5 or 6 course are encouraged to apply. Applicants must meet the following criteria in order to be eligible:
- Be a UK national or have permanent residence or indefinite leave to remain in the UK, or be the relevant family member of a UK national
- Have been ordinarily resident in the UK for three years prior to the start date of the course
- Have a household income below £30,000 (for technology bursaries) or £25,000 (for production and journalism bursaries)
- Have accepted an offer from a university as their firm choice

Further eligibility guidelines are available on the society's website.

Types of grant
The society offers two bursary schemes for undergraduates – a Television Production and Broadcast Journalism Bursary and a Technology Bursary. Grants are paid in yearly instalments of £1,000, for undergraduates on specified relevant courses. Successful applicants will also receive a free student membership of the Royal Television Society while studying, and one year's free full membership (after graduation), as well as affiliate membership of the Hospital Club while studying, and mentoring and placement opportunities. Full guidance notes and FAQs are available on the RTS website. Broadcast Journalism applicants will also automatically be considered for the Steve Hewlett Scholarship which offers an extra £1,000 per year.

Applications
Application forms are available on the society's website during submission windows. Applications must be submitted electronically and be accompanied by a copy of the applicant's UCAS personal statement and an example of previous work (although this is not a requirement). Details of a referee will also be required. Applications must be submitted by the deadline, details of which can be found on the charity's website. The society advises that applications should not be left until the last minute as IT systems will be busy and applications may take some time to upload.

Financial information

Year end	31/12/2018
Income	£3,930,000
Total expenditure	£3,510,000

Further financial information
In 2018, 32 bursaries were awarded, 25 of these were production and broadcast journalism bursaries and seven were technology bursaries. We were unable to determine the grant total.

Other information
Successful applicants of the Technology Bursary are also offered tours of eight organisations including the BBC, Channel 4, ITV, and Sky. The society runs a number of events including conferences, masterclasses, careers fairs and award ceremonies.

Sources of information
Accounts; annual report; Charity Commission record; funder's website.

George Viner Memorial Fund Trust

 £27,100 (2017/18)

Correspondent: Lorna Jones, Fund Administrator, National Union of Journalists, Headland House, 72 Acton Street, London WC1X 9NB (tel: 020 7843 3700; email: georgeviner@nuj.org.uk)

 www.nuj.org.uk/rights/george-viner-memorial-fund

CC number: 328142

Eligibility

Students from black and Asian backgrounds who have received a formal offer of a place on an industry recognised course based in the UK or Ireland, but have not yet commenced their studies. Courses must be within the fields of print, broadcasting, photographic or online journalism. Applicants must be UK or Irish citizens who intend to continue their education or start a career within the British/Irish media industry.

Types of grant

Grants are awarded for tuition fees, travel expenses, books and other necessities. Course fees are paid in instalments directly to the institution. Opportunities to attend open days, conferences and meetings in the relevant area of journalism are also provided. Successful applicants will be expected to assist with the fund's publicity, attend an awards ceremony and produce a report at the end of their course.

Exclusions

Individuals who have already received a student loan/sponsorship and previous recipients of an award from the trust are not supported.

Applications

Application forms and guidelines can be obtained from the trust's website once the funding round opens. Applications must include examples of journalistic work, a course offer letter and the names of two referees. Completed application forms must be returned with a signed conditions form to the correspondent by email or post. Shortlisted applicants will be invited to an interview. For current opening dates and deadlines, consult the trust's website. Note that late submissions will not be accepted.

Financial information

Year end	28/02/2018
Income	£36,300
Total expenditure	£29,000

Sources of information

Accounts; annual report; Charity Commission record; funder's website.

Yr Ymddiriedolaeth Ddarlledu Gymreig (The Welsh Broadcasting Trust)

 £24,100 (2017)

Correspondent: The Trustees, Islwyn, Lôn Terfyn, Morfa Nefyn, Pwllheli, Gwynedd LL53 6AP (tel: 01758 720132; email: post@ymddiried.cymru)

 ymddiried.cymru/home

CC number: 700780

Eligibility

Applicants must meet at least one of the following criteria:
- Applicant was born in Wales
- Applicant is a Welsh Speaker
- Applicant has lived in Wales full time for at least two years prior to the application

Applicants should be wishing to expand their skills in film, TV and new media.

Applicants applying for the 'Owen Edwards Scholarship' must have lived in Wales for at least five years and have already embarked on a career in the creative industries.

Types of grant

The trust supports participation in appropriate part-time/full-time and short training courses as well as higher education courses (not including first degrees or performing arts courses). The trust also provides travel grants to help applicants to display their work at festivals or recognised media marketing events. In addition, the trust administers the 'Owen Edwards Scholarship' which awards a maximum of £30,000 over a period of three years towards a specific professional development plan. Activities supported include higher level vocational courses, a doctorate in relevant a subject, internships and work experience. Successful applicants will also be provided with a personal mentor throughout the scholarship period.

Exclusions

The trust does not fund first degrees, production costs, time off work to develop an idea and performing arts or journalism courses.

Applications

Application forms for financial assistance are available from the trust's website. Those wishing to apply for the Owen Edwards Scholarship must submit a comprehensive document of around 5,000 words including a CV, relevant skills and experience, personal development plan, details of the company/organisation where the activity will take place, a financial plan and two personal references. Further information is available on the trust's website. There are three official closing dates every year: 1 March, 1 July, and 1 November.

Financial information

Year end	31/12/2017
Income	£13,200
Total expenditure	£53,600

Further financial information

Full accounts were not available to view on the Charity Commission's website due to the charity's low income. We have therefore estimated the grant total based on the charity's total expenditure.

Other information

Grants are also made to organisations that promote educational resources and skills development for the benefit of the media sector.

Sources of information

Charity Commission record; funder's website.

Medicine

Alzheimer's Society

Correspondent: Grants Team, 43–44 Crutched Friars, London EC3N 2AE (email: grantenquiries@alzheimers.org.uk)

 https://www.alzheimer's.org.uk/research/researchers/our-funding-schemes/phd-studentships

CC number: 296645

Eligibility

Students who are planning on studying a PhD at a UK university, with the ultimate aim of gaining a career in dementia research. The proposed research project must fall into one of the following areas:
- Biomedical research
- Care, implementation and public health research

Medical/healthcare students who are half way through their undergraduate degree (year two of a three/four-year degree or year three of a four-year degree) are also eligible for funding.

Types of grant

Studentships of up to £85,000 for up to three years (or for up to five years for part-time study) towards PhD fees, consumables, equipment, etc. London-based applications will receive up to £91,000 for the duration of the course. Grants include a stipend of around £15,000 to £16,000 per year.

Undergraduate bursaries of £200 per week for up to eight weeks (up to a maximum of £1,600) are awarded for short research projects. Up to £500 can also be claimed for project expenses.

Exclusions

Applications can be made online on the charity's website. If successful at the shortlisting stage, applicants will be invited to attend an interview at the charity's office in London.

Applications

Funding is not available for studentships that have already commenced. The society will provide PhD fees up to the UK/EU rate only. For undergraduate bursaries, those who have had the opportunity to undertake research (for example, those on intercalated BSc degrees) are not eligible to apply. Bursaries cannot be awarded for projects that make up part of the degree, or for projects that will take place overseas. Applications from graduates, first year and final year students will not be accepted.

Financial information

Year end	31/03/2018
Income	£106,950,000
Total expenditure	£112,480,000

Further financial information

We were unable to determine the grant total.

Other information

The Alzheimer's Society funds various organisations and universities for research projects aimed at understanding the underlying causes of dementia, improving diagnosis and care, identifying ways to prevent dementia and searching for a cure. A list of all previous and current research projects funded by the charity can be found on its website.

Sources of information

Accounts; annual report; funder's website.

The Worshipful Society of Apothecaries General Charity Ltd

 £38,000 (2017/18)

Correspondent: The Trustees, Apothecaries Hall, Black Friars Lane, London EC4V 6EJ (tel: 020 7236 1189; email: clerk@apothecaries.org)

www.apothecaries.org

CC number: 284450

Eligibility

Candidates must be final-year medical or pharmaceutical students who are in

need. Undergraduates taking courses in history of medicine and the ethics and philosophy of healthcare can also be supported.

Types of grant

Grants of £1,000 provided on a one-off basis to final year medical or pharmacy students in the UK.

Applications

Every year, the trustees write to the deans of medical schools, and to the charity Pharmacist Support, seeking the nomination of one undergraduate to receive financial assistance to be submitted by 30 June. Recommendations are considered in July and the grants are disbursed in August. Additional meetings can also be held as required.

Financial information

Year end	31/08/2018
Income	£104,900
Total expenditure	£112,900

Other information

The charity also supports a student at the Guildhall School of Music and Drama and provides awards at the London medical schools, Christ's Hospital School and the City of London Academy (Southwark).

Sources of information

Accounts; annual report; Charity Commission record; funder's website.

The Barbers' Company General Charities

 £7,400 (2017/18)

Correspondent: Clerk, Barber Surgeons Hall, 1A Monkwell Square, London EC2Y 5BL (tel: 020 7606 0741; email: clerk@barberscompany.org)

https://barberscompany.org

CC number: 265579

Eligibility

Students involved in the medical profession.

Types of grant

The charity carries out most of its charitable activities through making grants to organisations who then distribute the funds to students. One of its main grants is to provide The McNee Awards, of £2,500 a year, which are made to London medical students who already have a degree and so are not eligible for grants. To find out more information on the different awards see the 'How to Apply' section on the charity's website.

Applications

Each award has a different application process and correspondent. For

information see the 'How to Apply' section on their website. For all general enquiries contact the correspondent.

Financial information

Year end	31/08/2018
Income	£423,200
Total expenditure	£260,200

Further financial information

Grants totalling £7,400 were made to six individuals in 2017/18. The charity also made grants of £245,800 to organisations, including a grant of £25,000 to the BMA Charities to provide the McNee Awards.

Other information

The Worshipful Company of Barbers administer three funds: Barbers' Company General Charities (Charity Commission No: 265579); Barbers' Amalgamated Charities (Charity Commission No: 213085); The Haymarket Charitable Trust (Charity Commission No: 276231). These funds make grants to individuals for educational and welfare purposes. The company was originally established to benefit both barbers and surgeons but the latter is now its main focus.

Sources of information

Accounts; annual report; Charity Commission record; funder's website.

BMA Charities Trust Fund

 £278,500 (2018)

Correspondent: BMA Advisors, BMA Charities, BMA House, Tavistock Square, London WC1H 9JP (tel: 020 7383 6142; email: info.bmacharities@ bma.org.uk)

https://www.bma.org.uk/about-us/ who-we-are/bma-charities

CC number: 219102

Eligibility

Doctors and medical students who are in financial difficulty are eligible to apply. Membership of the BMA is not required in order to apply.

Types of grant

A list of what can be supported can be found on the charity's website. Typically the trustees award grants for essential items such as: utility bills, travel and disability equipment; GMC fees and professional indemnity insurance; the costs of taking the PLAB exams.

Exclusions

Grants are not made for debts, private medical expenses, legal fees, career development costs, mortgages, or childcare costs.

Applications

Contact the correspondent for information on which funds are currently available and how to apply.

Financial information

Year end	31/12/2018
Income	£554,700
Total expenditure	£402,900

Further financial information

In 2018 the trust awarded 175 grants to individuals.

Sources of information

Accounts; annual report; Charity Commission record; funder's website.

British Pharmacological Society

 £92,900 (2018)

Correspondent: The Trustees, The Schild Plot, 16 Angel Gate, London EC1V 2PT (tel: 020 7239 0171; email: info@bps.ac.uk)

https://www.bps.ac.uk

CC number: 1030623

Eligibility

There are currently two schemes open to non-members of the society. The **A.J. Clark Studentship** is available to graduates in pharmacology or a related discipline who are intending to carry our research in pharmacology, leading to the degree of PhD in a recognised department in the UK or Ireland. **Vacation Studentships** are open to undergraduates in universities across the UK and Ireland for projects into exploratory or applied pharmacology and experimental/translational medicine and clinical research.

Types of grant

A.J. Clark Studentship: grants are made towards course fees (paid at the rate applicable to EU students), research costs (up to £10,000) and travel/other fees to support attendance at non-society meetings (up to £1,000).

Vacation Studentships: up to £1,850 is paid for up to ten weeks to help with living costs during a research project.

Applications

Refer to the society's website for details on the application process and current deadlines.

Financial information

Year end	31/12/2018
Income	£4,190,000
Total expenditure	£4,920,000

Further financial information

During 2018, just one AJ Clark Studentship was awarded totalling

£92,900. No Vacation Studentships were awarded.

Other information

Most of the society's grants and prizes are available only to current members of the society. During 2018, the charity awarded over £40,000 in bursaries to members for travel to conferences. For more information, see the website.

Sources of information

Accounts; annual report; Charity Commission record; funder's website.

Pathological Society

 £563,000 (2018)

Correspondent: The Trustees, 7th Floor, 6 Alie Street, London E1 8QT (tel: 0207 484 8046/7; email: admin@pathsoc.org)

https://www.pathsoc.org

CC number: 1154851

Eligibility

Students who are studying medicine, veterinary medicine, dentistry or biomedical sciences based in the UK and/or Ireland. Early career researchers in pathology, including clinical lecturers, clinician scientists and senior lecturers (within the first five years of their role) in histopathology are eligible for PhD funding. Research funding is also awarded to postdoctoral histopathology trainees. All applicants must be members of the society.

Types of grant

Undergraduate Bursary: funding of £150 per week for a maximum of eight weeks) to support research in pathology or gain experience in diagnostic departments during elective or vacation periods.

Intercalated Degree Awards: grants are awarded to students on intercalated BSc or MSc degrees for fees (up to £9,000) and £1,500 for consumables. Awards also include a stipend of £4,000.

PhD Sponsorship: funding covers tuition fees (at the level set for UK students) and research consumables up to £15,000 per annum.

Small Grants Scheme: postdoctoral researchers can apply for up to £10,000 for essential equipment, staff costs, etc. incurred when undertaking investigative research. This scheme is particularly aimed at projects generating research data which may contribute towards a substantive application to a research funding body.

Exclusions

The charity states that it is 'not in a position to provide full economic costs

or overheads with regard to any funds awarded.'

Applications

Applications can be made on the charity's website using an online form. Terms and conditions for each scheme can also be found on the website.

Financial information

Year end	31/12/2018
Income	£1,270,000
Total expenditure	£1,680,000

Other information

Grants are made to organisations, particularly to schools and further education colleges, for activities and ventures aimed at enhancing understanding of pathological diseases. Grants are also made to established student societies who wish to organise regular local activities/events promoting engagement and education in pathology. Prizes are awarded for undergraduate essays and academic achievements.

Sources of information

Accounts; annual report; Charity Commission record; funder's website.

Rhona Reid Charitable Trust

 £9,200 (2017/18)

Correspondent: Kerry Clayton, c/o Rathbone Investment Management, Port of Liverpool Building, Pier Head, Liverpool, Merseyside L3 1NW (tel: 0151 236 6666; email: kerry.clayton@ rathbones.com)

CC number: 1047380

Eligibility

People wishing to excel in a chosen field who would be unable to achieve without the trust's help. Preference is given to the study and advancement of medicine (particularly ophthalmology) and to music and the arts.

Types of grant

One-off and recurrent grants are available to support necessities and activities which would enable someone to excel in their chosen field.

Applications

Apply in writing to the correspondent. Applications are considered in March and September.

Financial information

Year end	05/04/2018
Income	£5,700
Total expenditure	£40,700

Further financial information

Full accounts were not available to view on the Charity Commission's website due to the charity's low income. We have therefore estimated the grant total based on the charity's total expenditure.

Other information

Grants are also given to organisations.

Sources of information

Charity Commission record; University of Worcester website.

Sandra Charitable Trust

£ £64,500 (2017/18)

Correspondent: Martin Pollock, Secretary to the Trustees, BDO LLP, 150 Aldersgate Street, London EC1A 4AB (tel: 020 7334 9191)

CC number: 327492

Eligibility

Nurses and nursing students who are in financial need. Postgraduate, overseas and part-time students can all be supported.

Types of grant

Financial assistance is available for nursing students to enable them to finish their studies. Grants can be used towards courses, equipment and so on.

Applications

Application forms can be requested from the correspondent. The trustees meet on a frequent basis to consider applications.

Financial information

Year end	30/06/2018
Income	£771,400
Total expenditure	£644,400

Other information

The trust also provides support to other charitable institutions and organisations with a wide variety of objectives including animal welfare and research, environment protection, relief of poverty and youth development. At the time of writing, (November 2019), the trustees were in the process of developing a website to deal with all applications.

Sources of information

Accounts; annual report; Charity Commission record; University of Worcester website.

Dr Meena Sharma Memorial Foundation

See record on page 64

The Victoria Foundation

 £21,000 (2017/18)

Correspondent: Lorna Votier, Development Director, St David's House, 15 Worple Way, Richmond, Surrey TW10 6DG (tel: 020 8332 1788; email: enquiries@thevictoriafoundation. org.uk)

https://www.thevictoriafoundation. org.uk

CC number: 292841

Eligibility

UK medical students from disadvantaged backgrounds who are studying medicine at a UK university.

Types of grant

Support is given in the form of bursaries towards the cost of medical electives overseas. In addition, 'toolkit grants' are awarded towards books, equipment and medical instruments.

Exclusions

The foundation will not provide grants for the following:
- Work that has already taken place
- Grants that replace or subsidise statutory funding
- Festivals, leisure or fundraising activities
- Websites, publications, conferences or seminars

Applications

Application forms can be downloaded from the foundation's website and can be made directly by the individual or through a third party. Applications are reviewed each month.

Financial information

Year end	31/03/2018
Income	£17,090,000
Total expenditure	£19,070,000

Further financial information

In 2017/18 grants to individuals totalled £36,000. Grants for mobility aids totalled £15,000. No grants were given to individuals for medical treatments in 2017/18 (£6,000 was awarded for medical treatments in 2016/17). Bursaries for medical students totalled £21,000.

Other information

The foundation also makes grants to charities with shared objectives and has funded five accessible mini-buses for older people in Richmond and Kingston. The foundation aims to support over 100 medical students from disadvantaged backgrounds each year. The Victoria Foundation is the parent charity of the New Victoria Hospital in Kingston.

Sources of information

Accounts; annual report; Charity Commission record; funder's website.

Wellbeing of Women

 £114,000 (2018)

Correspondent: Jeremy Barratt, Head of Research, First Floor, Fairgate House, 78 New Oxford Street, London WC1A 1HB (tel: 020 3697 6350; email: jbarratt@wellbeingofwomen.org.uk)

https://www.wellbeingofwomen.org. uk

CC number: 239281

Eligibility

People wanting to undertake research in the following areas:
- Pregnancy, birth and the postpartum period
- Gynaecological cancers
- General wellbeing surrounding women's health

Research training fellowships are only open to medical graduates, nurses, midwives or allied health professionals who are pursuing a career in obstetrics, gynaecology or focused on women's reproductive health. For postdoctoral funding, candidates must have been awarded an MD or PhD within the previous seven years, and be employed by the NHS, HEI or on a postdoctoral research fellowship with at least 40% of their time funded to undertake research.

Types of grant

Research Training Fellowships: funding of up to £250,000 (for up to three years) to cover the cost of a full-time salary up to Specialty Registrar grade (or equivalent), consistent with current NHS or academic scales, when undertaking research.

Entry-level Research Scholarships: funding of up to £20,000 is given towards salary and/or research costs for a period of one year.

Entry-level Research Scholarships for midwives: funding of up to £20,000 for members of the Royal College of Midwives (RCM) towards salary and/or research costs for a period of one year.

Postdoctoral Research Fellowships: funding of up to £30,000 (for up to three years) is awarded towards 'new and directly incurred costs of research'.

Exclusions

Postdoctoral funding cannot be used to pay for salary.

Applications

Application forms and guidelines are available to download from the charity's website. Two email versions of the application form (one Word document and one fully signed PDF copy) should be sent to the Head of Research by email. Opening and closing dates for applications can also be viewed on the website.

Financial information

Year end	31/12/2018
Income	£2,190,000
Total expenditure	£2,140,000

Other information
Grants are also made to established research institutions for projects which align with the charity's research interests.

Sources of information
Accounts; annual report; Charity Commission record; funder's website.

Social work

Social Workers' Educational Trust

 £15,500 (2017/18)

Correspondent: Catherine Poulter, Secretary, The British Association of Social Workers, Wellesley House, 37 Waterloo Street, Birmingham, West Midlands B2 5PP (tel: 01269 824454; email: swet@basw.co.uk)

https://www.basw.co.uk/financial-support/social-workers-educational-trust

CC number: 313789

Eligibility
Qualified social workers, with at least two years of post-qualifying experience, who work or are looking for work in the UK, and are undertaking post-qualifying training to improve their knowledge and skills for social work practice. Membership of the British Association of Social Workers (BASW) will be taken into account.

Types of grant
Grants of up to £500 for research, study, travel or other costs that will improve social work practice where sufficient funding is not available from other sources. The trust can also provide up to £1,000 to assist team learning, for example, to organise team events. The grant could be used for a speaker, organisational costs or books and resources. In addition three scholarships are available each year: Elizabeth O'Dell Memorial Award; Anne Cummins Memorial Scholarship; and SWET Research Scholarship. They all award £3,000, with the aim of improving social work. For detailed information on the scholarships see the trust's website.

Exclusions
The trust cannot assist those undertaking initial social work training or qualifications. Successful applicants may not reapply within three years of the completion of a supported training course or project.

Applications
Application forms can be downloaded from the trust's website along with guidelines. Applications can be submitted at any time and are normally considered in February, July and October.

Financial information

Year end	30/09/2018
Income	£25,900
Total expenditure	£17,000

Further financial information
In 2017/18 grants were awarded to 38 individuals. The trust can award three scholarships, but in 2017/18 no successful applications were submitted.

Sources of information
Accounts; annual report; Charity Commission record; funder's website.

Religion

The All Saints Educational Trust
See record on page 35

Culham St Gabriel's Trust (The Culham Institute)

 £47,100 (2017/18)

Correspondent: Mark Chater, Director, Culham St Gabriel's, 60–62 Banbury Road, Oxford, Oxfordshire OX2 6PN (tel: 01865 612035; email: enquiries@cstg.org.uk)

www.cstg.org.uk

CC number: 309671

Eligibility
People who are, or intend to become, teachers in religious education or are otherwise involved in the work, development, research and studies of the Church of England.

Types of grant
Grants are for further/higher education students and to promote the life-long learning of teachers. Financial support is available towards books, equipment, necessities and the costs of classes,

lectures or various development opportunities.

Exclusions
Grants are not given for work outside the UK, for general running costs, deficit reduction or religious instruction (as distinct from education).

Applications
Application forms can be obtained from the trust's website and should be submitted by January, May and September (specified dates may be subject to change; see the trust's website for further information).

Financial information

Year end	31/08/2018
Income	£737,400
Total expenditure	£1,050,000

Further financial information
Grants were awarded to 15 individuals.

Other information
The trust will also award grants to organisations.

Sources of information
Accounts; annual report; Charity Commission record.

Lady Hewley's Charity
See record on page 100

Hockerill Educational Foundation

 £62,300 (2017/18)

Correspondent: Derek Humphrey, The Trustees, 3 Swallows, Harlow, Essex CM17 0AR (tel: 01279 420855; email: info@hockerillfoundation.org.uk)

www.hockerillfoundation.org.uk

CC number: 311018

Eligibility
The following information has been taken from the foundation's website:

We make grants in the following categories for study in the United Kingdom, with priority given to Religious Education courses.

- Students and teaching assistants taking teaching qualifications, or first degrees leading to teaching.
- Teachers, teaching assistants and others in an educational capacity seeking professional development through full-time or part-time courses.
- Those undertaking research related to the practice of Religious Education in schools or further education
- Students taking other first degree courses, or courses in further education.

Others involved in teaching and leading in voluntary, non-statutory education, including those concerned with adult and Christian education.

Grants are not usually awarded for the first year of a three or four year course, but exceptions may be made for mature students.

Types of grant

University fees; further education; part-time/full-time courses; research in relation to religious education; students from the dioceses of Chelmsford and St Albans undertaking gap-year projects with an educational focus.

Exclusions

According to the foundation's website, the foundation will not support the following:

- Teachers who intend to move out of the profession
- Those training for ordination or mission, or clergy who wish to improve their own qualifications, unless they are also involved in teaching in schools
- Those taking courses in counselling, therapy, or social work
- Training for other professions, such as accountancy, business, law, or medicine
- Courses or visits abroad, including gap-year courses
- Primary or secondary schoolchildren
- Those training to teach English as an additional language

Applications

An application form is available to download from the foundation's website.

Financial information

Year end	31/03/2018
Income	£328,300
Total expenditure	£330,600

Further financial information

Grants were awarded to 68 individuals during 2017/18.

Other information

The majority of annual funding is committed to long-term projects or activities in education, but funding is also given to other projects, namely: training and support for the Church of England's educational work, particularly in the dioceses of Chelmsford and St Albans; research, development and support grants to organisations in the field of religious education (RE). The charity also supports conferences for new RE teachers and a 'Prize for Innovation in the Teaching of RE'.

Sources of information

Accounts; annual report; Charity Commission record; funder's website.

The Foundation of St Matthias

 £120,300 (2018)

Correspondent: Karine Prescott, Clerk to the Trustees, First Floor, Hillside House, 1500 Parkway North, Newbrick Road, Stoke Gifford, Bristol BS34 8YU (tel: 0117 906 0100; email: stmatthiastrust@bristoldiocese.org)

 www.stmatthiastrust.org.uk

CC number: 311696

Eligibility

Further and higher education students, including mature students and occasionally postgraduates, who are studying in accordance with the doctrine of the Church of England. This includes:

- People who are, or intend to become, engaged in social welfare work as social workers, community workers, youth workers, teachers or supervisors of pre-school groups, etc.
- People who are intending to become ministers of the Church of England or of a church in communion therewith

Preference is given to applicants from the dioceses of Bath and Wells, Bristol and Gloucester, although applicants from elsewhere are considered.

Types of grant

One-off grants can be given for books, fees, maintenance/living expenses, childcare and for some study or travel abroad. Overseas courses may be supported only if the visit is integral to the course or research. PhD scholarships are also available.

Exclusions

No retrospective grants are awarded.

Applications

Applicants should telephone in the first instance to discuss their applications with the correspondent. Applications must be made on a form available from the foundation's website. They should be submitted by 31 May for consideration in July or 30 September for consideration in November.

Financial information

Year end	31/12/2018
Income	£280,700
Total expenditure	£388,700

Further financial information

A total of 87 individuals received grants during 2018.

Other information

The foundation advises applicants to apply to as many sources of funding as possible as funding is not guaranteed and often, the foundation cannot offer the full amount requested. There is a link to other religious education trusts on its website. The foundation is not able to cover the costs of fees, maintenance or travel, etc., of students from overseas, but small contributions may be offered should evidence be supplied that substantial funding is available from other sources. The foundation also makes grants to organisations

Sources of information

Accounts; annual report; Charity Commission record; funder's website.

The Spalding Trusts

 £36,300 (2017)

Correspondent: Tessa Rodgers, Secretary, The Spalding Trust, PO Box 85, Stowmarket, Suffolk IP14 3NY

 https://www.spaldingtrust.org.uk

CC number: 209066

Eligibility

People undertaking research projects into world religions, particularly comparative studies, who are in need of financial support. Projects must primarily have a religious focus rather than sociological or anthropological.

Types of grant

Awards of up to £2,000 for the comparative study of the major religions. Support is available for research projects, publications, occasionally travel costs, conferences and related expenses. Applications may not necessarily be academically orientated, provided they have a sufficient practical and beneficial aspect. Recurrent grants extending over one year are only considered in exceptional circumstances.

Exclusions

Grants are not given retrospectively and will rarely be provided towards expenses related to a first degree.

Applications

Apply in writing to the correspondent. Visit the trust's website for full details on how to make an application.

Financial information

Year end	31/12/2017
Income	£84,800
Total expenditure	£94,800

Other information

The trust also makes grants to institutions, such as libraries, colleges, other educational establishments. A subsidiary of the trust, the Ellen Rebe Spalding Memorial Fund, makes grants to disadvantaged women and children.

Sources of information
Accounts; annual report; Charity Commission record; funder's website.

Turath Scholarship Fund

 £10,000 (2018/19)

Correspondent: Imran Satia, Trustee, 4 West Park Road, Blackburn BB2 6DG (tel: 07825 346320; email: scholarship@turath.co.uk)

www.turath.co.uk/front/turath-scholarship-fund

CC number: 1138153

Eligibility
UK citizens between the ages of 18 and 24. Preferably, applicants will have a 2:1 degree from a good UK university and some teaching experience. Applicants must be intending to study any aspect of the Islamic sciences outside their university degree and be committed to studying their chosen discipline for a prolonged period of time.

Types of grant
Financial assistance can be given for a wide range of activities such as study in the UK or abroad, long-term or short-term courses, tuition, vocational training and so on. Visit the fund's website for examples of projects that will be supported. After completing the proposed study, individuals are expected to produce a report and go on to teach others in their communities.

Applications
Application forms can be downloaded from the fund's website and should be returned by email. Shortlisted applicants will be required to discuss their proposal with the trustees and provide references. An in-person or phone interview may also be requested. Successful candidates should be informed of the decision within 30 days of the deadline date.

Financial information
Year end	20/12/2019
Income	£20,000
Total expenditure	£20,000

Further financial information
Full accounts were not available to view on the Charity Commission's website due to the charity's low income. We have therefore estimated the grant total based on the charity's total expenditure.

Sources of information
Charity Commission record; funder's website.

Skilled crafts

The William Barry Trust
See record on page 42 *See record on page 42*

The British Jewellery, Giftware and Finishing Federation Benevolent Society

 £32,600 (2018)

Correspondent: Laura Banner, Secretary to the Trustees, Federation House, 10 Vyse Street, Hockley, Birmingham, West Midlands B18 6LT (tel: 0121 237 1138; email: laura.b.banner@gmail.com)

www.thebenevolentsociety.co.uk

CC number: 208722

Eligibility
People who are, or have been, engaged in the trades embraced by the British Allied Trades Federation (BATF) who are in need as a result of older age, illness, disability or other medical conditions. Trades include: National Association of Jewellers, British Travelgoods and Accessories Association, The Giftware Association, Jewellery Distributors' Association and the Surface Engineering Association.

Types of grant
Bursaries of up £9,000 towards educational/vocational fees involved in training to work in any trade covered by the BATF.

Exclusions
Welfare grants cannot be made for items or services where provision is deemed to be the responsibility of the state.

Education/training grants cannot be awarded towards the purchasing of tools and materials.

Applications
Application forms are available to download from the society's website. The charity's qualified counsellor will usually make arrangements to visit the applicant, to fully assess their need. The charity is able to help with the completion of the application form if necessary. The trustees meet quarterly to consider grant applications.

Financial information
Year end	31/12/2018
Income	£113,500
Total expenditure	£107,100

Further financial information
The charity awarded ten bursaries during 2018.

Sources of information
Accounts; annual report; Charity Commission record; funder's website.

Charities Administered by the Worshipful Company of Founders

 £22,000 (2017/18)

Correspondent: The Trustees, The Founders Co., Founders Hall, 1 Cloth Fair, London EC1A 7JQ (tel: 020 7796 4800; email: office@foundersco.org.uk)

www.foundersco.org.uk

CC number: 222905

Eligibility
Young people studying for degrees in metallurgy or material sciences. Equally important is the support given to apprenticeship schemes.

Types of grant
Bursaries, scholarships and other costs associated with education and research in the material sciences and related fields in engineering.

Applications
Apply in writing to the correspondent.

Financial information
Year end	29/10/2018
Income	£35,700
Total expenditure	£26,200

Sources of information
Accounts; annual report; Charity Commission record; funder's website.

The Cotton Industry War Memorial Trust
See record on page 80 *See record on page 80*

The Worshipful Company of Framework Knitters Education Charity

 £33,500 (2018/19)

Correspondent: Capt. Shaun Mackaness, Clerk, The Grange, Walton Road, Kimcote, Lutterworth, Leicestershire LE17 5RU (tel: 01455 203152; email: clerk@frameworkknitters.co.uk)

www.frameworkknitters.co.uk/student-bursaries

CC number: 292630

Eligibility

Students in further and higher education about to enter the final year of a diploma or first degree, on a postgraduate course, or registered for a research degree, are eligible to apply. Students of design, management, marketing, science and technology relevant to the knitting/knitwear industries are eligible for consideration.

Types of grant

Bursaries of £1,500 or £2,500 for exceptional projects and research that benefits the British knitting/knitwear industries.

Applications

Application forms and information are sent to heads of departments or tutors and students' unions at the start of each academic year, with a closing date for the receipt of completed applications around mid-October. The project or research should benefit the British knitting/knitwear industries and applicants should include a CV and an outline of the project. For information on how applications are assessed see the charity's website.

Financial information

Year end	31/03/2019
Income	£61,900
Total expenditure	£52,400

Other information

During 2018/19 the committee visited 17 universities and colleges, interviewed 50 candidates and gave 19 bursaries and awards. If the applicant is successful they will be mentored until the completion of the project.

Sources of information

Accounts; annual report; Charity Commission record; funder's website.

The Gunmakers' Company Charitable Trust

 £22,900 (2017/18)

Correspondent: Mr A. J. Mundin, Secretary, Proof House, 48–50 Commercial Road, London E1 1LP (tel: 020 7481 2695; email: clerk@gunmakers.org.uk)

 www.gunmakers.org.uk

CC number: 1100227

Eligibility

Individuals wishing to undertake an apprenticeship in the gun and allied trades and in associated crafts. The trades and crafts that can be supported include metalwork, woodwork, leatherwork, casemaking, engraving, computer sciences connected with machinery and ballistics and environmental sciences connected with noise and cartridge design.

Types of grant

Bursaries of up to £5,000 per year are provided to support apprenticeships for up to three years. Those receiving grants are also mentored by a trustee and visited in their workplace to monitor progress. The trust aims to provide at least five bursaries each year. The grants are paid to the organisation offering the apprenticeship on behalf of the individual.

Applications

Apply in writing to the correspondent. The trustees meet at least twice a year to consider applications.

Financial information

Year end	31/10/2018
Income	£38,400
Total expenditure	£28,200

Sources of information

Accounts; annual report; Charity Commission record; funder's website.

The Leathersellers' Company Charitable Fund

See record on page 36

Social sciences

The Airey Neave Trust

 £30,400 (2018/19)

Correspondent: Sophie Butler, PO Box 111, Leominster, Herefordshire HR6 6BP (tel: 01568 760195; email: aireyneavetrust@gmail.com)

 www.aireyneavetrust.org.uk

CC number: 297269

Eligibility

Fellows of 'established university departments' who plan to undertake research on any topic which falls under the definition of 'helping to protect and/or enhance personal freedom under the rule of democratic law against the threat of political violence (either nationally or internationally)' are eligible to apply, according to the trust's website. Preference is given to projects designed to contribute in a practical way to the struggle against international terrorist activity.

Types of grant

Grants are made towards the cost of writing a report or publication in the form of an article, series of articles or monograph. A salary, equivalent to that of a university lecturer (depending on age, qualifications and experience) may be covered by, or contributed towards, by the trust.

Exclusions

Due to limited funds, financial assistance to refugees is no longer provided.

Applications

From time to time, the trust will approach universities requesting research proposals for consideration, but is also open to receiving unsolicited applications. Applicants should send their proposals to the trust by email. Applicants should demonstrate how their proposed research relates to the objectives of the trust, what outputs are to be expected from their research and how these outputs can be observed or measured.

Financial information

Year end	31/03/2019
Income	£13,500
Total expenditure	£33,700

Further financial information

Full accounts were not available to view on the Charity Commission's website due to the charity's low income. We have therefore estimated the grant total based on the charity's total expenditure.

Sources of information

Charity Commission record; funder's website.

The Barry Amiel and Norman Melburn Trust

 £105,700 (2017/18)

Correspondent: Administrator, PO Box 59542, London SE21 9BR (tel: 07949 716043; email: apply@amielandmelburn.org.uk)

 www.amielandmelburn.org.uk

CC number: 281239

Eligibility

Groups and individuals working to advance public education in the philosophy of Marxism, the history of socialism, and the working-class movement.

Types of grant

Grants are available for a range of projects which include: conferences; seminars; publications; research;

archiving; translations; arts and culture; and documentaries. The trust funds both national and international projects. Applications can be made for either 'Regular or Major Project' awards.

Exclusions

The trust does not award funds: to subsidise the continuation or running of university/college courses; to cover transport costs to or from conferences; or to subsidise fees/maintenance for undergraduate/postgraduate students.

Applications

Application forms are available to download from the trust's website and must be returned in hard copy via post, and uploaded to the online form. Applications are considered in January and July. Funding bids for £7,000 or more (Major Project Awards) are only considered in January.

Financial information

Year end	05/04/2018
Income	£40,000
Total expenditure	£123,300

Further financial information

According to the trust's 2017/18 accounts, direct charitable expenditure comprised of the following:

Conferences and seminars	£56,300
Annual fellowship	£16,300
Summer school	£10,700
Research and archiving	£9,400
Publications and pamphlets	£8,000
Nina Fishman award	£4,800

Other information

Grants are also awarded to groups and bodies; however, it appears to be for the work of individuals.

Sources of information

Accounts; annual report; Charity Commission record; funder's website.

Economic History Society

 £61,800 (2017/18)

Correspondent: Dr H. J. Paul, Honorary Secretary, Univeristy of Glasgow, Adam Smith Building, 40 Bute Gardens, Glasgow G12 8RT (tel: 01865 778171; email: ehsocsec@arts.gla.ac.uk)

https://www.ehs.org.uk

CC number: 228494

Eligibility

University students (at all levels) undertaking research into any aspect of economic and/or social history at a UK university or college. It is expected that applicants will be, or will become, members of the society.

Types of grant

Bursaries: students registered for a higher degree in history can apply for funding to attend a course entitled 'An Introduction to Methods and Sources for Historical Research'. Grants are made to cover fees and accommodation (where required).

Bursary Scheme for PhD Students: one-year bursaries of up to £5,000 are awarded to doctoral students at any stage of their PhD career.

Fellowships: stipends are paid at the ESRC level (which in 2018–19, was £16,777 per annum for students within London and £14,777 for those based outside London), to students undertaking advanced research with a view to publication.

Small Research Grants Scheme: grants of up to £5,000 are made towards the direct costs of research that is aimed at a specific publication outcome and/or pilot projects that will form the foundation for applications to other bodies for more substantial funding.

Research Fund for Graduate Students: grants of up to £1,000 are made towards any travel and accommodation costs incurred when undertaking research.

Undergraduate Project Facility Grant: small grants of up to £250 are awarded to undergraduates for projects contributing to their final degree classification. Projects must be for final degree examinations only.

Exclusions

See the charity's website for exclusions.

Applications

Application processes vary between grant schemes. See the charity's website for more information.

Financial information

Year end	30/06/2018
Income	£410,300
Total expenditure	£393,200

Sources of information

Accounts; annual report; Charity Commission record; funder's website.

Gilbert Murray Trust – International Studies Committee

 £9,200 (2017/18)

Correspondent: Richard Alston, Classics Department, Royal Holloway University of London, Egham Hill, Surrey TW20 0EX (tel: 07786 543925; email: r.alston@rhul.ac.uk)

www.gilbertmurraytrust.org.uk

CC number: 212244

Eligibility

People under the age of 25 who are studying, or have studied, international relations (including international law, security, peace, development studies, global governance) at an institution of higher education in the UK. Applicants above the age of 25 could be considered if there are specific reasons for a delay in their education, such as ill-health or financial problems.

Types of grant

Grants of up to £1,000 are available towards a specific project relevant to the work and purposes of the United Nations (for example, research-related visits to a specific country/headquarters of an international organisation, or a short course at an institution abroad) which will directly contribute towards the applicant's studies.

Exclusions

Grants are not intended to support international affairs students with general educational expenses and needs.

Applications

Applications should be submitted to Dr Peter Wilson in writing. It should include a brief CV, a short statement of career intentions, a detailed description of the project with associated costs and sources of additional funding (if required), a reference letter by someone suitable to judge the suitability of the applicant, and reasons for delayed education (if required). Applications and all the relevant information should be provided in five copies.

Financial information

Year end	05/04/2018
Income	£10,200
Total expenditure	£10,200

Further financial information

Full accounts were not available to view on the Charity Commission's website due to the charity's low income. We have therefore estimated the grant total based on the charity's total expenditure.

Other information

The charity's Classical Committee also offers recurring support and awards for various projects and initiatives which seek to promote the study of ancient Greek civilisation, culture and language. Organisations can also be supported.

Sources of information

Funder's website.

Cultural studies

British Association for Irish Studies

Correspondent: Dr Maggie Scull, Chair of the Bursaries Committee, Moore Institute, NUI Galway University, Clifton, Galway, Ireland (email: baisbursaries@gmail.com)

 https://bairishstudies.wordpress. com/prizes-and-funding

Eligibility
Postgraduates who are researching Irish related topics at British universities.

Types of grant
Bursaries of £300 to £1,000 are available for three to six students annually for travel expenses, payments of fees, subsistence or other expenses related to the completion of their research project. The association's website states that it aims to support research that uncovers new or neglected areas in the field.

Applications
Applicants must be members of the British Association for Irish Studies, or should join when they apply. Application forms are available to download from the association's website and must be submitted with two completed referee forms. Check the website for submission deadlines. Applicants are encouraged to produce a specific and targeted funding request, detailing how the award will support the research.

Other information
BAIS also offer a postgraduate essay prize for essays between 5,000 and 8,000 words in length. The winning author will receive £500 of Cambridge University Press books of their choice and have their essay published in Irish Studies Review.

Sources of information
Funder's website.

Il Circolo Italian Cultural Association Ltd

 £3,700 (2017)

Correspondent: Lady Belinda Aylmer, Secretary, 22–24 Ely Place, London EC1 N6TE (email: grants@ilcircolo.org. uk)

 www.ilcircolo.org.uk

CC number: 1108894

Eligibility
UK/EU residents who are enrolled or have been accepted onto a course at a British or Italian university or higher education institution, either at undergraduate or postgraduate level.

Types of grant
Scholarships for students who wish to further their education in the field of Italian and related studies. Funding is given for educational purposes such as tuition fees, thesis preparation, conferences and associated travel.

Applications
Application forms can be downloaded from the association's website or by contacting the correspondent. Application forms should be submitted along with two academic references and shortlisted candidates will be invited to interview. Consult the website for current deadlines.

Financial information
Year end	31/12/2017
Income	£48,500
Total expenditure	£31,100

Further financial information
In 2017 a total of £3,700 was awarded as scholarships to students.

Other information
The association also sponsors research and holds a Christmas Bazaar every year in London to promote Italian culture in the UK.

Sources of information
Accounts; annual report; Charity Commission record; funder's website.

Geography

The Mount Everest Foundation

£64,900 (2017/18)

Correspondent: Glyn Hughes, Hon. Secretary, 73 Church Street, Chesham, Buckinghamshire HP5 1HY (tel: 01494 792073; email: glynhughes@waitrose. com)

CC number: 208206

Eligibility
Support is given for education and research across a wide range of subjects including geography, glaciology, and the effects of altitude.

Types of grant
Expedition grants to explore mountain regions. Unless an expedition has research as its primary objective, it must have a strong exploratory element to be deemed eligible for support. Applications from expeditions proposing to visit little-explored or formerly inaccessible areas are particularly encouraged, as are those pursuing worthwhile research.

Exclusions
The foundation will not make grants for an expedition that has already been completed.

Applications
Full application details and guidance can be found on the foundation's website.

Financial information
Year end	31/03/2018
Income	£212,800
Total expenditure	£68,400

Sources of information
Accounts; annual report; Charity Commission record; funder's website.

Royal Geographical Society (with the Institute of British Geographers)

£57,000 (2017)

Correspondent: Grants Office, 1 Kensington Gore, London SW7 2AR (tel: 020 7591 3073; email: grants@rgs. org)

www.rgs.org

CC number: 208791

Eligibility
People over the age of 16 who are carrying out geographical research and projects. Teachers, undergraduate and postgraduate students, scientists, and non-academics (e.g. independent travellers) are all eligible. The society has previously stated that its grants programme aims to promote geographical research and a wider understanding of the world. Applicants are not required to have a geography degree, work in a geography department or define themselves as a geographer, but must share the society's interest in the world, people and environment. Note: some grants are only open to fellows of the society.

Types of grant
The society administers a large number of grants each with separate eligibility criteria and application processes. The awards are broken down into the following categories: established researchers; early career researchers; postgraduate; undergraduate; expeditions, fieldwork and independent travel; teaching. For full details of each award see the society's website. Support can be given for work both in the UK and overseas in the range of £250 to £30,000.

Exclusions

Grants are not made retrospectively or given for fees/living costs associated with degrees.

Applications

All grant details, guidelines, application forms and specific deadlines can be obtained from the society's website. Generally, the application process takes between three and four months. All candidates are informed about the outcome of their application.

Financial information

Year end	31/12/2017
Income	£5,580,000
Total expenditure	£5,540,000

Other information

The society also supports institutions and offers information, advice, resources and training to support anyone planning a fieldwork or scientific expedition.

Sources of information

Accounts; annual report; Charity Commission record; funder's website.

National charities classified by type of beneficiary

Asylum seekers and refugees

Ruth Hayman Trust

 £34,300 (2017/18)

Correspondent: The Trustees, PO Box 17685, London N6 6WD (email: info@ ruthhaymantrust.org.uk)

🌐 www.ruthhaymantrust.org.uk

CC number: 287268

Eligibility

Adults who have come to settle in the UK, and whose first language is not English and cannot afford the full fees for their studies. Preference is given to refugees, asylum seekers and survivors of modern slavery, domestic violence and trafficking. Applicants must be resident in the UK, either as a citizen of the UK or EU, or as a spouse or partner of a UK citizen.

Types of grant

One-off and recurrent grants of up to £500 (on average £150) are available to help with the following:

- Registration and course fees
- Exam fees
- Disclosure and Barring Service (DBS) fees
- Costs of joining professional bodies if these are essential for participation on the course

- Dictionaries (kindly donated by Oxford University Press and sent out four times a year) and essential textbooks
- Equipment essential to the course such as chef's knives, hairdresser's scissors, steel-capped boots for bricklaying apprentices
- Travel for students with disabilities. A letter from a doctor must be enclosed with your application

There is an additional annual Rose Grant Special Award of £500 available to 'applicants who can show exceptional academic achievement, an outstanding commitment to the community or human rights as well as financial need'.

Exclusions

Grants cannot be given towards:

- Travel costs (except for students with disabilities who can provide an accompanying statement from a doctor)
- Computers
- Accommodation
- Childcare
- Living expenses
- University education unless the course leads directly to employment
- PhDs

At the time of writing (September 2019) the trustees were not accepting applications for any university course fees, unless the course leads directly to employment. This is due to a high demand of grants.

Applications

Application forms can be found on the trust's website or requested from the correspondent. Grants are awarded about five times a year and applications should be submitted in February, late April, late June, early September or late

November. Candidates are required to provide an academic reference. Applications for the Rose Grant Special Award should be made on the same form providing evidence that the candidate satisfies the additional requirements. The trust reminds that it is crucial to fill in the application form in full (do not forget to demonstrate financial need, state your first language, include a reference and specify what the support is needed for). Further application guidelines can be found on the trust's website; read them carefully to avoid your application being rejected on technical grounds.

Financial information

Year end	31/03/2018
Income	£37,200
Total expenditure	£36,900

Other information

Applications that show a small amount of funding has already been sourced from other organisations will be looked upon favourably.

Sources of information

Accounts; annual report; Charity Commission record; funder's website.

The Prisoners of Conscience Appeal Fund

 £59,400 (2018/19)

Correspondent: The Trustees, PO Box 61044, London SE1 1UP (tel: 020 7407 6644; email: info@prisonersofconscience. org)

🌐 www.prisonersofconscience.org

CC number: 213766

Eligibility
People, and their families, who have been persecuted for their conscientiously-held beliefs and are in need.

Types of grant
Educational grants are made in the form of bursaries for postgraduate or re-qualification study to improve employment prospects.

Exclusions
The charity does not help those who have used or advocated for violence, or members of violent organisations.

Applications
Applications must be made by approved organisations as the charity does not deal with individuals directly. The charity advises that prospective applicants contact a solicitor, Citizens Advice or other refugee organisation or official bodies to make an application on their behalf. If the applicant does not know of any organisation who could help, then they should contact the charity by email: grantsofficer@prisonersofconscience.org for advice.

Financial information
Year end	31/03/2019
Income	£342,500
Total expenditure	£365,100

Further financial information
The charity awarded grants to 315 beneficiaries. Note: the grant total has been estimated.

Other information
The charity has recently launched an Employability Panel comprised of specialist organisations who can assist with finding meaningful and skill-related employment for its beneficiaries.

Sources of information
Accounts; annual report; Charity Commission record; funder's website.

The Walter and Liesel Schwab Charitable Trust (also known as Schwab and Westheimer Trust)

 £234,000 (2017/18)

Correspondent: The Trustees, PO Box 12327, Colchester CO6 4XE (tel: 07711 386974; email: info@swtrust.org.uk)

swtrust.org.uk

CC number: 1091870

Eligibility
Young refugees and asylum seekers under the age of 28 who are in education or need educational support. Applicants must have claimed asylum in the UK or have been recognised as a refugee by the Home Office.

To be eligible to apply for the Westheimer Scholarships, applicants must meet the following criteria:
- Be an asylum seeker, or the dependant of an asylum seeker, who is awaiting a decision or appealing a decision for asylum; a person, or a dependant of a person, who claimed asylum in the UK and has been granted limited leave to remain (without refugee status or humanitarian protection) or some other form of temporary status; or a person with limited leave to remain for unaccompanied minors
- Have been accepted onto an undergraduate university course in social care, medicine, nursing or related professions
- Be under the age of 28

Types of grant
The trust has two grant-making programmes:
- Schwab Educational Grants: grants of up to £2,000 to help young refugees and asylum seekers with their studies. Assistance can be given towards materials, equipment, travel costs, computers, books and fees
- Westheimer Scholarships: awards up to three people each year scholarships of a maximum of £11,500 per year for a first degree or professional qualification in the field of health and social care. Support can be given towards tuition fees and living expenses

Further information about eligible courses is available on the trust's website.

Exclusions
The Westheimer scholarship will only fund undergraduate degrees.

Applications
Applications for both programmes can be made using online forms on the trust's website. Applicants can apply in person or any professional may apply on their behalf. Further information, application guidelines and current deadlines can be found on the website. Both programmes require a personal reference. Applicants may be asked to attend an interview.

Financial information
Year end	01/05/2018
Income	£69,600
Total expenditure	£280,200

Other information
The trust has developed close working partnerships with the Helena Kennedy Foundation and Refugee Support Network, which also supports refugees and asylum seekers seeking access to education. In 2017/18 the trust began the 'Brittan Scholarship' which is at postgraduate level. The trust is also linked to the Isle and Frieda Westheimer Charitable Trust, which has similar aims.

Sources of information
Accounts; annual report; Charity Commission record; funder's website.

Children and young people

Buttle UK

 £896,000 (2017/18)

Correspondent: Grants Team, 15 Greycoat Place, London SW1P 1SB (tel: 020 7828 7311; email: info@ buttleuk.org)

www.buttleuk.org

CC number: 313007/SC037997

Eligibility
Grants are awarded to young people aged 16 to 20 who are estranged, orphaned or living outside the family home and who are committed to pursuing a defined goal in relation to education, training or employment. This criteria may be waived if the young person has been a victim of domestic abuse and lives in London. The trustees prioritise young people facing exceptional difficulties or crisis, particularly living in severe poverty or facing domestic violence, drug and alcohol misuse, estrangement, illness, distress, abuse, neglect, behavioural or mental health issues.

Types of grant
Educational grants have been made for travel costs and course fees for students in further education. Grants are also available to cover the cost of boarding school fees when there is a strong case as to why a child cannot stay within the family home with their parent or carer.

Exclusions
A list of exclusions for each programme can be found on the charity's website.

Applications
Applications can be made online on the charity's website and should be completed by a statutory or voluntary

organisation that supports the family or the individual and is capable of assessing their needs and can also administer a grant on behalf of the charity. Contact details for applicants resident in the UK are as follows:

- England: Buttle UK, 15 Greycoat Place, London, SW1P 1SB; Tel: 020 7828 7311
- Scotland: Buttle UK, PO Box 2081, Glasgow, G32 2BR; Tel: 0141 7782839
- Wales: Buttle UK, PO Box 116, Pontypridd, CF37 9ER; Tel: 014 43408209
- Northern Ireland: Buttle UK, PO Box 1534, Dungannon, BT70 9BR; Tel: 028 87746778

Both parties must agree to the plan. Once the application has been received, a telephone interview will be arranged with the young person.

Further information, contact details for specific programmes, and deadlines are detailed on the charity's website.

Financial information

Year end	31/03/2018
Income	£5,820,000
Total expenditure	£7,000,000

Further financial information

According to the 2017/18 annual report, the charity awarded grants worth £4.6 million to over 35,000 children and young people.

Other information

As of 2018, Buttle UK no longer provides the Emergency Essentials Programme on behalf of BBC Children in Need. The charity also stopped its Day School Fees programme in March 2016.

Sources of information

Accounts; annual report; Charity Commission record; funder's website.

The Chizel Educational Trust

£ £7,600 (2018/19)

Correspondent: The Trustees, Burgage Manor Cottage, Burgage, Southwell, Nottingham, Nottinghamshire NG25 0EP (tel: 01636 081 685)

CC number: 1091574

Eligibility

People under the age of 25 who live in the UK and who are in need of financial assistance.

Types of grant

Bursaries and maintenance allowances for students at school, university or any other educational establishment. Grants are available towards equipment, clothing, instruments, books and travel in the UK or abroad.

Applications

Applications should be made in writing to the correspondent and must be submitted in May or November. Applications must also enclose an sae.

Financial information

Year end	05/04/2019
Income	£21,600
Total expenditure	£33,800

Further financial information

Full accounts were not available to view on the Charity Commission's website due to the charity's low income. We have therefore estimated the grant total based on the charity's total expenditure. We estimate that in 2018/19 around £15,200 was awarded in grants to individuals. It is estimated that this can be broken down as follows: £7,600 was awarded to individuals for welfare purposes and around £7,600 for education.

Other information

Financial assistance is also provided towards the maintenance of Ackworth School, Yorkshire and the Inverness Royal Academy Mollie Stephens Trust.

Sources of information

Charity Commission record.

The Emmott Foundation Ltd

£ £375,800 (2017/18)

Correspondent: Julie Spillane, Education Officer, 136 Browns Lane, Stanton-on-the-Wolds, Nottinghamshire NG12 5BN (tel: 0115 937 6526; email: emmottfoundation@btinternet.com)

 emmottfoundation.org

CC number: 209033

Eligibility

Students aged 16 to 18 in fee-paying schools (including state boarding schools) who have high academic achievements (a majority of actual or predicted A*s or As at GCSE). The following is taken from the 2017/18 trustees' annual report:

Accordingly grants are primarily intended for children whose parents or guardians can no longer meet their considered financial commitments for education in either state or independent sixth forms as a result of a family crisis such as death, severe illness, accident, divorce, desertion or loss of employment. Consequently support is often given to children of families where the household income is very low. Consideration will also be given to cases where there is a major educational or pastoral problem, including the impact of parental drug and/or alcohol abuse, domestic violence and bullying.

Awards may be granted to students with lower grades in circumstances of exceptional need or where there is a major educational, social or pastoral problem, including domestic violence, bullying, or parental drug/alcohol abuse. Note: grants are made only where the school is willing to make a significant contribution to the fees.

Types of grant

Grants are for sixth form students only. Their purpose is to enable pupils to enter or remain in the sixth form in their present school. The grants help only with basic fees, not with incidental expenses (music lessons, travel, books, expeditions and so on). Grants are usually of between £500 and £1,500 per term, paid directly to the school at the start of each sixth form term.

Exclusions

Students in other age groups than those specified above are not considered.

Applications

Apply initially in writing to the correspondent. Application forms will be sent to eligible applicants. The trustees meet in March, June and November to consider applications. Enquiries and applications should be made to the correspondent.

Financial information

Year end	31/08/2018
Income	£452,200
Total expenditure	£485,800

Further financial information

Grants were awarded to 77 students during 2018. Of these, 41 were in the upper sixth, with three completing their IB courses and 39 their A-levels.

Sources of information

Accounts; annual report; Charity Commission record; funder's website.

The William Gibbs Trust

£ £2,700 (2017)

Correspondent: The Trustees, Kingwell House, Hayeswood Road, Timbury, Bath BA2 0HH

CC number: 282957

Eligibility

Children and young people in education.

Types of grant

One-off and recurrent grants according to need.

Applications

Apply in writing to the correspondent.

Financial information

Year end	31/12/2017
Income	£11,200
Total expenditure	£5,900

Further financial information

Full accounts were not available to view on the Charity Commission's website due to the charity's low income. We have therefore estimated the grant total based on the charity's total expenditure.

Other information

Grants are also given to organisations for educational purposes.

Sources of information

Charity Commission record.

The McAlpine Educational Endowments Ltd

£ £9,800 (2018/19)

Correspondent: Gillian Bush, Secretary, Eaton Court, Maylands Avenue, Hemel Hempstead, Hertfordshire HP2 7TR (tel: 0333 566 2069; email: g.bush@srm.com)

CC number: 313156

Eligibility

Children and young people undertaking education.

Types of grant

Grants are awarded for educational purposes. Grants can be renewed for further years subject to a satisfactory school report.

Applications

Apply in writing to the correspondent.

Financial information

Year end	31/03/2019
Income	£28,000
Total expenditure	£22,300

Further financial information

In 2018/19 a total of £19,600 was awarded as seven bursaries to individuals. We estimate that around £9,800 was given for welfare purposes and £9,800 was given for educational purposes.

Sources of information

Accounts; annual report; Charity Commission record.

One Me

£ £3,960 (2017/18)

Correspondent: The Trustees, Welton House, Lime Kiln Way, Lincoln, Lincolnshire LN2 4WH (tel: 01522 574100; email: administrator@one-me.org.uk)

CC number: 1159762

Eligibility

Young people between the ages of 16 and 25.

Types of grant

Funding is awarded for a wide range of purposes with the aim of allowing people to achieve their potential through education, training and employment. Grants may be given to enable access to training, support for further education, extracurricular activities, or starting up a business.

Applications

Apply in writing to the correspondent.

Financial information

Year end	31/03/2018
Income	£22,200
Total expenditure	£17,600

Further financial information

Full accounts were not available to view on the Charity Commission's website due to the charity's low income. We have therefore estimated the grant total based on the charity's total expenditure.

Sources of information

Accounts; annual report; Charity Commission record; funder's website.

The Prince's Trust

£ £353,500 (2017/18)

Correspondent: Wendy Becker, Chair of the Young Persons Committee, Prince's Trust House, 6–9 Eldon Street, London EC2M 7LS (tel: 0800 842842; email: info@princes-trust.org.uk)

 www.princes-trust.org.uk

CC number: 1079675/SC041198

Eligibility

Young people between the ages of 11 and 30 who have struggled at school, are not in education or training, are in or leaving care, are long-term unemployed, have been in trouble with the law, are facing issues such as homelessness or mental health issues, or are otherwise disadvantaged.

Types of grant

The Prince's Trust aims to change the lives of young people, helping them to develop confidence, learn new skills and get practical and financial support. A wide range of support is offered, including the trust's Development Awards – cash grants of up to £500, although typical amounts are between £175 and £250, that are available to assist young people aged 16 to 30 to access education, training or employment. Examples of what can be funded include tools and equipment, course fees, interview clothes, transport or childcare costs.

Exclusions

Development Awards cannot be given for:

- Living expenses
- Retrospective costs
- Gap-year or overseas projects
- Fees for courses higher than Level 3 (e.g. NVQ Level 4, HNC, HND, degree or postgraduate courses)
- Business start-up (see the Enterprise programme instead)

For restrictions from other programmes, and further information, refer to the trust's website.

Applications

An initial enquiry form can be completed online on the trust's website. Alternatively, the trust can be contacted by phone on 0800 842842, seven days a week from 9am – 9pm.

Financial information

Year end	31/03/2018
Income	£72,892,000
Total expenditure	£71,150,000

Further financial information

In total £1.179 million was awarded in grants to individuals in 2017/18. Grants totalling £425,000 were made to 1,402 individuals for welfare purposes through the Enterprise programme grants and £707,000 was awarded to 4,012 individuals for both welfare and educational purposes through the Development Awards. The grant totals have been estimated from the 2017/18 accounts.

Other information

The Prince's Trust also have a number of programmes to help individuals into work, education or training, or to build the skills and confidence of those aged 11 to 30, including work experience programmes; personal development programmes; mentoring; courses to help individuals discover new talents; and courses to boost confidence and skills. For up-to-date and more detailed information on the current programmes and support available, refer to the trust's website.

Sources of information

Accounts; annual report; Charity Commission record; funder's website.

The Stanley Stein Deceased Charitable Trust

 £8,700 (2017/18)

Correspondent: Brian Berg, Trustee, 14 Linden Lea, London N2 0RG (email: brianberg369@yahoo.co.uk)

CC number: 1048873

Eligibility

Educational grants are available to young people under the age of 21.

Types of grant

Educational grants are made to young people to help with the costs of pursing education or training.

Applications

Apply in writing to the correspondent.

Financial information

Year end	05/04/2018
Income	£5,300
Total expenditure	£19,300

Further financial information

Full accounts were not available to view on the Charity Commission's website due to the charity's low income. We have therefore estimated the grant total based on the charity's total expenditure. Grants are also awarded to individuals for welfare purposes.

Sources of information

Charity Commission record.

Ethnic minorities in the UK

Armenian General Benevolent Union London Trust

 £88,200 (2017)

Correspondent: The Trustees, Kent House, 14–17 Market Place, London W1W 8AJ

www.agbu.org.uk

CC number: 282070

Eligibility

University students of Armenian descent studying full-time at accredited UK educational organisations. Both undergraduate and postgraduate programmes are eligible. Preference can be given for courses in Armenian studies

or subjects which may benefit the Armenian community.

Types of grant

Scholarships generally range from £1,000 to £3,000 and are awarded annually for up to three years. The trust offers both grants and interest-free loans. Students studying performing arts have the opportunity to apply for funding to study in the USA. For undergraduates, see the AGBU Performing Arts Fellowship. For postgraduates (master's and above), see the USA Graduate Fellowship programme.

Exclusions

Citizens of Armenia studying in Armenia are not eligible for the scholarship. The trust does not offer travel grants, support for conferences, semesters of study abroad, non-degree courses, research studies and similar short-term educational or professional experience.

Applications

Applications can be made online on the AGBU Scholarship program website. There is a convenient eligibility checking programme. There arc various scholarships and fellowships with different deadline dates, check the website carefully before submitting an application.

Financial information

Year end	31/12/2017
Income	£158,300
Total expenditure	£125,300

Further financial information

Grants were awarded to 42 students during 2017.

Other information

Support is also given for the relief of poverty among Armenians, and for the promotion of Armenian history, culture, literature, language and religion.

Sources of information

Accounts; annual report; Charity Commission record.

The Armenian Relief Society of Great Britain Trust

 £840 (2016/17)

Correspondent: Jacqueline Karanfilian, Secretary, 19 Somervell Road, London HA2 8TY

CC number: 327389

Eligibility

Armenians in need as a result of illness, bereavement or financial hardship.

Types of grant

Scholarships and general financial assistance is available for students.

Applications

Apply in writing to the correspondent.

Financial information

Year end	31/10/2017
Income	£47,100
Total expenditure	£48,300

Further financial information

The 2016/17 accounts were the latest available at the time of writing (November 2019).

Other information

The charity collects food, medicines and clothing which is distributed in disaster situations. Grants are also made to organisations, particularly relief centres and similar organisations that are involved in providing relief in times of crisis.

Sources of information

Accounts; annual report; Charity Commission record.

Aviva Scholarships

Correspondent: (email: contact form available on the website)

 https://www.avivascholarships.com

Eligibility

Asian students who are citizens of China, Hong Kong, Singapore, Indonesia or Vietnam and who, or whose parents, are current Aviva customers. They must have an offer of admission (conditional or unconditional) at one of the 11 participating UK universities on an eligible undergraduate or postgraduate course. The participating universities are: University of London; Durham University; Northumbria University; University of Birmingham; University of Dundee; University of Bristol; University of East Anglia; University of Leicester; University of Liverpool; University of Stirling; York St John University.

Types of grant

Scholarships cover 20% of the tuition fees. For detailed information on specific courses covered by the scholarship and for which Aviva customers are eligible see the scholarship's website.

Exclusions

Only students who have yet to begin their studies are considered.

Applications

Applications are made via an online form. To see up-to-date closing dates for applications check the website.

Sources of information
Funder's website.

The Bestway Foundation

£ £104,500 (2017/18)

Correspondent: Mohammed Sheikh, Trustee, Bestway Foundation, Abbey Road, London NW10 7BW (tel: 020 8453 1234; email: zulfikaur.wajid-hasan@bestway.co.uk)

 www.bestwaygroup.co.uk/page/Bestway-Foundation.html

CC number: 297178

Eligibility
Higher education students who are of Indian, Pakistani, Bangladeshi or Sri Lankan origin are eligible to apply.

Types of grant
One-off and recurrent scholarships, grants and loans towards tuition fees. Payments are normally made directly to academic institutions.

Applications
Apply in writing to the correspondent. Considerations are usually made in January.

Financial information
Year end	30/06/2018
Income	£409,100
Total expenditure	£400,900

Further financial information
The grant total in the foundation's 2017/18 accounts included grants to charities overseas and individuals. We have therefore estimated how much was given in grants to individuals.

Other information
Grants are also made to organisations and academic institutions in the UK and overseas.

Sources of information
Accounts; annual report; Charity Commission record.

Canadian Centennial Scholarship Fund (UK)

£ £60,000 (2017/18)

Correspondent: Michelle Cassidy, Commercial Officer, Financial Services, Canada House, Trafalgar Square, London SW1Y 5BJ (tel: 07912 647473; email: scholarship@canadianscholarshipfund.co.uk)

 www.canadianscholarshipfund.co.uk

CC number: 313966

Eligibility
Canadian citizens who are studying for a postgraduate degree (or equivalent) in the UK and are in need of financial assistance. Applicants must have completed at least one term of study and have at least one term remaining at the time of applying.

Types of grant
Scholarships ranging from £3,000 to £5,000 to assist with the costs of studying in the UK. Previous scholarships have been awarded to people studying a wide range of subjects including engineering, social science and humanities, music, creative arts, design and so on.

Exclusions
Applicants undertaking a one-year programme are not eligible for support.

Applications
Application forms and guidelines are available to download from the fund's website. Shortlisted applicants will be required to attend an in-person interview in London and successful applicants will be notified soon after. Applications must include the following: details of two referees; a statement of financial need; a personal statement and programme overview; a short CV; a copy of Canadian passport; and copy of the transcript from the most recent completed degree. Current deadlines for each stage of the application are available on the fund's website.

Financial information
Year end	31/03/2018
Income	£73,400
Total expenditure	£71,800

Further financial information
In 2017/18 a total of £60,000 was awarded to 15 individual students.

Sources of information
Accounts; annual report; Charity Commission record; funder's website.

Churches International Student Network Hardship Fund

£ £18,200 (2017)

Correspondent: Applications Secretary, Churches Together in Britain and Ireland, Interchurch House, 35 Lower Marsh, London SE1 7RL (tel: 020 3794 2288; email: hardship@ctbi.org.uk)

 https://ctbi.org.uk/hardship-fund

CC number: 1113299

Eligibility
Full-time international students from developing countries studying at British or Irish institutions who are facing unexpected financial problems during the final stages of their course (six months). Both undergraduate and postgraduate students on a degree course lasting a minimum of one year are eligible. Applicants should be intending to return to their home country after completion of the course.

Types of grant
Small grants of up to, but not exceeding £1,000 to enable the applicant to complete their course. The same person will not be funded twice.

Exclusions
Funding is not given to:
- Permanent residents of Britain, Ireland, EU and other developed countries
- Students who began the course without assured funding to meet the education costs
- Asylum seekers or refugees
- Those who have not begun their course, or those who have already finished
- Those studying outside Britain/Ireland or those seeking help for a field trip abroad
- Those whose studies relate to arms manufacture or experimentation on live animals
- Students whose fees and living expenses have been covered by major award(s)

Applications
Potential applicants should request an application form from the correspondent (providing their postal address). Requests for application forms should be made by mid-December, mid-April and mid-August. Grants are usually considered three times a year, in February (for studies finishing April-July), June (for August-November) and October (for December-March).

Financial information
Year end	31/12/2017
Income	£15,700
Total expenditure	£19,100

Further financial information
In 2017, grants to 21 students totalled £18,200.

Other information
The fund is administered by Churches Together in Britain and Ireland, the fund's financial information can be found in that charity's accounts.

Sources of information
Accounts; annual report; Charity Commission record; funder's website.

Koning Willem Fonds – The Netherlands Benevolent Society

Correspondent: Ms M. Koomans, Social Work Coordinator, 7 Austin Friars, London EC2N 2HA (tel: 01932 840285; email: info@koningwillemfonds.org.uk)

 https://www.koningwillemfonds.org.uk

CC number: 213032

Eligibility
Dutch citizens living in the UK who are in need. Support is extended to surviving widows/widowers of Dutch nationals and children with at least one parent of Dutch nationality.

Types of grant
The charity has recently set up an Education Fund to deal with requests for educational support. Financial assistance has been given to students who, due to circumstances beyond their control, would otherwise be unable to finish their studies. Support has been given to those studying paramedic courses and catering diplomas.

Exclusions
The charity does not normally support university students applying for additional funding.

Applications
Initial enquires can be made using the contact form on the funder's website. The trustees meet on a monthly basis to consider grant applications.

Financial information
Year end	31/12/2018
Income	£39,500
Total expenditure	£55,410

Further financial information
The charity awarded 30 grants to its beneficiaries. Note: the charity's Education Fund was set up during 2019 and therefore, we were unable to determine a grant total for educational grants.

Sources of information
Accounts; annual report; Charity Commission record; funder's website.

The Henry Lester Trust

£65,000 (2017/18)

Correspondent: The Trustees, The Barn House, Lees Hill, South Warnborough, Hook, Hampshire RG29 1RQ (email: info@henrylestertrust.com)

 https://www.henrylestertrust.com

CC number: 313892

Eligibility
Citizens of the People's Republic of China studying/researching architecture, medicine, computer development and mechanical sciences at postgraduate level at a UK university. Particular emphasis is given to:

- Those seeking support for (so far) unfunded studies in terms of materials, technical assistance or extra tuition calculated to achieve the aim of, or enhance, their course of study
- Those in the later stages of their studies who can demonstrate that their studies may be negatively affected by an unexpected lack of finances

Applicants must be returning to China upon completion of their studies.

Types of grant
Grants up to £3,500 per year are made towards course materials/equipment and general living expenses.

Exclusions
Grants are not given for study or research outside the UK, nor for seminars or conferences.

Applications
Applications should be made to the trust by email. Applications must enclose a formal letter of support (on official headed paper) written by the applicant's professor, head of department or similar senior person. Full details of the course/area of research, a detailed CV, a calculation of the amount being sought and an indication of the applicant's intention to return to China in due course must also be included.

Financial information
Year end	30/04/2018
Income	£42,400
Total expenditure	£79,200

Further financial information
During 2017/18, the trust awarded grants to 26 beneficiaries.

Sources of information
Accounts; annual report; Charity Commission record; funder's website.

Schilizzi Foundation in Memory of Eleutherios and Helena Veniselos (The Schilizzi Foundation)

£72,900 (2017/18)

Correspondent: The Secretary, Rowan, Turweston, Brackley, Northamptonshire NN13 5JX (tel: 01295 710356; email: admin@schilizzifoundation.org.uk)

 www.schilizzifoundation.org.uk

CC number: 314128

Eligibility
Greek nationals who are pursuing an undergraduate degree course or vocational training in Britain and are in need. Priority is given to undergraduates in their final year. Children of Greek nationals living in Britain may also be eligible for support to further their education in the language, history, literature and institutions of Greece.

Types of grant
The foundation provides 'special awards' to support Greek nationals who are studying in Britain and are able to demonstrate financial hardship. Grants are awarded towards the cost of books, tuition fees and living expenses. In addition, the foundation offers bursaries of £3,500 a year (for up to three years) to Greek nationals wishing to study an undergraduate degree at King's College London. The Gordon Hedley Scholarship, which is also administered by the foundation, offers bursaries of £3,500 a year (for up to three years) to Greek nationals wishing to study an undergraduate degree at King's College, Cambridge.

Exclusions
The foundation is currently unable to support PhD students.

Applications
Apply in writing to the correspondent to request an application. Applications for scholarships to King's College London should be made directly to the college (contact details can be found on the foundation's website).

Financial information
Year end	30/06/2018
Income	£68,500
Total expenditure	£102,200

Further financial information
Grants were distributed as follows: grants totalling £31,500 were awarded to three students at King's College London and special awards totalling £37,900 were awarded to 14 students. The were no new Gordon Hedley Scholarships awarded in 2017/18; however, the third instalment of a three-year scholarship amounting to £3,500 was paid to one existing student.

Sources of information
Accounts; annual report; Charity Commission record; funder's website.

W. Wing Yip and Brothers Foundation

Correspondent: The Trustees, W. Wing Yip plc, The Wing Yip Centre, 375 Nechells Park Road, Birmingham B7 5NT (tel: 0121 327 6618; email: foundation@wingyip.com)

 https://www.wingyip.com/supporting-our-communities/wing-yip-foundation

CC number: 326999

Eligibility

UK and overseas students of Chinese origin who are undertaking an undergraduate degree in the UK.

Types of grant

Grants can be made to contribute towards fees and living expenses while studying.

Applications

Students must be nominated through their university.

Financial information

Year end	31/07/2018
Income	£98,400
Total expenditure	£43,600

Further financial information

No grants were made to individuals in 2017/18; however, in previous years the total of grants have ranged from £6,000 to £100,000.

Other information

Grants are also made to other charities who are engaged in community welfare, medical research, care for the sick and religious activities. The foundation has recently began a scheme with Loughborough University by which four students are given funding for the duration of their degree course.

Sources of information

Accounts; annual report; Charity Commission record; funder's website.

Gender

Broadlands Home Trust

 £3,100 (2017/18)

Correspondent: The Secretary, 2 Winchester Close, Newport, Isle of Wight PO30 1DR (tel: 01983 525630; email: broadlandstrust@btinternet.com)

CC number: 201433

Eligibility

Educational support is given to girls and young single women (under the age of 22) in need who are at school, starting work or are in further or higher education.

There may be some preference for women living on the Isle of Wight.

Types of grant

Grants can be made in the form of pensions or Christmas gifts to women over the age of 40. Younger women can receive grants to cover the costs of books, fees, travelling expenses or other educational equipment.

Exclusions

Grants are not made for married women or graduates.

Applications

Application forms are available from the correspondent and should be submitted either directly by the individual or a family member. They should include the applicant's name, date of birth, address, financial details (family income and expenditure), details of course undertaken, a reference and confirmation of attendance, and specify the support needed. Requests are considered quarterly in January, April, July and October. If applying by post, applicants should enclose an sae.

Financial information

Year end	31/03/2018
Income	£10,300
Total expenditure	£6,900

Further financial information

Full accounts were not available to view on the Charity Commission's website due to the charity's low income. We have therefore estimated the grant total based on the charity's total expenditure.

Sources of information

Charity Commission record.

Edinburgh Association of University Women – President's Fund

 £17,100 (2018)

Correspondent: Eileen Brownlie, Trustee/Honorary Secretary, 12 Dean Park Mews, Edinburgh EH4 1ED (email: eileencbrownlie2706@gmail.com)

 https://www.hw.ac.uk/study/scholarships/presidents-fund-edinburgh-association.htm

OSCR number: SC004501

Eligibility

Women experiencing unforeseen financial hardship who are in their final year of study for a degree (undergraduate or postgraduate) at a university in the UK.

Types of grant

Previous grants have been awarded towards books, equipment and maintenance/living expenses.

Exclusions

Grants are not given for access courses, diplomas, certificates, or for courses with a duration of just one year. The fund does not support study or work overseas. Grants are capped at one award per person.

Applications

Request an application form from the Honorary Secretary by email. Applications are considered three times each year, usually in October, January and April.

Financial information

Year end	31/12/2018
Income	£19,200
Total expenditure	£19,000

Further financial information

Full accounts were not available to view on the Charity Commission's website due to the charity's low income. We have therefore estimated the grant total based on the charity's total expenditure.

Sources of information

Heriot Watt University website; OSCR record.

FfWG (Funds for Women Graduates)

 £224,600 (2018)

Correspondent: Jean Collett-Flatt, Grants Administrator, 4 St Michaels Gate, Shrewsbury SY1 2HL (tel: 01743 383047; email: grants@ffwg.org.uk)

 www.ffwg.org.uk

CC number: 312903

Eligibility

Women who are studying for a postgraduate degree in the UK. Students must have already completed at least six months of their course at the time of application. Eligibility criteria varies between grant schemes. See the charity's website to confirm your eligibility.

Types of grant

Foundation grants and emergency grants are made towards general living expenses. The Theodora Bosanquet Bursary is also made towards living expenses, but is awarded specifically to history and English literature students for accommodation in London for up to four weeks between mid-June and mid-September. The FfWG Fellowship, with a value of £6,000, is awarded for original research 'relevant to the mission of the Graduate Women International (GWI)'.

The fellowship requires the applicant to have worked in a country other than the one in which they were born for a minimum of eight months. This is reserved for applicants wishing to undertake research in Britain.

Exclusions

The charity cannot award funding for:

- Undergraduate degrees
- A second first degree
- University or college fees
- Fieldwork outside Britain
- Travel costs outside Britain
- Any conferences, exhibitions or seminars

Students who are planning to defer their place/start their course in the next academic year cannot apply.

Applications

For foundation grants, emergency grants and the Theodora Bosanquet Bursary, contact the charity for information on how to apply. For the FfWG Fellowship, refer to the GWI website (https://graduatewomen.org/) for details. The fellowship is normally awarded every three years.

Financial information

Year end	31/12/2018
Income	£226,700
Total expenditure	£321,400

Further financial information

Grants are broken down as follows:

Foundation grants	38	£161,000
Emergency grants	28	£61,500
Theodora Bosanquet Bursary	2	£2,100

The FfWG Fellowship was not awarded during 2018. The next fellowship is due to be made in 2019.

Sources of information

Accounts; annual report: Charity Commission record; funder's website.

The Girls of the Realm Guild (Women's Careers Foundation)

 £16,700 (2018)

Correspondent: Beth Hayward, Secretary, 2 Watch Oak, Blackham, Tunbridge Wells, Kent TN3 9TP (tel: 01892 740602)

CC number: 313159

Eligibility

Women over the age of 21 who are UK citizens and are seeking assistance to continue educational and vocational training. Younger applicants (over the age of 16) may be supported for music or dance studies.

Types of grant

One-off grants of around £250 to assist with costs relating to education or training, preferably to lead to a career.

Exclusions

Grants are not given for PhD or postgraduate studies if the subject indicates a complete change of direction.

Applications

For application forms and further guidelines, write to the correspondent and include an sae.

Financial information

Year end	31/12/2018
Income	£9,400
Total expenditure	£18,600

Further financial information

Full accounts were not available to view on the Charity Commission's website due to the charity's low income. We have therefore estimated the grant total based on the charity's total expenditure.

Other information

The charity also provides low interest loans (which may be included in the grant total).

Sources of information

Charity Commission record; University of Worcester website.

The Hilda Martindale Educational Trust

Correspondent: The Trustees, c/o The Registry, Royal Holloway, University of London, Egham, Surrey TW20 0EX (tel: 01788 434455; email: HildaMartindaleTrust@royalholloway.ac.uk)

 https://www.royalholloway.ac.uk/aboutus/governancematters/thehildamartindaletrust.aspx

Eligibility

Women over the age of 21 who are British nationals and pursuing a profession or career requiring vocational training in the areas where women are underrepresented. Priority is given to postgraduates and undergraduates in their final year of study. Courses/training must be the minimum of a full year in length and preferably start in September/October of the relevant academic year.

Types of grant

A small number of one-off grants of up to £3,000 are offered for training courses and are normally paid in three instalments, in October, January and April. Awards can be used for fees, books, equipment, living expenses, childcare and so on. A limited number of awards can also be given towards the costs of any graduate training (MSc/MA and PhD) in an area which is underrepresented by women e.g. science, technology, engineering, architecture and some branches of medicine (such as surgery), and leadership roles in all fields at a UK institution approved by the trustees.

Exclusions

Assistance is not given for:

- Short courses
- Access courses
- Courses attended abroad
- Elective studies
- Intercalated BSc years during a UK medical, dental, veterinary or nursing course
- Academic research
- Special projects in the UK or abroad
- First year undergraduates
- People holding grants from research councils, the British Academy and other public sources
- Retrospective awards

Funding can only be given to women who cannot access any other funding. Medical, dental, or veterinary students will only be considered if they are pursuing an area within that field where women are underrepresented.

Applications

Application forms are available from the Council of Royal Holloway website. Applications open in August and should be submitted, together with two references and a personal statement, by February for the courses taking place in the following academic year. See the website for up-to-date closing dates for applications and further guidance notes. The trustees normally meet in spring to consider awards.

Sources of information

Funder's website.

The Muirhead Trust

£ £6,100 (2017/18)

Correspondent: The Trustees, c/o Franchi Law LLP, Queens House, 19 St Vincent Place, Glasgow G1 2DT (email: ann@franchilaw.co.uk)

www.themuirheadtrust.org.uk

OSCR number: SC016524

Eligibility

Female students of Scottish origin and almost exclusively those who are studying in Scotland. Support is available to students of medicine, veterinary science, pharmacy, nursing, dentistry, science and engineering, including biological and chemical engineering.

Types of grant

One-off and recurrent grants according to need.

Exclusions

Biomedical or forensic science students are outside the remit of the trust as is PhD funding.

Applications

Application forms can be downloaded from the trust's website and should be submitted together with a CV and an academic transcript. The deadline for applications is 31 August annually.

Financial information

Year end	30/06/2018
Income	£7,700
Total expenditure	£6,800

Sources of information

Funder's website; OSCR record.

Dr Meena Sharma Memorial Foundation

£ £3,600 (2017/18)

Correspondent: The Trustees, 14 Magdalene Road, Walsall, West Midlands WS1 3TA (tel: 01922 629842; email: gwalior@onetel.com)

CC number: 1108375

Eligibility

Children and women in the UK and India, especially those who are disadvantaged or have disabilities.

Types of grant

Scholarships and grants are awarded towards education. Teachers, other educational professionals, medical personnel or medical students may also be supported.

Applications

Apply in writing to the correspondent.

Financial information

Year end	31/03/2018
Income	£24,300
Total expenditure	£32,300

Further financial information

Full accounts were not available to view on the Charity Commission's website due to the charity's low income. We have therefore estimated the grant total based on the charity's total expenditure.

Other information

Grants are also made to organisations and to support women and children in India.

Sources of information

Charity Commission record.

Yorkshire Ladies' Council of Education (Incorporated)

 £24,100 (2017/18)

Correspondent: Mrs P. Hollis, Honorary Secretary, Ground Floor Office, Forest Hill, 11 Park Crescent, Leeds, West Yorkshire LS8 1DH (tel: 0113 269 1471; email: info@ylce.org)

🌐 www.ylce.org.uk

CC number: 529714

Eligibility

Women aged 21 and over who are British citizens and have a confirmed offer at a British educational institution. Applicants cannot be related to a member of the Yorkshire Ladies' Council of Education and must not be eligible for student finance support.

Types of grant

Grants in the range of £100 to £500 (average grant £200 to £300) are given to contribute to course fees only.

Applications

Application forms and further guidelines are available on the charity's website. Applications are usually considered three times a year in September, March and June and completed forms must be received by the first day of the relevant month. The award is available for one year, candidates must reapply if they wish to receive further funding.

Financial information

Year end	31/08/2018
Income	£81,000
Total expenditure	£35,500

Further financial information

In 2017/18 a total of £24,100 was awarded as scholarships and educational grants.

Other information

The charity also provides grants to local community bodies and institutions.

Sources of information

Accounts; annual report; Charity Commission record; funder's website.

Homelessness

Crisis

 £47,000 (2017/18)

Correspondent: Welfare Team, 66 Commercial Street, London E1 6LT (tel: 0300 636 1967; email: enquires@ crisis.org.uk)

🌐 www.crisis.org.uk

CC number: 1082947/SC040094

Eligibility

People over the age of 18 who are homeless in the UK.

Types of grant

Grants to assist people with the costs of courses and training, equipment to get started in the world of work or set up a business (where a robust plan is presented).

Applications

Grant applications can be made by individuals who are supported by a coach working at a Crisis Skylight centre.

Financial information

Year end	30/06/2018
Income	£40,914,000
Total expenditure	£39,720,000

Further financial information

Grants were made to 62 members with an average grant of £1,500. The grant totals have been estimated from the 2017/18 accounts.

Other information

Crisis is a national charity for homeless people that delivers education, employment, housing and health services. It also undertakes research into the causes and consequences of homelessness and campaigns for change. In 2017/18 it helped more than 11,300 people out of homelessness. Visit the charity's website for more information.

Sources of information

Accounts; annual report; Charity Commission record; funder's website.

Illness and disability

Ataxia UK

 £1,500 (2017/18)

Correspondent: Susan Millman, Secretary and CEO, Ground Floor, Lincoln House, 1–3 Brixton Road, London SW9 6DE (tel: 020 7582 1444; email: office@ataxia.org.uk)

🌐 www.ataxia.org.uk

CC number: 1102391

Eligibility
Grants from The Mark Dower Trust (administered by Ataxia UK), are available to young people between the ages of 16 and 30 who have been diagnosed with ataxia.

Types of grant
Grants are available to support young people 'in their quest for independent living through enabling them to develop skills or hobbies or to pursue educational goals', according to the charity's website. The grant can be used for purposes such as participation in training or development of a skill, hobby or creative activity, or purchase of equipment which will enable this.

Applications
An application form is available to download from the charity's website which can be submitted by either email or post. Along with the form the application should include a recent letter from a doctor and evidence of commitment to the skill/hobby/sport/activity concerned. Applications are usually submitted by the end of January each year but see the charity's website for current information on submission dates.

Financial information
Year end	31/03/2018
Income	£831,900
Total expenditure	£836,800

Further financial information
The Mark Dower Trust can award up to £3,000 annually for both educational and welfare purposes. In 2017/18 it was divided between three recipients for art courses, equipment for university and driving lessons to reduce isolation.

Other information
The charity previously provided the Jerry Farr Travel Fellowship, which offered up to £3,500 for individuals with ataxia to undertake travel abroad, broadening their horizons. It appears from the website that the final grant from this scheme was made in 2017. Ataxia UK also offers help with applications made to three other grant schemes: The Headley Trust, which provides grants towards equipment for use at home; the Florence Nightingale Aid in Sickness Trust, which provides grants towards equipment and also respite breaks; and Barchester's Church Foundation, which seeks to improve the independence and mobility of older people and those with disabilities.

Sources of information
Accounts; annual report; Charity Commission record; funder's website.

The Douglas Bader Foundation

 £29,500 (2017/18)

Correspondent: David Bickers, Chief Executive Officer, 14 Raynham Road, London W6 0HY (tel: 020 8748 8884; email: david.bickers@ douglasbaderfoundation.com)

🌐 https://www.douglasbader foundation.com/bader-grants

CC number: 800435

Eligibility
People who were either born without, or who have lost, one or more limbs or those who have a physical disability. Adults and children with a diagnosed mental health issue can also be supported.

Types of grant
The Bader Grant Scheme offers financial support towards the pursuance of achievements. Funding can be given towards education and training, including further education, and for other practical support and equipment. Lady Bader Memorial grants and special awards may also be awarded at the trustees discretion to applicants who reflect Lady Bader's own lifetime interests and achievements.

Exclusions
Grants cannot be given towards living aids.

Applications
Application forms are available to download from the foundation's website.

Financial information
Year end	31/10/2018
Income	£304,300
Total expenditure	£448,800

Further financial information
In 2017/18 a total of £58,900 was awarded to individuals. We estimate that around £29,500 was awarded for welfare purposes and a further £29,500 was awarded for educational purposes.

Other information
Support is also given to organisations. The foundation administers a scheme called the Bader Braves which offers children and young people the opportunity to fly in a light aircraft at events throughout the UK as well as the Team Bader scheme that offers children experiences that encourage teamwork to instil a sense of self-confidence. In addition, the foundation provides advice and information and the one-to-one support line, 'Limbline'.

Sources of information
Accounts; annual report; Charity Commission record; funder's website.

Cambrian Educational Foundation for Deaf Children in Wales

 £16,600 (2018)

Correspondent: Mrs P. Brown, Clerk to the Trustees, 30 Lon Cedwyn, Sketty, Swansea SA2 0TH (tel: 01792 207628; email: pam-brown@homecall.co.uk)

🌐 www.cambrianeducational foundationfordeafchildren.org.uk

CC number: 515848

Eligibility
Young people under 25 who are deaf or partially deaf and live or have a parent living in Wales.

Types of grant
Grants up to a maximum of £500 per year. Grants can be used at any school, college, university or institution of further (including professional and technical) education that has been approved by the trustees. The foundation also offers financial assistance, clothing, equipment or books for school and university leavers to enable them to enter a profession, trade or calling. Bursaries or maintenance allowances are offered to enable students to travel to pursue their education in both the UK and abroad as well as financial assistance to enable young people to study music or the arts.

Applications
Application forms are available to download from the foundation's website. If the applicant is under the age of 18, the form should be completed by a parent/guardian or another authorised person. Applications should be supported in writing by the applicant's teacher or tutor.

Financial information

Year end	31/12/2018
Income	£20,000
Total expenditure	£18,500

Further financial information

Full accounts were not available to view on the Charity Commission's website due to the charity's low income. We have therefore estimated the grant total based on the charity's total expenditure.

Sources of information

Charity Commission record; funder's website.

Cystic Fibrosis Trust

 £59,600 (2017/18)

Correspondent: Welfare Team, 1 Aldgate, Second Floor, London EC3N 1RE (tel: 020 3795 2184; email: helpline@cysticfibrosis.org.uk)

www.cysticfibrosis.org.uk

CC number: 1079049

Eligibility

People in need who have cystic fibrosis and live in the UK.

Types of grant

Education grants – help for adults with cystic fibrosis over the age of 18 with the costs of higher education or other professional qualifications including vocational training. The fund also accepts applications from people with cystic fibrosis aged 16 or 17 who are not moving into formal further education and who wish instead to undertake vocational training.

Applications

Application forms can be downloaded from the trust's website.

Education grants are administered by the Joseph Levy Foundation. Further information can be found on its website at: www.jlef.org.uk.

Financial information

Year end	31/03/2018
Income	£15,170,000
Total expenditure	£17,650,000

Other information

The trust also provides confidential advice, support and information on all aspects of cystic fibrosis in the form of factsheets and a dedicated helpline which can provide advice and support on a range of issues, including help with financial issues (020 3795 2184).

Sources of information

Accounts; annual report; Charity Commission record; funder's website.

Gardner's Trust for the Blind

 £14,200 (2017/18)

Correspondent: Angela Stewart, 117 Charterhouse Street, London EC1M 6AA (tel: 020 7253 3757)

CC number: 207233

Eligibility

Registered blind or partially-sighted people who live in the UK.

Types of grant

One-off and recurrent grants of up to £600 towards the costs of education, course fees, assistive technology and so on.

Applications

Apply in writing to the correspondent. Applications must be supported by confirmation of the applicant's disability from a third party.

Financial information

Year end	30/09/2018
Income	£102,600
Total expenditure	£96,300

Other information

The trust may also make grants to organisations.

Sources of information

Accounts; annual report; Barnet London Borough website; Charity Commission record; Sightline Directory website.

Kidney Care UK

 £25,800 (2018)

Correspondent: The Trustees, 3 The Windmills, St Mary's Close, Turk Street, Alton, Hampshire GU34 1EF (tel: 01420 541424; email: info@kidneycareuk.org)

https://www.kidneycareuk.org

CC number: 270288

Eligibility

Dialysis patients and their families who are on a low income. Transplant patients and those receiving conservative care whose health and quality of life is being seriously affected by their renal condition are also eligible for support. Support may be extended more generally to people whose lives have been affected by kidney disease, at the trustees' discretion.

Types of grant

Educational grants are awarded to eligible people in further education and training, to help cover the cost of university or college fees and IT equipment.

Exclusions

The charity is unable to help with travel costs for ongoing dialysis.

Applications

Application forms (and full guidelines) are available to download from the funder's website. Applications must be submitted by a renal social worker or a member of the patient's renal team, who must sign a declaration and attach a detailed social report on the hospital's headed paper.

Financial information

Year end	31/12/2018
Income	£2,400,000
Total expenditure	£3,330,000

Further financial information

During 2018, the charity awarded grants to 1,533 beneficiaries.

Other information

The charity operates a counselling and support service for patients and their families. To access this service, contact the charity by telephone to book an appointment with a renal counsellor. The charity also runs a National Advocacy Service, with 11 advocacy officers covering different regions across the UK. The service is totally confidential and provides information and support to patients and their families (or carers) on a wide range of issues including treatment options, benefits, housing, etc. To find your local advocacy officer, see the charity's website.

Sources of information

Accounts; annual report; Charity Commission record; funder's website.

The Leukaemia Care Society

£19,600 (2017/18)

Correspondent: The Trustees, One Birch Court, Blackpole East, Worcester, Worcestershire WR3 8SG (tel: 01905 755977; email: info@leukaemiacare.org.uk)

www.leukaemiacare.org.uk

CC number: 259483

Eligibility

People with leukaemia and allied blood disorders and their families. Support is also available to haematology nurses who wish to study at a postgraduate level.

Types of grant

Grants are awarded for a variety of welfare needs, for example, the charity's Hospital Travel Fund makes grants of £200 towards the cost of travel (including bus or train tickets, fuel, parking, etc.) to hospitals and treatments for patients and their families. The Ann Ashley Leukaemia Counselling Fund awards grants of £400 for a maximum of six counselling sessions with BACP or UKCP registered counsellors.

The Nurse Bursary Scheme makes grants of up to £2,500 for postgraduate university study or professional short courses. Grants are awarded towards fees, travel costs involved in study, accommodation costs e.g. for attending conferences and additional childcare costs incurred as a result of learning activities.

Applications

Application forms for any of the above-mentioned funds are available to download from the charity's website. Completed forms can be sent to the charity's postal address or by email, although email addresses differ for each fund. See the charity's website for details.

Financial information

Year end		31/03/2018
Income		£1,260,000
Total expenditure		£1,280,000

Other information

The charity operates a free helpline (9am to 10pm during Monday to Friday, 9am to 10pm during on Saturdays) for advice and support. The helpline can also be accessed via Whatsapp. For a limited time each day, the helpline can be used to speak with a nurse. Details of when this service is available can be found on the charity's website, although it may be useful to contact the helpline to book a time slot to speak with a nurse. The charity also operates 24 support groups nationwide for patients and their families affected by blood cancer to share their experiences with local people.

Sources of information

Accounts; annual report; Charity Commission record; funder's website.

The Joseph Levy Memorial Fund

 £60,000 (2017/18)

Correspondent: Maria Zava, 1st Floor, 1 Bell Street, London NW1 5BY (tel: 020 7616 1207; email: education@jlef.org.uk)

🌐 www.jlef.org.uk

CC number: 1079049

Eligibility

Young people with cystic fibrosis who are UK residents and are wishing to undertake a higher education course at an accredited university, college or other educational institution or vocational training. Applicants must be aged 18 or over at the time their course is due to start; however, those wishing to undertake vocational training may apply when they are 16/17.

Types of grant

Grants are available to assist with the financial costs associated with studying while living with cystic fibrosis, such as travel to college and to hospital visits, high calorie foods and accommodation costs (the additional costs of having an en-suite and keeping the accommodation at a suitable temperature). Financial assistance is also available towards books, materials and course fees.

Exclusions

The charity will not fund: studies at a private institution unless it can be demonstrated that there is no alternative course available at a statutory provider, gym fees, or the repayment of student loan or other debts.

Applications

Application forms can be downloaded from the charity's website and should be completed and returned to the correspondent by post. Applications can be made at any time and are considered twice a year, usually in June and December. Further guidelines and current deadlines can be found on the charity's website.

Financial information

Year end		31/03/2018
Income		£35,000
Total expenditure		£60,000

Other information

The fund is part of the Cystic Fibrosis Trust and is administered by the Joseph Levy Foundation.

Sources of information

Accounts; annual report; Charity Commission record; funder's website.

Meningitis Now (formerly known as Meningitis Trust)

Correspondent: The Trustees, Fern House, Bath Road, Stroud, Gloucestershire GL5 3TJ (tel: 0808 801 0388; email: helpline@meningitisnow. org)

 https://www.meningitisnow.org

CC number: 803016/SC037790

Eligibility

People in the UK who are in need as a result of meningitis and meningococcal septicaemia, or those who have a disability as a result of the illness. Support is extended to the immediate family (parent, step-parents, siblings, partners or grandparents) of those affected by meningitis.

Types of grant

Grants of up to £1,000 are given for various welfare needs, from the following schemes:

Health and wellbeing grants: grants of this type are awarded for counselling, creative therapies, complementary therapies (such as acupuncture), travel expenses for hospital visits, health and exercise (swimming lessons, horse riding, etc.) and short breaks and days out.

Specialist equipment grants: grants are made towards the cost of specialist bikes and trikes, mobility aids, specialist beds, sensory toys, home adaptations and prosthetics.

Bereavement grants: grants are awarded to help with the cost of funerals, headstones and bereavement counselling.

Opportunities grants: grants of up to £1,000 are awarded for education support, books/equipment required for a training course, technology to support learning (laptops, iPads, etc.) and tuition and re-training costs.

Exclusions

Grants are **not** awarded towards the following:
- Holidays
- Building, home and garden adaptations on rental property (without prior written consent from the landlord)
- Domestic bills and arrears (telephone, gas, mortgage, loan repayments, etc.)
- Non-specialist clothing, bedding, furniture
- Purchasing a private vehicle
- Purchasing animals/pets
- Nursery placements
- Legal fees
- Private tuition fees
- Medical treatment

The charity does not make payments in cash.

Applications

Contact the charity's helpline to request an application form. If the beneficiary is under the age of 18, the application must be completed on their behalf by the individual's parent or carer. First time applicants will have to include a written confirmation of the diagnosis. A support statement from a relevant third party (health professional, social services, etc.) may also be required. In most cases, applications will be subject to a support assessment which involves a discussion about the individual's needs and award request with a member of the Meningitis Now Helpline or one of the charity's community support officers. Where appropriate, a community support officer may visit the applicant in their home to conduct the assessment.

Financial information

Year end	31/03/2018
Income	£3,460,000
Total expenditure	£2,730,000

Further financial information

During 2017/18, the charity's grants programme was temporarily suspended.

Other information

The charity's research programme funds research projects in universities across the UK, to help improve meningitis vaccines and develop new ones. The charity also operates a free helpline on 0808 80 10 388 (Monday to Thursday 9am until 4pm, Fridays 9am until 1pm) for advice and support with meningitis-related issues. The charity has access to a telephone interpreting service in over 240 languages to ensure that the helpline is accessible to all. Those who have a hearing or speech impairment can also contact the helpline using the Next Generation Text Service, prefix 18001.

Sources of information

Accounts; annual report; Charity Commission record; funder's website.

Snowdon Trust

💷 £226,700 (2017/18)

Correspondent: Selection Panel, Unit 18, Oakhurst Business Park, Wilberforce Way, Southwater, Horsham, West Sussex RH13 9RT (tel: 01403 732899; email: info@snowdontrust.org.uk)

 www.snowdontrust.org

CC number: 282754

Eligibility

Individuals with a physical disability or sensory impairment who are studying in the UK in further or higher education, or training towards employment.

Types of grant

The trust runs two funding programmes: **Core Grants Programme** – funds to cover the additional costs that students incur as a result of their disability e.g. carers, translators for students who are deaf, computers, specialist software, wheelchairs or special accommodation/equipment; **Scholarships Programme** – aims to fully fund around 50 exceptional students who have a disability, through a master's degree. About 100 grants are awarded each year, ranging from £250 to £3,000, and up to £5,000 in exceptional circumstances.

Exclusions

The trust does not normally cover expenses for tuition fees or standard living, accommodation and childcare costs, but can occasionally help with tuition fees if the need is justifiably and directly related to the applicant's disability. Retrospective awards are not made.

Applications

Application forms and guidelines can be completed online or downloaded from the trust's website. Applicants are required to provide academic and personal references and supporting documentation such as medical information of disability if applicable. The awarding selection panel usually meets in July and October, with applicants receiving results soon after each meeting. Acceptance of an award must normally be made within two weeks of a funding offer.

Financial information

Year end	30/04/2018
Income	£373,900
Total expenditure	£417,700

Further financial information

The trust awarded 109 student grants during 2017/18, and awarded its first two scholarships to students studying at The Royal College of Art and Design (RCA) and Cambridge University.

Other information

In 2015 the trust removed a previously stated preference for students between 17 and 25 years of age, reflecting the fact that the trust supports a significant number of applications from those retraining following later onset of disability, or those undertaking postgraduate study. This trust also provides mentoring support and advice to beneficiaries and occasionally undertakes research. The trust's Scholarships Programme was launched in 2017 and is planned to be a seven-year programme funded by a large legacy received in the financial year 2016/17.

Sources of information

Accounts; annual report; Charity Commission record; funder's website.

Miscellan-eous

The Buchanan Society

💷 £7,400 (2018)

Correspondent: Ian Buchanan, Secretary, 16 Ribblesdale, East Kilbride, Lanarkshire G74 4QN (tel: 01355 243437; email: contact form on the website)

 www.buchanansociety.com

OSCR number: SC013679

Eligibility

People who through birth, adoption or marriage bear the following surnames: Buchanan, MacAuslan (all spellings), MacWattie and Risk. Those whose mother's maiden name is or was any of the above-mentioned surnames are also eligible.

Types of grant

Educational grants are made to students in higher and further education (including vocational training) towards costs such as purchasing equipment.

Exclusions

Grants can be paid in instalments but no grant can continue for more than three years.

Applications

Application forms are available to download from the charity's website. For educational grants, university and college students need to confirm that they have been accepted for a course. The charity will also require a progress update for each year a grant is given. Apprentices and vocational students must provide details of the course or programme they are following. Applications for educational grants are considered in meetings in February, June and October. Applicants are advised to send completed application forms to the charity in the month before the next meeting.

Financial information

Year end	31/12/2018
Income	£73,600
Total expenditure	£59,500

Other information

The charity also makes grants for welfare purposes.

Sources of information

Accounts; annual report; funder's website; OSCR record.

The Marie Duffy Foundation

💷 £560 (2017/18)

Correspondent: Mike Pask, Trustee/Secretary and Awards Manager, 2 Aspin Lodge, 38 North Park, Gerrard's Cross, Buckinghamshire SL9 8JP (tel: 07775 905440; email: mike@marie-duffy-foundation.com or enquiries@marie-duffy-foundation.com)

 www.marie-duffy-foundation.com

CC number: 1145892

Eligibility

Irish dancers and musicians over the age of ten who are 'passionate about excellence in dance, music, composition or choreography'.

Types of grant

Educational grants have been awarded in the form of bursaries (particularly to Limerick University) and scholarships to study the Irish language.

Applications

Application forms are available to download from the funder's website. Applicants must also provide:

▶ Their dance or music CV
▶ Details of their proposed project
▶ Why they think they should receive an award/details on how their project will benefit Irish dancing, culture and/ or music

Financial information

Year end	08/08/2018
Income	£3,000
Total expenditure	£1,700

Further financial information

Full accounts were not available to view on the Charity Commission's website due to the charity's low income. We have therefore estimated the grant total based on the charity's total expenditure.

Other information

Grants are mainly awarded to individuals/groups of individuals, but the charity does make an annual donation to the World Academy of Music and Dance at the University of Limerick.

Sources of information

Charity Commission record; funder's website.

Masonic Charitable Foundation

Correspondent: Enquiries Team, Freemasons Hall, 60 Great Queen Street, London WC2B 5AZ (tel: 0800 035 6090; email: help@mcf.org.uk)

 https://mcf.org.uk

CC number: 1164703

Eligibility

Children or grandchildren of Freemasons, under the age of 25, who are in full-time education are eligible for funding.

Types of grant

Educational grants are made to families being supported with daily living expenses grants. Grants are made to assist with the cost of IT equipment, course materials and may assist with higher or further education scholarships. TalentAid grants are awarded to young people with the potential to develop an exceptional talent into a career in music,

sport or the performing arts. Grants are made for school fees at Dance and Drama Award (DaDA) or Music and Dance Scheme (MDS) accredited schools. Grants for choir schools, specialist music schools or sports colleges are also available.

Applications

Initial enquiries should be made by contacting the local lodge almoner or the charity directly by telephone, email or post. If deemed eligible, a representative of the foundation will visit the applicant to help complete an application form.

Financial information

Year end	31/03/2019
Income	£68,400,000
Total expenditure	£79,900,000

Further financial information

The charity made welfare grants to 6,365 beneficiaries. Note: we were unable to determine the grant total for education.

Other information

Masonic care homes are operated by the RMBI Care Company. The charity currently has 17 locations across England and Wales offering a range of nursing, residential and dementia care to meet the needs of older people. The charity also operates a free Counselling Careline for people experiencing mental health issues. In addition to awarding individual grants, the charity makes grants to local and national charities, whose work is focused on children and young people, older people, medical research and hospice care.

Sources of information

Accounts; annual report; Charity Commission record; funder's website.

The Vegetarian Charity

 £9,800 (2017/18)

Correspondent: Mrs C. George, Grants Secretary, PO Box 496, Manchester M45 0FL (tel: 01249 443521; email: grantssecretary@vegetariancharity.org. uk)

 www.vegetariancharity.org.uk

CC number: 294767

Eligibility

Vegetarians and vegans up to the age of 26 who are in need.

Types of grant

One-off grants, usually up to £500, for those who are attending an educational course. Grants can be used for equipment/ books, computers, art materials, etc.

Exclusions

Grants are not given: to start up businesses; if the funds will go directly to fundraising for another charity; to pay off debts.

Applications

Application forms are available to download, complete, and return to the correspondent on the charity's website. The charity prefers to receive applications via email. The application form requires details of income, expenditure and debts in order to assess financial eligibility. The applicant also needs to provide two referees who can vouch that the applicant is vegetarian or vegan (not family, house-mates or fellow students). The process usually takes around three months.

Financial information

Year end	31/03/2018
Income	£55,500
Total expenditure	£44,100

Further financial information

In 2017/18 grants were awarded to 50 individuals for both welfare and educational purposes. The grant totals have been estimated from the 2017/18 accounts.

Other information

Grants are also made to organisations running projects for vegetarians and vegans under the age of 26.

Sources of information

Accounts; annual report; Charity Commission record; funder's website.

Offenders and ex-offenders

The Hardman Trust

 £43,600 (2018/19)

Correspondent: Ian Wilson, Director, PO Box 108, Newport PO30 1YN (tel: 01983 550355; email: info@ hardmantrust.org.uk)

 https://www.hardmantrust.org.uk

CC number: 1042715

Eligibility

People who are serving a prison sentence of seven years or more, and are within two years of release, who have specific career goals upon leaving prison. Grants are currently available to people in 30 prisons across the UK. For full eligibility criteria, see the trust's website.

Types of grant

Educational grants of up to £900 for vocational courses, HGV and LGV training and support costs for academic courses, including postgraduate courses.

Applications

Application forms are available to download from the trust's website. The trust has staff representatives in all qualifying prisons, who prospective applicants can contact for an application form and for guidance throughout the process. All applications must include positive endorsements from two prison staff members. All applicants will be required to attend an interview with an assessor from the trust.

Financial information

Year end	31/03/2019
Income	£204,400
Total expenditure	£221,300

Further financial information

During 2018/19, the charity awarded 177 grants. Note: the grant total has been estimated.

Other information

The trust also produces The Hardman Directory, a practical guide to supplementary funding and other forms of financial support that may be available to prisoners and those recently released from prison.

Sources of information

Accounts; annual report; Charity Commission record; funder's website.

The Longford Trust

 £109,400 (2018)

Correspondent: Philippa Budgen, Scholarship Manager, PO Box 64302, London NW6 9JP (tel: 07747 365037 (Tuesday and Thursday, 8am–12pm); email: scholars@longfordtrust.org)

https://www.longfordtrust.org

CC number: 1164701

Eligibility

People who have offended or those awaiting release in the near future whose sentence was or is still being served in a UK prison and who cannot afford education. Applicants must have identified a specific course they want to study at degree level offered by an institute of higher education (including the Open University) and have obtained a provisional offer of a place. Eligibility remains open for up to five years after release. The chosen course should improve the applicant's career chances and advance the rehabilitation process.

Types of grant

Scholarships are given to enable individuals to continue their rehabilitation through education at a UK university or equivalent institute.

- **The Longford Scholarship** is available for any subject at any UK university. A small number of awards are made under the Patrick Pakenham Awards Scheme to those who want to study law
- **Nat Billington Awards Scheme** for those who want to study computer science. Grants are intended to cover both the cost of tuition fees on higher education courses and offer a contribution to living expenses, books and other course materials
- **The Frank Awards** are available for serving prisoners to cover the costs of individual modules towards degrees at the Open University

Exclusions

Grants are not made for postgraduate study.

Applications

Application forms can be found on the trust's website or can be downloaded, printed off and posted to the correspondent. Applications for courses beginning in September must be made by 1 June in that year. A personal statement with educational plans and two referees must also be provided. There is more information available on the trust's website about applying to each award.

Financial information

Year end	31/12/2018
Income	£237,500
Total expenditure	£250,700

Further financial information

In the academic year 2018–2019, 57 people were in receipt of a scholarship and 13 people received an award to study with the Open University.

Other information

The trust also puts on lectures and awards academic prizes.

Sources of information

Accounts; annual report; Charity Commission record; funder's website.

Prisoners' Education Trust

 £744,000 (2018)

Correspondent: Access to Learning Team, The Foundry, 17 Oval Way, London SE11 5RR (tel: 020 3752 5680; email: accesstolearning@prisonerseducation.org.uk)

www.prisonerseducation.org.uk

CC number: 1084718

Eligibility

Individuals over the age of 18 who are serving a custodial sentence in the UK and still have at least six months of their sentence to serve.

Types of grant

Grants are made from the Access to Learning programme to pay for: distance learning courses; beginning study with the Open University; and art/creative hobby materials. Priority is given to subjects and qualifications that cannot usually be found in prison education provision. Courses are available at a range of different levels, including GCSEs and IGCSEs, A-levels and Open University courses, as well as other vocational qualifications – the Distance Learning Curriculum is distributed to prisons and this is available to download from the trust's website.

Exclusions

Applications for retrospective funding are not accepted.

Applications

Applicants should speak to prison staff about applying who can obtain and application form. This should be submitted with a 200 to 300-word letter stating why the applicant would like to undertake the course and how it will benefit them. An endorsement by a prison education manager is also required. Applications are considered every month and the outcome is communicated to all applicants. Further detailed guidance is given on the trust's website and in the Distance Learning Curriculum. Any enquiries can be directed to the correspondent.

Financial information

Year end	31/12/2018
Income	£1,670,000
Total expenditure	£1,890,000

Further financial information

Grants were broken down as follows:

General education courses, arts and hobby materials	£549,800
Open University courses	£221,300

Other information

The organisation also provides advice about distance learning courses and how they relate to employment paths and possibilities. It supports learners in prisons, trains people to act as peer learning mentors and commissions research, projects, reports and conferences to help in evaluating and advancing prison education. It has an alumni network for those who have studied a course funded by the trust to share experience, support and advice. Note: applications are welcomed from any prison in the UK, Isle of Man and the Channel Islands.

Sources of information
Accounts; annual report; Charity Commission record; funder's website.

Older people

The Stanley Stein Deceased Charitable Trust
See record on page 59

Religion

Manse Bairns Network

 £18,300 (2017/18)

Correspondent: Jennifer Law, Secretary and Treasurer, Scott-Monicrieff, Exchange Place 3, Semple Street, Edinburgh EH3 9BL (tel: 0131 473 3500; email: jennifer.law@scott-moncrieff.com)

mansebairnsnetwork.org

OSCR number: SC010281

Eligibility
Children of ministers of the Church of Scotland. There are no geographical constraints.

Types of grant
One-off grants, up to £1,700, for education or training in preparation for employment. Preference will be shown to those training for the ministry.

Applications
Application forms are available to download from the charity's website. Applications should be submitted to the correspondent no later than 31 May each year and grants are distributed by early September.

Financial information

Year end	30/09/2018
Income	£61,500
Total expenditure	£75,800

Further financial information
Grants were awarded to 12 individuals for educational purposes. Grants were also awarded for welfare purposes.

Other information
The registered name of the charity is: Glasgow Society of the Sons and Daughters of Ministers of The Church of Scotland. Further information on the charity is available from its website or from the 'charities' page of Scott Moncrieff, the charity's administrator

(www.scott-moncrieff.com/services/charities/charitable-trusts).

Sources of information
Accounts; annual report; funder's website; OSCR record.

Christianity

The French Huguenot Church of London Charitable Trust

 £79,900 (2017)

Correspondent: The Trustees, Haysmacintyre, 10 Queen Street Place, London EC4R 1AG (tel: 020 7969 5500; email: dmcgowan@haysmacintyre.com)

CC number: 249017

Eligibility
People under the age of 25. Support is given in the following priority: people who/whose parents are members of the Church; people of French Protestant descent; other people as the trustees think fit (see the type of grants section for preferences).

Types of grant
Bursaries, special allowances and project grants to help with costs associated with education. Overseas projects and expeditions are also supported.

Applications
Apply in writing to the correspondent.

Financial information

Year end	31/12/2017
Income	£399,200
Total expenditure	£375,500

Further financial information
The following information has been taken from the 2017 annual report: '50 pupils at various colleges, boys and girls day schools and choir schools received special allowances, bursaries and emergency grants.'

Other information
In addition to the educational fund there are also church and hardship funds, mostly supporting organisations.

Sources of information
Accounts; annual report; Charity Commission record; funder's website.

Islam

The Aziz Foundation

 £370,200 (2018/19)

Correspondent: The Trustees, 16 Babmaes Street, London SW1Y 6HD

(tel: 020 7432 2444; email: enquiries@azizfoundation.org.uk)

azizfoundation.org.uk

CC number: 1169558

Eligibility
British young Muslims committed to improving British society through representation and advocacy or community development. The young person must lack the financial means to fund the course themselves.

Types of grant
There is a scholarship available to masters students which will fund all of the applicant's tuition fees and provide a maintenance allowance. The bursary scheme supports exceptional men and women who want to positively transform attitudes towards muslims in the UK and are in their final year of their PhD. The bursary covers their tuition fees.

Applications
Application forms along with further guidance can be downloaded from the foundation's website. Also check the website for dates when the applications can be submitted.

Financial information

Year end	31/03/2019
Income	£514,200
Total expenditure	£550,700

Sources of information
Accounts; annual report; Charity Commission record; funder's website.

Hidden Pearls Bursaries

Correspondent: The Administrator, Hidden Pearls Ltd, 20–24 Tooting High Street, London SW17 0RG (email: bursaries@hidden-pearls.co.uk)

https://www.hidden-pearls.co.uk/hidden-pearls-bursaries

Eligibility
Young women of Islamic faith who are in their second year of an undergraduate degree at a UK university. Applicants must be predicted to obtain 2:1 grade or above, and must have an annual household income of less than £16,000.

Types of grant
Bursaries of £1,000 are awarded towards university costs.

Exclusions
Bursaries are not given for part-time or online degrees.

Applications
Application forms are available to download from the funder's website.

Applications should include a letter of recommendation from a third party. Details of what should be included in the letter can be found on the website. Completed forms can be returned by email. Applications close on 30 June every year. Beneficiaries are announced on 15 August every year. If a bursary winner fails to respond within ten days of notification (by email), the bursary will be offered to another candidate.

Sources of information

Funder's website.

Judaism

AJA-UJS Student Welfare Fund

 £64,800 (2017/18)

Correspondent: The Trustees, UJS, Office 1, 353 – 359 Finchley Road, London NW3 6ET (tel: 020 7424 3288; email: admin@ujs.org.uk)

https://www.ujs.org.uk/aja_ujs_student_welfare_fund

CC number: 313503

Eligibility

British undergradate or postgraduate Jewish students obtaining their first degree of that level, or equivalent, from a recognised UK based educational organisation. The charity's website states that it looks favourably on applicants that:

▸ Also apply for grants elsewhere;
▸ Are actively involved in the Jewish community and/or demonstrate that they have potential to be involved in the future;
▸ Demonstrate commitment and drive, indicated by a high quality and detailed application form, with all areas fully completed

Types of grant

Up to £1,500 per student per year as a contribution towards essential living or studying costs such as utilities, travel, books or other study material. Students can apply every year of their course.

Exclusions

Part-time courses cannot be supported. Years abroad are also not supported nor courses with a year in industry that is not mandatory.

Applications

Application forms are available on the charity's website along with application closing dates and full guidance notes. Two references also need to be submitted – one academic and one personal.

Financial information

Year end	30/06/2018
Income	£1,120,000
Total expenditure	£1,300,000

Other information

The charity also runs campaigns and events and provides a range of services to Jewish students. See the charity's website for further information.

Sources of information

Accounts; annual report; Charity Commission record; funder's website.

The Anglo Jewish Association

 £69,300 (2017/18)

Correspondent: Jonathan Walker, Trustee, 75 Maygrove Road, West Hampstead, London NW6 2EG (tel: 020 7449 0909; email: admin@ujs.org.uk)

www.anglojewish.org.uk

CC number: 256946

Eligibility

British undergraduate and postgraduate Jewish students in need who are studying a full-time course at a recognised UK university or further education college. Part-time courses are not eligible for funding.

Types of grant

Means-tested grants to assist Jewish students (who are British citizens) with the costs of further education.

Applications

Application forms can be downloaded from the association's website.

Financial information

Year end	30/06/2018
Income	£29,500
Total expenditure	£91,500

Further financial information

A total of 45 students were supported during 2017/18. Grants totalling £42,300 were awarded to Jewish students with the costs of further education. Grants totalling £27,000 were awarded for Israeli postgraduates.

Other information

The association also administers grants to Israeli postgraduate (master's or PhD) students in the UK through its Karten Scholarship Programme.

Sources of information

Accounts; annual report; Charity Commission record; funder's website.

Finnart House School Trust

 £323,800 (2017/18)

Correspondent: The Trustees, Radius Works, Back Lane, Hampstead, London NW3 1HL (tel: 020 7794 9835; email: info@finnart.org)

www.finnart.org

CC number: 220917

Eligibility

Young people under the age of 21 who are of the Jewish faith and are wishing to obtain a recognised qualification from a UK university/college (a degree or diploma). Grants are usually awarded to students in need of financial assistance while moving directly from sixth form into higher/further education. Applicants must have Jewish parents, a Jewish mother or evidence of conversion by a Rabbinic authority to be eligible and must qualify for UK home fees.

Types of grant

Scholarships are awarded for the duration of the course, usually for three to four years but occasionally longer in some situations, for example, medical students. Funding will be subject to regular attendance reports from the college or university.

Exclusions

Funding is not given for study abroad, international students or to support postgraduate study.

Applications

Application packs can be downloaded from the trust's website.

Financial information

Year end	31/03/2018
Income	£84,200
Total expenditure	£374,300

Further financial information

Scholarships of between £1,000 and £6,000 were awarded to 33 students and the trust continued to pay scholarships awarded in previous years.

Other information

This trust also gives grants to schools and charities who work with children and young people of the Jewish faith who are in need. The trust is committed to providing £100,000 per year for three years (beginning 2016/17) to the Gateways programme at JW3 that provides education, training and support to young people of the Jewish faith.

Sources of information

Accounts; annual report; funder's website.

The Jewish Widows and Students Aid Trust

£ £27,300 (2017/18)

Correspondent: The Trustees, 5 Raeburn Close, London NW11 6UG (email: alan@gapbooks.com)

CC number: 210022

Eligibility
The trustees will support the following: Jewish students from the UK, Ireland, Israel, France and the British Commonwealth who are aged between 16 and 30; widows; and schoolchildren not younger than ten who reside in the UK.

Types of grant
Grants are awarded for university students to cover the cost of fees.

Applications
Apply in writing to the correspondent.

Financial information
Year end	05/04/2018
Income	£65,900
Total expenditure	£55,000

Other information
Welfare grants are also available to widows with young children.

Sources of information
Accounts; annual report; Charity Commission record.

Specific circumstances

The Capstone Care Leavers' Trust

£ £27,600 (2017/18)

Correspondent: Maggie Moloney, Trust Manager, Wootton Chase, Wootton St Lawrence, Basingstoke, Hampshire RG23 8PE (tel: 0121 374 2601; email: info@capstonetrust.org)

 https://www.capstonecareleavers trust.org

CC number: 1149717

Eligibility
Young people between the ages of 17 and 25 who have been in care at any time in the past, and are in need. Those who have received a leaving care grant or any other financial support from a local authority department are still eligible to apply.

Types of grant
Grants are awarded towards further or higher education courses and training. Funding will also be considered for items that assist with studies such as a laptop or textbooks as well as for travel to and from the place of study. Most grants will fall between £300 and £2,000 however, grants up to £3,000 may be considered in relation to higher education fees.

Exclusions
Grants are not generally given towards the following:

- Private accommodation costs (such as deposits or rent)
- Arrears or debts
- Daily living costs
- Food or utility bills
- Credit card bills, overdraft or bank charges
- Overseas trips or courses
- Driving theory test

Applications
Application forms can be completed online or downloaded from the trust's website. Applications require the names of two referees who are able to confirm the applicants circumstances such as a support worker, social worker or tutor. The trust aims to make a decision within four weeks; however, it could take up to 12 weeks. Individuals may apply more than once but must wait 12 months before reapplying if they have already received a grant from the trust. Further guidelines are available on the trust's website.

Financial information
Year end	30/09/2018
Income	£71,700
Total expenditure	£73,500

Further financial information
Grants were awarded to 73 individuals for welfare and educational purposes.

Sources of information
Accounts; annual report; Charity Commission record; funder's website.

The Spark Foundation

£ £18,500 (2017/18)

Correspondent: The Trustees, Hugh House, Hugh Place, Faversham, Kent ME13 7AD (tel: 01795 534260; email: admin@sparkfoundation.org.uk)

 www.sparkfoundation.org.uk

CC number: 1097058

Eligibility
Young people under the age of 26 who either are, or have been, in care in England and Wales and are undertaking education.

Types of grant
One-off grants of up to £600 are available for students and people undertaking vocational training or starting work towards tools, protective clothing, laptops and so on.

Exclusions
The foundation does not fund items which are the responsibility of the local authority, fostering agency or carer.

Applications
Application forms can be downloaded from the foundation's website along with examples of successful applications and current deadlines.

Financial information
Year end	31/03/2018
Income	£46,100
Total expenditure	£39,100

Further financial information
In 2017/18 grants totalling £37,000 were awarded to 66 individuals. We estimate that £18,500 was awarded for social welfare purposes and £18,500 as educational grants.

Other information
The foundation previously provided a University Grants Scheme which offered individuals £1,000 for the duration of the course. However, at the time of writing (December 2019), this scheme is closed to new applicants. Students have instead been funded through the small grants programme.

Sources of information
Accounts; annual report; Charity Commission record; funder's website.

The Unite Foundation

£ £1,380,000 (2017/18)

Correspondent: Helen Arber, Foundation manager, South Quay House, Temple Back, Bristol BS1 6FL (tel: 0117 302 7073; email: info@unitefoundation.co.uk)

 www.unitefoundation.co.uk

CC number: 1147344

Eligibility
Students aged 25 or under who are care-leavers or estranged from their family, and are starting their first undergraduate degree at one of the foundation's partner universities (listed on the Unite Foundation's website).

Types of grant
The scholarship provides rent-free accommodation for 365 days a year for a maximum of three years, in a Unite Students property (including household bills, wi-fi, on-site support, communal kitchen). These years do not have to be

73

consecutive as long as the candidate remains eligible. The foundation may also be able to provide additional support to students through donors and supporters such as paid internships, employability coaching and mentoring.

Exclusions

Only students with UK home university fee status are eligible. Students on the following years of study are not eligible for support: foundation year, years involving study credits towards a master's degree (whether as a postgraduate qualification or as part of an integrated bachelor's degree), resit years, and repeat years arising from changing courses and years in which the applicant is the age of 26 or older on 1 September.

Applications

Application forms will become available on the Unite Foundation's website and from partner universities between October and December. Once the applicant has confirmed their first choice university via UCAS, the forms can be submitted between January and May for the following academic year, via the universities. Each university will have their own deadlines. Successful applicants will receive confirmation of awards and accommodation arrangements will be made in between July and August. Further information and guidance notes can be found on the website.

Financial information

Year end	30/09/2018
Income	£1,810,000
Total expenditure	£1,520,000

Further financial information

In 2017/18 the foundation supported 165 students across the UK. A total of £1,380,000 was paid in grants. This is broken down to: £246,600 paid for student bursaries and £1,140,000 for student rental payments.

Other information

The foundation has 29 partner universities, which are listed on its website. The foundation previously provided living allowances to students in addition to accommodation however, this was discontinued. Those previously receiving the allowance will continue to do so until graduation.

Sources of information

Accounts; annual report; Charity Commission record; funder's website.

National charities classified by occupation or parent/ guardian occupation

Armed forces

The Black Watch Association

 £22,400 (2018)

Correspondent: The Trustees, c/o Morris & Young, 6 Atholl Crescent, Perth, Perthshire PH2 6ST (tel: 01738 623214; email: bwassociation@btconnect. com)

theblackwatch.co.uk/regimental-association

OSCR number: SC016423

Eligibility

Serving and retired soldiers of the Black Watch, and their dependants, who are in need.

Types of grant

Education and training grants are awarded to soldiers who are retired or are about to retire. In some cases, this type of grant can be awarded to spouses and dependants.

Applications

Initial enquiries should be made to The Soldiers, Sailors, Airmen and Families Association (SSAFA) Forces Help, who are responsible for making referrals to the association and administering

expenditure once a grant is awarded. For details of your local SSAFA branch, see the website https://www.ssafa.org.uk/ Alternatively, prospective applicants may wish to contact SSAFA Forcesline on 0800 731 4880 or the general enquiries line on 020 7403 8783 The committee meets once a month to consider grant applications.

Financial information

Year end	31/12/2018
Income	£141,700
Total expenditure	£177,400

Further financial information

Note: the grant total has been estimated.

Other information

Grants are also made to organisations, mainly to other armed forces charities.

Sources of information

Accounts; annual report; funder's website; OSCR record.

Greenwich Hospital

Correspondent: The Trustees, Head Office, 1 Farringdon Street, London EC4M 7LG (tel: 020 7396 0150; email: enquiries@grenhosp.org.uk)

 www.grenhosp.org.uk/general/ bursaries

Eligibility

Former members of the Royal Navy and Royal Marines, or the children of current

and former members of the Royal Navy and Royal Marines. For undergraduate support, applicants must be studying (or planning to study) a degree at any Greenwich Hospital partner university. These are:

- University of Greenwich
- University of Portsmouth
- Newcastle University

Types of grant

Bursaries of up to £3,000 are awarded to undergraduate students for a maximum of three years. Training grants are available to former Royal Navy and Royal Marines personnel.

Applications

For undergraduate funding, contact the charity for more information on how to apply. For training grants, applicants should approach a caseworker at either The Soldiers, Sailors, Airmen and Families Association (SSAFA), or the Royal British Legion, who will make an application on their behalf.

Other information

The charity awards various bursaries to students of the Royal Hospital School. Bursaries (and discounts for school fees) are also made to prospective students of the school whose parent(s) have a minimum of three years' seafaring service in the Royal Navy, Royal Marines, WRNS or RFA. The charity awards grants to former pupils of the school who are in their first of study in English language and journalism, aerospace and aviation engineering and real estate at university. The children of current and former members of the Royal Navy or Royal Marines can apply for a bursary (without having been a former pupil of the school) to study at the Trinity Laban Conservatoire of Music and Dance.

Sources of information
Funder's website.

Help for Heroes

Correspondent: The Grants Team, Unit 14 Parker's Close, Downton Business Park, Downton, Salisbury, Wiltshire SP5 3RB (tel: 01980 844280; email: getsupport@helpforheroes.org.uk)

 www.helpforheroes.org.uk

CC number: 1120920, SC044984

Eligibility
Current and former members of the armed forces who have suffered a life-changing injury or illness while serving, or as a result of their service, and their families.

Types of grant
Grants are provided through the Quick Reaction Fund (QRF). Support is given towards vocational and employment opportunities. In urgent cases, the fund aims to provide support within 72 hours.

Applications
To apply for a grant, contact the correspondent via telephone or email. For advice and signposting, contact 01980 844255.

Financial information
Year end	30/09/2018
Income	£26,090,000
Total expenditure	£36,810,000

Further financial information
In 2017/18 a total of £1.31 million was awarded to 982 beneficiaries. We were unable to determine the split between welfare and educational grants.

Other information
Help for Heroes provides a wide range of support and advice services, details of which can be found on the charity's website. The charity works with the armed forces and other military charities. Support is given towards rehabilitation, mental health, wellbeing, careers and so on. The charity provides access to a range of recreational activities such as art and sports. Individuals and their families or carers are also welcome to visit one of the 'Support Hubs' to receive further advice and support on a range of issues from finance to education and training. For more details and contact information of the recovery centres, see the charity's website.

Sources of information
Accounts; annual report; Charity Commission record; funder's website.

Officers' Association Scotland

Correspondent: Laura Darling, Welfare Services Administrator, New Haig House, Logie Green Road, Edinburgh EH7 4HR (tel: 0131 550 1575/1581; email: oasadmin@oascotland.org.uk)

 www.oascotland.org.uk

OSCR number: SC010665

Eligibility
Those 'who have held a Sovereign's Commission with embodied service in HM Naval, Military or Air Forces', and their dependants who are in need. Ex-officers who were commissioned into the Reserve, Auxiliary, or Territorial Forces are also eligible. Applicants must be resident in Scotland at the time of their initial application and be planning to undertake training/education within a Scottish organisation.

Types of grant
Single payments are paid each year direct to the learning organisation. Consideration may also be given to costs such as learning materials and childcare.

Applications
Application forms are available to download or complete on the association's website.

Financial information
Year end	31/03/2019
Income	£281,100
Total expenditure	£336,700

Further financial information
We were unable to determine a grant total for educational grants.

Other information
The association has a Centenary Bursary Award for further and higher education fees. In 2018/19 no grants were made from this, although in the past grants have been awarded for vocational training. The association runs a 'Friendship Visits programme' to provide company for retired officers and their dependants who are feeling isolated. It also offers support and advice to officers making the transition from service to civilian employment and for the rest of their working lives.

Sources of information
Accounts; annual report; funder's website; OSCR record.

Poppyscotland

 £37,000 (2017/18)

Correspondent: Gary Gray, Head of Welfare Services, New Haig House, Logie Green Road, Edinburgh EH7 4HQ (tel: 0131 550 1557; email: gethelp@ poppyscotland.org.uk)

 www.poppyscotland.org.uk

OSCR number: SC014096

Eligibility
Employment grants are available to ex-service people who are unemployed or have a low household income, and their dependants.

Types of grant
Employment grants are awarded to pay for short vocational courses and work-related tools. There must be a strong likelihood that the training will lead to employment.

Applications
For general welfare and employment grants, initial enquiries should be made by contacting the charity by telephone or email. Application forms for Break Away grants are available to download from the funder's website.

Financial information
Year end	30/09/2018
Income	£9,850,000
Total expenditure	£7,680,000

Other information
The charity operates two welfare centres in Ayrshire and Inverness for those needing advice on issues such as benefits or housing, debt and employment. The charity also provides financial support to various housing organisations in Scotland, to help veterans find appropriate accommodation. Poppyscotland works closely with veteran mental health organisations to ensure that veterans receive adequate support. The charity has partnered with the Scottish Association for Mental Health (SAMH) to create a specialised employment service (Employ-Able) for veterans and their partners whose mental health is having an impact on their ability to work. SAMH employment advisers can help with CV writing, finding employment and/or volunteering experience, making job applications and other employment-related issues.

Sources of information
Accounts; annual report; funder's website; OSCR record.

The Rifles Benevolent Trust

 £215,400 (2018)

Correspondent: The Rifles Regimental Secretary, Peninsula Barracks, Romsey Road, Winchester, Hampshire SO23 8TS (tel: 01962 828527 or 01962 828530; email: benevolence@the-rifles.co.uk or admin@the-rifles.co.uk)

https://theriflesnetwork.co.uk/page/benevolence

CC number: 1119071

Eligibility
Serving and ex-serving members of the Rifles, and their dependants, who are in need.

Types of grant
Educational grants, typically of up to £1,500, are made for retraining costs. Grants have been made for vocational courses for training as paramedics, plumbers, fitness instructors, etc. Grants have also been made for college courses in theology.

Applications
Initial enquiries should be made by contacting your local Unit Welfare Officer (UWO) who will make an application on your behalf. For weekly pensions, applications should be made to the ABF The Soldiers' Charity.

Financial information

Year end	31/12/2018
Income	£1,470,000
Total expenditure	£821,500

Further financial information
During 2018, the charity awarded 596 grants. Note: the grant total has been estimated.

Sources of information
Accounts; annual report; Charity Commission record; funder's website.

The Royal Air Force Benevolent Fund

 £2,560,000 (2018)

Correspondent: The Trustees, 67 Portland Place, London W1B 1AR (tel: 0800 169 2942 or 0300 102 1919 (helpline); email: info@rafbf.org.uk or mail@rafbf.org.uk)

www.rafbf.org

CC number: 1081009

Eligibility
Educational grants are available to the children of deceased RAF service people and those who have left the RAF

unexpectedly (due to medical discharge or other unexpected life events) and are unemployed or in low-paid employment.

Types of grant
Educational grants of £3,000 per annum are available to the children of deceased servicemen/women who are studying an undergraduate degree at university. Grants are also made towards the cost of retraining in cases where training is likely to lead to sustainable employment.

Exclusions
The charity is unable to provide support for: business and credit card debts, financial advice, legal costs and private medical costs. Grants cannot be awarded retrospectively as reimbursements for funds already expended.

Applications
Requests for assistance can be made using an online form featured on the funder's website. Alternatively, prospective applicants may wish to contact the charity's helpline on **0300 102 1919** to begin the application process.

Financial information

Year end	31/12/2018
Income	£22,520,000
Total expenditure	£26,640,000

Further financial information
The charity states that it made nearly 6,000 grants to individuals during 2018, including 60 retraining grants and 21 university scholarship awards. Note: the grant total has been estimated.

Other information
The charity offers subsidised welfare/respite breaks to serving members of the RAF and their families. The charity can also offer access to relationship counselling through its partnership with Relate, as well as access to an online relationship course Building Stronger Families, which teaches couples how to deal with common relationship problems. The charity's Listening and Counselling Service (operated in partnership with Anxiety UK) provides confidential emotional support to members of the RAF who are experiencing issues with their mental wellbeing. Tailored support services for help with the transition back into civilian life (such as help with housing and employment) and for issues related to gambling are also available.

Sources of information
Accounts; annual report; Charity Commission record; funder's website; guidelines for applicants.

The Royal British Legion

Correspondent: The Trustees, 199 Borough High Street, London SE1 1AA (tel: 0808 802 8080 (helpline, 8am to 8pm everyday); email: info@britishlegion.org.uk)

 www.britishlegion.org.uk

CC number: 219279

Eligibility
Serving and ex-serving members of the armed forces, and their dependants, who are in need. The charity is dedicated to supporting 'the whole armed forces community' and its eligibility criteria reflects this premise. For a detailed list of all eligible people, see the charity's website.

Types of grant
Employment grants of up to £1,000 are made for training and costs associated with pursing training such as travel, accommodation, equipment, childcare, etc. The charity can also award a licences grant (of up to £250) to fund the provision of a professional licence required for work, such as a Security Industry Authority (SIA) licence. Scholarships for postgraduate study at Seoul University in South Korea are also available, to cover the cost of course fees, flights, accommodation, etc. Scholarships are open to all members of the public, but preference is given to applicants with a family connection to the armed forces.

Applications
Initial enquiries can be made by contacting the charity by telephone or email. Application processes vary between grant schemes. See the charity's website for further information on how to apply for a specific grant. Note: applications for home adaptations must be made through the applicant's local council.

Financial information

Year end	30/09/2018
Income	£163,180,000
Total expenditure	£165,290,000

Further financial information
We were unable to determine the grant total for educational grants.

Other information
The Royal British Legion is the country's largest armed forces charity, and direct financial assistance is just one aspect of its charitable work. The charity operates six care homes across the country, five of which with specialist dementia care, and are available to veterans and their families. The charity also runs four break centres in Southport, Weston-Super-

Mare, East Yorkshire and Portrush for people experiencing hardship to take a holiday. Recovery and rehabilitation centres are designed to ensure that wounded, injured and sick armed forces personnel get the support they need. These are available in various areas of the UK such as Catterick, Colchester, Edinburgh, Tidworth and also in Germany. The charity's expert guidance services cover a range of common issues affecting members of the armed forces community. Referrals can be made for advice on housing, debt and pensions. The charity's teams of experienced solicitors can also help those who have been bereaved as a result of service and who can offer guidance throughout the often-complicated process of and inquiry and inquest after death. For access to any of the above services, contact the helpline or see the charity's website for further information. Other voluntary organisations that are running or planning charitable activities in support of the armed forces community can apply for funding of up to £50,000 from the Royal British Legion. Applications are usually prioritised based on a particular outcome, theme or need that has been identified within the armed forces community, and the charity is unlikely to support projects or services which duplicate (or risk duplicating) support already provided by the Royal British Legion.

Sources of information
Accounts; annual report; Charity Commission record; funder's website.

The Royal Caledonian Education Trust

 £20,000 (2017/18)

Correspondent: Karen Stock, Children and Family Support Service Co-ordinator, 121 George Street, Edinburgh EH2 4YN (tel: 0131 240 2224; email: familysupport@rcet.org.uk)

www.rcet.org.uk

CC number: 310952/SC038722

Eligibility
The offspring of Scottish members of Her Majesty's Armed Forces. The child or young person can be non-Scottish as long as the parent is Scottish. Scottish being any of the following: a born Scot; living and serving with their family in Scotland; veterans who have made Scotland their family home

The Scottish offspring of members of Her Majesty's Armed Forces. The parent can be non-Scottish as long as the child is Scottish (whether living with the parent or not). Scottish being any of the

following: a born Scot; living in Scotland; currently being educated in Scotland

The child or children must have reached statutory pre-school age and higher/further education applicants must be aged 21 and under on the commencement of the programme.

Exceptional circumstances may be considered at the trustees' discretion.

Types of grant
School Children Fund - school uniforms/clothing, sports equipment, after school clubs/activities, residential school trips (UK only), special equipment for educational/wellbeing needs, and education costs in exceptional circumstances.

Crisis Intervention Fund/Wellbeing Support – children's needs, essential clothing, essential food and groceries, essential household expenses, essential travel costs and exceptional general needs.

College and University Students Fund - living expenses (undergraduate degree only), books, special equipment and essential course materials.

Exclusions
The trust will not provide funding where the need should be met by statutory authorities.

Applications
Applications for the School Children Fund and Crisis Intervention Fund must come from a parent or guardian and be made via the local branch of The Soldiers, Sailors, Airmen and Families Association (SSAFA).

Applications for the College and University Students Fund must come directly from the young person using the form available on the trust's website.

Documentary proof of service and place of birth will be required.

Financial information
Year end	31/03/2018
Income	£293,500
Total expenditure	£443,800

Further financial information
The grant total has been estimated from the 2017/18 accounts.

Other information
In addition to making grants to individuals, the trust also works through its education programme with schools, local authorities, armed forces charities and military communities to support the armed forces children, teachers and families in the school environment, especially in relation to children's emotional wellbeing.

Sources of information
Accounts; annual report; Charity Commission record; funder's website; guidelines for applicants.

The Royal Naval Benevolent Trust

 £86,100 (2018/19)

Correspondent: Grants Administrator, Castaway House, 311 Twyford Avenue, Portsmouth, Hampshire PO2 8RN (tel: 023 9269 0112; email: rnbt@rnbt.org.uk)

www.rnbt.org.uk

CC number: 206243

Eligibility
People who are serving, or have served as ratings in the Royal Naval or as other ranks in the Royal Marines (including reservists) who are in need. Support is extended to the dependants of such people.

Types of grant
Educational grants are made to help with costs associated with education and training for second careers.

Exclusions
The charity does not normally help with debts.

Applications
Prospective applicants should first contact their local Royal Navy/Royal Marines Welfare. Alternatively, applicants may wish to contact The Soldiers, Sailors, Airmen and Families Association (SSAFA) (www.ssafa.org.uk) or the Royal British Legion (www.britishlegion.org.uk). Representatives from the above organisations will then visit the applicant to discuss their case and if eligible, will make an application on their behalf. The committee meets weekly to consider grant applications.

Financial information
Year end	31/03/2019
Income	£6,190,000
Total expenditure	£5,610,000

Further financial information
During 2018/19, the charity awarded 1,631 grants for welfare and 91 grants for education and employment.

Other information
The trust can also make quarterly grants of up to £10,000 to organisations, particularly smaller ones, whose work has a direct impact on members of the RNBT. The trust operates a care and nursing home (Pembroke House) in Kent, as well as a subsidised housing

facility at the John Cornwell VC National Memorial in Hornchurch.

Sources of information
Accounts; annual report; Charity Commission record; funder's website.

The Royal Navy and Royal Marines Children's Fund

 £82,500 (2017/18)

Correspondent: Sara Smith, Senior Caseworker, Castaway House, 311 Twyford Avenue, Stamshaw, Hampshire PO2 8RN (tel: 023 9263 9534; email: caseworkers@ rnrmchildrensfund.org.uk)

www.rnrmchildrensfund.org

CC number: 1160182

Eligibility
Children (under the age of 25) of serving/ex-serving members of the following:
- The Royal Navy
- The Royal Marines
- The Queen Alexandra's Royal Naval Nursing Service (QARNNS)
- The Women's Royal Naval Service
- The Royal Fleet Auxiliary
- Reserves of the above forces

Types of grant
Educational grants are made to schoolchildren, college students, undergraduates and vocational students where there is a special need. Grants are awarded towards the cost of assessments, extra tuition and other educational requirements.

Applications
Application forms are available to download from the funder's website. Alternatively, applicants can contact The Soldiers, Sailors, Airmen and Families Association (SSAFA), Royal Navy/Royal Marines Welfare or the Royal British Legion who can make a referral on their behalf.

Financial information
Year end	31/03/2018
Income	£1,360,000
Total expenditure	£1,490,000

Further financial information
During 2017/18, the charity awarded 1,802 grants to beneficiaries.

Other information
The charity also awards grants to organisations.

Sources of information
Accounts; annual report; Charity Commission record; funder's website.

The Royal Navy Officers' Charity

 £104,300 (2018)

Correspondent: Director, 70 Porchester Terrace, Bayswater, London W2 3TP (tel: 020 7402 5231; email: rnoc@arno. org.uk)

https://www.arno.org.uk/rnoc

CC number: 207405

Eligibility
Serving and retired officers of the Naval Service (Royal Navy, Royal Marines and QARNNS), and their dependants, who are in need.

Types of grant
Educational grants are made for training costs and essential equipment for vocational training.

Applications
Contact the charity by telephone or email. If necessary, the charity may ask serving personnel to contact the appropriate Royal Navy Welfare team who will then apply on their behalf.

Financial information
Year end	31/12/2018
Income	£629,900
Total expenditure	£633,900

Further financial information
During 2018, the charity awarded grants to 142 individuals. Note: the grant total has been estimated.

Sources of information
Accounts; annual report; Charity Commission record; funder's website.

WRNS Benevolent Trust

 £4,500 (2017)

Correspondent: Roger Collings, Grants Administrator, Castaway House, 311 Twyford Avenue, Portsmouth, Hampshire PO2 8RN (tel: 023 9265 5301; email: grantsadmin@wrnsbt.org. uk)

www.wrnsbt.org.uk

CC number: 206529

Eligibility
Former Wrens (i.e. members of the Regular Service, who served between 3 September 1939 and 1 November 1993), who live in the UK or abroad. Applicant's do not need to be a member of the Association of Wrens.

Types of grant
Grants are also available for former Wrens who are mature students to help

with training courses, study costs, computers, books, etc.

Exclusions
People who deserted are not eligible. The trust does not make grants for retrospective costs, nor is assistance given to settle secondary debts (e.g. credit cards or amounts owed to family or friends).

Applications
Applications can be made directly to the correspondent although most applications are received through the Royal British Legion and The Soldiers, Sailors, Airmen and Families Association (SSAFA). Applications can be made directly by the individual or, with their consent, by a relation or friend.

Financial information
Year end	31/12/2017
Income	£281,900
Total expenditure	£429,900

Other information
The trust's website notes the following:

'Despite publicity, one of our biggest problems is raising awareness; it is surprising how many former Wrens do not even know of our existence. If you hear of a former Wren who you think may be having difficulties, do please tell her about us or, if given her permission, contact us on their behalf. Many people are too proud to ask for help, but we always stress that we are their special charity, and one that they may well have donated to during their time in the Women's Royal Naval Service. Alternatively, you may wish to help us to help those in need by supporting our work through donations and/or legacies.'

Sources of information
Accounts; annual report; Charity Commission record; funder's website.

Arts and heritage

The Actors' Children's Trust (ACT)

 £11,500 (2017/18)

Correspondent: Robert Ashby, General Secretary, 58 Bloomsbury Street, London WC1B 3QT (tel: 020 7636 7868; email: robert@actorschildren.org)

www.tactactors.org

CC number: 1177106

Eligibility
Children of professional actors may be eligible for a grant. Grants are usually given to families where the household income is less than £40,000. The parent/

guardian may need to send the trustees a CV of acting work if they are not in Spotlight or Mandy.

Types of grant

The trust provides the following types of educational support:

- Grants to cover school meals, uniforms, trips and afterschool clubs
- SEND support grants for children, to cover the cost of fast-track private assessments
- Sponsorship for coaching and tuition in performing arts or sport for talented young people
- Start-up grants are available to young people over the age of 18 who are beginning an apprenticeship or starting university

Exclusions

The trust is not able to fund presenters or people who have mainly played as extras. Grants are not usually given for private school fees or legal fees. Postgraduate students are not supported.

Applications

Details on how to apply can be found on the trust's website. The trustees encourage potential applicants to get in touch.

Financial information

Year end	31/03/2018
Income	£293,200
Total expenditure	£987,200

Sources of information

Accounts; annual report; Charity Commission record; funder's website.

The June Baker Trust

£ £5,100 (2018)

Correspondent: Mr D. Jones, Trustee, 9 Kirk Wynd, Cupar, Fife KY15 5AW (email: junebakertrust@gmail.com)

 https://icon.org.uk/groups/ scotland/june-baker-trust

OSCR number: SC020311

Eligibility

Individuals working in the restoration, renovation and conservation of historic and artistic artefacts in Scotland, or those training to do so.

Types of grant

Awards are usually up to £300, and are made available for travel, training, fees, purchase of equipment, short courses and other suitable projects to students, mature and vocational students and people starting work.

Exclusions

Fees for long, full-time courses are not given.

Applications

Application forms are available to download from ICON's website.

Financial information

Year end	31/12/2018
Income	£1,700
Total expenditure	£5,700

Further financial information

Full accounts were not available to view on the Charity Commission's website due to the charity's low income. We have therefore estimated the grant total based on the charity's total expenditure.

Sources of information

Charity Commission record; ICON website.

The Nicholas Boas Charitable Trust

£ £19,500 (2017/18)

Correspondent: Helena Boas, Secretary, 22 Mansfield Street, London W1G 9NR (tel: 020 7436 0344; email: boas22m@ btinternet.com)

 www.nicholasboastrust.org.uk

CC number: 1073359

Eligibility

Young musicians beginning their careers and students of architecture.

Types of grant

Grants are awarded to young musicians towards masterclasses, travel to auditions, vocal coaching, recordings and commissioning new work. Travel grants are awarded to architecture students from The Architectural Association or Cambridge University to attend the British School at Rome.

Exclusions

The trust does not give funding for tuition fees.

Applications

An application form can be requested from the correspondent via email.

Financial information

Year end	31/03/2018
Income	£31,900
Total expenditure	£39,500

Further financial information

In 2017/18 we estimate that around £19,500 was awarded to individuals, this includes grants to 24 young musicians.

Other information

The trust also awards grants to musical organisations and festivals such as the English National Opera, English Music Festival and IMA Prussia Cove.

Sources of information

Accounts; annual report; Charity Commission record; funder's website.

The Cotton Industry War Memorial Trust

£ £8,000 (2018)

Correspondent: Peter Booth, Trust Secretary, 19 Shepherd Street, Bewerley, Rochdale, Lancashire OL11 5SU (tel: 01706 341731; email: theciwmt@ btinternet.com)

CC number: 242721

Eligibility

Educational grants are available to textile students.

Types of grant

Educational grants are awarded to help with costs associated with studying textiles. Recently, the charity awarded a grant to a student studying a master's in textile conservation.

Applications

Apply in writing to the correspondent. Applications should be made by other voluntary organisations (such as the Royal British Legion, Age Concern, SSAFA, etc.) on the applicant's behalf. The trustees meet quarterly to consider grant applications.

Financial information

Year end	31/12/2018
Income	£367,600
Total expenditure	£291,100

Further financial information

During 2018, the charity awarded 80 grants for recuperative holidays, one one-off welfare grant and one grant for educational purposes. Note: we were unable to determine the grant total for recuperative holidays.

Other information

This charity also makes grants to organisations, mainly to help with administrative and core running costs. Grants are also made in support of various textile projects.

Sources of information

Accounts; annual report; Charity Commission record.

Dancers' Career Development

 £195,300 (2018/19)

Correspondent: Jennifer Curry, Executive Director, Plouviez House, 19–20 Hatton Place, London EC1N 8RU (tel: 020 7831 1449; email: dancers@ thedcd.org.uk)

https://thedcd.org.uk

CC number: 1168958

Eligibility

Professional dancers of any artistic background wishing to make a transition to a new career. Only those who have been a professional dancer for at least eight years and have worked for a minimum of five years in the UK are eligible. Applications can be made up to ten years after stopping work as a professional dancer. There are different categories:

▶ Independent dancers – must have earned an income as a dancer for a minimum of 16 weeks each year, on average
▶ Company dancers – have spent at least five years as a dancer with one of the partner companies (see list on the charity's website)
▶ Medical grounds – dancers who do not fulfil the criteria for independent or company dancers, but have been forced to retire due to illness or injury may also be eligible for support

Types of grant

Grants to help with retraining for a new career after professional dancing. Grants may be given for course and training fees, equipment, books and materials, living expenses, travel costs and childcare costs. There are also some bursaries for specific fields of training – refer to the charity's website for current information.

Applications

Potential applicants should first contact the charity for a one-to-one consultation in person or by telephone. Application forms and guidelines are available to download from the charity's website and should be submitted along with a dance career CV, a personal statement, an application budget and information on the course or equipment required. Applications should be submitted at least three months prior to starting training.

Financial information

Year end	31/03/2019
Income	£557,400
Total expenditure	£544,800

Further financial information

Retraining grants totalling £195,300 supported 76 dancers.

Other information

The charity was formerly known as The Independent Dancers Resettlement Trust (Charity Commission no. 327747). The charity also offers advice, support, coaching, mentoring and workshops.

Sources of information

Accounts; annual report; Charity Commission record; funder's website.

Equity Charitable Trust

 £92,000 (2018/19)

Correspondent: Kaethe Cherney, Company Secretary, Plouviez House, 19–20 Hatton Place, London EC1N 8RU (tel: 020 7831 1926; email: kaethe@ equitycharitabletrust.org.uk)

www.equitycharitabletrust.org.uk

CC number: 328103

Eligibility

Professional performers who are able to demonstrate ten years' adult professional work.

Types of grant

Grants are awarded to enable retraining or developing skills for a second income stream.

Exclusions

The trust will not provide support for the following:

▶ Amateur performers, musicians or drama students
▶ Credit card debt
▶ Overseas courses
▶ Courses that do not lead to a recognised qualification
▶ Courses designed to improve acting and performance skills
▶ Maintenance grants
▶ Student loans
▶ Full tuition fees

Applications

Application forms for each grant can be downloaded from the trust's website. Applications should be submitted to the trust's relevant email (see details on its website), along with a professional CV and any supporting documents.

The trustees meet every two months to consider welfare applications. The education committee meets in May, July and early September to consider applications.

Financial information

Year end	31/03/2019
Income	£501,400
Total expenditure	£450,700

Further financial information

Education grants were given to 57 individuals.

Other information

The trust also supports theatres and theatre directors.

Sources of information

Accounts; annual report; Charity Commission record; funder's website.

The Gerald Finzi Trust

 £13,500 (2017/18)

Correspondent: The Trustees, PO Box 137, Stour Row, Shaftesbury, Dorset SP7 0WX (tel: 01244 320300; email: admin@geraldfinzi.org)

www.geraldfinzi.org

CC number: 313047

Eligibility

Musicians between the ages of 18 and 80. Formal qualifications are not necessary.

Types of grant

Scholarships ranging from £2,000 to £5,000 are awarded to people wanting to undertake music-related research, or to compose a work of art, in the UK or overseas. For overseas projects, grants are made to cover travel, accommodation and living costs. Insurance costs (at a reasonable rate) are also covered. Recent scholarships have been awarded for projects in Canada, Estonia, Finland, France, India and other parts of the world. Grants are also available for the purchase of, or renovation of, musical instruments.

Exclusions

Equipment costs are not usually covered by scholarships. The trust does not typically make grants to supplement any lost income when undertaking a project. Grants are generally capped at one per applicant.

Applications

Applications can be made using an online form on the trust's website. Alternatively, applicants may wish to download a copy of the application form, or request a form be sent to them by post.

Financial information

Year end	31/03/2018
Income	£699,400
Total expenditure	£181,500

Further financial information

During 2017/18, the charity awarded four scholarships and three grants for musical instruments.

Other information

Grants are also awarded to organisations.

Sources of information

Accounts; annual report; Charity Commission record; funder's website.

The Gane Charitable Trust

 £18,300 (2018)

Correspondent: The Trustees, Deign Study Centre KSC, 48 Park Row, Bristol BS1 5JY (tel: 0117 926 5548; email: secretary@ganetrust.org.uk)

www.ganetrust.org.uk

CC number: 211515

Eligibility
Students of arts and crafts, architecture and design. There is a preference for applicants from Bristol and south Wales and those in further education.

Types of grant
Grants are available to help meet the educational costs of college students, vocational students and mature students and their children.

Applications
A contact form is available on the trust's website.

Financial information
Year end	31/12/2018
Income	£43,600
Total expenditure	£23,100

Sources of information
Accounts; annual report; Charity Commission record; funder's website.

The Derek Hill Foundation

 £13,000 (2017/18)

Correspondent: The Trustees, c/o Rathbone Trust Company Ltd, 8 Finsbury Circus, London EC2M 7AZ (tel: 020 7399 0835; email: bsr@britac.ac.uk)

www.bsr.ac.uk/awards/fine-arts# Hill

CC number: 801590

Eligibility
Artists who are UK or Irish nationals and are aged 24 or over on 1 September in the year in which the award would be taken up.

Types of grant
A three month scholarship of around £950 per month with the aim of encouraging artists whose central practice involves paint or drawing. In addition, the foundation funds meals and accommodation in a residential studio at the British School at Rome.

Applications
Application forms and further guidelines can be found on the British School at Rome's website. Applications also require examples of the applicant's recent work as well as details of two referees. There is an application fee of £25. Consult the website for current deadlines.

Financial information
Year end	09/05/2018
Income	£46,200
Total expenditure	£166,200

Further financial information
In 2017/18 we estimate that £13,000 was awarded in scholarships to the British School in Rome.

Other information
The scholarship is administered by the British School at Rome.

Sources of information
Accounts; annual report; Charity Commission record; funder's website.

Worshipful Company of Musicians Charitable Fund

 £34,900 (2016)

Correspondent: Mr H. Lloyd, Clerk, The Worshipful Company of Musicians, 1 Speed Highwalk, Barbican, London EC2Y 8DX (tel: 020 7496 8980; email: clerk@wcom.org.uk)

www.wcom.org.uk

CC number: 310040

Eligibility
Young musicians and music students starting their professional career (including those working in/studying performance, composition, musicology and music technology).

Types of grant
There are a number of different scholarships and bursaries funded through schools, conservatoires and other academic institutions, as well as awards and prizes for outstanding musicians. Support is given towards purposes such as courses, training and study. All award winners can compete for the Prince's Prize, which offers £10,000 from the company. Details of the awards given by the charity are on its website.

Applications
Refer to the charity's website for information on specific awards and how to apply.

Financial information
Year end	31/12/2016
Income	£382,000
Total expenditure	£405,500

Further financial information
The grant total comprises of scholarships, awards and prizes and was estimated from the 2016 accounts as they were the last available at the time of writing (October 2019).

Other information
The Worshipful Company of Musicians Charitable Fund administers two other funds: The Musicians' Company Fund (Charity Commission no. 264303) and Concordia Foundation Artists Fund (Charity Commission no. 1132981). The charity also carries out outreach work with children and young people in London, particularly focusing on those from disadvantaged backgrounds.

Sources of information
Accounts; annual report; Charity Commission record; funder's website.

Construction

The Worshipful Company of Plaisterers Charitable Trust

 £8,300 (2018/19)

Correspondent: Nigel Bamping, Clerk, Plaisterers' Hall, One London Wall, London EC2Y 5JU (tel: 020 7796 4333; email: clerk@plaistererslivery.co.uk)

plaistererslivery.co.uk/education-training

CC number: 281035

Eligibility
Individuals who are training or pursuing education within the UK plastering industry.

Types of grant
Bursaries of up to £500 can be awarded to students who are undergoing training or experienced practitioners looking to develop their knowledge within the trade. According to the trust's website, bursaries may be given towards: the costs of travel to attend a course overseas; fees for existing courses (where no other support is available); wage subsidies to enable students to pursue extracurricular activities; funding to a mentor to support achievement of advanced qualifications; or the costs of enhancing access to training for people with disabilities. The trust also runs a number of awards programmes, including the Annual Training Awards and the Student

of the Year Award. See the trust's website for details of awards available.

Applications

See the trust's website for details on how to apply.

Financial information

Year end	05/04/2019
Income	£118,600
Total expenditure	£84,400

Sources of information

Accounts; annual report; Charity Commission record; funder's website.

Scottish Building Federation Edinburgh and District Charitable Trust

 £20,300 (2018)

Correspondent: Jennifer Law, Trust Administrator, c/o Scott-Moncrieff, Exchange Place 3, Semple Street, Edinburgh EH3 8BL (tel: 0131 473 3500; email: jennifer.law@scott-moncrief.com)

https://scott-moncrieff.com/ services/charities/charitable-trusts/scottish-building-federation-edinburgh

OSCR number: SC029604

Eligibility

Students studying skills relating to the building industry in the following universities and colleges: Heriot-Watt University; Napier University; West Lothian College; and Edinburgh College. Grants may also be given more generally to college and university students in need.

Types of grant

Scholarships, bursaries and academic prizes.

Applications

Application forms are available to download from the Scott-Moncrieff website. Applications for welfare grants should be returned to the correspondent by post. Applications for education grants should be completed and forwarded to the appropriate department of the university or college.

Financial information

Year end	31/12/2018
Income	£56,300
Total expenditure	£57,500

Further financial information

Educational grants are broken down as follows: £15,300 was given directly to individuals in the form of scholarships and bursaries and £5,000 was paid to universities for individual academic prizes.

Sources of information

Accounts; annual report; OSCR record; Scott-Moncrieff website.

Education and training

Farmington Institute Scholarships

Correspondent: Sir Ralph Walker, The Director, The Farmington Institute, Harris Manchester College, Mansfield Road, Oxford OX1 3TD (tel: 01865 271985; email: farmington@hmc.ox.ac.uk)

 www.farmington.ac.uk

Eligibility

Teachers of religious education and headteachers in primary and secondary schools in the UK.

Types of grant

Two types of scholarship are offered: university based and school/home based. Scholars studying any aspect of religious education (RE) or associated subjects but preference is given to applicants whose work will directly benefit the teaching of RE in schools. The scholarship will cover the cost of tuition, essential local travel and, by negotiation with the school, the salary of a replacement teacher. Teachers that live within a reasonable distance from one of the selected universities or colleges (listed below) may be awarded a university-based scholarship.

▶ Bath: Bath Spa University, Religions, Philosophies and Ethics, Department of Humanities
▶ Belfast: St Mary's University College; Stranmillis University College; Queen's University Belfast
▶ Cambridge: University of Cambridge, Faculty of Education/Homerton College
▶ Durham: University of Durham, St Chad's College
▶ Exeter: University of Exeter, School of Education (preferably spring or summer term)
▶ Glasgow: University of Strathclyde, School of Education
▶ Lampeter/Carmarthen: University of Wales Trinity Saint David
▶ Lincoln: Bishop Grosseteste University
▶ Liverpool: Liverpool Hope University, Department of Theology and Religious Studies; and Liverpool John Moores University

▶ Norwich: University of East Anglia, Centre for Spirituality and Religion in Education, School of Education and Lifelong Learning
▶ Warwick: University of Warwick, Institute of Education, Warwick Religions and Education Research Unit
▶ York: York St John University

Applications

Application forms can be downloaded from the charity's website. Applicants may be asked to attend an interview. All scholars are expected to produce an outline study plan of their project, which must be sent to the Farmington Institute before the start of the scholarship. Towards the end of the scholarship, the scholar will give a presentation on their work at the University/School and produce a written report on the work they have undertaken.

Occasionally a particular research opportunity will be advertised. See the charity's website for details.

Further financial information

The Farmington Trust Ltd (Charity Commission number: 237934) makes an annual grant to Harris Manchester College, Oxford to carry out the Farmington Institute's work which includes offering scholarships and conducting research.

Sources of information

Charity Commission record; funder's website.

The National Association of Schoolmasters Union of Women Teachers (NASUWT) Benevolent Funds

 £15,600 (2018)

Correspondent: Legal and Casework Team, Hillscourt Education Centre, Rose Hill, Rednal, Birmingham B45 8RS (tel: 0121 453 6150 (weekdays from 8am to 5:30pm); email: legalandcasework@mail.nasuwt.org.uk)

https://www.nasuwt.org.uk/contact-us/legal-support/benevolent-fund.html

CC number: 285793

Eligibility

Educational grants are awarded to the children of members (alive or deceased) who are in need.

Types of grant

Educational grants are made for costs associated with further education.

Applications

Applicants are advised to contact their local association secretary. Alternatively, applicants may wish to contact the correspondent by telephone, post or email. Once initial enquiries have been made, a benevolence visitor will visit the applicant to complete an application form on their behalf.

Financial information

Year end	31/12/2018
Income	£413,000
Total expenditure	£444,900

Further financial information

During 2018, the charity awarded grants to 701 individuals. The charity awards grants for both educational and welfare purposes.

Sources of information

Accounts; annual report; Charity Commission record; funder's website.

Engineering

The Worshipful Company of Engineers Charitable Trust Fund

 £44,800 (2018)

Correspondent: The Clerk to the Trustees, Ironmongers' Hall, Shaftesbury Place, Barbican, London EC2V 8AA (tel: 020 7726 4830; email: clerk@ engineerscompany.org.uk)

 www.engineerstrust.org.uk

CC number: 289819

Eligibility

Qualified engineers and those training to be chartered engineers, incorporated engineers and engineering technicians. Eligibility criteria differs depending on the award. See the trust's website for more information.

Types of grant

The trust supports a number of award schemes providing monetary prizes with the aim of encouraging excellence in engineering, many of which are open to students. Visit the trust's website for further information on the different awards.

Applications

Apply in writing, or by email to the correspondent.

Each award has a different application process. See the trust's website for more details.

Financial information

Year end	31/12/2018
Income	£94,900
Total expenditure	£157,600

Further financial information

We estimate that in 2018 the total amount awarded to individuals was £64,900 and that grants for welfare purposes totalled £20,100. Monetary prizes totalling £44,800 were awarded to 11 individuals.

Other information

Support can be given to organisations concerned with engineering or organisations in the City of London that further the interest of the history, traditions and customs of the city. The trust also supports two Arkwright Scholarships each worth £600 over two years.

Sources of information

Accounts; annual report; Charity Commission record; funder's website.

The Institution of Engineering and Technology (IET)

 £515,000 (2018)

Correspondent: The Trustees, The Institution of Engineering and Technology, 2 Savoy Place, London WC2R 0BL (tel: 020 7344 5415; email: awards@theiet.org)

 www.theiet.org

CC number: 211014, SC038698

Eligibility

Scholarships and awards are open to those pursuing a career in engineering whether as an apprentice, student or researcher. There are various scholarships and awards on offer, check the charity's website to see eligibility for each specific one. For scholarships being awarded to apprentices or students the organisation has to be linked to IET.

Types of grant

The IET offers a range of scholarships, prizes and travel awards. These include undergraduate and postgraduate scholarships, travel grants to members of the IET (for study tour, work in the industry, to attend a conference), apprenticeship and technician awards and various prizes for achievement and innovation. See the charity's website for more information on the scholarships and how much can be awarded.

Applications

Further details and application forms are available from the IET website. The deadlines vary for different awards.

Financial information

Year end	31/12/2018
Income	£68,712,000
Total expenditure	£65,380,000

Further financial information

The 2018 accounts detail that £33,000 was awarded to 24 individuals who are members of the IET via its linked and newly re-branded charity Foothold (Charity Commission no. 208925), and £515,000 was awarded to 154 individuals for scholarships, awards and prizes. Some of these awards are for engineers in their professional careers but these awards are usually small compared to the amounts that are awarded to students.

Other information

The charity also promotes knowledge sharing and education within the industry.

Sources of information

Accounts; annual report; Charity Commission record; funder's website.

The Benevolent Fund of the Institution of Mechanical Engineers (IMechE) (known as Support Network)

 £163,600 (2017)

Correspondent: Maureen Hayes, Support and Casework Officer, 1 Birdcage Walk, Westminster, London SW1H 9JJ (tel: 020 7304 6816; email: supportnetwork@imeche.org)

 www.imeche.org/support-network

CC number: 209465

Eligibility

Current and former members (at *any* grade of membership or duration) of the Institution of Mechanical Engineers, and their dependants, who are in need.

Members of the Institution of Mechanical Engineers who are currently studying a mechanical engineering (or related) undergraduate degree, master's or PhD. Other courses at another level are also eligible for support. Preference is given to applicants who:
- Have a disability
- Are in their final year or stage of their programme
- Are local authority care-leavers
- Are estranged from their parents
- Are aged 25 and over with additional financial commitments
- Are parents with children under the age of 18 (especially single parents)
- Are managing significant debts incurred before commencing their course

Are repeating a year due to circumstances outside their control

Cannot access other funding sources

IMechE members who are currently studying for mechanical engineering apprenticeships are also eligible for support. IMechE members (at a paying grade of membership) who have already completed an apprenticeship, undergraduate degree, master's, PhD or any other forms of training/education which would enable STEM employment can also apply for funding.

Types of grant
Student grants: grants of £2,000 per academic year are awarded towards general living costs, rent, course materials, software, laptops and other equipment required for study. The charity can also make grants for any expenses involved in attending industrial placements. **Apprenticeship grants:** grants of this type are awarded to pay for vital equipment and easing financial need during study. The charity can also help with any disability-related costs or additional disability needs. **Newly Qualified fund:** grants are made to help with the 'transitional costs of entering employment' such as train and/or underground season tickets, rent/rent deposits, relocation costs and childcare.

Applications
Initial enquiries should be made by contacting the charity either by telephone or email. The trustees meet quarterly to consider grant applications.

Financial information
Year end	31/12/2017
Income	£1,400,000
Total expenditure	£626,500

Further financial information
During 2017, the charity made a total of 1,424 payments to 485 IMechE members. Note: the grant total has been estimated.

Other information
The charity partners with different organisations to offer a range of advice services. The charity works with the National Autistic Society (Charity Commission no. 269425) for support related to the condition, with PayPlan for advice on debt and budgeting, with Renovo for specialist employment support, with British Dyslexia Association (Charity Commission no. 289243) for support related to dyslexia and with Independent Age (Charity Commission no. 210729) for help with the needs of older members, particularly in terms of accessing care and local authority funding options.

Sources of information
Accounts; annual report; Charity Commission record; funder's website.

Environment

Forest Industries Education and Provident Fund

 £700 (2018)

Correspondent: Edward Mills, Bleacott Farm, Witherslack, Grange-over-Sands, Cumbria LA11 6RZ (tel: 07875 248115; email: info@edwardmills.co.uk)

www.confor.org.uk/resources/education-provident-fund

CC number: 1061322

Eligibility
People who have been a member of the Confederation of Forest Industries, either as a student or other individual member, continuously for one year.

Types of grant
Grants of up to £750 are awarded to students on technical and professional courses within the field of forestry. Support is also given towards educational trips, activities and professional development opportunities such as conferences.

Exclusions
Applications for retrospective funding will not be considered.

Applications
Application forms can be downloaded from the fund's website. Applicants will be required to declare any other sources of financial aid they may have received.

Financial information
Year end	31/12/2018
Income	£7,900
Total expenditure	£1,600

Further financial information
Full accounts were not available to view on the Charity Commission's website due to the charity's low income. We have therefore estimated the grant total based on the charity's total expenditure.

Other information
Successful applicants are required to write an article which may be used in the FTN magazine. Grants are also awarded to Confederation of Forest Industries members and their dependants for welfare purposes.

Sources of information
Charity Commission record; funder's website.

Gamekeepers Welfare Trust

 £1,200 (2017)

Correspondent: The Trustees, Keepers Cottage, Tanfield Lodge, West Tanfield, Ripon, North Yorkshire HG4 5LE (tel: 0300 1233088 (helpline) or 01677 470180; email: enquiries@thegamekeeperswelfaretrust.com or gamekeeperwtrust@btinternet.com)

thegamekeeperswelfaretrust.com

CC number: 1008924

Eligibility
Young people under the age of 24 who wish to make gamekeeping their career and are in need of financial assistance to do so. The trust will also support a mature student considering a course due to special circumstances such as redundancy. Further eligibility information can be found on the trust's website.

Types of grant
Grants are awarded towards accommodation and transport for college courses, equipment and so on. In extenuating circumstances grants may be awarded towards course fees.

Applications
Application forms and further guidelines are available from the trust's website. Applications can be made at any time.

Financial information
Year end	31/12/2017
Income	£162,800
Total expenditure	£70,600

Further financial information
Educational grants totalled £1,200 and were distributed as follows: educational maintenance grants totalling £870 were awarded to two individuals and one grant was given towards college fees totalling £330.

Other information
In addition, the charity maintains a Job Register for gamekeepers, stalkers, ghillies and their families in difficult times to help them find gainful employment. The trustees have estimated that a further 600 people and their families were assisted in some way, either through signposting to other organisations, or through telephone support.

Sources of information
Accounts; annual report; Charity Commission record; funder's website.

Gardeners' Royal Benevolent Society (Perennial)

 £126,100 (2018)

Correspondent: Sheila Thomson, Director of Services, 115–117 Kingston Road, Leatherhead, Surrey KT22 7SU (tel: 0800 093 8510; email: info@ perennial.org.uk)

 www.perennial.org.uk

CC number: 1155156/SC040180

Eligibility

People studying horticulture training courses and those working in horticulture who are wishing to make a career change.

Types of grant

The Lironi Training Fund, administered by the trustees, supports students undertaking horticultural training courses and full-time placements as well horticulturalists wishing to retrain.

Applications

Different schemes have different application processes, consult the charity's website for further information or contact the society directly via email, telephone or the contact form on the charity's website.

Financial information

Year end	31/12/2018
Income	£6,430,000
Total expenditure	£3,140,000

Other information

The society provides a range of resources and advice for people working in horticulture.

Sources of information

Accounts; annual report; Charity Commission record; funder's website.

The Royal Horticultural Society (RHS)

 £140,000 (2017/18)

Correspondent: RHS Bursaries Manager, 80 Vincent Square, London SW1P 2PE (tel: 01483 479719; email: bursaries@rhs. org.uk)

 https://www.rhs.org.uk/education-learning/bursaries-grants

CC number: 222879/SC038262

Eligibility

Professional and student gardeners/horticulturalists, plant and soil scientists, botanists, arboriculturalists, landscapers, botanical artists and related professionals. While priority is given to professional horticulturists and students, applications are also considered from serious amateur gardeners. Eligible proposals must be closely identified with horticulture.

Types of grant

Grants can be awarded for horticultural projects, expeditions, study tours, voluntary work placements, conferences, educational and training courses, artwork, taxonomy, research and other purposes with clear horticultural relevance. Grants can be used towards the costs of travel, accommodation, food, essential equipment, administration, publication and other costs. There are a number of different funds and bursaries administered by the RHS; the committee selects the most appropriate fund for each application. For further information on the funds available, refer to the RHS website.

Exclusions

Funding is not awarded for:

- Salaries
- Household expenses (e.g. utility bills)
- Infrastructure (e.g. poly-tunnels, pergolas or buildings)
- Commercial enterprises
- Courses which lead to a qualification or accreditation
- Costs related to undertaking a course (e.g. purchase of books or materials)

Applications

Application forms can be obtained from the society's website. Completed forms should be submitted by email by 31 March, 30 June, 30 September or 15 December, unless otherwise indicated on the website.

Financial information

Year end	31/01/2018
Income	£95,930,000
Total expenditure	£84,890,000

Further financial information

A combined total of £140,000 was awarded to professional and student horticulturists.

Other information

Organisations, charities and gardens open to the public may also be supported. The Royal Horticultural Society administers a number of bursary funds, established and maintained through generous bequests and donations, to support professional and student gardeners/horticulturalists. It also runs an exchange programme between British and American university graduates and students, which aims to further educate on horticulture.

Sources of information

Accounts; annual report; Charity Commission record; funder's website.

Financial services

The Bankers Benevolent Fund (The Bank Workers Charity)

 £623,400 (2017/18)

Correspondent: Selam Shibru, Company Secretary, Suite 686–695, Salisbury House, Finsbury Circus, London EC2M 5QQ (tel: 0800 0234 834 (9am to 5pm, Monday to Friday); email: info@ bwcharity.org.uk)

 www.bwcharity.org.uk

CC number: 313080

Eligibility

Current and former bank employees, and their dependants, who are in need.

Types of grant

Grants are made to the children of current or former bank workers for 'the advancement of education'.

Exclusions

The charity is unable to make grants for personal debt or loans, medical fees, legal expenses, private school fees and items and/or services for which statutory funding exists.

Applications

Initial enquiries can be made by contacting the charity's helpline (9am to 5pm, Monday to Friday). Alternatively, prospective applicants may wish to complete an enquiry form on the funder's website. The charity will then contact the applicant via telephone or email to discuss their application further.

Financial information

Year end	31/03/2018
Income	£1,690,000
Total expenditure	£4,410,000

Further financial information

Note: the grant total has been estimated.

Other information

The charity can make referrals to counselling and other therapies for those struggling with their mental health, or for those experiencing difficulties in their personal life such as relationship breakdown or bereavement. The charity also operates a range of advice services, for guidance on debt and money, disability (for information on benefit entitlements, statutory funding, etc.), housing (for information on housing benefit, repossession, eviction, etc.), as well as advice for carers.

Sources of information
Accounts; annual report; Charity Commission record; funder's website.

The Chartered Institute of Management Accountants Benevolent Fund

 £67,000 (2018)

Correspondent: Caroline Aldred, Manager, CIMA Benevolent Fund, 1 South Place, London EC2M 2RB (tel: 07711 368894; email: benevolent. fund@aicpa-cima.com)

www.cimaglobal.com

CC number: 261114

Eligibility
Grants are available to dependants of members of CIMA in higher education.

Types of grant
The fund awards educational grants.

Exclusions
No grants are awarded towards non-priority debts (such as credit card bills), school fees where education is available free of charge, legal costs (except for bankruptcy fees) or business and career development costs.

Applications
Prospective applicants should contact the Manager of the Benevolent Fund by post or email. Application forms are available to download from the funder's website. Note: there are two different application forms; one for UK residents and one for applicants outside the UK. After making an application, the Manager of the Benevolent Fund will usually contact the applicant to ask further questions about their current circumstances. Decisions on grants are usually made within one or two weeks.

Financial information
Year end	31/12/2018
Income	£212,000
Total expenditure	£205,000

Further financial information
During 2018, grants were awarded to 54 beneficiaries. Note: the grant total has been estimated.

Other information
The charity also funds referrals to an outplacement organisation for people who are currently out of work and need support to find employment.

Sources of information
Accounts; annual report; Charity Commission record; funder's website.

The Insurance Charities

 £219,400 (2017/18)

Correspondent: Mrs Kirsten Watson, Chair of the Grants Committee, Third Floor, 2 St Andrews Hill, London EC4V 5BY (tel: 020 7606 3763; email: info@theinsurancecharities.org.uk)

www.theinsurancecharities.org.uk

CC number: 206860

Eligibility
The charity's website states:

> You can apply if you are a:
> - Current or past insurance employee:
>   - with at least five years' work in insurance within the last ten years
>   - with less than five years' insurance work but where insurance has made up the majority of your career to date
>   - with at least five years' work in insurance immediately prior to retirement
>   - in receipt of a pension or deferred pension from an insurance employer in respect of at least five years' insurance service.
>
> OR you are:
> - A dependant of a current or former insurance employee.
>
> In all cases:
> - Service must be/have been within the UK or Irish insurance industry.
> - There must be restricted financial means in terms of income and capital.
> - An element of misfortune has arisen.
>
> You do not need to be a CII member to apply for help.

Types of grant
Grants are awarded for general educational purposes.

Applications
In the first instance, an initial application form is available to complete and submit online. From this, the charity may request more information or arrange a home visit with a welfare adviser. The adviser will discuss the applicant's financial situation in detail and may suggest changes to their income and expenditure habits. After this meeting, the grants committee will advise the applicant of their decision.

Financial information
Year end	31/03/2018
Income	£1,287,000
Total expenditure	£1,570,000

Further financial information
Grants were made to support 235 individuals for both welfare and educational purposes. The grant totals have been estimated.

Other information
The charity also provides practical support and advice.

Sources of information
Accounts; annual report; Charity Commission record; funder's website.

Scottish Chartered Accountants' Benevolent Association

 £58,400 (2018)

Correspondent: Charity Administrator, PO Box 28843, Edinburgh EH14 9BY (tel: 07722 932120; email: admin@scaba. org.uk)

https://www.icas.com/scaba-the-charity-for-cas-in-need

OSCR number: SC008365

Eligibility
Current and former members of the Institute of Chartered Accountants of Scotland (ICAS), and their dependants, who are in need. Prospective members of ICAS who are in higher/further education, or those who have recently entered into a training contract, are also eligible for support.

Types of grant
Educational grants are made towards, for example, the costs of retraining when working in a current profession is no longer possible. Previous grants have been given for maintenance costs. Loans are also available.

Applications
Application forms are available to download from the funder's website. Completed forms should be returned to the charity by post.

Financial information
Year end	31/12/2018
Income	£146,800
Total expenditure	£172,100

Other information
Beneficiaries will be visited by a support worker who will act as a listening ear and provide practical support based on their circumstances. Beneficiaries may also be assigned a financial adviser who can help with money management.

Sources of information
Accounts; annual report; funder's website; OSCR record.

Hospitality

The Savoy Educational Trust

 £920 (2017/18)

Correspondent: Margaret Georgiou, Secretary to the Trustees, Room 160, 90 Long Acre, London WC2E 9RZ (tel: 020 7849 3001; email: info@savoyeducationaltrust.org.uk)

www.savoyeducationaltrust.org.uk

CC number: 1161014

Eligibility

Individuals undertaking a hospitality-related course.

Types of grant

Grants of up to £500 are available to help with fees or to purchase items required for the course such as uniforms, books and equipment.

Applications

Initially in writing to the correspondent. Eligible applicants will then be provided with an application form. Grants are normally considered at meetings in March, July, September and December, and completed forms must be submitted at least five weeks before the meeting date.

Financial information

Year end	31/03/2018
Income	£1,573,000
Total expenditure	£1,900,000

Further financial information

Grants totalling £920 and ranging from £170 to £500 were made to three individuals.

Other information

There is a scholarship scheme run in partnership with the Worshipful Company of Innholders which introduces those in middle management in hospitality to senior/general manager techniques through short intensive courses. The trust gave £60,000 to the scheme and in total awarded £1.527 million to educational institutions for hospitality training in 2017/18.

Sources of information

Accounts; annual report; Charity Commission record; funder's website.

Manufac-turing

The BTMA Trust

 £86,900 (2017/18)

Correspondent: Jane Pocock, Case Secretary, PO Box 3157, Caterham, Surrey CR3 4BH (tel: 01883 371280; email: secretary@bmtatrust.org.uk)

bmtatrust.org.uk

CC number: 273978

Eligibility

People who are or have been employed in the motor industry and their children.

Types of grant

Grants of up to £1,000 to young people to help them overcome financial barriers to achieve their education, training or employment goals in the motor industry. Examples include: course fees, tools and help with living costs.

Applications

Applicants first need to contact the correspondent by phone or email to have a chat about their situation. If eligible the individual will be sent an application form to complete.

Financial information

Year end	30/06/2018
Income	£244,400
Total expenditure	£235,900

Other information

The trust also makes grants for welfare purposes.

Sources of information

Accounts; annual report; Charity Commission record; funder's website.

The Coats Foundation Trust

 £17,100 (2017/18)

Correspondent: Andrea McCutcheon, Coats Pensions Office, 107 West Regent Street, Glasgow G2 2BA (tel: 0141 207 6835; email: andrea.mccutcheon@coats.com or pensions.services@coats.com)

https://www.coatspensions.co.uk/about-us/coats-foundation-trust

CC number: 268735

Eligibility

Students across the UK are eligible for educational assistance. Priority is given to those studying textile-related courses.

Types of grant

Educational grants are awarded towards course fees and materials required for study.

Exclusions

Educational grants cannot be given towards rent and living expenses.

Applications

Application forms are available to download from the funder's website.

Financial information

Year end	05/04/2018
Income	£1,300
Total expenditure	£75,800

Further financial information

Full accounts were not available to view on the Charity Commission's website due to the charity's low income. We have therefore estimated the grant total based on the charity's total expenditure.

Other information

The charity also makes welfare grants to individuals and to organisations to provide, (or assist the provision of) recreational facilities.

Sources of information

Charity Commission record; funder's website.

W. W. Spooner Charitable Trust

 £6,200 (2017/18)

Correspondent: The Trustees, 2 Elliot Road, Watford, Hertfordshire WD17 4DF

CC number: 313653

Eligibility

Scholarships are available to young employees of Spooner Industries Ltd.

Types of grant

One-off and recurring grants according to need.

Applications

Apply in writing to the correspondent.

Financial information

Year end	05/04/2018
Income	£86,000
Total expenditure	£147,200

Further financial information

Note: the grant total has been estimated.

Other information

The charity purchases works of art 'for the benefit of the public'. The charity also supports community projects and causes by making grants to organisations.

Sources of information
Accounts; annual report; Charity Commission record.

Maritime

The Corporation of Trinity House of Deptford Strond

 £1,750,000 (2018/19)

Correspondent: Graham Hockley, Secretary, Trinity House, Tower Hill, London EC3N 4DH (tel: 020 7481 6914; email: graham.hockley@thls.org)

www.trinityhouse.co.uk

CC number: 211869

Eligibility
Educational grants are available to young people (usually aged between 16 and 18.5) who are of good general health and physique, sufficient enough to pass the Maritime and Coastguard Agency medical examination. There are certain academic standards expected of applicants which differ depending on the chosen entry route. These are:

- **Foundation Degree/Scottish Professional Diploma:** GCSEs at grades A to C, or Scottish Standard level 1 to 3, in English, Mathematics (must be at grade A or B), Physics or Combined Science and at least two other subjects. Applicants must have attained at least 120 UCAS points in any A-level subjects or equivalent. Continuation on to a full honours degree may be possible
- **Higher National Diploma (HND):** GCSEs at grades A to C, or Scottish Standard level 1 to 3, in English, Mathematics (must be at grade A or B), Physics or Combined Science and at least two other subjects

UKSA Superyacht Cadetships are available to young people aged between 15 and 18. Applicants are expected to have excellent oral and written skills, a good understanding of mathematics and have GCSE grades 9 to 4 (A* to C) in English, Maths and Science. If applying for a foundation degree alongside the Superyacht Cadetship, applicants must have 48 UCAS points.

Types of grant
The Merchant Navy Scholarship Scheme funds cadetships for young people seeking careers in the Merchant Navy. Cadets can train as deck officers, engineer officers and electro-technical officers. The qualifications gained from a cadetship vary from a Higher National Diploma to a full honours degree.

Grants of up to £11,000 are available for UK Sailing Academy (UKSA) Superyacht Cadetships.

Applications
Application forms for Merchant Navy Scholarships are available to download from the charity's website. Prospective applicants for the UKSA Superyacht Cadetship can also register their interest on the website.

Financial information
Year end	31/03/2019
Income	£12,910,000
Total expenditure	£9,780,000

Further financial information
During 2018/19, scholarships were awarded to 105 cadets.

Other information
The charity owns and operates 18 almshouses in Walmer (Kent), which are available to ex-mariners, typically aged 60 and above, who are in need. Residents normally have over 15 years' service at sea. Occupancy is also extended to the dependants of such people.

Sources of information
Accounts; annual report; Charity Commission record; funder's website.

The Marine Society and Sea Cadets

Correspondent: Mark Hallam, Director of Finance and Company Secretary, 202 Lambeth Road, London SE1 7JW (tel: 020 7654 7000; email: info@ms-sc.org)

 https://www.marine-society.org/91-funding

CC number: 313013/SC037808

Eligibility
Professional seafarers, active or retired, serving in the Royal Navy, the British Merchant Navy or fishing fleets. The charity also supports people who are serving in the navies, merchant navies or fishing fleets of other countries as the trustees from time to time determine. Members of the Sea Cadet Corps and those preparing to enter a maritime career are also eligible for support.

Types of grant
Grants are awarded to assist with financial hardship among seafarers and their dependants.

Bursaries, scholarships and loans are given towards education and training for those entering a maritime career. Support can be given towards fees, maintenance and other expenses. The society administers a range of scholarships to support professional

development, details of each scheme can be found on the charity's website.

Applications
Application forms for each scholarship can be found on the charity's website. A contact form is also available to use for any other enquires.

Financial information
Year end	31/03/2019
Income	£19,830,000
Total expenditure	£17,870,000

Further financial information
In 2019 a total of £1,020,000 was awarded as grants to individuals. We were unable to determine how much was awarded for educational purposes.

Other information
Grants are also made to sea cadet units and support can be given to 'nautical or other schools or training establishments which are charities or to other organisations established for charitable purposes'. In addition, grants are provided to volunteers for the upkeep or purchase of uniforms on promotion or for wear and tear.

Sources of information
Accounts; annual report; Charity Commission record; funder's website.

The Honourable Company of Master Mariners and Howard Leopold Davis Charity

 £16,400 (2018)

Correspondent: Honourable Company of Master Mariners, HQS Wellington, Temple Stairs, Victoria Embankment, London WC2R 2PN (tel: 020 7836 8179; email: info@hcmm.org.uk)

www.hcmm.org.uk/activities/charitable-giving

CC number: 1172234

Eligibility
People intending to serve in the Merchant Navy or with an interest in seamanship or sailing are eligible to apply.

Types of grant
The charity's website states: 'The objectives and aims of the Education Fund are to assist and encourage the education, instruction and training whether generally, technically or professionally, of people serving or intending to serve in the Merchant Navy. Grants are available for anyone who fulfils these requirements.'

Applications
Apply in writing to the correspondent.

Financial information

Year end	31/12/2018
Income	£95,000
Total expenditure	£114,400

Other information

The charity also makes grants for welfare purposes.

Sources of information

Accounts; annual report; Charity Commission record; funder's website.

Reardon Smith Nautical Trust

 £104,100 (2018/19)

Correspondent: Sarah Fox, FoxSE Consultancy, 4 Bessemer Road, Cardiff CF11 8BA (tel: 029 2002 2143; email: sarah@foxseconsultancy.co.uk)

CC number: 1153623

Eligibility

Residents of Wales up to the age of 25 studying recognised nautical or maritime courses in the UK or abroad. The courses should relate to shipping, maritime law and commerce, navigation, sailing, oceanography and marine related environmental issues, in particular those which give the individual first hand practical experience of being at sea. Preference is given to residents of the city and county of Cardiff.

Types of grant

Grants, scholarships, exhibitions and bursaries towards general educational expenses.

Applications

Apply in writing to the correspondent or through an educational institution.

Financial information

Year end	05/04/2019
Income	£140,400
Total expenditure	£124,300

Further financial information

Grants were made directly to five individuals totalling £9,100 and to six organisations that provide maritime education, totalling £95,000. Grants are paid through sail training providers, which include Island Trust, Tall Ships Youth Trust and Challenge Wales.

Sources of information

Accounts; annual report; Charity Commission record.

The Royal Liverpool Seamen's Orphan Institution (RLSOI)

 £87,600 (2018)

Correspondent: Mr M. Finn, Secretary, Suite 315, Cotton Exchange Building, Old Hall Street, Liverpool, Merseyside L3 9LQ (tel: 0151 227 3417 or 07747 607062 (mobile); email: enquiries@rlsoi-uk.org)

www.rlsoi-uk.org

CC number: 526379

Eligibility

Educational grants are available to the children of merchant seafarers and fishermen.

Types of grant

Educational grants are made to help with costs associated with pursing higher and further education, including monthly maintenance allowances.

Applications

Application forms are available to download from the funder's website.

Financial information

Year end	31/12/2018
Income	£220,300
Total expenditure	£275,200

Further financial information

The grant total has been estimated from the 2018 accounts.

Other information

Note: the charity was in the process of revising its application forms/grant criteria at the time of writing (November 2019). Grants are also awarded for welfare purposes.

Sources of information

Accounts; annual report; Charity Commission record; funder's website.

Royal Merchant Navy Education Foundation

 £111,700 (2017/18)

Correspondent: Cdr Charles Heron-Watson, Secretary, 1A Charnham Lane, Hungerford, Berkshire RG17 0EY (tel: 01488 567890; email: office@rmnef.orh.uk)

www.rmnef.org.uk

CC number: 1153323

Eligibility

British children of Merchant Navy seafarers, professional sea-going fishermen and RNLI lifeboat crew members, who have served or are serving at sea and who are unable to meet their children's educational needs. The foundation's website states: 'The length of sea-service is considered when determining whether a young person is eligible for support and, in all instances, the Trustees will use their discretion[...] In each case, we need to identify a genuine 'need' and this will be based upon factors such as domestic environment, locality, health, finance and education.'

Types of grant

Support is available for children and young people at any stage of education – from pre-school, primary school, secondary school, right up to further education, higher education (to professional entry qualification) and career training and apprenticeships (to professional entry qualification). Support can be given towards some or all of the following: school fees, educational extras, school uniforms, travel between home and school, educational equipment, educational visits, educational books and some university expenses.

Applications

Initial contact should be made with the correspondent via letter or email. Phone enquiries to discuss individual circumstances are welcomed, and some applicants make contact through and associated charity (see the foundation's website for further details). Application forms will then be provided to eligible applicants. Candidates will be paid a home visit and may be required to provide an assessment by a relevant professional. A submission is then put to the trustees for a final decision.

Financial information

Year end	31/08/2018
Income	£466,200
Total expenditure	£533,200

Further financial information

The grant total has been estimated from the 2017/18 accounts.

Other information

Previously known as the Royal Merchant Navy School Foundation (Charity Commission no. 309047), the assets and liabilities of the foundation were transferred to the Royal Merchant Navy Education Foundation, a charitable incorporated organisation, in 2013. The foundation also assists beneficiaries over the age of 18 who have previously been supported by the Royal Liverpool Seamen's Orphan's Institution.

Sources of information

Accounts; annual report; Charity Commission record; funder's website.

Marketing and PR

The Manchester Publicity Association Educational Trust

 £2,500 (2017/18)

Correspondent: The Trustees, The Candidate, 5th Floor, Clayton House, 59 Piccadilly, Manchester M1 2AQ (email: theeducationaltrust@btinternet.com)

https://www.theeducationaltrust.org.uk

CC number: 1001134

Eligibility
People studying for a recognised marketing communications qualification at a course centre or distance learning company who are in need of financial assistance.

Types of grant
One-off grants to assist with course fees and additional costs such as exam fees and books.

Exclusions
Bursaries are not intended to replace a student loan or fully fund the course. Funding is not available for international students who require a Tier 4 (General) study visa to remain in the UK.

Applications
Application forms can be completed by the individual online on the trust's website. Applications must be submitted with a CV and written approval from the applicant's course leader. Further guidelines are available on the trust's website.

Financial information
Year end	31/03/2018
Income	£2,400
Total expenditure	£2,800

Further financial information
Full accounts were not available to view on the Charity Commission's website due to the charity's low income. We have therefore estimated the grant total based on the charity's total expenditure.

Sources of information
Charity Commission record; funder's website.

Media

The Grace Wyndham Goldie (BBC) Trust Fund

 £23,200 (2018)

Correspondent: Cheryl Miles, Secretary, BBC Pension and Benefits Centre, Broadcasting House, Cardiff CF5 2YQ (tel: 0303 080 5801)

www.bbc.co.uk/corporate2/charityappeals/about/grants/grace-wyndham-goldie

CC number: 212146

Eligibility
Individuals currently or previously engaged in broadcasting and their dependants.

Types of grant
One-off grants are awarded to help with educational costs such as school or college fees, travel expenses, school uniforms, books and equipment, living expenses or to supplement existing educational awards. Support can also be given to help support young people gain professional or trade qualifications.

Exclusions
The application form states: 'It is important to recognise that the fund has been established to act as a safety net and not to fund expensive lifestyle choices. If you therefore have expenses such as holidays, gym membership, digital services for tv, high mobile telephone charges or non-essential car costs then you will be expected to be able to pay for these yourself.'

Applications
Application forms are available to download from the fund's page on the BBC website. Applicants are asked to provide full information about the circumstances supporting their application. All applications are considered in confidence. Completed forms should be returned to the correspondent by post.

Financial information
Year end	31/12/2018
Income	£61,500
Total expenditure	£39,000

Further financial information
In 2018, 11 grants were made for education and seven for the alleviation of hardship.

Other information
The fund was created in memory of BBC producer Grace Wyndham Goldie, who recruited and trained many well-known broadcasters at the BBC as well as pioneering political programming such as the first televised general election.

Sources of information
Accounts; annual report; Charity Commission record; funder's website.

The GPM Charitable Trust

 £6,700 (2017/18)

Correspondent: Keith Keys, Secretary, c/o 43 Spriggs Close, Clapham, Bedford MK41 6GD (tel: 07733 262991; email: gpmcharitabletrust82@gmail.com)

www.gpmtrust.org

CC number: 227177

Eligibility
Workers, former workers and their dependants in the printing, graphical, papermaking and media industries who are in need.

Types of grant
Grants for retraining, skills enhancement and other educational requirements especially following redundancy or other reduction in income.

Exclusions
The trust is unable to assist with regular grants or debt relief.

Applications
An application form can be downloaded from the trust's website or requested from the correspondent. It must be printed and completed in black ink before being returned to the trust. The dates of application deadlines for subsequent trustee meetings are also listed on the website.

Financial information
Year end	31/03/2018
Income	£25,700
Total expenditure	£22,300

Further financial information
The grant total has been estimated from the 2017/18 accounts.

Sources of information
Accounts; annual report; Charity Commission record; funder's website.

The Printing Charity

 £109,900 (2018)

Correspondent: Neil Lovell, Chief Executive/Secretary, Underwood House, 235 Three Bridges Road, Crawley, West Sussex RH10 1LS (tel: 01293 542820; email: info@theprintingcharity.org.uk)

www.theprintingcharity.org.uk

CC number: 208882

Eligibility

People who work, or have worked, for at least three years (not necessarily consecutively or for the same employer) in printing, paper, publishing, packaging, graphic arts or allied trades who are in need. Support is extended to the dependants of such people.

Young people aged between 18 and 30 who are:
- UK residents
- Studying for a UK printing, paper, publishing, packaging or graphic arts qualification and are planning to take up their first role in the sector
- An apprentice or studying for an NVQ in a UK print-related organisation
- Already working in printing, paper, publishing, packaging or graphic arts in the UK and wish to develop their workplace skills

Types of grant

Print Futures Awards of up to £1,500 for young people working in the sector or intending to join it. Grants can be made for post-education internships, relevant training courses, professional accreditation, and kit and equipment.

Applications

Application forms and guidelines are available to download from the charity's website. Prospective applicants are advised to contact the charity by email (awards@theprintingcharity.org.uk) or by telephone (as given above) for further information about the scheme.

Financial information

Year end	31/12/2018
Income	£1,670,000
Total expenditure	£2,870,000

Further financial information

During 2018, the charity awarded welfare grants to 544 beneficiaries and educational grants to 91 beneficiaries.

Other information

Along with making Print Future Awards, the charity supports various bursaries and apprenticeships run by other organisations such as the Papermaking Apprenticeship Programme, the Queen's Bindery Apprenticeship Scheme and the Stationers' Foundation Postgraduate Bursary Scheme. The charity also operates two sheltered housing facilities containing 72 apartments, which are available to retired printers and their dependants.

Sources of information

Accounts; annual report; Charity Commission record; funder's website.

ScreenSkills

 £54,100 (2017/18)

Correspondent: The Trustees, 94 Euston Street, London NW1 2HA (tel: 020 7713 9800; email: bursaries@screenskills.com)

https://www.screenskills.com

CC number: 1015324

Eligibility

People aged 18 and over looking to enter, progress in, or return to the screen industries. Applicants must:
- Be eligible to work in the UK
- Have a UK bank account
- Currently be working in the UK screen industries, or demonstrate their intention to work in the UK screen industries

Types of grant

Bursaries are made towards the cost of items such as accommodation, travel, care, equipment (hire and purchase), training costs, living costs, etc. The amount awarded is dependent on the candidate. To see how much applicants may be entitled to, see the guidance notes on the charity's website.

Exclusions

The charity is unable to:
- Provide bursary funding for undergraduate or postgraduate courses
- Provide bursary funding for course fees or any associated costs for training courses which are already funded by ScreenSkills
- Cover costs which should be paid for by an employer (for example, accommodation or travel costs for training provided by the employer)

Applications

Applications can be made online on the funder's website. Applications are considered over the course of a calendar month.

Financial information

Year end	31/03/2018
Income	£7,970,000
Total expenditure	£7,780,000

Further financial information

During 2017/18, bursaries were awarded to 94 recipients.

Other information

Grants are also made to various organisations in the screen industry,

Sources of information

Accounts; annual report; Charity Commission record; funder's website.

Medicine and health

British Veterinary Nursing Association

Correspondent: The Bursary Administrator, 79 Greenway Business Centre, Harlow Business Park, Harlow, Essex CM19 5QE (tel: 01279 408644; email: bvna@bvna.co.uk)

 www.bvna.org.uk/members/bursaries

Eligibility

Those studying veterinary nursing at college or university, or those in need of funding for a continuing professional development (CPD) certified course or research project. Applicants must be members of the association.

Types of grant

The association administers a number of bursary schemes, further details of which can be found on its website. Current grants/bursaries include:
- **BVNA Educational Bursary:** up to £500 for veterinary nurses or students towards training and education
- **The Kennel Club Charitable Trust Bursary:** up to £3,000 towards course fees and other expenses incurred as part of veterinary nurse training
- **The Kennel Club Charitable Trust Degree Bursary:** £1,000 per academic year (£3,000) is awarded to one degree student
- **AWF Student Research Grants:** students (who have completed at least two years of study and wish to undertake a research project designed to have a practical and positive impact on raising animal welfare standards
- **MSD Veterinary Nurse Research Bursary:** a bursary of £1,000 is given to one student or qualified veterinary nurse with the best research project application
- **Petsavers Student Research Projects:** veterinary nurses can apply for clinical research aimed at understanding the conditions affecting small animals kept as pets, to ultimately understand the cause

and/or management of clinical disorder'

Applications

Contact the association for information on how to apply for your chosen scheme. Applications typically open in January.

Other information

The association also administers RCVS Knowledge Grants and Awards. Prizes of £250 are awarded to individuals and teams who are 'focused on driving continuous improvements in their practice for better outcomes for their patients, better service provision to their clients and an improved business case or better working conditions for the team.' Students can enter for a Veterinary Evidence Award and if successful, will have their work published in a veterinary journal and win a prize of up to £200.

Sources of information

Funder's website.

The Cameron Fund

 £57,000 (2018)

Correspondent: David Harris, Company Secretary, BMA House, Tavistock Square, London WC1H 9HR (tel: 020 7388 0796; email: info@cameronfund. org.uk)

www.cameronfund.org.uk

CC number: 261993

Eligibility

Registered and formerly registered general practitioners, and their dependants, who are in need. Support is also extended to doctors who are training to be GPs.

Types of grant

Student allowances of £3,000 per academic year (£1,000 per term) are made towards living costs when undertaking a first degree course or vocational training.

Applications

Application forms are available to download from the funder's website.

Financial information

Year end	31/12/2018
Income	£388,300
Total expenditure	£322,400

Other information

The charity also makes grants for welfare purposes.

Sources of information

Accounts; annual report; Charity Commission record; funder's website.

The Elizabeth Casson Trust

 £96,800 (2017/18)

Correspondent: Pamela Anderson, 6 Langdale Court, Witney, Oxfordshire OX28 6FG (email: ec.trust@btinternet. com)

https://www.elizabethcasson.org.uk

CC number: 227166

Eligibility

Training and practising occupational therapists.

Types of grant

Funding is available to cover the costs of: courses and conferences; bespoke research; scholarships; and postdoctoral career development.

Exclusions

The trust will not fund pre-registration education.

Applications

Application forms are available to complete online. Applications for grants under £2,000 will need to include a current copy of the applicant's CV and a letter from their line manager or academic supervisor. For applications for grants over £2,000, applicants will need to include a current copy of their CV, a letter from their line manager or academic supervisor, a CPD (continuing professional development) or PDP (personal development plan) statement, and a personal statement.

Financial information

Year end	31/08/2018
Income	£246,100
Total expenditure	£191,600

Other information

In 2015/16, the trust committed to a grant of £250,000 to Oxford Brookes University, payable over five years, to support the development of a sustainable research stream focused on occupational therapy.

Sources of information

Accounts; annual report; Charity Commission record; funder's website.

The Chartered Society of Physiotherapy Charitable Trust

 £70,400 (2018)

Correspondent: Shamina Begum, 14 Bedford Row, London WC1R 4ED (tel: 020 7306 6646; email: debooss@csp. org.uk)

www.csp.org.uk/charitabletrust

CC number: 279882

Eligibility

Qualified, associate and student members of the society.

Types of grant

Grants can be given for fees of academically accredited research courses, UK and overseas presentations, overseas development projects, research visits, master's research dissemination and student elective placements.

Applications

Applications for educational awards should be submitted using the CSP ePortfolio, which can be accessed on the society's website. The deadlines for applications for different awards vary – for the most up-to-date information see the website.

Financial information

Year end	31/12/2018
Income	£501,600
Total expenditure	£689,000

Other information

Awards can also be made for experienced researchers and those only starting their research career. Research funding comprises Physiotherapy Research Foundation (PRF) awards, paediatric research funding and a special care of older people research award. For specific details and latest available awards in this category, see the trust's website. During 2018, grants totalling £180,000 were awarded to the Physiotherapy Research Foundation.

Sources of information

Accounts; annual report; Charity Commission record; funder's website.

The Nightingale Fund

 £11,900 (2017/18)

Correspondent: Katie Hyatt, Honorary Secretary, 16 Liphook Crescent, Forest Hill, London SE23 3BW (tel: 020 8291 5984; email: honorary.secretary@ thenightingalefund.uk)

http://www.thenightingalefund.org. uk

CC number: 205911

Eligibility

Nurses, midwives and community public health nurses who are registered with the Nursing and Midwifery Council and healthcare assistants in the UK.

Types of grant

Grants are awarded for course fees only. Support is given towards further education and training to allow individuals to improve and develop their nursing practice. During 2017/18 grants ranged from £350 to £1,500.

Applications

A candidate can apply for a grant by completing the application form and returning it to the correspondent with a current CV and two references. Application forms are available to download from the fund's website.

Financial information

Year end	30/06/2018
Income	£28,900
Total expenditure	£20,100

Further financial information

A total of 14 grants were awarded during 2017/18.

Other information

Each year the fund is able to support around 30 nurses, healthcare assistants, midwives and public health nurses.

Sources of information

Accounts; annual report; Charity Commission record; funder's website.

The Florence Nightingale Foundation

£ £816,600 (2018/19)

Correspondent: The Trustees, Deans Mews, 11–13 Cavendish Square, London W1G 0AN (tel: 020 7730 3030; email: admin@florence-nightingale-foundation.org.uk)

 www.florence-nightingale-foundation.org.uk

CC number: 229229/SC044341

Eligibility

Nurses and midwives in the UK who are Nursing and Midwifery Council (NMC) registered. Nurses and midwives studying for a PhD or writing a master's dissertation are also eligible for support, provided that their research aligns with one of the following topics:

- Researching an aspect of care for adolescents and young adults with depression and/or other mental health issues
- Researching an aspect of mental healthcare

Nurses and midwives who wish to undertake doctoral of postdoctoral level research are also eligible for funding, provided that their research falls into one of the following practice-related areas:

- The management of pain
- The management of end of life care
- Enhancing patient safety

Types of grant

Leadership scholarship: scholarships of up to £10,000 are made for leadership development programmes. There are three types of leadership programmes aimed at senior leaders, aspiring directors of nursing/midwifery and emerging leaders (Band 7 or 8, or equivalent, nurses and midwives).

Travel scholarship: scholarships of up to £3,000 are awarded for travel aboard to study new models of care, patient safety and quality improvement.

Research scholarship: scholarship awards will support a nurse or midwife's release from their roles for a 12 month period based on an NHS band 6 salary. Contributions may also be made towards essential travel costs.

Research scholarship (fees): scholarships are awarded to master's and PhD students for course fees.

Exclusions

Applications for Leadership scholarships will not be accepted without confirmation of a 10% contribution from the applicant's employer.

Applications

Application forms are available to download from the foundation's website. Applications should be made by the applicant's chief nurse or line manager on their behalf. Applications should include a copy of the applicant's NMC registration documentation and their personal, employment and educational information. See the foundation's website for further information on what should be included in the application.

Financial information

Year end	31/03/2019
Income	£1,430,000
Total expenditure	£1,290,000

Further financial information

During 2018/19, the charity awarded 56 leadership scholarships, 13 travel scholarships and nine research scholarships.

Sources of information

Accounts; annual report; Charity Commission record; funder's website.

The Nurses' Memorial to King Edward VII Edinburgh Scottish Committee

£ £4,800 (2018)

Correspondent: Ann McQueen, c/o Johnston Smillie Ltd, Chartered Accountants, 6 Redheughs Rigg, Edinburgh EH12 9DQ (tel: 0131 317 7377; email: info@nursesmemorial.org.uk)

 www.nursesmemorial.org.uk

OSCR number: SC023963

Eligibility

Nurses or midwives with a strong connection to Scotland (including nurses who have worked in Scotland, or Scottish nurses working outside Scotland) who are retired, ill or otherwise in need.

Types of grant

Educational bursaries are available for further education and training.

Applications

Applications can be made via the charity's website.

Financial information

Year end	31/12/2018
Income	£85,300
Total expenditure	£152,300

Other information

The charity also makes grants to individuals for welfare purposes.

Sources of information

Accounts; annual report; funder's website; OSCR record.

The Queen's Nursing Institute

£ £8,400 (2018)

Correspondent: Joanne Moorby, Welfare and Grants Officer, 1A Henrietta Place, London W1G 0LZ (tel: 020 7549 1405; email: joanne.moorby@qni.org.uk or mail@qni.org.uk)

 www.qni.org.uk

CC number: 213128

Eligibility

Educational grants are available to working nurses, up to and including band 6 (or equivalent), who are in need of assistance to further their education. Nurses must be studying accredited courses or modules in community nursing which demonstrate a clear clinical benefit to patients.

Types of grant

Educational grants of up £1,000 are awarded for course fees and books required for study.

Exclusions

Welfare grants cannot be awarded for residential or nursing home fees, debt, medical treatment or funeral expenses. Educational grants can only be paid once, and are not normally given for travel costs. This charity is unable to support nurses in Scotland. Scottish nurses should instead consult The Queen's Nursing Institute Scotland (OSCR No. SC005751).

Applications

Application forms are available to download from the funder's website. Completed forms (along with a copy of the applicant's latest bank statement and utility bill if applying for a welfare grant) should be sent to the correspondent by post.

Financial information

Year end	31/12/2018
Income	£1,050,000
Total expenditure	£1,320,000

Further financial information

During 2018, the charity awarded 397 welfare grants and 18 educational grants.

Sources of information

Accounts; annual report; Charity Commission record; funder's website.

The RCN Foundation

 £281,000 (2018)

Correspondent: Ian Norris, Chair of the Grants Committee, 20 Cavendish Square, London W1G 0RN (tel: 020 7647 3489; email: rcnfoundation@rcn.org.uk)

www.rcnfoundation.org.uk

CC number: 1134606

Eligibility

Educational grants are available to current or former nurses, midwives, nursing support workers, students and nursing associates who are looking to develop their practice. There are several grant schemes, each with their own eligibility criteria. See the foundation's website for further information.

Types of grant

- **Student Grants:** one-off or recurrent grants of £2,500 for those studying nursing at undergraduate or postgraduate level
- **Professional Bursary Scheme:** grants of up to £5,000 for those who wish to develop their existing skills in the following fields: adult nursing, children's nursing, learning disability nursing, mental health nursing, history of nursing (up to £1,000) and occupational health nursing (up to £1,000)
- **Needlemakers Grant:** grants of up to £1,000 for nurses who use needles in their work and are studying a postgraduate or professional short course
- **Kelsey Bequest Grant:** grants of up to £5,000 for nurses who work or live in the Northumberland/Tyne and Wear area who are about to begin a course that will improve patient care in adult nursing, children's nursing, learning disability nursing or mental health nursing

- **Rae Bequest:** grants of up to £1,000 for registered nurses currently working in Northern Ireland (in any sector), who wish to undertake a course or programme that will 'benefit the education of nurses for work in Northern Ireland and enhance nursing practice and service delivery'
- **Marcia Mackie Bequest:** grants of up to £300 are available to nurses currently working in Northern Ireland (in any sector) who wish to 'enhance nursing through personal professional development or research investigation'

Applications

For educational grants, applicants can apply online through the foundation's website. The next round of funding will be in spring 2020.

Financial information

Year end	31/12/2018
Income	£2,360,000
Total expenditure	£1,380,000

Other information

Grants for research and practice development are available to organisations looking to fund a nursing-led project. Eligible organisations include registered charities, healthcare organisations, places of higher education and NHS trusts.

Sources of information

Accounts; annual report; Charity Commission record; funder's website.

The Royal Medical Foundation

 £20,800 (2017/18)

Correspondent: The Caseworker, RMF Office, Epsom College, College Road, Epsom, Surrey KT17 4JQ (tel: 01372 821010; email: rmf-caseworker@ epsomcollege.org.uk or rmf@ epsomcollege.org.uk)

www.royalmedicalfoundation.org

CC number: 312046

Eligibility

According to the foundation's website, its main focus is the assistance of 'registered doctors and their families who are in financial hardship'.

Types of grant

Educational grants have been made, 'in exceptional circumstances', for private tuition fees, including sixth form/college fees.

Applications

Initial enquiries can be made on the foundation's website using an online

form. All applicants will be visited by the caseworker before funding is awarded. Applicants must have already applied for any state benefits to which they may be entitled before applying for funding. The board meets quarterly in January, April, July and October. See the website for current application deadlines.

Financial information

Year end	30/06/2018
Income	£26,340,000
Total expenditure	£25,280,000

Further financial information

The charity awarded 22 welfare grants and 11 educational grants. Note: the grant total for education has been estimated.

Other information

This charity is one of several linked charities and funds. It is located at Epsom College, whose charitable activity includes providing access to day and boarding education through bursaries and scholarships.

Sources of information

Accounts; annual report; Charity Commission record; funder's website.

Society for Assistance of Medical Families

 £21,200 (2018)

Correspondent: The Secretary, First Floor, The Houses, 16–18 Blackfriars Lane, London EC4V 6EB (tel: 07771 300410 (Monday to Friday, 10am until 4pm); email: info@samf.org.uk)

https://www.samf.org.uk

CC number: 207473

Eligibility

Grants are awarded to the following people (in order of priority):
- Dependants of deceased members of the society
- Members of the society
- Dependants of members
- Doctors, and their dependants, who are in need but are not currently members of the society

Children of medical families who are studying for medical degrees and other medical students are eligible for educational support.

Types of grant

Educational grants have been made towards course fees, examination fees and maintenance costs. Grants are also made for retraining costs to help doctors remain, or return to, work after illness or other circumstances.

Applications

Contact the correspondent for information on how to apply. The trustees meet quarterly (in February, May, August and November) to consider grant applications. If possible, the secretary or a member of the court of directors will meet applicants.

Financial information

Year end	31/12/2018
Income	£241,900
Total expenditure	£150,300

Sources of information

Accounts; annual report; Charity Commission record; funder's website.

Mining and quarrying

The Coal Industry Social Welfare Organisation

 £86,700 (2018)

Correspondent: The Trustees, The Old Rectory, Rectory Drive, Whiston, Rotherham, South Yorkshire S60 4JG (tel: 01709 728115; email: mail@ciswo. org.uk)

 www.ciswo.org.uk

CC number: 1015581

Eligibility

Former mineworkers and their dependants who are experiencing financial difficulties.

Types of grant

Grants are provided for general educational needs.

Applications

Applicants should contact their nearest office, details of which can be found on the charity's website.

Financial information

Year end	31/12/2018
Income	£9,140,000
Total expenditure	£4,180,000

Other information

The charity provides a range of support to former miners including: a home visiting service, advocacy, emotional support, assistance applying for benefits, support on mining-related issues and support at times of hardship.

Sources of information

Accounts; annual report; Charity Commission record; funder's website.

Miners' Welfare National Educational Fund (MWNEF)

 £133,650 (2017/18)

Correspondent: Secretary, The Old Rectory, Rectory Drive, Whiston, Rotherham, South Yorkshire S60 4JG (tel: 01709 728115)

 www.ciswo.org/other-services/ education-fund

CC number: 313246/SC038771

Eligibility

People who are employed in the coal mining industry of Britain, or who have been employed in the industry and took up full-time further education within five years of leaving the industry, or people who had to leave employment in the industry due to age or disability. Individuals between the ages of 17 and 25 who are the dependants of such employees or former employees are also eligible if the employee either completed 20 years of employment in the industry or left due to age or ill-health and was not able to obtain further employment.

Types of grant

Grants are awarded towards higher and further education courses. Any full-time courses of education for which statutory higher education student support is available (e.g. from Student Finance England, Student Finance Wales or Student Awards Agency Scotland) can be supported.

Applications

Application forms are available from the correspondent.

Financial information

Year end	31/08/2018
Income	£16,200
Total expenditure	£148,500

Further financial information

Full accounts were not available to view on the Charity Commission's website due to the charity's low income. We have therefore estimated the grant total based on the charity's total expenditure.

Other information

The eligibility criteria is quite specific but those who do not meet the requirements might be supported by CISWO (Coal Industry Social Welfare Organisation).

Sources of information

Charity Commission record; funder's website.

Mining Institute of Scotland Trust

 £51,500 (2018)

Correspondent: Keith Donaldson, Hon. Secretary/Treasurer, 14/9 Burnbrae Drive, Edinburgh EH12 8AS (tel: 0131 629 7861)

 https://www.iom3.org/mining-institute-scotland/mining-institute-scotland-trust

OSCR number: SC024974

Eligibility

Former members of the Mining Institute of Scotland (MIS) and members or former members of the Institute of Materials, Minerals and Mining who live in Scotland or people who worked in connection with Scottish mining for at least five consecutive years. The dependants of eligible people can also be supported.

Types of grant

The trust's webpage describes the three components of its educational fund:

- **Norman Henderson Prize** – each year, the trustees can purchase a medal for presentation to the author of any paper considered by them to be of 'outstanding merit'
- **Sam Mavor Travelling Scholarship** – bursaries or prizes can be awarded to an MIS student or students to allow them to visit places, works or mines in any such place of special interest to them as may be determined by the trustees
- **Cunningham Scholarship** – scholarships for education in the science of mining, insight into contemporary mining methods, or visiting/studying mines anywhere in the world may be provided

Applications

Applications for assistance should be made in writing to the correspondent.

Financial information

Year end	31/12/2018
Income	£30,600
Total expenditure	£67,200

Other information

The trust also makes grants to organisations.

Sources of information

Accounts; annual report; funder's website; OSCR record.

Other specific industries

Trades Union Congress Educational Trust

 £5,800 (2017)

Correspondent: Julie Lawrence, Administrator, Unionlearn, Congress House, Great Russell Street, London WC1B 3LS (tel: 020 7467 1251; email: jlawrence@tuc.org.uk)

https://www.unionlearn.org.uk/bursaries-tuc-educational-trust

CC number: 313741

Eligibility
Members of Trades Union Congress affiliated trade unions, to attend courses at selected colleges and universities.

Types of grant
The trust offers a range of scholarships and bursaries:

- **One Year Awards** – bursaries for people offered a place on a Higher Education (HE) Diploma at Northern College and Fircroft College. Course subjects include: Labour Studies, History and Social Studies. The TUC provides three additional bursaries of £925 to people who have been accepted onto one of these courses
- **Ruskin College Bursaries** – three annual bursaries of £1,000 (or two payments of £500 if part-time) to study an MA in Global Labour and Social Change
- **Clive Jenkins European Study Bursary** – two bursaries of £800 each to cover travel and subsistence costs for a visit to a European Union country, to study aspects of trade unionism, industrial relations or training and employment

Further information about the grants available is given on the trust's website.

Applications
Application forms for each award can be found on the Unionlearn website. Further information and current deadlines are available from the website or by contacting the correspondent.

Financial information
Year end	31/12/2017
Income	£26,900
Total expenditure	£723,800

Other information
The trust also awards grants to educational institutions.

Sources of information
Accounts; annual report; Charity Commission record; funder's website.

The Feltmakers Charitable Foundation

 £5,600 (2017/18)

Correspondent: Major J. T. H. Coombs, Clerk to the Trustees, Post Cottage, The Street, Greywell, Hook, Hampshire RG29 1DA (tel: 01256 703174; email: jcpartnership@btopenworld.com)

www.feltmakers.co.uk

CC number: 259906

Eligibility
Retired people who have been engaged in the felt or hatting trade. Support is also available to fashion students or apprentices in the headwear industry.

Types of grant
The foundation also makes grants in the form of 'Feltmaker Awards' to fashion students and apprentices. The first prize winner of the award receives £1,500 and two weeks of work experience. Runners-up receive funding ranging from £250 to £1,000.

Applications
Apply in writing to the correspondent for welfare grants.

For the Feltmaker Award, see the funder's website for full details on how to apply.

Financial information
Year end	31/03/2018
Income	£62,100
Total expenditure	£40,300

Other information
The foundation also makes donations to organisations in the City of London, where the founder is based.

Sources of information
Accounts; annual report; Charity Commission record; funder's website.

The Stationers' Foundation

 £140,000 (2018)

Correspondent: Pamela Butler, Administrator, Stationers' Hall, Stationers' Hall Court, Ave Maria Lane, London EC4M 7DD (tel: 020 7246 0990; email: foundation@stationers.org)

www.stationers.org

CC number: 1120963

Eligibility
People in need with preference given to Liverymen and Freemen of the Stationers' Company who are over the age of 60, and their spouses, partners and dependants. In addition, support for education is available for UK residents aged 25 and under and in need of financial assistance. Preference may be given to: former pupils of the Stationers' Company School; children of Liverymen and Freemen of the Company; and those people wishing to enter the communications and content industries.

Types of grant
The foundation offers support for those in education through a number of different schemes:

- **Postgraduate Bursary Scheme** – postgraduate students under the age of 25 (students between 25 and 30 should contact the relevant course director and the foundation's administrator) who hold an offer on one of the specific courses listed on the foundation's website, supporting progression in or entry into the communications and content industries. There are 12 bursaries of £6,000 awarded each year, alongside mentoring from a member of the Stationers' Company. Upon completion of the course, students are awarded freedom of the company
- **Financial assistance** – to assist students starting or continuing their education
- **Major Awards** – around £2,000 for young people under the age of 25 who wish to study a course or educational project associated with printing, bookbinding, paper conservation, stationery, papermaking, publishing, book selling or newspaper production
- **Francis Mathew Stationers' Company Scholarships** – travel scholarships of around £2,000 for those aged between 18 and 35 studying or working in the industries supported by the foundation
- **Prize and Scholarship Fund** – for the children of members of the Stationers' Company studying for a degree, undertaking further education or carrying out research at a university, as well as prizes for those studying in the communication and content industries
- **Evening Standard Media Diversity Bursary Scheme** – two years of training, including on the job training at the Evening Standard, The Independent and London Live Television for people 16 or over who have not been to university

Further information and guidelines for each category of grant is available on the foundation's website.

Applications

Application forms are available from the foundation's website along with detailed guidance notes and current deadlines, specific to each award. Any queries should be addressed to the foundation's correspondent.

Financial information

Year end		31/12/2018
Income		£390,900
Total expenditure		£334,600

Further financial information

Grants were broken down as follows: 13 postgraduate students received grants totalling £75,100; a total of £64,800 for special educational projects.

Other information

The foundation also supports a number of specific schools, organisations, charities and organises the Shine School Media Project as well as funding two Saturday Supplementary Schools for disadvantaged children. The foundation also administers a library.

Sources of information

Accounts; annual report; Charity Commission record; funder's website.

Public sector

The Fire Service Research and Training Trust

See record on page 3

The Gurney Fund

 £102,500 (2018/19)

Correspondent: Christine McNicol, Fund Manager, 9 Bath Road, Worthing, West Sussex BN11 3NU (tel: 01903 237256; email: gurneyfund@btconnect. com)

www.gurneyfund.org

CC number: 1156903

Eligibility

Children of police officers from 22 subscribing forces in England and Wales, where a parent has died or retired on the grounds of ill-health. Step-children may also be eligible if they were substantially supported by a deceased or medically retired officer. The list of subscribing forces can be found on the fund's website.

Types of grant

Grants are available for higher and further education students for essential costs such as course books.

Exclusions

Grants will not be awarded for skiing trips.

Applications

Applications for medically retired officers can be made online via the online form. Widows/widowers/ guardians should contact the correspondent directly to discuss eligibility. The trustees meet at least four times each year. A copy of the child's birth certificate will be required. Successful candidates will be asked to complete an income and expenditure form and produce receipts if assistance is requested for specific expenditure. Each year beneficiaries will be asked to complete an online annual review.

Financial information

Year end		31/03/2019
Income		£476,300
Total expenditure		£844,300

Further financial information

Grants were broken down as follows:

Quarterly allowances	211	£453,600
One-off additional support	112	£52,500
Christmas gifts	211	£24,900

In 2018/19, 70 students were supported.

Sources of information

Accounts; annual report; Charity Commission record; funder's website.

Police Care UK

 £37,000 (2017/18)

Correspondent: The Trustees, Nova Scotia House, 70 Goldsworth Road, Woking, Surrey GU21 6LQ (tel: 0300 012 0030; email: hello@policecare.org. uk)

https://www.policecare.org.uk

CC number: 1151322

Eligibility

Educational grants are available to the children of serving or veteran police officers, staff or volunteers, who are aged 15 to 18 and are in full-time education. This includes stepchildren, adopted children or grandchildren (where parental responsibility exists). Applicants must already be enrolled in, or have confirmed status of enrolment to, a higher or further education course at a recognised place of education.

Types of grant

Educational grants of up to £3,000 per year are awarded towards living costs

when studying in higher or further education.

Exclusions

Grants cannot be used for repaying debts, legal costs or medical care. The charity does not make loans, nor does it award grants in cases where state assistance or statutory services are available.

Applications

Initial enquiries can be made using the 'make a referral' form featured on the charity's website. Applicants can self-refer if they wish. Alternatively, applicants may wish to contact the charity by telephone (9am to 5pm, Monday to Friday) to begin the application process. Applications for educational grants can be sent anytime up until 31 December and payments are made in January. The bursary panel meets once each year to consider grants.

Financial information

Year end		31/03/2018
Income		£5,810,000
Total expenditure		£1,450,000

Further financial information

Grants were broken down as follows:

Maintenance grants	37	£114,200
Assistance grants	33	£100,600
Specialist equipment grants	9	£71,500
Educational bursaries	37	£37,000
Retraining grants	6	£12,900
Christmas grants	53	£6,700

Other information

The charity operates a counselling service for those struggling with mental health problems or trauma. The services encompasses a range of psychiatric techniques such as Cognitive Behavioural Therapy (CBT), guided self-help, as well as Eye Movement Desensitisation and Reprocessing (EMDR) for people experiencing post-traumatic stress disorder.

Sources of information

Accounts; annual report; Charity Commission record; funder's website.

St George's Police Children Trust

 £353,900 (2018)

Correspondent: Trust Administrator, Northern Police Convalescent Home, St Andrews, Harlow Moor Road, Harrogate, North Yorkshire HG2 0AD (tel: 01423 504448; email: enquiries@ stgeorgespolicechildrentrust.org)

www.stgeorgespolicechildrentrust. org

CC number: 1147445/SC043652

Eligibility

Children of serving, retired or deceased police officers who are in need due to life-changing circumstances such as the loss of a parent, or the parent who is a police officer being unable to work due to illness or injury sustained on or off duty. Each grant scheme has separate eligibility criteria, further details can be found on the trust's website. **Note:** usually, to be eligible, the police officer parent must have donated to the trust while serving.

Types of grant

The trust offers three grant schemes to support education:

- **Higher Education Grants:** support is given to beneficiaries who are undertaking any form of further education such as a university degree, HNC, HND or NVQ level four. Grants are available from the age of 18 for a maximum of four years or up to the age of 25
- **Ex-gratia Grant:** funding is available for trade tools, musical instruments, text books, etc.
- **School Leavers Grant:** grants of up to £500 are available for young people not attending university towards tools for apprenticeships, work uniforms and so on

Exclusions

The trust will not support people in education beyond first degree level. Grants are not made for gap-year activities. Applicants applying for a Further Education Grant after a gap-year will only be considered if a single gap period from education was no longer than 12 months. The trust does not pay allowances or grants to beneficiaries who are in work and earning money.

Applications

Application forms are available to download from the trust's website. Applications must be completed in full by a responsible adult or guardian, validated and countersigned either by a representative of the force's Police Federation office, HR/Occupational Health Department or Benevolent Fund. Applications should be submitted along with any supporting documents such as birth, death, adoption and incapacity certificates.

Financial information

Year end	31/12/2018
Income	£1,190,000
Total expenditure	£922,700

Further financial information

Note: the grant total has been estimated.

Other information

The trust offers a one week stay at their holiday home in Harrogate to all new members. The trust covers the following police forces: British Transport Police; Cheshire Constabulary; Civil Nuclear Constabulary; Cleveland Police; Cumbria Constabulary; Derbyshire Police; Durham Constabulary; Greater Manchester Police; Humberside Police; Lancashire Constabulary; Lincolnshire Police; Merseyside Police; Ministry of Defence Police North Wales; North Yorkshire Police; Northumbria Police; Nottinghamshire Police; Police Scotland; South Yorkshire; Staffordshire; West Mercia; West Yorkshire; Isle of Man.

Sources of information

Accounts; annual report; Charity Commission record; funder's website.

Religious occupations

Clergy Support Trust

 £174,800 (2018)

Correspondent: The Trustees, 1 Dean Trench Street, Westminster, London SW1P 3HB (tel: 0800 389 5192; email: grants@clergysupport.org.uk)

https://www.clergysupport.org.uk

CC number: 207736

Eligibility

Current and former Anglican clergy and ordinands, and their dependants, who are in need. Support is extended to the dependants of deceased Anglican clergy members and ordinands. Eligibility criteria varies between each grant scheme. The charity's website features an 'eligibility checker' which can be used to confirm eligibility.

Types of grant

Educational grants of up to £2,000 are awarded for academic courses or vocational training for beneficiaries who have mental, physical or learning disabilities. Training grants are also given to current and former spouses/civil partners of clergy. Grants for extra tuition fees are made to children of clergy who are aged 18 or under. Grants have been made previously for children of clergy in higher education (at £1,500 per year) but the charity's 2018 annual report states that it is in the process of phasing out this support.

Applications

Applications can be made online using a form on the charity's website. Alternatively, applicants may wish to contact the charity to request that a physical copy of the application form be sent to them by post.

Financial information

Year end	31/12/2018
Income	£4,680,000
Total expenditure	£4,000,000

Further financial information

Note: the grant total for education has been estimated. This figure also includes university maintenance grants and the charity has since begun to phase out this type of support (as stated in the annual report).

Sources of information

Accounts; annual report; Charity Commission record; funder's website.

Esdaile Trust Scheme 1968

 £9,200 (2017/18)

Correspondent: Jennifer Law, Scott-Moncrieff, Exchange Place 3, Semple Street, Edinburgh EH3 8BL (tel: 0131 473 3500; email: jennifer.law@ scott-moncrieff.com)

www.scott-moncrieff.com/services/ charities/charitable-trusts/esdaile-trust

OSCR number: SC006938

Eligibility

Daughters of ministers of the Church of Scotland, daughters of missionaries appointed or nominated by the Overseas Council of the Church of Scotland, and daughters of widowed deaconesses. Applicants must be between the ages of 12 and 25. Preference is given to families with a low income.

Types of grant

Annual grants towards general educational costs.

Applications

Application forms can be obtained from the trust's website and should be completed by a parent/guardian. Applications should be submitted to the correspondent no later than 31 May each year. Grants are distributed by early September.

Financial information

Year end	31/08/2018
Income	£39,600
Total expenditure	£39,400

Further financial information

In 2017/18 grants were made to 20 individuals for both welfare and educational purposes totalling £18,400 and ranging from £250 to £1,730. We have estimated the grant total for educational grants.

Sources of information

Accounts; annual report; funder's website; OSCR record.

Lady Hewley's Charity

£ £65,200 (2017/18)

Correspondent: Neil Blake, Clerk to the Trustees, Military House, 24 Castle Street, Chester CH1 2DS (tel: 01244 400315)

CC number: 230043

Eligibility

Support is available for students who are studying for ministries in United Reformed, Congregational and Baptist churches or 'attending certain specified colleges'.

Types of grant

One-off and recurring grants according to need.

Applications

Applications are invited through contact with respective churches at local church, regional and provincial levels. Individual applications are considered twice a year.

Financial information

Year end	05/04/2018
Income	£298,200
Total expenditure	£453,700

Other information

This charity owns and operates almshouses which are available to people belonging to the Protestant faith, aged 55 and over, who are in need.

Sources of information

Accounts; annual report; Charity Commission record.

Powis Exhibition Fund

£ £11,400 (2017/18)

Correspondent: The Trustees, The Representative Body of the Church in Wales, 2 Callaghan Square, Cardiff CF10 5BT (tel: 029 2034 8200)

CC number: 525770

Eligibility

Students or graduates of theology, who already are, or who are intending to train as ordinands in the Church in Wales. Applicants must have been born, or currently reside in Wales and have an adequate knowledge of the Welsh language.

Types of grant

Promoting the study of theology by awarding grants that are tenable at any university or theological college approved by the governors.

Applications

Application forms are available from the correspondent.

Financial information

Year end	30/06/2018
Income	£13,500
Total expenditure	£12,700

Further financial information

Full accounts were not available to view on the Charity Commission's website due to the charity's low income. We have therefore estimated the grant total based on the charity's total expenditure.

Sources of information

Charity Commission record.

Society for the Benefit of Sons and Daughters of the Clergy of the Church of Scotland

£ £8,300 (2018)

Correspondent: Jennifer Law, Scott-Moncrieff, Exchange Place, 3 Semple Street, Edinburgh EH3 8BL (email: jennifer.law@scott-moncrieff.com)

 www.scott-moncrieff.com/services/charities/charitable-trusts/society-for-the-benefit-of-sons-and-daughters

OSCR number: SC008760

Eligibility

Children of ministers of the Church of Scotland aged between 12 and 25. Preference is given to low-income families.

Types of grant

Grants are awarded towards general educational purposes, and are made for one year only but renewals may be granted following a fresh application.

Applications

Application forms can be downloaded from the Scott-Moncrieff website and should be posted to the correspondent. Applications should provide full details of the family income and need, and should be submitted by a parent/guardian before 31 May each year. Grants are distributed by early September.

Financial information

Year end	31/12/2018
Income	£46,500
Total expenditure	£36,500

Further financial information

General grants were awarded to 12 individuals for both welfare and educational purposes. We have estimated the grant total for educational purposes.

Sources of information

Accounts; annual report; funder's website; OSCR record.

Sola Trust

£ £425,200 (2017/18)

Correspondent: The Trustees, Green End Barn, Wood End Green, Henham, Bishop's Stortford CM22 6AY (tel: 01279 850819; email: admin@solatrust.org.uk)

 www.solatrust.org.uk

CC number: 1062739

Eligibility

Individuals training for full-time Christian work, either at a theological college or at a church, as well as to those already involved in full-time ministry.

Types of grant

Grants are available to support those undertaking education and training, whether at a Theological college or apprentice style at a church.

Exclusions

The trust generally will not provide support beyond one year and aims to avoid being the sole source of funding for any applicant.

Applications

Apply in writing to the correspondent. Applications can be submitted at any time during the year. The trust states it prefers to receive applications from those who have already sought help from family, friends, churches, other trusts and personal savings. Detailed guidelines and advice for completing the application can be found on the trust's website. References will be required.

Financial information

Year end	31/03/2018
Income	£820,400
Total expenditure	£808,000

Further financial information

In 2017/18 the trust awarded five grants to PhD students totalling £26,800, and 121 grants totalling £398,400 for individuals undertaking theological and ministry training. The trust also awarded one grant towards relief of poverty totalling £4,700.

Other information

The trust also supports churches and the allocation of trained gospel workers to new geographical areas.

Sources of information

Accounts; annual report; Charity Commission record; funder's website.

Retail

The George Drexler Foundation

 £87,700 (2016/17)

Correspondent: The Trustees, 35–43 Lincolns Inn Fields, London WC2A 3PE (tel: 020 7869 6086; email: info@georgedrexler.org.uk)

www.georgedrexler.org.uk

CC number: 313278

Eligibility

Grants are made to former employees of the Ofrex group and their families and are awarded for undergraduate and postgraduate study in all fields. The foundation's website states; 'It is a strict requirement of the Foundation that *a personal or family link with commerce is established for an application to be considered.* To qualify either the applicant, the applicant's parents or grandparents must have worked in or owned a commercial business.' This does not include professional people i.e. doctors, accountants, architects, solicitors, etc. If applicants are studying medicine or music at: University College London, University of Nottingham, University of Liverpool, Peninsula College of Medicine and Dentistry, Royal College of Music, Royal Academy of Music, Guildhall School of Music and Drama or The Purcell School, the foundation has separate schemes with them so contact the school directly.

Types of grant

Annual bursaries, between £500 and £2,000, to relieve financial hardship while studying.

Exclusions

Support is not given for:
- Overseas students
- Volunteering
- Part-time study
- Study abroad
- Medical electives
- Gap-year projects
- Non-UK citizens

Applications

Initial enquiries can be submitted via the contact form on the foundation's website.

The application guidelines state: 'Bursaries are made annually, with applications considered by the Trustees in May each year. Completed applications must be submitted online via the Foundation's website by 31 March. All applicants will be notified of the outcome by early June. We no longer accept applications by email or post.' The application requires a personal statement which should be no longer than one side of A4 to be submitted and an academic reference.

Financial information

Year end	30/06/2017
Income	£279,000
Total expenditure	£371,400

Other information

The foundation also makes grants to the eight educational organisations listed above.

Sources of information

Accounts; annual report; Charity Commission record; guidelines for applicants; funder's website.

The Ruby and Will George Trust

 £97,200 (2017/18)

Correspondent: The Trustees, 125 Cloverfield, West Allotment, Newcastle upon Tyne, Tyne and Wear NE27 0BE (tel: 0191 266 4527; email: admin@rwgt.co.uk)

www.rwgt.co.uk

CC number: 264042

Eligibility

People who have a connection to commerce. Applicants themselves could be/have been employed in commerce. Their dependants, wider family (grandparents, aunties and uncles) and widows also qualify for a connection. Preference is given to applicants from north east England where the charity has its roots.

Types of grant

Grants for educational purposes, predominantly to those in higher education.

Applications

Applications can be made through the trust's website. Applicants will need to provide a brief explanation of their commerce connection and a recent payslip or a letter from an employer. The trustees meet four times a year to consider applications.

Financial information

Year end	05/04/2018
Income	£131,900
Total expenditure	£180,100

Further financial information

Grants were made to 27 individuals in 2017/18.

Sources of information

Accounts; annual report; Charity Commission record; funder's website.

Leverhulme Trade Charities Trust

 £1,500,000 (2018)

Correspondent: Katrina Moore, 1 Pemberton Row, London EC4A 3BG (tel: 020 7042 9885; email: info@ leverhulme-trade.org.uk)

www.leverhulme-trade.org.uk

CC number: 1159171

Eligibility

Students (undergraduate or postgraduate) at a recognised UK university who are in need and whose parent or spouse has worked as a commercial traveller, grocer or pharmacist for at least five years, and is either still currently working in one of these occupations, or has retired within the last ten years. Individuals are still eligible if their parent/spouse is unemployed (or deceased) but who fell within one of the three categories when the employment ceased (or at the time of death).

Types of grant

One-off or recurrent grants of up to £3,000 a year to full-time undergraduate students and of up to £5,000 a year to postgraduate students. Support is given towards general educational needs, including tuition and examination fees, living expenses, books, equipment, travel costs and accommodation. Awards are paid to the applicant's university.

Exclusions

The trust is not able to award grants for any previous years of study.

Applications

Applications for undergraduate funding can be made on the trust's website, where further guidance is also provided. There are two funding rounds each year – one which opens in August and closes in November, and one which opens in January and closes in March (refer to the website for exact dates). Applications for postgraduate funding are also made online – applications open in August and close in October. The trust aims to decide on applications within four to six weeks of the closing date. The trust states that if there are a large number of applications, awards may be reduced accordingly.

Financial information

Year end	31/12/2018
Income	£3,100,000
Total expenditure	£1,945,000

Further financial information

Grants totalling £1,157,000 were awarded as undergraduate bursaries and £348,000 as postgraduate bursaries. We were unable to determine the amount given in welfare grants.

Other information

The Leverhulme Trust (Charity Commission no. 1159154) is a sister charity which provides grants for researchers at any point in their careers.

Sources of information

Accounts; annual report; Charity Commission record; funder's website.

Retail Trust

Correspondent: The Trustees, Marshall Hall, Marshall Estate, Hammers Lane, London NW7 4DQ (tel: 0808 801 0808; email: helpline@retailtrust.org.uk)

 www.retailtrust.org.uk

CC number: 1090136

Eligibility

People in need who have worked in retail or in manufacturing, wholesale or distribution for the supply of retail businesses, and their dependants. To be eligible for support, applicants must have worked in retail for a particular amount of time, the length of which varies depending on the applicant's employment situation (e.g. if they are currently employed in retail, unemployed, or retired). See the trust's website for more information.

Types of grant

Education grants can cover university costs such as course fees and accommodation. The trust also offers a number of scholarships each year.

Exclusions

No grants are awarded for private medical treatment, legal fees, most personal debts or for items purchased prior to the application.

Applications

Applications can be made via the online grant portal. The application requirements are quite specific and potential applicants should read the information provided by the trust on its website before making an application.

Financial information

Year end	30/04/2018
Income	£8,720,000
Total expenditure	£8,080,000

Further financial information

Grants to individuals totalled £410,200. We were unable to determine the split between welfare and education grants.

Other information

Retail Trust provides free financial, legal, emotional, career and redundancy advice and support services for people who have been involved in retail through

'retailHUB'. More information on how to access these services is available from the website or through the trust's confidential helpline (0808 801 0808). The trust also operates Cottage Homes, which has five retirement estates across the UK (in London, Derby, Glasgow, Liverpool and Salford), providing sheltered and extra-care accommodation for people who have retired from the retail sector. More information is available from the trust's website.

Sources of information

Accounts; annual report; Charity Commission record; funder's website.

The Royal Pinner School Foundation

 £112,000 (2018/19)

Correspondent: David Crawford, Company Secretary, 110 Old Brompton Road, South Kensington, London SW7 3RB (tel: 020 7373 6168; email: admin@royalpinner.co.uk)

 www.royalpinner.co.uk

CC number: 1128414

Eligibility

Children of commercial travellers, travelling sales and technical representatives and manufacturer's agents, where the family has experienced adversity or hardship. Preference is given to individuals under the age of 25 and those whose parents are deceased.

Types of grant

One-off or recurrent grants are available to students at university and further/higher education colleges. Support is given in the form of bursaries, maintenance allowances, grants towards accommodation and educational travel in the UK or abroad, and financial assistance to support the study of music and the arts. The foundation will support a wide range of subjects.

Applications

Apply in writing to the correspondent. The foundation may arrange a home visit as part of the assessment process. The grants committee meets about five times a year to consider applications.

Financial information

Year end	31/03/2019
Income	£793,400
Total expenditure	£605,200

Further financial information

In 2018/19 grants to 150 individuals totalled £454,900, some beneficiaries received grants in more than one category. This is broken down as follows:

Children at day and boarding schools	95	£274,600
Students at universities and colleges of further and higher education	55	£112,000
Special education needs, dance, drama, travel and clothing grants	33	£68,200

Other information

The foundation also offers pastoral support through home visits and other contact with the families it supports. Over a third of its beneficiaries have lost a parent or have a parent with a long-term illness.

Sources of information

Accounts; annual report; Charity Commission record; funder's website.

Science

The Royal Society of Chemistry – Chemists' Community Fund

£238,000 (2018)

Correspondent: Chemists' Community Fund Team, Thomas Graham House, Science Park, Milton Road, Cambridge CB4 0WF (tel: 01223 432227; email: contact form on the website)

www.rsc.org/membership-and-community/chemists-community-fund

CC number: 207890

Eligibility

Current members of the society who have been a member for a minimum of three consecutive years. Former members of the society are also eligible for support, provided they have resigned after ten years of membership rather than allowing their membership to lapse. Partners and other dependants of deceased members of the society can apply for support irrespective of membership length. There are exceptions to these criteria (particularly for students and recent graduates) so it is advised that prospective applicants contact the charity to confirm their eligibility.

Types of grant

Students, apprentices and those undertaking vocational training are eligible for **student hardship grants**. **Retraining grants** are available to members who wish to enhance their employment prospects. Grants can be used to help pay for course fees and other associated costs such as books and equipment. **Breathing Space** grants are awarded to recent graduates who are looking for their first jobs. One-off grants are made to help with general living costs.

Applications

Initial enquiries should be made by contacting the charity. If deemed eligible, the charity will then send the applicant an application form. Completed forms can be sent by post or email. The committee meets quarterly to consider grant applications but if a request is deemed urgent, the committee can make decisions between meetings.

Financial information

Year end	31/12/2018
Income	£63,590,000
Total expenditure	£59,650,000

Other information

The charity provides a variety of advice and guidance services and through its partnerships with accredited counsellors, can make referrals for fast-track access to face-to-face and telephone counselling services. The charity also has a partnership with the National Autistic Society to provide its members with autism with specialist support, including guidance on how to disclose an autism diagnosis at work and tips for interacting with colleagues. The charity's careers team can offer confidential consultations and coaching on all aspects of job seeking, professional development and making difficult career decisions.

Sources of information

Accounts; annual report; Charity Commission record; funder's website.

The Worshipful Company of Scientific Instrument Makers

 £48,200 (2017/18)

Correspondent: Clerk, Glaziers Hall, 9 Montague Close, London SE1 9DD (tel: 020 7407 4832; email: theclerk@ wcsim.co.uk)

 www.wcsim.co.uk

CC number: 221332

Eligibility

Schoolchildren, sixth formers, undergraduates and postgraduates with outstanding ability in science and mathematics, and a creative and practical interest in branches of engineering connected with instrumentation and measurement.

Types of grant

Postgraduate scholarships of £2,000 are available for 'exciting research and design' and two postdoctoral awards of £5,000 support high flying researchers. Travel grants are also available for any apprentices, scholars or freemen wishing

to attend a scientific conference to present a paper.

Applications

Apply in writing to the correspondent.

Financial information

Year end	30/09/2018
Income	£112,100
Total expenditure	£106,300

Sources of information

Accounts; annual report; Charity Commission record; funder's website.

Service industry

The Worshipful Company of Launderers Benevolent Trust Fund

 £2,000 (2017/18)

Correspondent: David Hart, Benevolent Fund Chair, Launderers Hall, 9 Montague Close, London Bridge, London SE1 9DD (tel: 020 7378 1430; email: treasurer@launderers.co.uk)

 www.launderers.co.uk

CC number: 262750

Eligibility

Educational grants are made to apprentices who are preparing to enter the laundry industry.

Types of grant

One-off grants according to need.

Applications

Apply in writing to the correspondent.

Financial information

Year end	31/03/2018
Income	£67,240
Total expenditure	£40,820

Further financial information

The fund awarded £2,200 in grants to individuals and £4,000 to recipients of the Travelling Scholarship, which funds a trip to Girbau Experience Centre in Barcelona. The fund awarded a further £2,000 under the TSA Apprenticeship Scheme.

Other information

A large portion of the fund's charitable spending is awarded to other charities local to the City of London. The fund also makes grants to national charities, such as the RNLI and Samaritans.

Sources of information

Accounts; annual report; Charity Commission record; funder's website.

Skilled crafts and trades

Queen Elizabeth Scholarship Trust Ltd

 £317,100 (2017)

Correspondent: Deborah Pocock, Executive Director, 1 Buckingham Place, London SW1E 6HR (tel: 020 7798 1535; email: info@qest.org.uk)

 www.qest.org.uk

CC number: 1152032

Eligibility

Scholarships are available to UK residents over the age of 17 who are already skilled in their craft but are wishing to improve. Apprenticeships are available to individuals aged 17 and over (with no upper age limit) who are permanently living and working in the UK, and are already learning craft skills from a company or a master craftsperson. In particular, the trust is looking to support those who are intending to become an established craftsperson contributing to the British craft sector. The trust encourages applications from a broad range of crafts including contemporary and innovative applications of traditional craft techniques.

Types of grant

Scholarships of up to £18,000 are awarded to fund traditional college courses, vocational training or one to one training with a master craftsperson. Financial assistance can be given towards anything directly related to training such as travel, equipment, materials, accommodation, living expenses. In addition the apprenticeship programme offers up to £6,000 a year for a maximum of three years which will contribute to the apprentice's salary.

Exclusions

The trust will not award funding to purposes not related to craft, retrospective applications, business start-ups or loss of income.

Applications

Applications for scholarships and apprenticeships usually open in January and again in July. Application forms will be made available on the trust's website, along with guidance on how to answer each section of the application. The application process is competitive and it is advised that applicants make sure their applications are clear and concise. The trust will contact applicants approximately two months after applications close to inform them of the outcome.

Financial information

Year end	31/12/2017
Income	£922,000
Total expenditure	£773,800

Further financial information

In 2017, a total of £317,100 was awarded in grants to individuals. This can be broken down as: £151,700 towards scholarships and £165,500 towards apprenticeships.

Other information

Grants are also awarded to educational institutions.

Sources of information

Accounts; annual report; Charity Commission record; funder's website.

The Fashion and Textile Children's Trust

Correspondent: Grants Team, Victoria Charity Centre, 11 Belgrave Road, London SW1V 1RB (tel: 0300 123 9002; email: grants@ftct.org.uk)

 www.ftct.org.uk

CC number: 257136

Eligibility

Children and young people under 18 whose parents or full-time carer work or have worked in the UK fashion and textile retailing and manufacturing industry for at least one year (within the last nine years).

Types of grant

The trust makes grants for education support (for children with a disability or additional needs).

Applications

In the first instance, contact the trust by telephone or by using the online enquiry form to discuss the child's needs. If the trust feels that it may be able to assist, an application form will be sent by post or email. Completed forms must be returned to the trust along with the required supporting documents.

Financial information

Year end	30/06/2018
Income	£422,300
Total expenditure	£776,700

Further financial information

Grants were awarded to support 680 children: 643 were new and 37 were ongoing. We were unable to determine a grant total solely for educational grants.

Sources of information

Accounts; annual report; Charity Commission record; funder's website.

The Doctor Dorothy Jordan Lloyd Memorial Fund

 £900 (2017/18)

Correspondent: Kerry Senior, UK Leather Federation, Leather Trade House, Kings Park Road, Northampton, Northamptonshire NN3 6JD (tel: 01604 679955; email: info@uklf.org)

 https://leatheruk.org

CC number: 313933

Eligibility

People working in the leather industry or who are studying leather related subjects.

Types of grant

Grants are available for travel overseas to study leather science and technology or work on related projects.

Applications

Apply in writing to the correspondent.

Financial information

Year end	30/09/2018
Income	£6,400
Total expenditure	£1,000

Further financial information

Full accounts were not available to view on the Charity Commission's website due to the charity's low income. We have therefore estimated the grant total based on the charity's total expenditure.

Other information

The charity's website has links to other grants and training opportunities in the leather industry.

Sources of information

Charity Commission record; funder's website.

The Worshipful Company of Plumbers' Charitable and Educational Trust

 £1,400 (2017/18)

Correspondent: The Clerk, Carpenters' Hall, 1 Throgmorton Avenue, London EC2N 2JJ (tel: 020 7628 8880; email: clerk@plumberscompany.org.uk)

 www.plumberscompany.org.uk

CC number: 800043

Eligibility

Student plumbers who are enrolled on to NVQ Level 3 MES (Plumbing) or equivalent.

Types of grant

Bursaries of up to £1,000 are awarded towards the costs of tools and equipment.

Exclusions

Bursaries cannot be used to offset course fees provided by an employer.

Applications

Application forms can be downloaded from the trust's website. Students must obtain a reference from their lecturer or employer as well as proof of registration on NVQ Level 3 MES (Plumbing) or equivalent.

Financial information

Year end	29/09/2018
Income	£80,200
Total expenditure	£42,000

Further financial information

In 2017/18 the trust awarded £1,400 in the form of bursaries.

Other information

The trust also supports organisations and provides certificates and awards to high achieving plumbers. The trust supports projects both in the UK and financially developing countries that are focused on providing clean water, public health, sanitation and community welfare.

Sources of information

Accounts; annual report; Charity Commission record; funder's website.

Sports

Athletics for the Young

 £13,700 (2017/18)

Correspondent: Alan Barlow, Trustee, 12 Redcar Close, Hazel Grove, Stockport, Cheshire SK7 4SQ (tel: 0161 483 9330; email: runalan55@hotmail.com)

 www.englandathletics.org

CC number: 1004448

Eligibility

Young people under the age of 23 who are in full-time education, active in athletics and eligible to compete for England.

Types of grant

One-off educational grants (usually between £50 and £200) towards athletic pursuits, including equipment and travel expenses.

Exclusions

People already receiving funding from other sources are not normally supported.

Applications

Application forms can be downloaded from the England Athletics website and should be returned via post. The deadline for applications is usually mid-February but check the website for exact dates. Note that applications should be handwritten and provide a reference.

Financial information

Year end	30/09/2018
Income	£7,100
Total expenditure	£24,600

Further financial information

Full accounts were not available to view on the Charity Commission's website due to the charity's low income. We have therefore estimated the grant total based on the charity's total expenditure.

Other information

Grants can also be made to organisations supporting young athletes.

Sources of information

Charity Commission record; funder's website.

National Trainers' Federation (NTF) Charitable Trust

 £22,200 (2018)

Correspondent: Welfare Officers, The Racing Centre, Fred Archer Way, Newmarket, Suffolk CB8 8EQ (tel: 0800 630 0443; email: info@racingwelfare.co.uk)

https://racingwelfare.co.uk

CC number: 1004308

Eligibility

Individuals who are engaged, or are intending to be engaged, in the UK thoroughbred horseracing and breeding industry.

Types of grant

Grants to support individuals attending further education and retraining courses.

Applications

Contact a racing welfare officer, using the contact details provided, to discuss making an application.

Financial information

Year end	31/12/2018
Income	£26,200
Total expenditure	£94,400

Further financial information

Grants were awarded to 17 individuals during 2018.

Other information

The trust is administered by Racing Welfare on behalf of the trustees. The trust also makes grants to the National Trainers Federation who offer different awards and scholarships. See its website for details (www.racehorsetrainers.org)

Sources of information

Accounts; annual report; Charity Commission record; funder's website.

The Professional Footballers' Association Charity

 £423,900 (2017/18)

Correspondent: The Trustees, 20 Oxford Court, Bishopsgate, Manchester M2 3WQ (tel: 0161 236 0575; email: info@thepfa.co.uk)

https://www.thepfa.com/charity

CC number: 1150458

Eligibility

Former professional footballers, current and former trainee footballers and young people registered with the professional football academies associated with a club (or centres of excellence associated with a club) wishing to pursue a career as a professional footballer.

Types of grant

Standard grants are made for all academic courses that carry a nationally recognised qualification. Grants are awarded towards course fees (usually 50% up to a maximum of £1,500 per year). University bursaries are also available.

Applications

Application forms are available to download from the funder's website. Full guidance notes can also be found on the website. Completed forms should be sent to PFA Education Department, 11 Oxford Court, Bishopsgate, Manchester, M2 3WQ.

Financial information

Year end	30/06/2018
Income	£26,390,000
Total expenditure	£24,550,000

Further financial information

During 2017/18, the charity awarded 393 welfare grants and 1,440 educational/vocational grants. Note: The grant total for education has been estimated.

Other information

The charity operates a 24/7 counselling helpline for current and former players, and concerned family/friends, to seek confidential advice and support. Contact the helpline on 07500 000 777. The charity also offers subsidised coaching courses (FA Level 2 and UEFA B qualifications) to current and former footballers. Grants are also made to organisations.

Sources of information

Accounts; annual report; Charity Commission record; funder's website.

The RFL Benevolent Fund (Try Assist)

 £132,100 (2018)

Correspondent: The Trustees, Red Hall, Red Hall Lane, Leeds, West Yorkshire LS17 8NB (tel: 0330 111 1113; email: info@tryassist.co.uk)

www.rflbenevolentfund.co.uk

CC number: 1109858

Eligibility

People who play or assist, or have played/assisted, in the game of Rugby League in the UK (or for a team affiliated to an association primarily based in the UK) who have sustained a serious/life-changing injury while engaging in the sport. Support is also extended to the dependants of such people.

Types of grant

Educational grants are available to support the education or re-training of beneficiaries.

Applications

Initial enquiries should be made by contacting the charity.

Financial information

Year end	31/12/2018
Income	£401,300
Total expenditure	£291,900

Further financial information

Note: the grant total has been estimated.

Sources of information

Accounts; annual report; Charity Commission record; funder's website.

Transport and travel

The Air Pilots Benevolent Fund

 £42,100 (2017/18)

Correspondent: Sqn Ldr C. J. Ford, Almoner, The Honourable Company of Air Pilots, Dowgate Hill House, 14–16 Dowgate Hill, London EC4R 2SU (tel: 01276 47050; email: office@airpilots. org)

www.airpilots.org

CC number: 212952

Eligibility

Members of The Honourable Company of Air Pilots and those who have been engaged professionally as air pilots, or air navigators in commercial aviation and their dependants. People who want to become pilots or wish to gain further qualifications in the aviation industry are supported by The Honourable Company of Air Pilots.

Types of grant

Scholarships and bursaries, including those to flying instructors. Academic bursaries awarded at City University to students. Awards towards the general educational needs of the dependants of aviators.

Applications

Apply in writing to the correspondent.

Financial information

Year end	30/09/2018
Income	£50,300
Total expenditure	£57,700

Other information

The charity was previously called The Guild of Air Pilots Benevolent Fund and provides both educational and welfare support. The fund is administered by The Honourable Company of Air Pilots which is also managing Air Safety Trust and Air Pilots Trust (see the separate record below).

Sources of information

Accounts; annual report; Charity Commission record; funder's website.

Air Pilots Trust

 £90,000 (2017/18)

Correspondent: Paul Tacon, Clerk, Air Pilots House, 52a Borough High Street, Gray's Inn, London SE1 1XN (tel: 020 7404 4032; email: office@airpilots.org)

https://www.airpilots.org

CC number: 313606

Eligibility

British, Irish or Commonwealth citizens who are or intend to be engaged professionally as air pilots or navigators in commercial aviation.

Types of grant

Scholarships and bursaries to assist further education and training within aviation.

Applications

Further information and application forms can be requested from the correspondent via email.

Financial information

Year end	30/09/2018
Income	£144,700
Total expenditure	£125,000

Further financial information

In 2017/18 the trust awarded a total of £90,000 as scholarships and bursaries for educational purposes. The table shows the full breakdown of awards:

Scholarships	£80,600
Academic bursaries	£9,000
Flying bursaries	£430

Other information

The trust makes awards to contribute to the establishment and maintenance of a technical library and information centre as well as the provision of lectures related to aviation . The trust also promotes the study and research into problems with aviation and flight. This trust is administered by the Honourable Company of Air Pilots.

Sources of information

Accounts; annual report; Charity Commission record; funder's website.

Go Make it Happen: a Project in Memory of Sam Harding

 £3,100 (2017/18)

Correspondent: Keith Harding, 39–40 Plumstead Green, Plumstead, Norfolk NR11 7LJ (tel: 01263 570246; email: keithhard@hotmail.co.uk)

gmih.co.uk/blog/?LMCL=rreRiw

CC number: 1145369

Eligibility

People between the ages of 18 and 30 who want to build a career in the tourism and travel industry. The charity has a particular, but not exclusive, focus on young people who have not necessarily followed a 'conventional' academic route through university.

Types of grant

Funding is available for training courses, travel expenses and other opportunities in the UK and overseas. Previous examples include: support for skills-based qualifications, London taxi driver qualification and bursaries for overseas work.

Applications

Application forms can be downloaded from the charity's website. Applicants may be required to attend an interview.

Financial information

Year end	30/03/2018
Income	£6,100
Total expenditure	£6,900

Further financial information

Full accounts were not available to view on the Charity Commission's website due to the charity's low income. We have therefore estimated the grant total based on the charity's total expenditure.

Other information

This charity campaigns for cycling safety and driver awareness in memory of Sam's tragic death at the age of 25. It also provides information and advice on opportunities for working overseas and in travel or tourism generally (both in the UK and abroad).

Sources of information

Charity Commission record; funder's website.

Voluntary sector

Diamond Education Grant (DEG)

 £10,100 (2017/18)

Correspondent: The Trustees, Second Floor, Beckwith House, 1 Wellington Road North, Stockport, Cheshire SK4 1AF (tel: 0161 480 7686; email: hq@ sigbi.org)

sigbi.org/our-charities/deg

CC number: 1139668

Eligibility

Women who are permanently resident in one of the countries of the Federation of Soroptimist International Great Britain and Ireland. Applicants should be intending to update their skills after an employment break, or obtain new skills to re-enter the employment market and improve their opportunities of employment/promotion.

Types of grant

Grants are awarded towards course fees, books or equipment.

Exclusions

Grants will not support living expenses.

Applications

Application forms will be made available from the charity's website once the grant scheme is open for submissions, usually in November each year for courses starting the following September. Consult the website for current deadlines.

Financial information

Year end	31/03/2018
Income	£16,900
Total expenditure	£11,200

Further financial information

Full accounts were not available to view on the Charity Commission's website due to the charity's low income. We have therefore estimated the grant total based on the charity's total expenditure.

Sources of information

Charity Commission record; funder's website.

WRVS Benevolent Trust

 £7,500 (2017)

Correspondent: John Fallon, Grants Manager, WRVS Benevolent Trust, PO Box 769, Chesterfield, Derbyshire S40 9NY (tel: 07894 060517; email: grants@wrvsbt.org.uk or enquiry@wrvsbt.org.uk)

www.wrvsbt.org.uk

CC number: 261931

Eligibility

People in need who have volunteered or worked for the WVS, WRVS or Royal Voluntary Service.

The trust runs a bursary scheme for current or past Women's Royal Voluntary Service (WRVS) volunteers between the ages of 16 and 25 taking part in events or opportunities which will benefit their personal development and future career.

Types of grant

Bursaries of up to £2,000 to help applicants take part in an unpaid event or opportunity which will assist their career development. Recent grants have been made to allow applicants to undertake medical placements, distance learning programmes for further education, and residential summer courses as part of their university studies.

Applications

Applications should be made on a form available to download from the trust's website, and are considered throughout the year. Applications can be made directly by the individual, or by a friend or family member on their behalf. Further information can be found on the trust's website.

Financial information

Year end	31/12/2017
Income	£56,300
Total expenditure	£39,100

Further financial information

In 2017, the trustees awarded five youth bursaries totalling £7,500. Further grants were also awarded for welfare purposes.

Sources of information

Accounts; annual report; Charity Commission record; funder's website.

Local charities

This section lists local charities that award grants to individuals for educational purposes. The information in the records applies, in the majority of cases, only to educational grants and concentrates on what the charity actually does rather than on what its governing document allows it to do.

Regional classification

We have divided the UK into 12 geographical areas, as numbered on the map on page 110. Scotland, Wales and England have been divided into unitary or local authorities, in some cases grouped in counties or regions. On page 111 you can find the list of unitary or local authorities within each county or area. (Please note: not all of these unitary authorities have a grant-making charity included in this guide.)

Northern Ireland

Unfortunately, the section for Northern Ireland remains limited, as very little information is available at present on charities based there. It is estimated that there are between 7,000 and 12,000 charities operating in Northern Ireland. The Charity Commission for Northern Ireland expects the completion of the registration process to take several years. In the meantime, up-to-date information on the progress of registration can be found on the Charity Commission for Northern Ireland's website: www.charity commissionni.org.uk.

Based on limited information available, the Northern Ireland section has been sub-divided into: general charities operating throughout Northern Ireland; charities operating in Belfast; and charities covering a specific county.

Within the other sections, charities are ordered as follows:

Scotland

- First, the charities which apply to the whole of Scotland, or at least two areas in Scotland, are listed.
- Second, Scotland is further divided into electoral board areas, and then again into council areas.
- Should an entry apply to at least two council areas, it will appear in the appropriate electoral board section.

Wales

- First, Wales is sub-divided into four regions. The records which apply to the whole region, or to at least two local government areas within it, appear first.
- Second, the remaining charities are listed under the relevant local government division.

England

- First, England is divided into nine regions. The records which apply to the whole region, or to at least two counties within it, appear first.
- Second, the regions are divided into counties.
- The counties are sub-divided into relevant local government areas.

Greater London

- First, the charities which apply to the whole of Greater London, or to at least two boroughs are listed.
- The charities serving London are further sub-divided into the relevant boroughs.

Within each geographical category, the charities are listed alphabetically.

To make sure you identify every relevant local charity, look at the records in each relevant category in the following order:

1. Unitary or local authority (for England, Scotland and Wales) or borough (for Greater London)
2. County (for England)
3. Region (for England, Wales and, in some cases, Scotland)
4. Country (for Northern Ireland, Scotland and Wales)

Having found grant-makers covering your area, please read any other eligibility requirements carefully. While some charities can and do give grants for any need for people in their area of benefit, most have other, more specific criteria which potential applicants must meet in order to be eligible.

Geographical areas

1. Northern Ireland 113

General 113

Belfast City 114

County Fermanagh 114

2. Scotland 115

General 115

Ayrshire and Arran 116

North Ayrshire; South Ayrshire

Central Scotland 117

Falkirk; Stirling

Dumfries and Galloway 118

Dunbartonshire and Argyll 119

Bute

Glasgow 120

Grampian 120

Aberdeenshire; Moray

Highlands and Western Isles (Na h-Eileanan Siar) 122

Highland; Na h-Eileanan Siar (Western Isles)

Lothian 123

City of Edinburgh; East Lothian; West Lothian

Scottish Borders 125

Tayside 125

Angus; Dundee; Perth and Kinross

3. Wales 127

Mid and West Wales 127

Pembrokeshire; Powys

North Wales 128

North Wales – Y Gogledd 129

Isle of Anglesey – Ynys Mon; Denbighshire – Sir Ddinbych; Flintshire – Sir Y Fflint; Gwynedd; Wrexham County – Wrecsam

South Wales 131

Caerphilly County – Caerffili; Cardiff City and County – Caerdydd; Monmouthshire – Sir Fynwy; Monmouthshire – Sir Fynwy; Neath Port Talbot County – Castell-nedd Port Talbot; Rhondda

Cynon Taff; Vale of Glamorgan – Bro Morgannwg

4. East Midlands 135

Derbyshire 135

Derby; Erewash; High Peak; South Derbyshire

Leicestershire 137

Charnwood; Hinckley and Bosworth; North West Leicestershire; Oadby and Wigston

Lincolnshire 140

Boston; East Lindsey; Lincoln; North Kesteven; South Holland; South Kesteven; West Lindsey

Northamptonshire 145

Daventry; Kettering; Northampton; South Northamptonshire

Nottinghamshire 148

Newark and Sherwood; Nottingham

Rutland 150

5. West Midlands Region 151

General 151

Herefordshire 153

Shropshire 154

Telford and Wrekin

Staffordshire 156

East Staffordshire; Stafford; Tamworth

Warwickshire 157

North Warwickshire; Nuneaton and Bedworth; Rugby; Stratford; Warwick

West Midlands Metropolitan Area 162

Birmingham; Coventry; Dudley; Sandwell; Walsall

Worcestershire 166

Bromsgrove; Malvern Hills; Redditch; Wychavon; Wyre Forest

6. East of England 171

General 171

Bedfordshire 172

Bedford; Central Bedfordshire

Cambridgeshire 174

East Cambridgeshire; Fenland; Huntingdonshire; South Cambridgeshire

Essex 175

Basildon; Chelmsford; Colchester; Epping Forest; Harlow; Rochford

Hertfordshire 179

Broxbourne; East Hertfordshire; North Hertfordshire; St Albans

Norfolk 182

Breckland; Kings Lynn and West Norfolk; Norwich; South Norfolk

Suffolk 187

Babergh; East Suffolk; Ipswich; Mid Suffolk; West Suffolk

7. Greater London 193

General 193

Barnet 196

Bromley 196

Camden 196

City of London 197

City of Westminster 198

Croydon 199

Ealing 199

Enfield 200

Greenwich 200

Hammersmith and Fulham 201

Haringey 201

Hillingdon 202

Islington 202

Kensington and Chelsea 202

Lambeth 203

Lewisham 204

Richmond upon Thames 204

Southwark 206

Waltham Forest 207

Wandsworth 208

8. North East 209

General 209

County Durham 210

Hartlepool

Northumberland 212

Tyne and Wear 213

Newcastle upon Tyne; South Tyneside; Sunderland

9. North West 215

General 215

Cheshire 216

Cheshire East; Cheshire West and Chester

Cumbria 217

Carlisle; South Lakeland

Greater Manchester 220

Bolton; Manchester; Rochdale; Salford; Stockport; Wigan

Lancashire 223

Blackburn with Darwen; Burnley; Lancaster; Preston; West Lancashire

Merseyside 225

Liverpool

10. South East 229

General 229

Berkshire 230

Reading; Windsor and Maidenhead

Buckinghamshire 231

Aylesbury Vale; Milton Keynes

East Sussex 234

Brighton and Hove; Hastings; Wealdon

Hampshire 236

Basingstoke and Deane; East Hampshire; Fareham; Gosport; New Forest; Winchester

Kent 239

Canterbury; Maidstone; Medway; Swale

Oxfordshire 242

Cherwell; Oxford; Vale of White Horse; West Oxfordshire

Surrey 245

Epsom and Ewell; Guildford; Mole Valley; Reigate and Banstead; Waverley

West Sussex 247

Arun

11. South West 249

General 249

Bristol 251

Cornwall 252

Devon 252

Mid Devon; North Devon; Plymouth; South Hams; Torridge; West Devon

Dorset 257

Bournemouth, Christchurch and Poole

Gloucestershire 260

Cheltenham; Cotswold; South Gloucestershire; Stroud

Somerset 262

Bath and North East Somerset; Mendip; North Somerset; South Somerset

Wiltshire 264

12. Yorkshire and the Humber 267

General 267

East Riding of Yorkshire 267

Kingston

Lincolnshire (formerly part of Humberside) 271

North Lincolnshire

North Yorkshire 272

Harrogate; Ryedale; York

South Yorkshire 275

Doncaster; Sheffield

West Yorkshire 276

Calderdale; Kirklees; Leeds; Wakefield

Northern Ireland

General

All Ireland Scholarships

Correspondent: The Administrator, Suite 25, The Mall, Beacon Court, Sandyford, Dublin D18 (tel: 01 295 3519; email: info@allirelandscholarships.com)

 https://www.allirelandscholarships.com

Eligibility

Talented students from across Ireland who are about to study a full-time undergraduate degree.

Applicants in the Republic of Ireland must:
- Attend a non-fee paying secondary school
- Be exempt from paying the Leaving Certificate Fee
- Not have already attempted/completed the Leaving Certificate
- Not hold another scholarship (as outlined in the Department of Education and Skills website)

Applicants in Northern Ireland must:
- Attend a grant-aided post-primary school or further education college
- Be in receipt of the Education Maintenance Allowance
- Not hold another scholarship (as outlined on the Northern Ireland Direct website)

Types of grant

Scholarships of €6,750 per year (one instalment of €1,500 followed by seven monthly instalments of €750) are made to help with costs associated with undergraduate study.

Exclusions

The organisation does not support master's degrees or postgraduate study. Payments will not be made during a year out from study, but are reinstated upon return to university. Once a scholarship is granted, scholars can defer their place at university for one year but no payments will be made during the period of deferral.

Applications

Contact the organisation for information on how to apply.

Further financial information

The organisation's website states that 125 scholarships were awarded in 2019.

Sources of information

Funder's website.

Belfast Association for the Blind

Correspondent: Ronnie Gillespie, Trustee, 30 Glenwell Crescent, Newtownabbey, County Antrim BT36 7TF (tel: 028 9083 6407; email: patrongillespie@yahoo.co.uk)

CC number: 106091

Eligibility

People who are registered blind in Northern Ireland.

Types of grant

Grants are awarded for support with 'education, training and skills'. Previous grants have been made for computers and course fees.

Applications

Apply in writing to the correspondent.

Further financial information

Financial information was unavailable at the time of writing (December 2019).

Other information

This charity also makes grants to organisations towards, for example, medical research into blindness and visual impairments.

Sources of information

CCNI record.

The Presbyterian Children's Society

(£) £193,400 (2018)

Correspondent: Jason Nicholson, Executive Secretary/Treasurer, 5th Floor, Glengall Exchange, 3 Glengall Street, Belfast BT12 5AB (tel: 028 9032 3737; email: info@presbyterianchildrenssociety.org or jasonnicholson1866@gmail.com)

 https://www.presbyterianchildrenssociety.org

CCNI number: NIC101444

Eligibility

Children and young people aged 23 or under who are in full or part-time education and are in need. Beneficiaries are usually from families where a parent is deceased or absent. Families must be under the pastoral care of a local Presbyterian congregation and within the charity's income limits (families receiving benefits or earning below the average wage are likely to be eligible).

Types of grant

Exceptional grants can also be awarded to help with educational expenses for children in full or part-time education.

Applications

Applicants are advised to contact the Minister of their local Presbyterian church, who will make an application on the individual's behalf. Ministers can download application forms for various grants on the funder's website.

Financial information

Year end	31/12/2018
Income	£902,600
Total expenditure	£863,900

Further financial information

During 2018, the charity awarded grants to 819 beneficiaries for both welfare and educational purposes. Note: the grant total for **education** has been estimated.

Other information

The charity can make small grants to recognised groups within Presbyterian congregations (youth clubs, parent and toddler groups, after-school clubs, crèches, etc.) to expand or improve their facilities. The charity also makes grants to Presbyterian congregations who are seeking to improve their provision and inclusion for children and families with additional needs, such as physical or cognitive disabilities.

Sources of information
Accounts; annual report; CCNI record; funder's website.

Belfast City

Aisling Bursaries

Correspondent: Angie Mervyn, West Belfast Partnership Board, Aisling Bursary Initiative, 218–226 Falls Road, Belfast BT12 6AH (tel: 028 9080 9202; email: angie@wbpb.org)

 www.westbelfast-partnership.com

Eligibility
Students in West Belfast who are aged 18 and over who are studying (or preparing to study) on a further education, higher education or vocational training course. The chosen course/award should contribute to the regeneration of West Belfast. Preference is given to students who have 'significant barriers and hardship preventing them from realising their full potential through education' such as those experiencing financial hardship or family circumstances.

Types of grant
Bursaries ranging from £500 to £1,000.

Exclusions
Except in the cases of personal or medical circumstances, bursaries are not given to students who are repeating part or all of an academic year. Bursary recipients who fail to complete a course of study will be required to pay back the award in part or in full. Previous recipients of the maximum £1,000 bursary/bursaries cannot reapply for funding.

Applications
Application forms are available to download from the West Belfast Partnership Board website. Completed forms can be returned in-person or by email or post. If successful, bursary recipients are required to attend the Aisling Bursary Award presentation ceremony and complete a six-monthly report for organisers and sponsors.

Further financial information
Financial information is unavailable.

Other information
Local businesses, organisations and individuals in West Belfast make donations to Aisling Bursaries, making funding possible.

Sources of information
West Belfast Partnership Board website.

County Fermanagh

The Fermanagh Trust

Correspondent: The Trustees, Fermanagh House, Broadmeadow Place, Enniskillen, County Fermanagh BT74 7HR (tel: 028 6632 0210; email: info@fermanaghtrust.org)

 www.fermanaghtrust.org

CC number: 102726

Eligibility
Individuals based in County Fermanagh.

Types of grant
The trust administers funds for a variety of purposes. Grants from these funds include:
- Equipment and bursaries for training or other activities which help equipment and in bursaries for training or other activities which will help individuals to develop their potential, particularly through recreation and sport from The Fermanagh Recreational Trust and The Oisin McGrath Foundation
- Care grants for specialist equipment or transport to visit a sick relative from Killesger and Cleenish Community Care
- Bursaries for young people to carry out voluntary work overseas from The Fisher Foundation
- Bursaries for young people to develop their skills in community service, sport or music and drama from The Greg Turley Bursary Awards
- Bursaries for young people to support training, education and practical experience in the creative/performing arts and Irish culture from the Joan Trimble Bursary awards

For more information on all the funds visit the trust's website.

Applications
Application forms for most funds are available to download from the trust's website. See the trust's website for up-to-date application information.

Financial information
Year end	05/04/2019
Income	£712,700
Total expenditure	£632,100

Further financial information
We were unable to determine the grant total for 2018/19.

Sources of information
Accounts; annual report; CCNI record; funder's website.

Scotland

General

The Cross Trust

£ £163,300 (2017/18)

Correspondent: Kathleen Carnegie, Secretary, McCash & Hunter LLP, Solicitors, 25 South Methven Street, Perth, Perthshire PH1 5ES (tel: 01738 620451; email: kathleencarnegie@mccash. co.uk)

 www.thecrosstrust.org.uk

OSCR number: SC008620

Eligibility
People aged between 16 and 30 who are of Scottish birth or parentage proposing 'a study or project that will extend the boundaries of their knowledge of human life.' Applicants must be in genuine financial need.

Types of grant
The trust offers support through the following:

- Awards for university or college (including music and art schools) students who can demonstrate outstanding academic achievements and who have taken full advantage of support available from local authorities, student loan opportunities and so on. Second degree and postgraduate studies are only considered in exceptional circumstances. Grants are made towards university or college costs, study/travel overseas, study visits and projects. Attendance at conferences, symposia, extracurricular courses, voluntary work and gap-year opportunities can also be considered
- Assistance towards projects and expeditions which do not form part of a degree. Candidates are required to provide evidence of efforts to secure funding elsewhere
- Awards for vacation studies in the arts (in its broad sense) to students at Scottish universities. The awards are designed 'to enable students of the highest academic merit and limited financial circumstances to attend conferences, symposia, workshops or master classes or to visit libraries, museums, galleries, concerts or centres of excellence in direct and demonstrable connection with their studies'
- Awards for medical electives studies abroad
- The John Fife Travel Award to people studying or working in horticulture

Exclusions
The trust reminds applicants that 'students who have already received support from the trust for a period of elective study abroad are not eligible for further support'.

Applications
Application forms for each of the awards can be found on the trust's website. Applicants are required to provide full information on their financial circumstances, attach a passport photo, provide an academic reference and details of applications for other funding. Further guidance and closing deadlines for applications for each of the awards can be found on the website.

Financial information
Year end	31/03/2018
Income	£230,100
Total expenditure	£371,300

Further financial information
Awards were made to 82 individuals in 2017/18 and varied between £250 and £6,000.

Other information
Grants are also awarded to organisations.

Sources of information
Accounts; annual report; funder's website; OSCR record.

The Caroline Fitzmaurice Trust

£ £23,800 (2018/19)

Correspondent: The Trustees, Thorntons Law LLP, Whitehall House, 33 Yeamen Shore, Dundee DD1 4BJ (tel: 01334 468604; email: ecalderwood@ thorntons-law.co.uk)

 www.carolinefitzmaurice.org.uk

OSCR number: SC000518

Eligibility
Individuals in full-time education and in financial need who live in the local authority areas of Perth and Kinross, Fife, Stirling, Clackmannanshire, Angus and Dundee in Scotland. Applicants must demonstrate a specific financial need and evidence of high promise.

Types of grant
Grants of between £200 and £5,000 are awarded.

Applications
Application forms can be obtained downloaded from the website and are considered only once a year. The closing date for applications is 30 April annually. A written report from the applicant's referee is required and applicants who are under the age of 18 at the time of the application are additionally asked to provide full information on their parent/s' financial circumstances. The trustees require successful applicants to make an effort in raising funds elsewhere through their own personal attempts.

Financial information
Year end	05/04/2019
Income	£19,300
Total expenditure	£26,400

Further financial information
Full accounts were not available to view on the Charity Commission's website due to the charity's low income. We have therefore estimated the grant total based on the charity's total expenditure.

Other information
Successful applicants are required to provide a written report to the trustees as soon as practicable after the end of each period of funding.

Sources of information
Funder's website; OSCR record.

Mathew Trust

£ £2,400

Correspondent: Fiona Bullions, Administrator, Henderson Loggie, The Vision Building, 20 Greenmarket, Dundee DD1 4QB (tel: 01382 200055; email: fiona.bullions@hendersonloggie. co.uk)

OSCR number: SC016284

Eligibility

People who live in the local government areas of the city of Dundee, Angus, Perth and Kinross and Fife and are over 18.

Types of grant

One-off grants, usually up to £400, for fees to study/travel abroad for college/ university students (including mature students), people in vocational or professional training/retraining, adult education, people starting work, overseas students and people with special educational needs.

Applications

Apply in writing to the correspondent. Applications can be submitted directly by the individual for consideration by the trustees every two months.

Financial information

Income	£347,000
Total expenditure	£465,500

Other information

Grants are also made to organisations.

Sources of information

LEAD Scotland website; OSCR record.

Scottish International Education Trust

£ £81,100 (2017/18)

Correspondent: Michael Ewart, Director, Turcan Connell, Princes Exchange, 1 Earl Grey Street, Edinburgh EH3 9EE (email: siet@turcanconnell. com)

 www.scotinted.org.uk

OSCR number: SC009207

Eligibility

Scottish people (by birth or upbringing) who wish to take their studies or training further in order to start a career. The trust looks for individuals who have 'ability and promise', generally with a good first degree (first-class honours or close to it) or an equivalent. Grants are rarely made to undergraduates and priority is given to postgraduate students, especially if assistance from public funds is not available (for

example, if the course is at an overseas institution).

Types of grant

One-off and recurrent grants of up to £2,000 for educational expenses, such as fees, books/equipment, research or travel. In 2017/18 grants were made in the following areas: medicine; music; arts and literature; scientific, engineering and technology; conservation and restoration; history; international affairs; film making and cinematography; language and linguistics; sport; and education.

Applications

Applications should be made in writing via post or email to the correspondent including: a completed information form (downloaded from the trust's website); a CV; details of the course; a statement of aims; the amount sought; two references. Full details of information required can be found on the website. Applications may be submitted at any time and will be initially assessed when received. The trustees meet twice a year for full assessments in late March and early September so applications must be submitted by 7 February (for the March meeting) or 7 August (for the September meeting).

Financial information

Year end	30/09/2018
Income	£28,575
Total expenditure	£127,100

Further financial information

Grants were awarded to 49 individuals in 2017/18.

Other information

The trust's website details: 'The Trust was the brainchild of Sir Sean Connery. Having had a scant education himself, Sean is well aware of the importance of learning and the empowerment it brings. He was given a helping hand when he needed it most at the start of his career. He believed other talented Scots deserved a 'leg up' too. So in 1971 proud Scot Sean joined with friends like Sir Jackie Stewart to establish the charity. Sean himself donated his entire fee from Diamonds Are Forever.'

Sources of information

Accounts; annual report; funder's website; OSCR record.

Ayrshire and Arran

Ayrshire Educational Trust

£ £40,500 (2018/19)

Correspondent: The Trustees, East Ayrshire Council, Council Headquarters, London Road, Kilmarnock, East Ayshire KA3 7BU (tel: 01563 555650; email: Education-Admin@east-ayrshire.gov.uk)

 https://www.east-ayrshire.gov.uk/ CouncilAndGovernment/About- the-Council/Grants-and-funding/ AyrshireEducationalTrust.aspx

OSCR number: SC018195

Eligibility

Individuals who live in the former county of Ayrshire.

Types of grant

Grants are awarded for a range of educational purposes. They are categorised as: competitive university/ college entrance bursaries; travel scholarships; foreign language grants; travel grants; assistance in obtaining practical experience of trades; special equipment grants; and adult education grants. More detailed information on each grant, how much is awarded and what it can be spent on can be found on the East Ayrshire Council website. Grants are awarded to candidates in both full- and part-time education.

Applications

Application forms can be downloaded from the trust's website. The trustees meet four times a year in February, May, September and November and some of the grants have deadlines attached. See the website for up-to-date information.

Financial information

Year end	15/05/2019
Income	£790
Total expenditure	£90,000

Further financial information

Full accounts were not available to view on the Charity Commission's website due to the charity's low income. We have therefore estimated the grant total based on the charity's total expenditure.

Other information

The trust also award to organisations, both for formal education and for less formal education within the community.

Sources of information

Funder's website; OSCR record.

North Ayrshire

John Longwill Education Trust

 £1,600 (2018)

Correspondent: The Trustees, J. & J. McCosh Solicitors, Clydesdale Bank Chambers, Dalry, Ayrshire KA24 5AB (tel: 01294 832112; email: info@ jjmccosh.co.uk)

OSCR number: SC005483

Eligibility

Students who are attending university in Scotland and who are native to Dalry and of Scottish descent.

Types of grant

Grants of around £100 each.

Applications

Apply in writing to the correspondent.

Financial information

Year end		31/12/2018
Income		£870
Total expenditure		£1,700

Further financial information

Full accounts were not available to view on the Charity Commission's website due to the charity's low income. We have therefore estimated the grant total based on the charity's total expenditure.

Sources of information

Glasgow Caledonian University website; OSCR record.

The Spier's Trust

Correspondent: Rosemary Fotheringham, Funding Officer, St John's Primary School Base, Morrison Avenue, Stevenson KA20 4HH (tel: 01294 475935; email: rosemaryfotheringham@north-ayrshire. gov.uk)

 www.north-ayrshire.gov.uk

Eligibility

Children and young people who live in the parishes of Beith, Dalry, Dunlop, Kilbirnie, Lochwinnoch or Neilston and who attend secondary education there and whose families are in financial difficulty.

Types of grant

Grants are available to secondary school and further/higher education students towards the cost of a course or special tuition in any academic, artistic, scientific or technological subject. Grants can be given for purposes including fees, travel costs, uniforms, books, equipment, accommodation and other educational necessities.

Applications

Application forms are available to download online or from the correspondent.

Other information

We were unable to determine a grants total for education.

Sources of information

Funder's website.

South Ayrshire

The C. K. Marr Educational Trust Scheme

£417,200 (2017/18)

Correspondent: Alan Stewart, Clerk, 1 Howard Street, Kilmarnock, East Ayrshire KA1 2BW (tel: 01563 572727)

OSCR number: SC016730

Eligibility

Students in tertiary education who live in Troon or the Troon electoral wards.

Types of grant

Bursaries, scholarships and educational travel grants to people at college or university, support towards postgraduate research and assistance to individuals with disabilities.

Applications

Apply in writing to the correspondent.

Financial information

Year end		15/05/2018
Income		£606,500
Total expenditure		£417,200

Other information

The trust also makes grants to organisations and funds the Marr Educational Resources Centre in Troon, which provides free access to computers, internet and other audio-visual equipment.

Sources of information

Accounts; annual report; Glasgow Caledonian University website; OSCR record.

Central Scotland

Falkirk

Stirlingshire Educational Trust

£37,000 (2018/19)

Correspondent: The Trustees, 68 Port Street, Stirling, Stirlingshire FK8 2LJ (tel: 01786 474956; email: stgedtrust@ btconnect.com)

www.stirlingeducationaltrust.org.uk

OSCR number: SC007528

Eligibility

People in need who live, or have lived in the past for a period of at least five consecutive years, in Stirlingshire (including Denny/Bonnybridge, Falkirk, Grangemouth, Kilsyth, Polmont, Stirling and their surrounding districts).

Types of grant

The trust offers:

- Post-graduation scholarships – for research work or advanced/special study for those on a postgraduate course
- Travel scholarships – for travel within the UK or abroad for educational purposes
- Special grants – to mature students (over the age of 21) for obtaining the necessary educational qualifications to enter university or an institute of further education. Grants may also be given to those undertaking an apprenticeship or practical experience of a profession
- John Allan Bursary – for apprenticeships and experiences of professions, trade or occupation
- Adult education – subsidising individuals

Support can be given towards fees, books, travel expenses, equipment/instruments or other educational necessities.

Applications

Applications can be made online on the trust's website. The trustees meet on the first Wednesday of June, September and March and applications should be submitted at least two weeks in advance of a meeting. An acknowledgement will be sent by email within seven working days of receipt of the application.

Financial information

Year end		31/03/2019
Income		£148,200
Total expenditure		£131,700

Further financial information

Grants were awarded to 101 individuals.

Other information

Organisations can also be supported.

Sources of information

Accounts; annual report; funder's website; OSCR record.

Stirling

Stirlingshire Educational Trust

See record on page 117

Dumfries and Galloway

The Dumfriesshire Educational Trust

£ £13,700 (2017)

Correspondent: Clerk, Municipal Chambers, Buccleuch Street, Dumfries, Dumfries and Galloway DG1 2AD (tel: 01387 245967; email: CommunitiesAdmin-CommunitiesDirectorate@dumgal.gov.uk)

 https://www.dumgal.gov.uk/article/17489/Dumfriesshire-Educational-Trust

OSCR number: SC003411

Eligibility

People normally living in Dumfriesshire who have had at least five years of education in Dumfriesshire and have secured a Student Awards Agency for Scotland bursary. The trust will also consider applications from looked-after children under the age of 18 who are attending an educational course. They must have been looked-after in the last three years or are currently being looked-after and their address must have been within the former boundary of Dumfriesshire within the last three years.

Types of grant

Grants can be awarded to attend courses, obtain qualifications or obtain practical experience in a trade. Postgraduate and mature students are also supported.

Applications

Application forms are available to download from the trust's website. Applications are usually considered in November but check the website for the latest information on application

deadlines. Payments will be made directly to the applicants bank account.

Financial information

Year end	31/12/2017
Income	£49,700
Total expenditure	£42,200

Sources of information

Accounts; annual report; funder's website; OSCR record.

The Holywood Trust

£ £17,800 (2017/18)

Correspondent: Claire Hanna, Grants Officer, Hestan House, Crichton Business Park, Bankend Road, Dumfries, Dumfries and Galloway DG1 4TA (tel: 01387 269176; email: funds@holywood-trust.org.uk)

 www.holywood-trust.org.uk

OSCR number: SC009942

Eligibility

Primarily young people aged 15 to 25 living in the Dumfries and Galloway region. The trust will also consider applications from people under the age of 15 who are vulnerable and if the measures are preventative in relation to health or social disadvantage, or if a child has an exceptional talent and requires funding to further this.

Types of grant

The trust's website states: 'The Trustees are particularly interested in applications which can contribute in some tangible way to your ongoing personal development.'

Grants usually up to £500, although larger grants are sometimes awarded, are available to contribute towards college and university expenses.

Exclusions

Grants are not given for second or postgraduate degrees. Retrospective awards are not made.

Applications

Application forms are available to download from the trust's website and should be returned to the correspondent via post in a large-letter envelope. The trust states it is beneficial to include a letter from a third party, such as a social worker or teacher. Applications are usually considered within four to six weeks of submission.

Financial information

Year end	05/04/2018
Income	£2,738,000
Total expenditure	£2,621,000

Further financial information

Grants were awarded to 358 young people in 2017/18 for both welfare and educational purposes.

Grants for welfare were broken down as follows:

Personal Welfare	£52,000
Personal Challenge	£21,600
Personal Development	£17,800
Personal 'Other'	£17,800

Other information

The majority of the trust's funds are used to award grants to organisations.

Sources of information

Accounts; annual report; Charity Commission record; funder's website.

John Primrose Trust

£ £4,500 (2017/18)

Correspondent: The Trustees, 1 Newall Terrace, Dumfries, Dumfries and Galloway DG1 1LN (tel: 01387 267316; email: enquiries@primroseandgordon.co.uk)

OSCR number: SC009173

Eligibility

People in need who live in Dumfries and Maxwelltown or have a connection with these places by parentage.

Types of grant

One-off and recurring grants according to need.

Applications

Application forms are available from the correspondent. They are generally considered in June and December.

Financial information

Year end	24/03/2018
Income	£17,900
Total expenditure	£20,400

Other information

The trust also awards grants to organisations for educational and social welfare purposes.

Sources of information

Accounts; annual report; funder's website; OSCR record.

John Wallace Trust Scheme

£ £3,200 (2017/18)

Correspondent: Joanne Dalgeish, The Administrator, Education Support Services, 122–124 Irish Street, Dumfries, Dumfries and Galloway DG1 2PB (tel: 01387 260493; email: educationsupport@dumgal.gov.uk)

www.dumgal.gov.uk/article/16432/
John-Wallace-Trust-Scheme

OSCR number: SC011640

Eligibility

Students living in the upper Nithsdale area of the Dumfries and Galloway region, who are attending/about to enter higher or further education.

Types of grant

The trust provides the following:

- Bursaries for higher and further education to students entering/attending any university or institution of higher or further education, or open university courses
- Agricultural bursaries – to students entering/attending Barony College Parkgate or any other institution specialising in agriculture and allied sciences
- Travel grants for those living in the area to travel in the UK or abroad for an educational purpose

Bursaries can be given for up to five years.

Applications

Application forms for bursaries can be downloaded from the trust's website or obtained from the correspondent or local schools. The closing date for bursary applications is 31 December and students will be informed of their success by the following May. People applying for travel grants are requested to do so in writing providing a statement of purpose for the journey, places to be visited, anticipated length and costs of the trip.

Financial information

Year end	31/03/2018
Income	£9,900
Total expenditure	£7,000

Further financial information

Full accounts were not available to view on the Charity Commission's website due to the charity's low income. We have therefore estimated the grant total based on the charity's total expenditure.

Sources of information

Funder's website; OSCR record.

Wigtownshire Educational Trust

(£) £810 (2018)

Correspondent: Trust Secretary, Business Support Wigtown, Dumfries and Galloway Council, Council Offices, Sun Street, Stranraer, Dumfries and Galloway DG1 2HP (tel: 01776 888423; email: committeeadmin-communitiesdirectorate@dumgal.gov.uk)

 https://www.dumgal.gov.uk/article/
16756/Wigtownshire-
Educational-Trust

OSCR number: SC019526

Eligibility

People who live in the former county of Wigtownshire and have exhausted/cannot find other areas of funding. Applicants must be receiving unemployment or disability benefits or if the student is still in school their parental circumstances will be taken into account.

Types of grant

Grants for college students, undergraduates, vocational students, mature students, people with special educational needs and people starting work. Grants given include those towards, clothing/uniforms, fees, study/travel abroad, books, equipment/instruments and excursions. Assistance is also given towards gaining practical experience of trades and promoting education in the visual arts, music and drama.

Applications

Application forms are available to download from the council website. Applications can be submitted at any time and the trustees meet every four months to consider them. If the applicant is a child/young person, details of parental income are required. The application form says that the trust will accept applications from schools for school trips but only on behalf of an individual pupil.

Financial information

Year end	31/12/2018
Income	£3,300
Total expenditure	£1,800

Further financial information

Full accounts were not available to view on the Charity Commission's website due to the charity's low income. We have therefore estimated the grant total based on the charity's total expenditure.

Sources of information

Dumfries and Galloway Council's website; OSCR record.

Dunbartonshire and Argyll

Bute

Charles and Barbara Tyre Trust

(£) £20,800 (2018/19)

Correspondent: Christine Heads, Clerk to the Governors, William Duncan & Co., Loch Awe House, Barmore Road, Tarbet, Argyll PA29 6TW (tel: 01880 820227; email: christine.heads@wdargyll.co.uk)

 www.charlesandbarbaratyretrust.org.uk

OSCR number: SC031378

Eligibility

Children and young people between the ages of 18 and 25 who live within the former county of Argyll (which includes Kinlochleven but excludes Helensburgh and the Island of Bute), have completed their school education and are of the protestant faith.

Types of grant

Grants are awarded to improve individuals' qualifications or for retraining. Support can be offered towards further/higher education, Open University courses and training and development courses, such as training in leadership and initiative, which are additional to the applicant's existing degree or qualification.

Applications

Application forms can be downloaded from the trust's website and should be emailed to the correspondent by 31 May annually. Successful applicants will be notified by the end of August. Applications received after the closing date are not considered other than in exceptional circumstances.

Financial information

Year end	31/03/2019
Income	£37,400
Total expenditure	£35,100

Further financial information

Grants between £1,400 and £1,600 were awarded to 17 individuals in 2018/19 for both welfare and educational purposes. The grant total has been estimated from the 2018/19 accounts.

Sources of information

Accounts; annual report; funder's website; OSCR record.

Glasgow

Glasgow Educational and Marshall Trust

 £62,200 (2017/18)

Correspondent: The Trustees, Merchants House of Glasgow, 7 West George Street, Glasgow G2 1BA (tel: 0141 221 8272; email: enquiries@gemt.org.uk)

www.gemt.org.uk

OSCR number: SC012582

Eligibility

Students who are in need and who have lived in the city of Glasgow (as at the re-organisation in 1975) for a minimum of five years (excluding time spent studying in the city with a home address elsewhere). The trust holds a list of the postcodes that qualify for support which can be found on its website. The trust states that awards to undergraduate students are made only in exceptional circumstances.

Types of grant

One-off and recurrent grants of up to £1,500. Support can be given to mature students, postgraduates, people in further/higher education and vocational training. See the trust's website for detailed information on what can be funded for each category.

Applications

Application forms and full guidelines are available on the trust's website and can be submitted directly by the individual together with two written references. Applications for grants for university courses which start in September/ October must be received by 31 July.

Financial information

Year end	31/03/2018
Income	£119,300
Total expenditure	£108,200

Further financial information

Grants were awarded to 68 individuals and were broken down as follows:

Postgraduate scholarships	£26,000
Trades experience	£11,600
Art, music and drama	£10,700
Grants to mature students	£10,300
Travel scholarships	£3,800

Sources of information

Accounts; annual report; funder's website; OSCR record.

The Glasgow Highland Society

 £7,400 (2018)

Correspondent: The Trustees, Alexander Sloan C. A, 180 St Vincent Street, Glasgow G2 5SG (tel: 0141 204 8989; email: info@alexandersloan.co.uk)

www.alexandersloan.co.uk/ghs

OSCR number: SC015479

Eligibility

Students (or at least one of their parents) who were born or brought up in the Highlands (the former Scottish counties Argyll, Inverness, Ross and Cromarty, Sutherland or Caithness) and who are undertaking a course of academic or vocational study at an educational organisation in Glasgow.

Types of grant

Grants of around £100 per year.

Applications

Application forms are available for download from the society's website. Application forms have to be submitted alongside a confirmation form from the educational organisation.

Financial information

Year end	31/12/2018
Income	£7,100
Total expenditure	£8,200

Further financial information

Full accounts were not available to view on the Charity Commission's website due to the charity's low income. We have therefore estimated the grant total based on the charity's total expenditure.

Sources of information

Funder's website; OSCR record.

The Trades House of Glasgow

 £43,500 (2017/18)

Correspondent: The Trustees, Trades Hall, 85 Glassford Street, Glasgow G1 1HU (tel: 0141 553 1605; email: info@tradeshouse.org.uk)

www.tradeshouse.org.uk

OSCR number: SC040548

Eligibility

People in need who live in Glasgow and surrounding areas. Several funds have different eligibility criteria around age or need, consult the charity's website before making an application.

Types of grant

The charity's Education Fund can provide financial help to students who lack the necessary funds to complete their studies.

Applications

Applications can be made online through the respective funding pages.

Financial information

Year end	30/09/2018
Income	£1,370,000
Total expenditure	£1,340,000

Other information

Guilds and Craft Incorporations are the Scottish equivalent of the craft guilds or livery companies which developed in the Middle Ages. The Trades House also operates the Drapers Fund which distributes around £80,000 annually to children in need under the age of 17. The fund has its own application form that is available to download from the charity's website.

Sources of information

Accounts; annual report; funder's website; OSCR record.

Grampian

Aberdeenshire

Aberdeenshire Educational Trust

 £23,000 (2018/19)

Correspondent: Allan Bell, Trust Section, Aberdeenshire Council, Woodhill House, Westburn Road, Aberdeen, Aberdeenshire AB16 5GB (tel: 01467 534562; email: trusts@ aberdeenshire.gov.uk)

www.aberdeenshire.gov.uk

OSCR number: SC028382

Eligibility

Students and schoolchildren of any age who, or whose immediate family, are resident in the former county of Aberdeenshire.

Types of grant

Grants up to £500 are awarded to students undertaking further or higher education courses.

Applications

Application forms are available from the correspondent via the email address provided.

Financial information

Year end	31/03/2019
Income	£277,000
Total expenditure	£95,000

Further financial information

The grant total has been estimated from the 2018/19 accounts.

Other information

Grants are also made to schools, clubs and educational groups. Annual school prizes are also awarded to individuals.

Sources of information

Accounts; annual report; funder's website; OSCR record.

Huntly Educational Trust 1997

 £2,500 (2017/18)

Correspondent: The Secretary, 3 The Square, Huntly, Aberdeenshire AB54 8AE

🌐 gordonschools.aberdeenshire.sch. uk/finance-grants

OSCR number: SC026920

Eligibility

Primarily people living in the district of Huntly. Applicants from elsewhere in Scotland may also be supported if there are remaining funds and at the trustees' discretion.

Types of grant

Grants are awarded towards tertiary education and training, including vocational courses.

Applications

Application forms can be downloaded from The Gordon Schools' website.

Financial information

Year end	31/07/2018
Income	£27,500
Total expenditure	£24,800

Sources of information

Accounts; annual report; Charity Commission record.

Kincardineshire Educational Trust

 £2,800 (2017/18)

Correspondent: Grant Administrator, Trust Section, Aberdeenshire Council, Woodhill House, Westburn Road, Aberdeen, Aberdeenshire AB16 5GB (tel: 01467 534562; email: trusts@ aberdeenshire.gov.uk)

🌐 https://www.aberdeenshire.gov.uk

OSCR number: SC028381

Eligibility

Students, or their parents, who permanently reside or are educated in the former county of Kincardineshire.

Types of grant

Supplementary bursaries for students attending a further or higher education course. Grants are also awarded to assist gaining practical experience of a trade, for example individuals undertaking an apprenticeship, to help towards the costs of books, equipment and tools. Travel grants are also available for travel in the UK or abroad for educational purposes.

Applications

Apply in writing to the correspondent.

Financial information

Year end	31/03/2018
Income	£6,600
Total expenditure	£6,200

Further financial information

Full accounts were not available to view on the Charity Commission's website due to the charity's low income. We have therefore estimated the grant total based on the charity's total expenditure.

Other information

Grants are also made to clubs, schools and other educational establishments.

Sources of information

Glasgow Caledonain University website; OSCR record.

Moray

Banffshire Educational Trust

Correspondent: Education and Social Care, Council Office, High Street, Elgin, Morayshire IV30 1BX (tel: 01343 563374; email: educationandsocialcare@moray. gov.uk)

 www.moray.gov.uk

Eligibility

Students who are resident in, or studying in, Banffshire. An applicant's household income should not exceed £34,000 per annum.

Types of grant

Welfare grants are awarded to schoolchildren for school trips, including travel costs.

Grants are made to help with costs associated with:

▷ Apprenticeships/traineeships
▷ Higher education
▷ Postgraduate study
▷ Second or subsequent degrees
▷ Mature study
▷ Any course for adult education

Applications

Application forms are available to download from the Moray Council website. Completed forms should be returned by post.

Further financial information

Financial information is unavailable.

Other information

Grants are also made to schools for special equipment and to organisations towards educational excursions, adult education, education research and so on.

Sources of information

Moray Council website.

James Gillan's Trust

£ £19,000 (2017/18)

Correspondent: The Trustees, St Leonard's Manse, Nelson Road, Forres, Morayshire IV36 1DR

OSCR number: SC016739

Eligibility

People who have lived in, or whose parents have lived in, Moray or Nairn for at least three years.

Types of grant

One-off grants according to need.

Applications

Apply in writing to the correspondent.

Financial information

Year end	05/04/2018
Income	£12,900
Total expenditure	£21,000

Further financial information

Full accounts were not available to view on the Charity Commission's website due to the charity's low income. We have therefore estimated the grant total based on the charity's total expenditure.

Sources of information

OSCR record.

Highlands and Western Isles (Na h-Eileanan Siar)

The Fresson Trust

£ £12,000 (2017/18)

Correspondent: Mr B. Spence, Trustee, The Pilk, 18 Academy Street, Fortrose, Ross-shire IV10 8TW (tel: 01381 620535; email: info@fressontrust.org.uk)

 www.fressontrust.org.uk

OSCR number: SC020054

Eligibility

People who live in or are visiting the Highlands and Islands and wish to further their career in aviation within the area as pilots, engineers or air traffic controllers.

Types of grant

Grants towards qualifications as a pilot, engineer, or air traffic controller. The trust's website states: 'Pilot training support is normally restricted to ground school costs associated with a commercial license, but exceptions can be made at the Trust's discretion especially regarding a PPL or ATC cadets who are just short of hours for the current Flying Scholarship'.

Applications

Fill in the enquiry form on the trust's website.

Financial information

Year end	31/07/2018
Income	£12,200
Total expenditure	£13,300

Further financial information

Full accounts were not available to view on the Charity Commission's website due to the charity's low income. We have therefore estimated the grant total based on the charity's total expenditure.

Sources of information

Charity Commission record; funder's website.

Highlands and Islands Educational Trust Scheme

£ £7,100 (2018/19)

Correspondent: The Trustees, Shepherd and Wedderburn LLP, 1 Exchange Crescent, Conference Square, Edinburgh EH3 8UL

OSCR number: SC014655

Eligibility

Students who live in the Highlands and Islands area of Scotland and who are embarking on a higher or further education course. Bursaries are awarded on academic merit and judged primarily on the results of SQA examinations although parental income and domestic circumstances are also taken into account. Specific awards can be made for those who study/speak Gaelic.

Types of grant

Recurring grants according to need and merit.

Applications

Application forms can be obtained from UCAS administrators or headteachers of secondary schools in the area. Alternatively apply in writing to the correspondent.

Financial information

Year end	30/06/2019
Income	£12,800
Total expenditure	£15,800

Further financial information

Full accounts were not available to view on the Charity Commission's website due to the charity's low income. We have therefore estimated the grant total based on the charity's total expenditure.

Sources of information

OSCR record.

Moray and Nairn Educational Trust

£ £7,800 (2017/18)

Correspondent: Education and Social Care, Grants and Bursaries, Council Office, High Street, Elgin, Morayshire IV30 1BX (tel: 01343 563374; email: educationandsocialcare@moray.gov.uk)

 www.moray.gov.uk/moray_standard/page_43905.html

OSCR number: SC019017

Eligibility

People who live (or whose parents have lived), in the former combined county of Moray and Nairn for at least five years and attend Moray and Nairn schools or further education organisations. Applicants' household income must be below £34,000 a year, plus an allowance for dependent children.

Types of grant

Bursaries are available to students (including mature and postgraduate) in Scottish universities and people pursuing education at a Scottish central institution or training college. Financial support can also be given for study/travel overseas.

Applications

Application forms can be found on the trust's website and should be submitted before 30 September annually.

Financial information

Year end	31/03/2018
Income	£17,600
Total expenditure	£17,400

Further financial information

Full accounts were not available to view on the Charity Commission's website due to the charity's low income. We have therefore estimated the grant total based on the charity's total expenditure.

Other information

Grants can also be made to local schools, further education centres or clubs and organisations operating in the area of benefit, for facilities, special equipment or promotion of adult education.

Sources of information

Funder's website; OSCR record.

Highland

Duncraig Educational Trust Scheme

Correspondent: Derek Martin, (tel: 01349 868532; email: cl.adminmid@highland.gov.uk)

 https://www.highland.gov.uk/info/899/schools_-_grants_and_benefits/30/duncraig_educational_trust_scheme

Eligibility

Young people under the age of 25 who are pupils or former pupils of Highland Council secondary schools are eligible to apply. There are limited funds (most likely one grant per year) available to young people who are of Highland descent i.e. applicants must have at least one parent or grandparent who has at one time attended a secondary school in the Highland Council area for a minimum of two years.

Types of grant

Sport grants are awarded to young people aged between 14 and 15 for specialist sports coaching, training or equipment required to participate in sporting events at a national or international level. Grants for study equipment are also provided to people aged between 16 and 25 on special courses in arts, language and heritage, or science and environment.

Applications

Applications must include two references, the first being the applicant's headteacher who will be contacted directly. The second referee must be someone independent who can comment on the applicant's talents and abilities. Ideally, this person should not be another member of staff from the school. Family members and Highland councillors cannot be referees under any circumstances.

Other information

We were unable to determine a grants total for education.

Sources of information

Highland Council website.

Highland Children's Trust

 £12,900 (2017/18)

Correspondent: The Trustees, 105A Castle Street, Inverness, Highlands IV2 3EA (tel: 01463 243872; email: info@ hctrust.co.uk)

www.hctrust.co.uk

OSCR number: SC006008

Eligibility

Children and young people in need who are under 25 and live in, or have a home address in the area covered by the Highland Council. The charity is the successor to the Highland Orphanage Trust and so there is some preference to provide grants for orphans.

Types of grant

Students at college or university can apply for the following:

- Hardship funding of between £1,000 and £1,500 a year if all other forms of support have been exhausted
- Expedition grants for research purposes, or demonstrable personal development, or overseas study. The current maximum grant available is £500 per person per trip, and no more than three applications will be considered for the same trip
- Grants to cover the expenses of travelling for a job, the cost of temporary accommodation, or the

cost of training courses or apprenticeships. In exceptional circumstances the trust can help with setting an applicant up in business or finding a home for them after your full-time education or apprenticeship is completed

Exclusions

Grants are not given for postgraduate study, to pay off debts, or to purchase clothing, footwear, food, furniture or cars, etc.

Applications

Application forms can be requested in writing from the correspondent, via email, or can be downloaded from the trust's website where there are also guidelines for applying.

If applicants are under 18, a parent or guardian should co-sign the application.

Financial information

Year end	05/04/2018
Income	£56,400
Total expenditure	£60,000

Sources of information

Accounts; annual report; funder's website; OSCR record.

Na h-Eileanan Siar (Western Isles)

Ross and Cromarty Educational Trust

Correspondent: Catriona Maciver, Senior Administrative Assistant, Department of Education and Children's Services, Comhairle Nan Eilean Siar, Sandwick Road, Stornoway, Isle of Lewis HS1 2BW (tel: 01851 822729 or 01851 709 546; email: catriona-maciver@ cne-siar.gov.uk)

 www.cne-siar.gov.uk

Eligibility

Residents in the Isle of Lewis. This is the area covered by postal codes HS1 and HS2 (sector 0 and sector 9).

Types of grant

Small grants ranging from £30 to £200 for various educational needs. Current schemes include:

- **Postgraduate scholarships:** scholarships are awarded for research work or advanced study for graduates of 'high attainment and promise'
- **Assistance in obtaining practical experience of trades:** grants are made to people undertaking apprenticeships or training courses for fees, books and equipment

- **Special grants:** people aged 21 or over who left school 'at a too early stage of their education' can apply for funding for higher or further education
- **Adult education:** grants are made to people in need who wish to undertake any course for adult education
- **Travel grants:** grants are made for travel abroad or in other parts of the UK for any educational purpose
- **Educational excursions:** students in further education can apply for funding for any organised educational excursions
- **Promoting education in music, drama and the visual arts:** grants are made to people with exceptional promise in any of the aforementioned fields for special tuition and private study

Applications

Application forms can be found on the Comhairle Nan Eilean Siar website.

Other information

The council supports local schools by making grants for special equipment and organisations in the area of benefit, by funding various educational activities. The council also maintains playing fields, swimming baths and other sports facilities in the county.

Sources of information

Comhairle nan Eilean Siar website.

Lothian

City of Edinburgh

James Scott Law Charitable Fund

 £1,100 (2017/18)

Correspondent: Gregor Murray, Secretary and Chamberlain, The Merchant Company, Merchants' Hall, 22 Hanover Street, Edinburgh EH2 2EP (tel: 0131 220 9284; email: gregor. murray@mcoe.org.uk)

www.mcoe.org.uk

OSCR number: SC008878

Eligibility

Children and young people who have a link to the Edinburgh Merchant Company.

Types of grant

Grants are awarded for a wide range of purposes including university bursaries.

Applications

Apply in writing to the correspondent.

Financial information

Year end	31/07/2018
Income	£260,214
Total expenditure	£7,300

Further financial information

Grants were made to seven individuals during 2017/18.

Other information

The fund is one of eight that are administered by the Edinburgh Merchant Company.

Sources of information

Accounts; annual report; further information provided by the funder; funder's website; OSCR record.

Scottish Building Federation Edinburgh and District Charitable Trust

See record on page 83

East Lothian

East Lothian Educational Trust

£ £22,800 (2017/18)

Correspondent: J. T. H. Peters, Department of Corporate Resources, John Muir House, Haddington, East Lothian EH41 3HA (tel: 01620 827273; email: eleducationaltrust@eastlothian. gov.uk)

 https://www.eastlothian.gov.uk/ info/210557/schools_and_ learning/12333/east_lothian_ educational_trust

OSCR number: SC010587

Eligibility

People in education or training who are residents of the 'old' county of East Lothian. This means that of the area currently covered by East Lothian Council, residents of Musselburgh, Wallyford and Whitecraig are excluded.

Types of grant

Support is available to people undertaking studies, courses or projects of an educational nature, including scholarships abroad and educational travel. Grants are normally one-off and means tested.

Applications

Application forms can be downloaded from the trust's website or requested from the correspondent. Applicants

should provide full costs of the course and associated expenses (such as fees, accommodation, travel, necessities, maintenance, special equipment), as well as give details of their household income. Applications can be submitted directly by the individual or through a parent/guardian. The trustees meet four times a year, usually in February, May, August and November.

Financial information

Year end	31/03/2018
Income	£72,700
Total expenditure	£62,500

Further financial information

The grants were broken down as follows:

Travel	£11,100
Postgraduate Study	£5,700
Research Work	£2,900
Undergraduate Study	£2,400
Sporting Talent	£640
Dramatic Art Talent	£150

Sources of information

Accounts; annual report; Charity Commission record; funder's website.

Red House Home Trust

£ £10,000 (2018)

Correspondent: Jennifer Law, Charity Accounts Manager, Scott-Moncrieff, Exchange Place 3, Semple Street, Edinburgh EH3 8BL (tel: 0131 473 3500; email: jennifer.law@scott-moncrieff.com)

 www.scott-moncrieff.com/services/ charities/charitable-trusts/red- house-home-trust

OSCR number: SC015748

Eligibility

Young people under the age of 22 who live in East Lothian and are in need of care, live in deprived circumstances or are adjusting to independent living.

Types of grant

Grants in 2018 were between £180 and £1,500 for general needs relating to education and training.

Applications

Application forms are available from the Scott Moncrieff website or can be requested from the correspondent. The trustees normally meet three times a year to review applications and award grants.

Financial information

Year end	31/12/2018
Income	£21,600
Total expenditure	£28,000

Further financial information

Full accounts were not available to view on the Charity Commission's website due to the charity's low income. We have therefore estimated the grant total based on the charity's total expenditure.

Sources of information

Funder's website; OSCR record.

West Lothian

West Lothian Educational Trust

£ £13,275 (2017/18)

Correspondent: Scott-Moncrieff, Exchange Place 3, Semple Street, Edinburgh EH3 8BL (tel: 0131 473 3500; email: jenniferlaw@scott-moncrieff.com)

OSCR number: SC015454

Eligibility

People who have lived in West Lothian for the last three years and who originate from the area.

Types of grant

Normally one-off grants of up to £500, although annual grants may be given if a training course lasts more than a year. Grants are awarded for:

- Postgraduate scholarships
- Supplementary bursaries for students attending universities
- Student apprenticeships or gaining experience in a trade
- Travel to study or for educational purposes
- Adult education
- Furtherance of education in music, visual arts and drama
- Educational experiments and research

Applications

Application forms are available from the Scott-Moncrieff website. They should be submitted no later than the 30 June or 31 December for consideration at the next trustee meeting. The trustees meet twice a year to review applications and agree grants.

Financial information

Year end	15/05/2018
Income	£14,100
Total expenditure	£29,500

Further financial information

Full accounts were not available to view on the Charity Commission's website due to the charity's low income. We have therefore estimated the grant total based on the charity's total expenditure.

Sources of information

OSCR record.

Scottish Borders

Berwickshire Education Trust

Correspondent: The Administrative Assistant, Community Learning and Development, Education and Lifelong Learning, Council Headquarters, Newton St Boswells TD6 0SA (tel: 01835 824000 (ext. 5833))

 https://www.scotborders.gov.uk/ directory_record/7080/ berwickshire_education_trust

Eligibility
Residents in Berwickshire or students whose family home is in Berwickshire.

Types of grant
Small grants are made towards 'educational pursuits or projects'. Grants are mainly made to help with costs associated with studying for a college or university course.

Applications
Application forms are available to download from the Scottish Borders Council's website. Applicants should enclose documentary evidence of their course (course acceptance, receipts, etc.) Completed forms should be returned to the Administrative Assistant by post.

Other information
Grants are also made to small clubs.

Sources of information
Scottish Borders Council's website.

Scottish Borders Council Charitable Trusts

 £21,700 (2018/19)

Correspondent: Administrative Assistant, Council Headquarters, Newtown St Boswells, Melrose, Scottish Borders TD6 0SA (tel: 01835 824000 or 01835 825249; email: krobb@ scotsborders.gov.uk)

 https://www.scotborders.gov.uk

OSCR number: SC043896

Eligibility
The Scottish Borders Council administers four educational trusts in Berwickshire, Peeblesshire, Roxburghshire and Selkirkshire. Applicants should be resident in these areas, or their family home should be in one of these areas.

Types of grant
Small grants are made to help with 'educational pursuits or projects', particularly in further education. Grants have been made for overseas study/travel and music and dance expenses.

Applications
Application forms are available to download from the Scottish Borders Council website. Applications must include documentary evidence of your course (such as a course acceptance letter). Completed forms should be sent to the Administrative Assistant by post.

Financial information
Year end	31/03/2019
Income	£27,300
Total expenditure	£386,600

Other information
Grants are also made to small clubs.

Sources of information
Accounts; annual report; OSCR record; Scottish Borders Council website.

Tayside

Angus

Angus Educational Trust

 £6,500 (2017/18)

Correspondent: The Administrator, Schools and Learning, Angus House, Orchardbank Business Park, Forfar, Angus DD8 1AE

 https://www.angus.gov.uk/media/ angus-educational-trust-student-application-form

OSCR number: SC015826

Eligibility
People in need residing in the Angus Council area that are attending or entering undergraduate courses in universities (both full- and part-time studies). **Note:** Any student entitled to apply for a loan under the Student Loans Scheme must have taken up this option before an application to the trust will be considered.

Types of grant
Grants for general educational purposes to students on undergraduate university courses as bursaries. The trust also offers travel grants for those studying on higher education courses outside Scotland.

Exclusions
Postgraduate studies and students at further education colleges are not supported.

Applications
Application forms can be downloaded from the trust's website or requested from the charity address. Applicants must state full details of their financial situation and enclose a copy of the letter from the awarding authority allocating or rejecting their grant/bursary application. The trustees meet twice a year normally in March and September to consider applications.

Financial information
Year end	15/05/2018
Income	£37,500
Total expenditure	£28,200

Further financial information
The grant total has been estimated from the 2017/18 accounts.

Other information
Grants are also available to various local clubs and groups working to improve educational opportunities and learning in Angus.

Sources of information
Accounts; annual report; funder's website; OSCR record.

Dundee

City of Dundee Educational Trust Scheme

 £21,600 (2018)

Correspondent: Jefffery Hope, Clerk, Miller Hendry Solicitors, 13 Ward Road, Dundee DD1 1LU (tel: 01382 200000; email: jeffhope@millerhendry.co.uk)

 https://www.dundeeeducational trust.org

OSCR number: SC015820

Eligibility
Higher education students who have lived in Dundee for at least five years.

Types of grant
Bursaries for both undergraduate and postgraduate students for general educational costs.

Exclusions
Students who have moved to Dundee to study and have not lived in the area previously are not eligible to apply for an award.

Applications
Application forms can be downloaded from the trust's website or requested

from the correspondent. Supporting evidence must be submitted alongside the application and further information can be found on the form. The trustees meet quarterly; see the trust's website for the next meeting and deadline for applications.

Financial information

Year end	31/12/2018
Income	£23,300
Total expenditure	£24,000

Further financial information

Full accounts were not available to view on the Charity Commission's website due to the charity's low income. We have therefore estimated the grant total based on the charity's total expenditure.

Sources of information

Funder's website; OSCR record.

Perth and Kinross

Guildry Incorporation of Perth

 £52,200 (2018/19)

Correspondent: Secretary, 42 George Street, Perth, Perthshire PH1 5JL (tel: 01738 623195; email: secretary@ perthguildry.org.uk)

www.perthguildry.org.uk

OSCR number: SC008072

Eligibility

Members of the guildry or their children who are attending a full-time course of study at a university or college in the UK. Assistance is also given to non-members who reside in Perth or Guildtown who have a place on a full-time education course in the UK, as well as students who reside outside Perth or Guildtown but attend one of the four local secondary schools in Perth.

Types of grant

In 2018/19 educational bursaries of £900 were awarded to non-members and on average £1,700 to members. Travel bursaries are also available.

Applications

Application forms can be downloaded from the charity's website or requested from the correspondent. They are considered trustees' meetings on the last Tuesday of every month and will be considered within two months of submission.

Financial information

Year end	31/03/2019
Income	£242,700
Total expenditure	£232,000

Further financial information

In 2018/19, 11 pensioners were supported and 58 students were awarded bursaries.

Sources of information

Accounts; annual report; Charity Commission record; funder's website.

Perth and Kinross Educational Trust

 £17,700 (2017/18)

Correspondent: Neighbourhood Manager, Perth and Kinross Council, Education and Children's Services, Perth, Perthshire PH1 5GD

www.pkc.gov.uk/article/17411/ Perth-and-Kinross-Educational-Trust

OSCR number: SC012378

Eligibility

Students in further or higher education who were born and attended school in Perth and Kinross. Mature students, postgraduates and people undertaking apprenticeships are all eligible.

Types of grant

Grants are to assist students in furthering their education, including travel grants/scholarships.

Applications

Application forms and further information can be obtained from the correspondent. Check the trust's website for the trust's opening and closing dates.

Financial information

Year end	31/03/2018
Income	£38,600
Total expenditure	£43,400

Further financial information

The grant total has been estimated from the 2017/18 accounts.

Other information

Organisations may also be supported.

Sources of information

Accounts; annual report; funder's website; OSCR record; University of St Andrews website.

Wales

Mid and West Wales

Pembrokeshire

The Charity of Doctor Jones

 £20,800 (2018)

Correspondent: The Trustees, Guinea Hill House, Norgans Hill, Pembroke, Pembrokeshire SA71 5EP (tel: 01646 622257; email: mcros94874@aol.com)

 drjonescharity.co.uk

CC number: 241351

Eligibility

Young people between the ages of 16 and 25 living in Pembroke or the previous Pembroke borough.

Types of grant

Grants are awarded for the furtherance of education.

Applications

Application forms can be downloaded from the charity's website, or requested from the correspondent, and should be returned by post or email.

Financial information

Year end	31/12/2018
Income	£45,100
Total expenditure	£40,000

Further financial information

Grants were awarded to 58 individuals.

Other information

The charity also maintains a number of properties in the area and assists the tenants with maintenance and repairs.

Sources of information

Accounts; annual report; Charity Commission record; funder's website.

Narberth Educational Charity

 £800 (2017/18)

Correspondent: Jude Stamp, PA to Director for Children and Schools, Pembrokeshire County Council, 2B County Hall, Haverfordwest, Pembrokeshire SA61 1TP (tel: 01437 775861)

 https://www.pembrokeshire.gov.uk/grants-and-financial-assistance/educational-charities

CC number: 1013669

Eligibility

People under the age of 25 who have lived in the community council areas of Narberth, Llawhaden, Llanddewi Velfrey, Lampeter Velfrey (including Tavernspite and Ludchurch), Templeton, Martletwy (including Lawrenny), Begelly, part of Jefferston, Minwere and Reynalton, for at least two years.

Types of grant

Grants are available towards educational costs.

Applications

Application forms can be obtained from the correspondent. Consult the Pembrokeshire County Council's website for current deadlines.

Financial information

Year end	31/03/2018
Income	£2,600
Total expenditure	£1,800

Further financial information

Full accounts were not available to view on the Charity Commission's website due to the charity's low income. We have therefore estimated the grant total based on the charity's total expenditure.

Other information

The charity also provides financial assistance for local organisations involved in youth activities and the promotion of education for young people/children living in the catchment area.

Sources of information

Charity Commission record; funder's website.

Tasker Milward and Picton Charity

 £2,600 (2017/18)

Correspondent: Anne Evans, Clerk to the Trustees, 11 Albert Street, Haverfordwest, Pembrokeshire SA61 1TA (tel: 07971 846801; email: mpaevans@lineone.net)

 https://www.haverfordwesthigh.pembrokeshire.sch.uk/Learners/Tasker-Milward-and-Picton-Charity-Student-Grants

CC number: 525678

Eligibility

Present and former pupils of Haverfordwest High VC School or the former Tasker Milward VC and Sir Thomas Picton Schools in Haverfordwest who are under the age of 25 and wish to further their education. The application will require details of family income and is means tested.

Types of grant

Grants are awarded to promote education including social and physical training. They aim to assist with the cost of pursuing further and higher education, this could include university or college courses, short specialist courses such as sport and music, or contributions towards books and living expenses. Grants are usually paid in termly instalments once evidence of attendance on the course is received from the university or college concerned.

Applications

Application forms can be requested from the correspondent or downloaded from the Haverfordwest High VC School website. Applicant's will need to provide details of their family's financial circumstances and the costs associated with the course. Applications are considered throughout the year. Deadlines for applications are usually the beginning of September and mid-November. Check the Haverfordwest High VC School website for current deadlines.

Financial information

Year end	31/03/2018
Income	£93,000
Total expenditure	£44,200

Further financial information

In 2017/18 grants were awarded to four individuals.

Other information

The charity also provides grants and other financial support to Tasker Milward VC and Sir Thomas Picton Schools, which in 2018 merged to become Haverfordwest High VC School.

Sources of information

Accounts; annual report; Charity Commission record; funder's website.

Powys

Edmund Jones' Charity

£ £7,500 (2017)

Correspondent: The Trustees, Steeple House, Brecon, Powys LD3 7DJ (tel: 07867 804108; email: edmundjonescharity@gmail.com)

CC number: 525315

Eligibility

People between the ages of 16 and 24 who have a registered address in the town of Brecon who are either; a student at college/university or vocational trainees/apprentices.

Types of grant

Grants of up to £400 are available to be used towards books, software, equipment or tools to support a university/college course or apprenticeship.

Exclusions

Grants cannot be used to cover the cost of courses or qualifications.

Applications

Contact the correspondent either via email or telephone to check eligibility and to request an application form. Applications are considered twice a year. Deadlines for applications are usually in mid-October and mid-April.

Financial information

Year end	31/12/2017
Income	£36,200
Total expenditure	£28,900

Further financial information

In 2017 the total amount of grants made to beneficiaries was lower than the previous year due to a fall in applicants.

Other information

Local organisations or groups in the area of benefit may also be assisted.

Sources of information

Accounts; annual report; Charity Commission record.

Thomas John Jones Memorial Fund for Scholarships and Exhibitions

 £62,000 (2017/18)

Correspondent: Mr D. W. Meredith, Clerk to the Trustees, Cilmery, The Avenue, Brecon, Powys LD3 9BG (tel: 01874 623373; email: tjjmemorialfund@gmail.com)

🌐 https://www.tjjonesmemorialfund.com

CC number: 525281

Eligibility

Students who live and were educated in the former county of Breconshire, who are wishing to study engineering or a course with a significant engineering aspect. Graduate, HND, or postgraduate levels can apply. Students from areas of the historic county of Breconshire that are part of Gwent and Mid Glamorgan, such as Penderyn, part of Hirwan, Cefn Coed, Pontsticill, Llanelly Hill, Clydach, Gilwern and most of Brynmawr, are encouraged to apply.

Types of grant

Grants of £2,500 per year for the duration of the course, subject to annual review. Engineering PhD scholarships award up to £2,500 per year with an additional £500 for those on full-time courses for up to three years, subject to annual review.

Exclusions

Grants are not available for time spent receiving practical or professional training from a company when a salary is received.

Applications

Application forms can be downloaded from the fund's website and should be submitted no later than 30 September for the academic year ahead. Successful applicants will be notified by the end of the calendar year.

Financial information

Year end	30/06/2018
Income	£68,800
Total expenditure	£65,700

Further financial information

Grants were awarded to 31 individuals.

Sources of information

Accounts; annual report; Charity Commission record; funder's website.

The St Chad's and St Alkmund's Charity

£ £500 (2017/18)

Correspondent: The Trustees, 1 St Chads Terrace, Shrewsbury, Shropshire SY1 1JL (tel: 07989 654134)

CC number: 231383

Eligibility

Young people under the age of 25, living in the ecclesiastical districts of St Chad's and St George's (Shrewsbury), Bicton, Oxon, Annscroft, Astley, Guilsfield, Kinnerly and Great Ness.

Types of grant

One-off and recurring grants according to need.

Applications

Apply in writing to the correspondent.

Financial information

Year end	30/09/2018
Income	£2,200
Total expenditure	£2,300

Further financial information

Full accounts were not available to view on the Charity Commission's website due to the charity's low income. We have therefore estimated the grant total based on the charity's total expenditure.

Other information

The charity makes grants to other organisations to further the religious and charitable work of the Church of England in the local area.

Sources of information

Charity Commission record.

North Wales

The Educational Charity of John Matthews

 £14,400 (2018)

Correspondent: Mr P. Smith, 6 Vernon Avenue, Hooton, Ellesmere Port, Cheshire CH66 6AL (tel: 0151 327 6103; email: pbsberllan@aol.com)

🌐 www.johnmatthewscharity.co.uk

CC number: 525553

Eligibility

People under the age of 25 who are either descendants of the founder of the trust (John Matthews) or live in the north Wales areas comprising Chirk, Llanarmon-Yn-Lal, Llandegla, Llangollen Rural, Llantysilio, the district of Glyndwr and the borough of Wrexham Maelor (both in the county of Clwyd and borough of Oswestry, in Shropshire). Applicants who live just outside the stated areas may still be considered, they are encouraged to email the correspondent with a postcode and address.

Types of grant
Grants have been given to a wide range of applicants, for example musicians, actors, journalists, tree surgeons, medical students. Grants can be offered for assistance with the purchase of equipment/lessons to assist further development of exceptional talent; financial help for school leavers for specialist books; equipment needed for apprenticeships or career related activities/courses and assistance with college or university course fees.

Exclusions
Financial assistance for those in ongoing education within the state or private education system will only be considered in exceptional circumstances.

Applications
Application forms and further guidelines can be found on the charity's website. Applications should be submitted with a covering letter giving as much information as possible about the applicant's course, career aspirations as well as personal and financial circumstances (including proof of identity and residence). The trustees usually meet four times a year, in April, June, September and December. Applicants should submit their applications at least one month before these dates in order to be considered at the next meeting. Those applying as descendants of the founder will be required to provide extensive supporting documentation.

Financial information
Year end	31/12/2018
Income	£16,000
Total expenditure	£16,000

Further financial information
Full accounts were not available to view on the Charity Commission's website due to the charity's low income. We have therefore estimated the grant total based on the charity's total expenditure.

Sources of information
Charity Commission record; funder's website.

The Richard Owen Scholarships and Exhibitions Foundation

£ £1,000 (2017/18)

Correspondent: The Trustees, c/o Town Hall, Lloyd Street, Llandudno, North Wales LL30 2UD (tel: 01492 879130; email: towncouncil@llandudno.gov.uk)

CC number: 525286

Eligibility
People under the age of 25 who were born in or live in Llandudno. Preference is given to undergraduates at the University of Bangor.

Types of grant
Scholarships are awarded for students at any university, college, teacher training college, or other institute of further education approved by the trustees as well as bursaries towards educational travel abroad. In addition, financial assistance is given towards clothing, tools, instruments or books to help people upon leaving education to enter a profession, trade or calling.

Applications
Apply in writing to the correspondent.

Financial information
Year end	31/03/2018
Income	£530
Total expenditure	£1,100

Further financial information
Full accounts were not available to view on the Charity Commission's website due to the charity's low income. We have therefore estimated the grant total based on the charity's total expenditure.

Sources of information
Charity Commission record.

North Wales – Y Gogledd

Isle of Anglesey – Ynys Mon

Charity of William Bold

£ £2,000 (2016/17)

Correspondent: The Trustees, Talfryn, Bodffordd, Llangefni, Anglesey LL77 7DJ (tel: 01248 750368; email: reestalfryn@ yahoo.co.uk)

CC number: 218152

Eligibility
Educational grants are available to young people in Gwalchmai and Heneglwys (Bodffordd) for support in continuing their studies.

Types of grant
One-off and recurring grants according to need.

Applications
Apply in writing to the correspondent.

Financial information
Year end	31/03/2017
Income	£16,500
Total expenditure	£11,100

Further financial information
Full accounts were not available to view on the Charity Commission's website due to the charity's low income. We have therefore estimated the grant total based on the charity's total expenditure. The 2016/17 expenditure was the latest available on the Charity Commission's website at the time of writing (November 2019).

Other information
This charity also makes grants to organisations and provides other services.

Sources of information
Charity Commission record.

Denbighshire – Sir Ddinbych

The Robert David Hughes Scholarship Foundation

£ £16,500 (2016/17)

Correspondent: The Trustees, Gardners Accountants, 21 Brynford Street, Holywell, Clwyd CH8 7RD (tel: 01352 710216)

CC number: 525404

Eligibility
University students who have connections with the community of Denbigh.

Types of grant
One-off and recurrent grants are offered to university students according to need.

Applications
Apply in writing to the correspondent.

Financial information
Year end	30/09/2017
Income	£19,400
Total expenditure	£18,400

Further financial information

Full accounts were not available to view on the Charity Commission's website due to the charity's low income. We have therefore estimated the grant total based on the charity's total expenditure. The 2016/17 expenditure was the latest available from the Charity Commission's website at the time of writing (December 2019).

Sources of information

Charity Commission record.

Flintshire – Sir Y Fflint

Owen Jones Charity

£ £6,700 (2017/18)

Correspondent: Jack Wolstenholme, Secretary, 18 St Peter's Park, Northop, Mold, Flintshire CH7 6DP (tel: 01352 840739; email: drjwolstenholme@aol. com)

CC number: 525453

Eligibility

Students in further or higher education who are in need and who live in Northop, Northop Hall, Sychdyn, Connah's Quay and Flint (the historic parish of Northop).

Types of grant

Grants are awarded to support costs associated with university or college. Grants are also given to assist apprentices who are entering trades to provide them with the necessary tools and equipment they need.

Applications

Apply in writing to the correspondent.

Financial information

Year end	31/03/2018
Income	£8,700
Total expenditure	£14,900

Further financial information

Full accounts were not available to view on the Charity Commission's website due to the charity's low income. We have therefore estimated the grant total based on the charity's total expenditure.

Other information

Grants are also awarded to organisations.

Sources of information

Charity Commission record.

Gwynedd
Minnie Morgan's Scholarship

£ £14,900 (2017/18)

Correspondent: The Trustees, Corporate Services Department, Carmarthenshire County Council, County Hall, Carmarthen SA31 1JP (tel: 01267 234567; email: corporateaccountancy@ carmarthenshire.gov.uk)

CC number: 504980

Eligibility

People under the age of 25 who have attended any of the secondary schools in Llanelli and who are studying drama or dramatic art at the University of Wales or any school of dramatic art approved by the trustees.

Types of grant

Scholarships to students to study and read drama or dramatic arts at university.

Applications

Apply in writing to the correspondent.

Financial information

Year end	31/03/2018
Income	£13,400
Total expenditure	£16,500

Further financial information

Full accounts were not available to view on the Charity Commission's website due to the charity's low income. We have therefore estimated the grant total based on the charity's total expenditure.

Sources of information

Charity Commission record.

Dr Daniel William's Educational Fund

£ £47,600 (2017/18)

Correspondent: Dwyryd Williams, Clerk to the Trustees, Bryn Golau, Pencefn, Dolgellau, Gwynedd LL40 2YP (tel: 01341 423494; email: dwyryd@ gmail.com)

CC number: 525756

Eligibility

People under the age of 25. Priority will be given to former pupils of Dr Williams' School, or their descendants, and people who are resident, or whose parents are resident, in the former administrative district of Meirionnydd.

Types of grant

Grants are awarded to promote education and can be used towards the costs of college fees, educational trips, clothing, uniforms, equipment/ instruments, books, travelling and other educational necessities.

Applications

Application forms can be requested from the correspondent.

Financial information

Year end	30/09/2018
Income	£55,300
Total expenditure	£55,400

Further financial information

During 2017/18 a total of £47,600 was awarded in grants to 368 applicants.

Sources of information

Accounts; annual report; Charity Commission record.

Wrexham County – Wrecsam

The Educational Foundation of Dame Dorothy Jeffreys

£ £3,600 (2018)

Correspondent: Frieda Leech, Clerk to the Trustees, Holly Chase, Pen Y. Palmant Road, Minera, Wrexham, Clwyd LL11 3YW (tel: 01978 754152; email: clerk.wpef@gmail.com)

CC number: 525430

Eligibility

People under the age of 25 who have attended school for at least two years in the former borough of Wrexham or the communities of Abenbury, Bersham, Broughton, Bieston, Brymbo, Esclusham Above, Esculsham Below, Gresford, Gwersyllt and Minera.

Types of grant

Grants are available for general advancement of education and to prepare or assist entry into a profession, trade or calling.

Applications

Application forms can be requested from the correspondent.

Financial information

Year end	31/12/2018
Income	£210
Total expenditure	£4,000

Further financial information

Full accounts were not available to view on the Charity Commission's website due to the charity's low income. We have therefore estimated the grant total based on the charity's total expenditure.

Sources of information

Charity Commission record.

The Wrexham (Parochial) Educational Foundation

£ £37,200 (2018)

Correspondent: Frieda Leech, Clerk to the Trustees, Holly Chase, Pen Y. Palmant Road, Minera, Wrexham, Clwyd LL11 3YW (tel: 01978 754152; email: clerk.wpef@gmail.com)

CC number: 525414

Eligibility
People who are under 25 who live in the county borough of Wrexham and who are former pupils of one of the following: Brymbo and Minera Voluntary Aided Schools, St Giles Voluntary Controlled School and St Joseph's Catholic and Anglican High School.

Types of grant
The foundation provides money for scholarships, exhibitions, bursaries or maintenance allowances that can be used at any school, university or any other educational establishment approved by the trustees. Financial assistance is offered for clothing, equipment or books for school/university leavers as well as grants towards travel, abroad or in the UK, to further education.

Applications
Application forms can be requested from the correspondent.

Financial information
Year end	31/12/2018
Income	£432,300
Total expenditure	£378,700

Further financial information
In 2018 the foundation gave a total of £37,200 in educational grants to 91 former students.

Other information
The foundation also gives grants to local schools and colleges.

Sources of information
Accounts; annual report; Charity Commission record.

South Wales

Caerphilly County – Caerffili

The Rhymney Trust

£ £500 (2017/18)

Correspondent: The Trustees, 16 Moriah Street, Rhymney, Gwent NP22 5JS

(tel: 01685 840064; email: gaynormiddleton@googlemail.com)

CC number: 517118

Eligibility
People in need who live in Rhymney.

Types of grant
Grants can be given towards the advancement of education.

Applications
Apply in writing to the correspondent.

Financial information
Year end	31/03/2018
Income	£20
Total expenditure	£2,400

Further financial information
Full accounts were not available to view on the Charity Commission's website due to the charity's low income. We have therefore estimated the grant total based on the charity's total expenditure.

Other information
Support is also given to organisations operating within the area of Rhymney.

Sources of information
Charity Commission record.

Cardiff City and County – Caerdydd

Cardiff Further Education Trust Fund

£ £77,700 (2017/18)

Correspondent: The Trustees, Cardiff City Council, City Hall, King Edward VII Avenue, Cardiff CF10 3ND

CC number: 525512

Eligibility
Young people over the age of 16 who live in the Cardiff area and have attended a secondary school there for at least two years.

Types of grant
Grants are awarded to enable students to undertake further education, vocational training, educational travel or special courses in connection with their education.

Applications
Apply in writing to the correspondent.

Financial information
Year end	31/03/2018
Income	£130,200
Total expenditure	£142,300

Further financial information
In 2017/18 grants totalling £77,700 were awarded to 23 individuals to attend special educational courses.

Other information
The trust also supports the University of Wales and local schools. The trust helps to fund Cardiff Council's 'Passport to Travel Scheme'.

Sources of information
Accounts; annual report; Charity Commission record.

Monmouthshire – Sir Fynwy

Monmouth Charity

£ £2,500 (2017/18)

Correspondent: The Trustees, 2 St John Street, Monmouth, Gwent NP25 3EA (tel: 01600 716202)

CC number: 700759

Eligibility
Children and young people living within a ten-mile radius of Monmouth town who are in education.

Types of grant
One-off and recurring grants according to need.

Applications
Apply in writing to the correspondent.

Financial information
Year end	26/08/2018
Income	£9,300
Total expenditure	£11,200

Further financial information
Full accounts were not available to view on the Charity Commission's website due to the charity's low income. We have therefore estimated the grant total based on the charity's total expenditure.

Other information
This charity also makes grants to organisations.

Sources of information
Charity Commission record.

The Monmouthshire County Council Welsh Church Act Fund

£ £1,300 (2017/18)

Correspondent: David Jarrett, Monmouthshire County Council, County Hall, The Rhadyr, Usk NP15 1GA (tel: 01633 644657; email: davejarrett@monmouthshire.gov.uk)

 www.monmouthshire.gov.uk/ welsh-church-fund

CC number: 507094

Eligibility

People studying at school, university or any other place of education, who live in the boundaries of Monmouthshire County Council. Grants are also made to apprentices and people starting work.

Types of grant

Scholarships, bursaries and maintenance allowances for people undertaking education, apprenticeships or starting work. Funding can be used towards items such as tools, clothing, equipment and books. Grants are also awarded for educational travel abroad and for the study of music and the arts.

Applications

Application forms can be downloaded from the Monmouthshire County Council's website and are considered seven times a year.

Financial information

Year end	31/03/2018
Income	£216,200
Total expenditure	£173,400

Further financial information

In 2017/18 £31,900 was awarded to individuals. Welfare grants totalled £30,600 and education grants totalled £1,300.

Other information

The charity also makes grants to organisations and assists with the provision of accommodation for older people. The charity may also offer loans to people undertaking education.

Sources of information

Accounts; annual report; Charity Commission record; funder's website.

Monmouthshire – Sir Fynwy

The Monmouthshire Farm School Endowment

 £27,500 (2017/18)

Correspondent: The Trustees, Monmouthshire County Council, Election office, The Rhadyr, Usk, Monmouthshire NP26 9AN (tel: 01633 644549; email: nicolawellington@ monmouthshire.gov.uk)

 https://www.monmouthshire.gov. uk/student-finance

CC number: 525649

Eligibility

Awards to students who live in Torfaen, Monmouthshire, Blaenau Gwent or Caerphilly who are attending Usk Agricultural College, or any other

educational institution to pursue courses of study in agricultural subjects.

Types of grant

Grants are awarded to help with the costs of study at Usk College of Agriculture or any other college/ university providing agricultural courses. Grants are awarded after the course fees have been paid, as a reimbursement.

Applications

Application forms are available from the Monmouthshire council website and should be submitted to the correspondent. Applications should be submitted by October and January of each academic year.

Financial information

Year end	31/03/2018
Income	£28,000
Total expenditure	£29,600

Further financial information

Grants were awarded to 19 individuals.

Sources of information

Accounts; annual report; Charity Commission record; funder's website.

The Monmouthshire Further Education Trust Fund

 £10,700 (2017/18)

Correspondent: Community Foundation in Wales, Community Foundation in Wales, 24 St Andrews Crescent, Cardiff CF10 3DD (tel: 029 2037 9580; email: info@cfiw.org.uk)

 https://communityfoundationwales. org.uk/grants/monmouthshire- further-education-trust-fund

CC number: 1146059

Eligibility

Individuals under the age of 25 who are pursuing further/higher education or training and who reside in the county of Monmouthshire as it existed in 1956. This includes the authorities which became Gwent, covering some or part of: Torfaen; Blaenau Gwent; Newport; Monmouthshire. Applicants must also have attended a school in the area for at least two years.

Types of grant

Grants ranging between £50 and £500 are available towards the costs associated with undertaking further or higher education or entering into a trade or profession, such as equipment, materials, travel, course/exam fees and training.

Exclusions

Awards cannot be made retrospectively.

Applications

Application forms and guidance notes are available to download from The Community Foundation in Wales' website. Application deadlines fall on the last day of each month and applicants should be notified of the outcome within four to six weeks. Successful applicants are paid upon proof of enrolment on their stated course.

Financial information

Year end	31/03/2018
Income	£3,700
Total expenditure	£11,900

Further financial information

Full accounts were not available to view on the Charity Commission's website due to the charity's low income. We have therefore estimated the grant total based on the charity's total expenditure.

Other information

The fund is administered by The Community Foundation in Wales (Charity Commmission no. 1074655).

Sources of information

Charity Commission record; funder's website.

The Roger Edwards Educational Trust (formerly the Monmouthshire Further Education Trust Fund)

 £6,900 (2018/19)

Correspondent: The Secretary, 17 Burrium Gate, Usk, Monmouthshire NP15 1TN (tel: 01291 673233; email: rogeredwardseducationaltrust@yahoo.co. uk)

 www.rogeredwardseducationaltrust. org.uk

CC number: 525638

Eligibility

Residents of Usk and the surrounding communities, including the majority of properties with an NP15 1 postcode. There is no age restriction for applicants, older people wishing to make a career change or gain new qualifications are encouraged to apply.

Types of grant

Scholarships, maintenance allowances and grants that are tenable at any university, college or institute of further education. In addition, grants can be used towards: travel intended to further education; assisting with entry into a trade or profession for those leaving education; vocational training; unpaid internships; retraining courses;

undergraduate placements for which funding was not available; postgraduate master's and PhD studies; and a wide variety of sporting activities including athletics, badminton, cricket, cycling, rowing, rugby and softball.

Exclusions

Grants will not normally be available to help with the basic costs of first degrees due to the system of student loans. However, activities for which funding is not available including field trips, unpaid placements or semesters abroad which students are expected to finance themselves will be considered.

Applications

Those interested in applying for a grant should email the correspondent stating the date, their name, contact details, the amount of grant sought, full projects costs and their contribution, a brief summary of the project and details of how the grant benefit the project. Information on how to apply and further guidelines are available on the trust's website. Applications are considered four times throughout the year. Deadlines are usually 1 January, 1 April, 1 July, 1 October. Applicants under 18 must have written permission from their parent or guardian.

Financial information

Year end	31/03/2019
Income	£82,800
Total expenditure	£94,000

Further financial information

Grants were awarded to 12 individuals.

Other information

Grants are also given to local primary schools, clubs and community projects such as Usk in bloom. Since 2010, the trust has made over 140 grants, totalling over £183,000, to individuals and local organisations.

Sources of information

Accounts; annual report; Charity Commission record; funder's website.

Neath Port Talbot County – Castell-nedd Port Talbot

Elizabeth Jones' Scholarships for Boys and Girls of Aberavon and Margam (Elizabeth Jones' Trust)

£ £5,800 (2017/18)

Correspondent: David Scott, Trustee, 28 Wildbrook, Port Talbot, Neath Port

Talbot SA13 2UN (tel: 01639 887953; email: scott-david11@sky.com)

CC number: 525517

Eligibility

Young people aged between 16 and 25 who live or whose parents live in the borough of Port Talbot and who have attended a county or voluntary school in/around the area of benefit for at least two years. In addition, students at the Margam College of Further Education.

Types of grant

Grants to be used for general educational purposes for young people and for nurse training.

Applications

Apply in writing to the correspondent.

Financial information

Year end	31/03/2018
Income	£2,200
Total expenditure	£6,400

Further financial information

Full accounts were not available to view on the Charity Commission's website due to the charity's low income. We have therefore estimated the grant total based on the charity's total expenditure.

Sources of information

Charity Commission record.

Rhondda Cynon Taff

Geoffrey Jones (Penreithin) Scholarship Fund

£ £4,200 (2017/18)

Correspondent: The Trustees, Marchant Harries, 17–19 Cardiff Street, Aberdare, Rhondda Cynon Taf CF44 7DP (tel: 01685 885500; email: simonbird@marchantharries.co.uk)

CC number: 501964

Eligibility

Students who are going into higher education and have been resident in the parishes or districts of Penderyn, Ystradfellte Vaynor or Taff Fechan Valley for at least 12 months prior to the application.

Types of grant

Financial aid is available to students in further or higher education.

Applications

Apply in writing to the correspondent.

Financial information

Year end	05/04/2018
Income	£7,900
Total expenditure	£4,700

Further financial information

Full accounts were not available to view on the Charity Commission's website due to the charity's low income. We have therefore estimated the grant total based on the charity's total expenditure.

Sources of information

Charity Commission record.

Vale of Glamorgan – Bro Morgannwg

Glamorgan Further Education Trust Fund

£ £32,000 (2018/19)

Correspondent: Director of Education, Leisure and Lifelong Learning, School and Family Support Team, Neath Port Talbot County Borough Council, Civic Centre, Port Talbot, Neath Port Talbot SA13 1PJ (tel: 01639 763937)

 https://www.npt.gov.uk/5062

CC number: 525509

Eligibility

People who have attended secondary school in the area of the former County Council of Glamorgan for at least two years. This includes Howells School, but excludes schools which were in the areas of the former county boroughs of Cardiff, Swansea and Merthyr Tydfil. Grants are intended to benefit those pupils who are attending approved courses not provided for under the normal award scheme, including professional and technical courses.

Types of grant

Grants towards the purchase of outfits, clothing, tools, books or instruments for those leaving school or college to assist their entry into a profession, trade or calling.

Exclusions

Applicants are not eligible for assistance if they:

▪ Are exempt from payment of tuition fees or are on a secondment
▪ Have received a mandatory award or a discretionary award
▪ Are prevented from receiving such an award due to financial circumstances
▪ Are receiving a bursary from a research council, government department, the British Academy or any other relevant body

This applies to all applicants unless there are exceptional or unusual circumstances relevant to the application.

Applications

Application forms can be requested from the correspondent, requests should be marked 'Glamorgan Further Education Trust Fund'. Information on how to apply and the criteria is available from the Neath Port Talbot Council's website. The closing date for applications is around 31 May each year.

Financial information

Year end	31/03/2019
Income	£46,900
Total expenditure	£44,600

Further financial information

The trust made grant payments totalling £32,000 to individuals during 2018/19.

Sources of information

Accounts; annual report; Charity Commission record; funder's website.

East Midlands

Derbyshire

Derbyshire Community Foundation

 £11,400 (2017/18)

Correspondent: Grants Team, Unit 2, Heritage Business Centre, Derby Road, Belper, Derbyshire DE56 1SW (tel: 01773 525860; email: hello@foundationderbyshire.org)

https://foundationderbyshire.org

CC number: 1039485

Eligibility

The John Weston Fund will support young people between the ages of 11 and 25, living in certain areas of Derbyshire (a list of eligible postcodes is available on the foundation's website). The Tom Carey fund supports individuals living in Abbey Ward.

Types of grant

The Tom Carey Fund offers grants of up to £2,000 to individuals to help them to access education and training courses. In addition, the fund will support young people to develop their skills in sports and performing arts.

Applications

Applications for The John Weston Fund can be requested from the correspondent.

Application forms The Tom Carey Fund can be completed on the foundation's website or requested from the correspondent.

Financial information

Year end	31/03/2018
Income	£703,400
Total expenditure	£641,600

Further financial information

In 2017/18 the foundation awarded £22,800 to 41 individuals. We estimate that £11,400 was awarded for welfare purposes and £11,400 was awarded for educational purposes.

Other information

This is one of the 46 community foundations, which distribute funding for a wide range of purposes. Grant schemes tend to change frequently; therefore, consult the foundation's website for details of current programmes and upcoming deadlines.

Sources of information

Accounts; annual report; funder's website.

Derby

Spondon Relief-in-Need Charity

Correspondent: Stephen Williams, Secretary and Treasurer, 13 Chapel Street, Spondon, Derby DE21 7JP (tel: 01332 544689; email: info@spondonreliefinneedcharity.org)

 www.spondonreliefinneedcharity.org

CC number: 211317

Eligibility

People who live in the ancient parish of Spondon within the city of Derby. A boundary map can be found on the charity's website.

Types of grant

Grants are also made to support students in higher education who need assistance purchasing books, other equipment and travel.

Exclusions

No grants are made for the relief of rates and taxes, or any expenses usually covered by statutory sources.

Repeat grants are only considered at the trustees' discretion and only if there are available funds.

Applications

Official application forms are available upon request from the correspondent. All returned applications should be accompanied by a letter of support from a social or professional worker. The

trustees meet to consider applications in February, May, September and November.

Financial information

Year end	31/12/2017
Income	£28,700
Total expenditure	£26,600

Further financial information

We were unable to determine a grant total.

Sources of information

Accounts; annual report; Charity Commission record; funder's website.

Erewash

Risley Educational Foundation

£15,300 (2017/18)

Correspondent: Margaret Giller, Clerk to the Trustees, 27 The Chase, Little Eaton, Derby, Derbyshire DE21 5AS (tel: 01332 883361; email: mgiller45@gmail.com)

CC number: 702720

Eligibility

People between the ages of 18 and 24 who live, or whose parents live, in the parishes of Breaston, Church Wilne, Dale Abbey, Draycott, Hopwell, Risley, Sandiacre or Stanton-by-Dale.

Types of grant

Grants are available for further education students towards the cost of books, equipment, educational travel, and for the study of music and the arts.

Applications

Application forms and more details can be requested from the correspondent.

Financial information

Year end	31/03/2018
Income	£63,400
Total expenditure	£82,200

Further financial information

Grants were awarded to 51 individuals.

Other information

The foundation also supports local schools, Sunday schools and organisations.

Sources of information

Accounts; annual report; Charity Commission record.

Scargill's Educational Foundation

 £10,900 (2018)

Correspondent: Clerk, Ashley House, Green Lane, Southwick, Trowbridge, Wiltshire BA14 9NF (tel: 07447 221922; email: stephen.marshall26@yahoo.com)

https://www.st-andrews-pri. derbyshire.sch.uk/scargill-trust

CC number: 527012

Eligibility

People under the age of 25 who live, or have a parent living, in the parishes of West Hallam, Dale Abbey, Mapperley and Stanley (including Stanley Common).

Types of grant

Grants are awarded to people undertaking higher/further education and apprenticeships towards the cost of books, tools, scientific instruments, educational travel and the study of music and the arts.

Exclusions

The foundation does not give grants towards school/college fees.

Applications

Application forms can be requested from the correspondent.

Financial information

Year end	31/12/2018
Income	£750
Total expenditure	£24,200

Further financial information

Full accounts were not available to view on the Charity Commission's website due to the charity's low income. We have therefore estimated the grant total based on the charity's total expenditure.

Other information

The foundation also supports local schools and organisations.

Sources of information

Charity Commission record; funder's website.

High Peak
The Bingham Trust

 £8,800 (2017/18)

Correspondent: Ms E. Marshall, Secretary, Unit 1, Tongue Lane Industrial Estate, Dew Pond Lane, Buxton, Derbyshire SK17 7LN (email: binghamtrust@aol.com)

www.binghamtrust.org.uk

CC number: 287636

Eligibility

People in need who live in and around Buxton, Derbyshire (the SK17 postcode area).

Types of grant

One-off grants ranging from £200 to £1,500. Grants are made to individuals for a wide variety of needs, including further education. Grants made to individuals are usually by cheque made out to the provider of the service or goods.

Exclusions

The trustees cannot consider applications from individuals outside the SK17 postcode area. Grants are not made to repay existing debts or for higher educational purposes (university and college level). No more than one application can be made in any 12-month period.

Applications

Applications can be made using the form available from the trust's website. Applications from individuals must always be supported by an agency familiar with the applicant's circumstances, such as social services or a charity or community organisation. Applications can be sent by post at the address above, or as an email attachment (with no additional attachments). All applications are acknowledged by post or email. They are usually considered in January, April, July and October/November each year; the date of the next meeting and the closing date for applications are noted on the trust's website. In cases of more complicated applications, the trustees may find it beneficial to arrange a visit if they feel it would help.

Financial information

Year end	05/04/2018
Income	£178,300
Total expenditure	£206,800

Further financial information

The trust mainly awards grants to organisations in the area. Although a breakdown of grants was not provided in the latest accounts, previous years

expenditure suggest that around 10% of the grant total is given to individuals each year.

Sources of information

Accounts; annual report; Charity Commission record; funder's website.

South Derbyshire
Hilton Educational Foundation

 £3,600 (2016/17)

Correspondent: The Trustees, 6 Willowbrook Close, Hilton, Derby, Derbyshire DE65 5JE (tel: 01283 734110; email: hiltoneducationalfoundation@ gmail.com)

https://www.hilton.derbyshire.sch. uk/useful-links

CC number: 527091

Eligibility

Young people between the ages of 18 and 25 in further/higher education or apprenticeships who live, or whose parents live, in the parish of Hilton.

Types of grant

Grants that are tenable at any school, university or institution of higher education. In addition, financial assistance is offered to those leaving school or higher education to help towards the cost of clothing, books, tools and equipment related to further study. The foundation also awards bursaries and maintenance allowances to assist with the cost of travel associated with education as well as financial support to enable people to study music and other arts.

Applications

Applications should be made in writing to the correspondent and should be submitted directly by the individual. Applications must include the applicants date of birth, details of their course or apprenticeship, the name of the university or college attending as well as a list of items purchased. Receipts/proof of the purchases will also be required for each listed item. Applications are considered twice a year.

Financial information

Year end	30/11/2017
Income	£10,600
Total expenditure	£8,100

Further financial information

Full accounts were not available to view on the Charity Commission's website due to the charity's low income. We have therefore estimated the grant total based on the charity's total expenditure.

Other information

Grants are also available to schools in the local area.

Sources of information

Charity Commission record; funder's website.

Leicester-shire

Mountsorrel Educational Fund

 £139,100 (2018)

Correspondent: Liz Resch, Clerk, 4 Rothley Road, Mountsorrel, Loughborough, Leicestershire LE12 7JU (tel: 0116 429 9946; email: clerkmef@gmail.com)

www.mountsorrelunitedcharities.com

CC number: 527912

Eligibility

People under the age of 25 who are pupils or former pupils of Christ Church and St Peters Church of England School or who have been (or whose parent/guardian has been) resident in the parish of Mountsorrel for at least a year.

Types of grant

Grants range in purpose and can be used for any educational purpose. This includes support for those in higher/further education and financial assistance towards training schemes, apprenticeships, music tuition, educational courses, books, clothing and educational visits.

Exclusions

Support is not normally available where assistance should be provided by the local authorities. Grants are not available for computers, uniform or travel.

Applications

Application forms for each category of grant can be found on the charity's website or can be requested from the correspondent. Consult the charity's website for current application deadlines.

Financial information

Year end	31/12/2018
Income	£152,900
Total expenditure	£200,000

Further financial information

Grants were made to 128 individuals during 2018 and were broken down as follows: education and training (£124,200 in 73 grants); other (£9,600 in 26 grants); A-level/college students

(£4,200 in 21 grants); music (£1,100 in 8 grants).

Other information

Together with Mountsorrel Relief in Need Charity (Charity Commmission no. 217615), the Mountsorrel Educational Fund is administered by Mountsorrel United Charities (Charity Commmission no. 1027652).

Sources of information

Accounts; annual report; Charity Commission record; funder's website.

Alderman Newton's Educational Foundation

 £59,600 (2017/18)

Correspondent: The Clerk to the Trustees, c/o Charity Link, 20A Millstone Lane, Leicester, Leicestershire LE1 5JN (tel: 0116 222 2200; email: info@charity-link.org)

anef.org.uk

CC number: 527881

Eligibility

People under the age of 25 who live, or whose parents live in the diocese of Leicester for a minimum of two years. Applicants must be able to demonstrate that they are in need of financial assistance.

Types of grant

Grants are available for general educational needs including tools, uniforms and books for those leaving an educational establishment and preparing to enter a trade/profession or for equipment required to complete vocational training courses. Financial assistance can be offered to help with the costs of taking up a place at a school, college, university or institution of further education as well as allowances for travel to pursue education. Support is also available for music/arts students and for religious education.

Exclusions

The foundation does not provide support for those who only live in Leicester for the purpose of study and for those classed as overseas students.

Applications

Application forms are available to download from the foundation's website. Applications must be accompanied by confirmation of the applicants place on the course and the details of three referees. Applications for over £1,000 will be required to provide evidence of household income. Applications are considered regularly throughout the year but should be submitted at least three months before the course start date.

Further guidelines can be found on the foundation's website.

Financial information

Year end	31/03/2018
Income	£190,500
Total expenditure	£199,300

Other information

The foundation also awards grants to educational institutions.

Sources of information

Accounts; annual report; Charity Commission record; funder's website.

The Oadby Educational Foundation

 £20,400 (2018)

Correspondent: The Secretary, St Peters Centre, Wigston Road, Oadby, Leicestershire LE2 5QE (tel: 0116 272 0080; email: Oadbyeducationalfoundation@gmail.com)

https://www.beauchamp.org.uk/about-us/partnerships-community/oadby-educational-foundation

CC number: 528000

Eligibility

People between the ages of 18 and 25 who are in full-time higher education or an apprenticeship.

Types of grant

Grants are awarded towards higher education and apprenticeships training costs.

Applications

Application forms are available from the correspondent or can be obtained from the applicants educational institution.

Financial information

Year end	31/12/2018
Income	£52,200
Total expenditure	£37,000

Further financial information

Grants were awarded to 100 students during the 2018.

Other information

Grants are also made for social welfare purposes as well as to local churches and organisations.

Sources of information

Accounts; annual report; Charity Commission record; funder's website.

The Marc Smith Educational Charity

£ £3,600 (2018)

Correspondent: Diana Jones, Secretary, 5 Laurel Fields, Claybrooke Magna, Lutterworth, Leicestershire LE17 5BD (tel: 01858 880741; email: dianajones929@gmail.com)

 ullesthorpe.org/marc-smith-grants

CC number: 1045965

Eligibility

People under the age of 25 who live or have attended school in the ancient parishes of Claybrooke Magna, Claybrooke Parva, Ullesthorpe or Wibtoft, or whose parents live there.

Types of grant

Support is available for people in further education or training, this can include university courses, apprenticeships and training schemes.

Applications

Initial applications should be made in writing to the correspondent, via post or email. Following this, applicants will be invited to a meeting in which they must attend in order to be considered. Contact the correspondent for current deadlines.

Financial information

Year end	31/12/2018
Income	£8,300
Total expenditure	£7,900

Further financial information

Full accounts were not available to view on the Charity Commission's website due to the charity's low income. We have therefore estimated the grant total based on the charity's total expenditure.

Other information

Grants are also given to local schools.

Sources of information

Charity Commission record; funder's website.

Charnwood

Babington's Charity

Correspondent: Helen McCague, Trustee, 14 Main Street, Cossington, Leicester, Leicestershire LE7 4UU (tel: 01509 812271)

CC number: 220069

Eligibility

People in need in the parish of Cossington, Leicestershire.

Types of grant

Educational grants are made for equipment, clothing, fees, books and other necessities, computer equipment, travel costs or maintenance expenses to people under the age of 25 to help with tertiary education costs, vocational training or entering a trade. One-off or recurrent support towards other educational needs may also be given, according to need. Mature students have been supported for re-training following a redundancy.

Applications

Applications may be made in writing to the correspondent. The trustees meet at least twice a year.

Financial information

Year end	31/12/2017
Income	£48,700
Total expenditure	£37,400

Further financial information

We were unable to determine a grant total for educational grants. Grants are also made to Cossington Church and Cossington School, which received £3,000 and £4,500 respectively during 2017.

Sources of information

Accounts; annual report; Charity Commission record.

The Dawson and Fowler Foundation

£ £600 (2018)

Correspondent: Lesley Cutler, PO Box 73, Loughborough, Leicestershire LE11 3XF (tel: 07765 934117; email: dawsonfowler73@gmail.com)

 www.dawsonfowler.co.uk

CC number: 527867

Eligibility

Young people between the ages of 11 and 25 who live in Loughborough or Hathern.

Types of grant

Grants are available to higher education students and apprentices towards the cost of equipment and clothing in connection with the course.

Applications

Further information and application forms can be requested from the correspondent.

Financial information

Year end	31/12/2018
Income	£55,700
Total expenditure	£69,400

Further financial information

In 2018 the foundation awarded grants totalling £12,200 to individuals. Grants for school uniforms totalled £11,000 and grants to individuals totalled £1,200. We estimate that around £600 of grants to individuals was awarded for welfare purposes and the remaining £600 towards education.

Other information

The foundation also awards grants to local senior schools and academies to be distributed to individual students in need. The foundation gives scholarships to students who attend the endowed schools of the charity.

Sources of information

Accounts; annual report; Charity Commission record; funder's website.

Wymeswold Parochial Charities

£ £880 (2017/18)

Correspondent: Jo Collington, Clerk, 94 Brook Street, Wymeswold, Loughborough, Leicestershire LE12 6TU (tel: 01509 880538; email: jocollington@sky.com)

CC number: 213241

Eligibility

People in need who live in Wymeswold.

Types of grant

Educational grants are awarded from the Thompson Educational Grants scheme.

Applications

Apply in writing to the correspondent.

Financial information

Year end	31/01/2018
Income	£5,100
Total expenditure	£3,900

Further financial information

Full accounts were not available to view on the Charity Commission's website due to the charity's low income. We have therefore estimated the grant total based on the charity's total expenditure.

Other information

Grants are also awarded to organisations.

Sources of information

Charity Commission record; Wymeswold village website.

Hinckley and Bosworth

The Dixie Educational Foundation

£ £12,800 (2017/18)

Correspondent: Mr P. Dungworth, Clerk to the Trustees, 31 Oakmeadow Way, Groby, Leicester, Leicestershire LE6 0YN (tel: 0116 291 3683; email: pdungworth@hotmail.co.uk)

CC number: 527837

Eligibility
Young people under the age of 25 who or whose parents/guardians live, or have lived for at least two years, in the civil parishes of Barlestone, Cadeby, Carlton, Market Bosworth, Osbaston, Shenton, Sutton Cheney or in such civil parishes situated in the former rural district of Market Bosworth, as the trustees decide.

Types of grant
Grants are available to support those in further education.

Applications
Apply in writing to the correspondent.

Financial information

Year end	31/03/2018
Income	£150,500
Total expenditure	£185,000

Other information
The foundation also supports local societies and organisations for young people as well as awarding students, on the basis of entrance examinations, at Dixie Grammar School.

Sources of information
Accounts; annual report; Charity Commission record.

Stoke Golding Boys' Charity

£ £5,400 (2017)

Correspondent: Tony Smith, Clerk, 2 Church Walks, Stoke Golding, Nuneaton, Warwickshire CV13 6HB (tel: 01455 212160)

CC number: 519728

Eligibility
Young men and boys under the age of 25 who live in Stoke Golding.

Types of grant
Grants are awarded to support educational needs.

Applications
Apply in writing to the correspondent. Applications are usually considered around the end of May.

Financial information

Year end	31/12/2017
Income	£6,600
Total expenditure	£6,100

Further financial information
Full accounts were not available to view on the Charity Commission's website due to the charity's low income. We have therefore estimated the grant total based on the charity's total expenditure.

Sources of information
Charity Commission record.

North West Leicestershire

The Mary Smith Scholarship Fund

£ £3,100 (2017/18)

Correspondent: The Trustees, FAO FAIT, Finance (Room 120), County Hall, Glenfield, Leicester, Leicestershire LE3 8RF (tel: 0116 305 5835; email: FAIT@leics.gov.uk)

CC number: 527890

Eligibility
People under the age of 25 who live in or around Ashby-de-la-Zouch, or who are a former student of either Ashby School or Ivanhoe High School.

Types of grant
The fund awards scholarships, bursaries and maintenance allowances and assists people entering a profession with the cost of clothing, equipment/instruments, books and tools. Funding to travel abroad in pursuance of education and help to study music or other arts can also be provided. Social and physical training, including coaching in athletics, sports and games is also available for anyone in primary, secondary or further education. Grants normally range from £25 to £150.

Exclusions
Funding is not available towards university tuition fees, living expenses, accommodation, laptops and similar devices or for regular travel costs and school trips.

Applications
Application forms are available from Ashby School, usually in February of each year or can be downloaded from the Ashby School website. Details of current deadlines can also be found on the school's website: www.ashbyschool.org.uk/mary-smith-fund.

Financial information

Year end	31/03/2018
Income	£3,400
Total expenditure	£6,800

Further financial information
Full accounts were not available to view on the Charity Commission's website due to the charity's low income. We have therefore estimated the grant total based on the charity's total expenditure.

Sources of information
Charity Commission record.

Oadby and Wigston

The Norton, Salisbury and Brailsford Educational Foundation

£ £1,300 (2017)

Correspondent: Clerk to the Trustees, 2 Midland Cottages, Wigston, Leicestershire LE18 2BU (tel: 0116 281 1245; email: ANT02CLEO@outlook.com)

CC number: 527930

Eligibility
People under the age of 25 who live in Wigston.

Types of grant
Grants are available for students at secondary school, college, university or other institutes of further education towards educational costs. Financial assistance is also available to people leaving school or university for outfits, tools, instruments or books.

Applications
Apply in writing to the correspondent.

Financial information

Year end	31/12/2017
Income	£2,400
Total expenditure	£1,400

Further financial information
Full accounts were not available to view on the Charity Commission's website due to the charity's low income. We have therefore estimated the grant total based on the charity's total expenditure.

Other information
The foundation may also support organisations.

Sources of information
Charity Commission record.

Lincolnshire

The Alenson and Erskine Educational Foundation

£ £4,000 (2017)

Correspondent: Edwina Arnold, Clerk, Crooks Cottage, Wrangle Bank, Wrangle, Boston PE22 9DL (tel: 01205 270352; email: wranglepc@aol.com)

CC number: 527671

Eligibility

People under the age of 25 who live in the parishes of Old Leake, New Leake and Wrangle. Preference is given to people who have attended a county or voluntary school for at least two years.

Types of grant

Annual grants can be given to further/higher education students at any institution of further education. In addition, financial assistance is offered to those leaving education to assist their entry into a trade, profession or calling.

Exclusions

Grants are not given towards A-levels.

Applications

Application forms can be requested from the correspondent. The trustees will usually advertise application deadlines in local newsletters.

Financial information

Year end	31/12/2017
Income	£3,700
Total expenditure	£4,400

Further financial information

Full accounts were not available to view on the Charity Commission's website due to the charity's low income. We have therefore estimated the grant total based on the charity's total expenditure.

Sources of information

Charity Commission record.

Deacon and Fairfax Educational Foundation

£ £4,200 (2018/19)

Correspondent: The Trustees, Coubro Chambers, 11 West End, Holbeach, Spalding, Lincolnshire PE12 7LW (tel: 01406 426739; email: holbeachpc@btconnect.com)

CC number: 527639

Eligibility

People between the ages of 16 and 25 who live, or have a parent living, in the parish of Fleet in Lincolnshire.

Types of grant

Grants are awarded to further and higher education students.

Applications

Apply in writing to the correspondent.

Financial information

Year end	31/03/2019
Income	£8,400
Total expenditure	£9,300

Further financial information

Full accounts were not available to view on the Charity Commission's website due to the charity's low income. We have therefore estimated the grant total based on the charity's total expenditure.

Other information

Grants are also made to schools in the area.

Sources of information

Charity Commission record.

Gainsborough Educational Charity

£ £4,800 (2017/18)

Correspondent: Mrs M. Bradley, Clerk to the Trustees, c/o Burton & Dyson Solicitors, 22 Market Place, Gainsborough, Lincolnshire DN21 2BZ (tel: 01427 610761; email: law@burtondyson.com)

 www.burtondyson.com/about-burton-and-dyson/corporate-social-responsibility/gainsborough-educational-charity

CC number: 527299

Eligibility

Children and young people between the ages of 11 and 25 who live, or whose parents live, in Gainsborough, Lea, Morton or Thonock.

Types of grant

The charity provides grants, bursaries and allowances to help with the cost of clothing, books, equipment/instruments and other educational costs to schoolchildren, further/higher education students and people starting work. Travel costs in the UK and abroad for educational purposes and music/arts studies are also supported.

Exclusions

Grants are not given towards the purchase of computers.

Applications

Application forms can be downloaded from Burton & Dyson Solicitors' website or requested from the correspondent.

Financial information

Year end	28/02/2018
Income	£5,900
Total expenditure	£7,000

Further financial information

Full accounts were not available to view on the Charity Commission's website due to the charity's low income. We have therefore estimated the grant total based on the charity's total expenditure.

Other information

Queen Elizabeth Grammar school in Gainsborough is also supported by the charity.

Sources of information

Charity Commission record; funder's website.

Gardiner Hill Foundation

£ £3,300 (2017/18)

Correspondent: The Trustees, NAViGO House, 3–7 Brighowgate, Grimsby, North East Lincolnshire DN32 0QE (tel: 01472 583053; email: NAV.GardinerHillFoundation@nhs.net)

 https://www.navigocare.co.uk/who-we-are/the-gardiner-hill-foundation

CC number: 1146433

Eligibility

Vulnerable people who live in Lincolnshire.

Types of grant

Grants to enable people to access education, housing and employment opportunities.

Applications

Apply in writing to the correspondent.

Financial information

Year end	31/03/2018
Income	£116,400
Total expenditure	£40,100

Further financial information

Full accounts were not available to view on the Charity Commission's website due to the charity's low income. We have therefore estimated the grant total based on the charity's total expenditure.

Sources of information

Charity Commission record; funder's website.

Kirton-in-Lindsey Exhibition Foundation

 £3,400 (2017/18)

Correspondent: Julia Melling, Clerk, 7 Darwin Street, Kirton Lindsey, Gainsborough, Lincolnshire DN21 4BZ (tel: 01652 649425; email: julia.melling@btinternet.com)

CC number: 529749

Eligibility
People who live in the parishes of Blyborough, Grayingham, Hibaldstow, Kirton-in-Lindsey, Manton, Northorpe, Redbourne, Scotter, Scotton or Waddingham and who have attended one of the following primary schools for at least two years: Hibaldstow, Kirton-in-Lindsey, Messingham, Scotter, or Waddingham.

Types of grant
The foundation awards junior exhibitions for students at secondary school or institution of technical, professional or industrial education, and senior exhibitions for students at any university or institution of technical, professional or industrial education. Grants are awarded to higher education students towards the cost of books. Additional support is also given to children resident in the beneficial area to continue their education at evening schools, day or evening classes. Grants are available for up to three years.

Applications
Application forms can be requested from the correspondent, either by post (including an sae) or by email. Deadlines are usually the end of September. Consult the correspondent for current deadlines. Grants are available for three years but separate applications must be made each year.

Financial information
Year end	31/03/2018
Income	£4,600
Total expenditure	£5,000

Further financial information
Full accounts were not available to view on the Charity Commission's website due to the charity's low income. We have therefore estimated the grant total based on the charity's total expenditure.

Other information
The foundation may also provide books or fittings for a school library in the parish of Kirton-in-Lindsey for the use of students.

Sources of information
Charity Commission record.

Lincolnshire Community Foundation

Correspondent: Sue Fortune, Joint CEO, 4 Mill House, Moneys Yard, Carre Street, Sleaford, Lincolnshire NG34 7TW (tel: 01529 305825; email: sue.lincolnshire@btconnect.com)

 www.lincolnshirecf.co.uk

CC number: 1092328

Eligibility
Individuals in need living in Lincolnshire. Visit the foundation's website for additional criteria specific to each grant.

Types of grant
A number of funds are available to individuals providing support towards health, wellbeing and education. Visit the foundation's website for further information on the grants available.

The foundation administers a number of funds that are available to individuals. The Make a Start fund awards small grants to individuals aged 16 and over to support education and training. Support can be given towards obtaining qualifications, clothing, equipment, course materials and travel expenses.

Applications
Each fund has a separate application process. See the foundation's website for further information.

Financial information
Year end	31/03/2019
Income	£1,200,000
Total expenditure	£1,170,000

Further financial information
In 2018/19 a total of £16,500 was awarded to individuals. We were unable to determine the split between social welfare grants and education grants.

Other information
This is one of the 46 community foundations, which distribute funding for a wide range of purposes. Grant schemes tend to change frequently; therefore, consult the foundation's website for details of current programmes and upcoming deadlines.

Sources of information
Accounts; annual report; Charity Commission record; funder's website.

Mapletoft Scholarship Foundation

 £4,700 (2017/18)

Correspondent: Patrick Purves, 43 Broadbank, Louth, Lincolnshire LN11 0EW (tel: 01507 605385; email: ppurves@aol.com)

parishes.lincolnshire.gov.uk/NorthThoresbyGrainsbyandWaithe/section.asp?docId=96498

CC number: 527649

Eligibility
People between the ages of 16 and 25 who are enrolled or are about to enrol in higher education or apprenticeship training. Applicants must have attended either North Thoresby primary school or any other state funded school in the parishes of North Thoresby, Grainsby and Waithe and have been resident there for at least five years.

Types of grant
Grants to help with further/higher education and apprenticeship costs.

Applications
Apply in writing to the correspondent.

Financial information
Year end	31/03/2018
Income	£5,100
Total expenditure	£5,200

Further financial information
Full accounts were not available to view on the Charity Commission's website due to the charity's low income. We have therefore estimated the grant total based on the charity's total expenditure.

Sources of information
Charity Commission record; funder's website.

Sir Thomas Middlecott's Exhibition Foundation

£22,500 (2017/18)

Correspondent: Frank Wilson, Clerk, 57A Bourne Road, Spalding, Lincolnshire PE11 1JR (tel: 01775 766117; email: info@middlecotttrust.org.uk)

www.middlecotttrust.org.uk

CC number: 527283

Eligibility
Students under the age of 25 who are either already in or are going into further education, who have, at any time, attended a maintained primary school in the parishes of Algarkirk, Fosdyke, Frampton, Kirton, Sutterton and Wyberton in Lincolnshire for at least two years.

Types of grant
Annual grants are awarded towards the cost of clothing, tools, instruments or

books for those in higher or further education.

Applications

Application forms can be found on the foundation's website and should be submitted by post. Applications should be submitted by 30 September each year.

Financial information

Year end	31/03/2018
Income	£36,700
Total expenditure	£25,000

Sources of information

Accounts; annual report; Charity Commission record; funder's website.

The Educational Foundation of Philip and Sarah Stanford

£ £7,700 (2018)

Correspondent: Mrs N. Ashton, Clerk to the Trustees, 2 Church Lane, Laceby, Grimsby, Lincolnshire DN37 7BW (tel: 01472 314102; email: nicola. ashton@outlook.com)

 www.stanfordschool.org/aboutus/ heritage.html

CC number: 529755

Eligibility

People under the age of 25 who live, or have parents living in the ancient parishes of Aylesby, Barnoldby-le-Beck, Bradley, Irby-upon-Humber and Laceby who are undertaking higher/further education or an apprenticeship.

Types of grant

Grants are awarded to assist with the cost of tools, specialist equipment and books required for apprenticeships and academic courses.

Exclusions

Grants are not normally given for A-level courses.

Applications

Application forms and guidance notes can be downloaded from the Stanford Junior and Infant School's website or requested from the correspondent. Completed applications should be returned to the correspondent, usually by 1 October each year.

Financial information

Year end	31/12/2018
Income	£35,800
Total expenditure	£19,500

Further financial information

In 2018 educational grants were awarded to 28 individuals.

Other information

Grants are also made to organisations. The foundation's Charity Commission record states that it provides a Bible or dictionary to those leaving primary school and also provides shopping vouchers for people in need at Christmas.

Sources of information

Accounts; annual report; Charity Commission record; funder's website.

Boston

Cowell and Porrill

£ £3,700 (2018)

Correspondent: Roger Hooton, Clerk, Come Bye, Sheepgate, Leverton, Boston, Lincolnshire PE22 OAR (tel: 01205 871236)

CC number: 240438

Eligibility

People under the age of 25 who live, or whose parents live, in the parishes of Benington and Leverton near Boston Lincolnshire.

Types of grant

One-off and recurrent grants according to need.

Applications

Apply in writing to the correspondent.

Financial information

Year end	31/12/2018
Income	£18,200
Total expenditure	£16,300

Further financial information

Full accounts were not available to view on the Charity Commission's website due to the charity's low income. We have therefore estimated the grant total based on the charity's total expenditure.

Other information

The charity also provides almshouses. We have taken this into account when estimating the grant total.

Sources of information

Charity Commission record.

Frampton Educational Foundation

£ £11,800 (2018/19)

Correspondent: The Trustees, Moore Thompson, Bank House, Broad Street, Spalding, Lincolnshire PE11 1TB (tel: 01775 711333; email: louise@ mooret.co.uk)

CC number: 527784

Eligibility

Children and young people who live in the parish of Frampton.

Types of grant

Grants are awarded to students studying in education higher than primary towards lectures and evening classes.

Applications

Apply in writing to the correspondent.

Financial information

Year end	31/03/2019
Income	£6,400
Total expenditure	£26,200

Further financial information

Full accounts were not available to view on the Charity Commission's website due to the charity's low income. We have therefore estimated the grant total based on the charity's total expenditure.

Other information

Grants are also given to local schools and organisations.

Sources of information

Charity Commission record.

East Lindsey

George Jobson's Trust

£ £5,100 (2017/18)

Correspondent: The Trustees, c/o Chattertons Solicitors, 5 South Street, Horncastle, Lincolnshire LN9 6DS (tel: 01507 522456; email: sarah. webster@chattertons.com)

CC number: 213875

Eligibility

Children and young people in need who live or attend/have attended school in the parish of Horncastle.

Types of grant

Grants to people in further education and training for general educational needs, including books, courses and equipment/instruments. Most funding for individuals appears to be for students in college.

Applications

Apply in writing to the correspondent.

Financial information

Year end	05/04/2018
Income	£30,000
Total expenditure	£16,900

Other information

Most of the trust's funding is awarded to schools and youth organisations. Grants are also given to Horncastle Town Band and the bell ringers of St Mary's Church in Horncastle.

Sources of information
Accounts; annual report; Charity Commission record.

Lincoln
Leeke Church Schools and Educational Foundation

 £37,200 (2017/18)

Correspondent: Anne Young, Leeke Educational Foundation, PO Box 1294, Lincoln, Lincolnshire LN5 5RD (tel: 07837 580917; email: leekeclerk@gmail.com)

https://adviceservice.lincoln.ac.uk/hardship-funds

CC number: 527654

Eligibility
People between the ages of 16 and 24 who live, or whose parents live, in the city of Lincoln and are in need of financial assistance due to low income or difficult circumstances.

Types of grant
One-off and recurring grants of around £150 to £360 per term are available to students towards the cost of further/higher education. Grants can be used towards the cost of fees for courses at schools, teacher training colleges, universities and other educational establishments. Financial assistance is also available for equipment, tools, books, travel and other costs that may arise during training for a profession or calling as well as leisure activities aimed at developing physical, mental and spiritual capacities.

Applications
Apply in writing to the correspondent.

Financial information

Year end	31/08/2018
Income	£57,000
Total expenditure	£41,800

Further financial information
Grants were made to 116 students, 20 of which were one-off grants.

Other information
The foundation may also support local schools.

Sources of information
Accounts; annual report; Charity Commission record; funder's website.

North Kesteven
The Navenby Town's Farm Trust

 £4,500 (2018/19)

Correspondent: The Trustees, 17 North Lane, Navenby, Lincoln, Lincolnshire LN5 0EH (tel: 01522 810273)

CC number: 245223

Eligibility
Students under the age of 25 who live in the village of Navenby and are undertaking further education and training.

Types of grant
Grants to assist with further education and training.

Exclusions
No grants can be given to individuals resident outside the village.

Applications
Applications can be obtained from the correspondent, the village baker, butcher and civic hall.

Financial information

Year end	31/03/2019
Income	£21,400
Total expenditure	£20,100

Further financial information
Full accounts were not available to view on the Charity Commission's website due to the charity's low income. We have therefore estimated the grant total based on the charity's total expenditure.

Other information
Grants are also made to organisations.

Sources of information
Charity Commission record.

The Pike and Eure Educational Foundation

 £3,500 (2018)

Correspondent: Mrs A. Sutton, Clerk to the Trustees, 39 Washingborough Road, Heighington, Lincoln, Lincolnshire LN4 1QW (tel: 01522 791030; email: anne.sutton46@ntlworld.com)

CC number: 527725

Eligibility
Young people between the ages of 16 and 25 who are in need and live in the parishes of Washingborough and Heighington in Lincolnshire.

Types of grant
Grants for students who are undertaking further or higher education courses at college, university or apprenticeship schemes. Financial assistance is available towards books, tools, travel and maintenance allowances. The foundation also makes grants to young people who need assistance to participate in sport, evening classes and other educational activities.

Applications
Application forms are available from the correspondent.

Financial information

Year end	31/12/2018
Income	£5,700
Total expenditure	£3,900

Further financial information
Full accounts were not available to view on the Charity Commission's website due to the charity's low income. We have therefore estimated the grant total based on the charity's total expenditure.

Sources of information
Charity Commission record.

South Holland
Allen's Charity (Apprenticing Branch)

 £10,200 (2018)

Correspondent: Mr Dale Frith, Clerk to the Trustees, 5 Gedney Road, Long Sutton, Spalding, Lincolnshire PE12 9HF (tel: 01406 365324)

CC number: 213842–1

Eligibility
Children and young people in need who live in the parish of Long Sutton. Higher education students between the ages of 18 and 25 are also supported.

Types of grant
Grants towards apprenticeships and related costs. University students can be assisted towards general educational necessities.

Applications
Application forms can be requested from the correspondent.

Financial information

Year end	31/12/2018
Income	£21,100
Total expenditure	£22,600

Further financial information
Full accounts were not available to view on the Charity Commission's website due to the charity's low income. We have therefore estimated the grant total based on the charity's total expenditure.

Other information
This charity is linked to Allen's Charity (Charity Commission no: 213842).

Farmer Educational Foundation

£ £9,000 (2017/18)

Correspondent: Michael Griffin, Clerk to the Trustees, 39 Church Street, Warmington, Peterborough, Cambridgeshire PE8 6TE (tel: 01832 281076; email: griffin325@btinternet.com)

CC number: 527636

Eligibility

People who live in the parish of Holbeach, South Lincolnshire.

Types of grant

Annual grants of around £200 per year to support those continuing in education beyond the age of 18. A small amount of funding is reserved for students of any age who need support, due to special circumstances, to take part in educational trips they would otherwise be unable to attend.

Applications

For an application form, contact the correspondent by email or post. Applications can be submitted in September.

Financial information

Year end	31/03/2018
Income	£34,300
Total expenditure	£25,600

Other information

The charity also awards grants to local schools and organisations.

Sources of information

Accounts; annual report; Charity Commission record; news article from Spalding Today.

The Moulton Harrox Educational Foundation

£ £9,600 (2017/18)

Correspondent: The Trustees, (email: john.grimwood@oldershawgroup.com)

CC number: 527635

Eligibility

People under the age of 25 who are resident in the district of South Holland, with a preference for those who live in the parishes of Moulton, Weston, or Whaplode.

Types of grant

Grants are available to support the education and training of young people who are in need of financial assistance.

Applications

Application forms are available from the correspondent.

Financial information

Year end	31/03/2018
Income	£49,600
Total expenditure	£51,000

Further financial information

A total of £9,600 was paid as grants to individuals in 2017/18.

Other information

Financial assistance is also provided to local schools.

Sources of information

Accounts; annual report; Charity Commission record.

The Sutton St James United Charities

£ £2,500 (2017/18)

Correspondent: Helen Minnis, Clerk, 6 St Vincent Close, Crowland, Lincolnshire PE6 0FD

 parishes.lincolnshire.gov.uk/SuttonStJames

CC number: 527757

Eligibility

Educational grants can be made to students over the age of 16.

Types of grant

One-off and recurring grants according to need.

Applications

Application forms can be requested from the correspondent or collected from the village post office.

Financial information

Year end	31/03/2018
Income	£22,500
Total expenditure	£11,000

Further financial information

Full accounts were not available to view on the Charity Commission's website due to the charity's low income. We have therefore estimated the grant total based on the charity's total expenditure.

Other information

Grants are also made to local organisations.

Sources of information

Charity Commission record.

South Kesteven

Deeping St James United Charities

£ £2,600 (2018)

Correspondent: Julie Banks, Clerk, The Institute, 38 Church Street, Deeping St James, Peterborough, Cambridgeshire PE6 8HD (tel: 01778 344707; email: dsjunitedcharities@btconnect.com)

 www.dsjunitedcharities.org.uk

CC number: 248848

Eligibility

People between the ages of 18 and 25 who are studying for their first degree or college qualification and are resident in Deeping St James can apply to the Tyghe Educational Foundation.

Types of grant

The Tyghe Educational Foundation provides annual grants towards the cost of studying for three years. Grants can be used towards books and equipment necessary for a degree or vocational qualification.

Applications

Application forms can be downloaded from the charity's website. Those who are starting higher education in the autumn are encouraged to apply as soon as their place has been awarded.

Financial information

Year end	31/12/2018
Income	£114,000
Total expenditure	£104,900

Other information

The trust is an amalgamation of a number of small charities from the local area. This trust also gives grants to local projects which benefit the community.

Sources of information

Accounts; annual report; funder's website.

West Lindsey

Kitchings Educational Charity

£ £6,400 (2017/18)

Correspondent: The Trustees, 71 Silver Street, Bardney, Lincoln, Lincolnshire LN3 5XG (tel: 01526 399529)

CC number: 527707

Eligibility

People under the age of 25 who live in Bardney, Bucknall, Southrey or

Tupholme and who are in need of financial assistance.

Types of grant

Grants to promote the education of young people under the age of 25 in ways in which the trustees see fit.

Applications

Apply in writing to the correspondent.

Financial information

Year end	28/02/2018
Income	£14,200
Total expenditure	£14,200

Further financial information

Full accounts were not available to view on the Charity Commission's website due to the charity's low income. We have therefore estimated the grant total based on the charity's total expenditure.

Other information

The charity also provides financial support to The Bardney Joint Church of England and Methodist Primary School or The Bucknall Primary School, where support is not already provided by the local authority.

Sources of information

Charity Commission record.

Tyler Educational Foundation

£ £7,400 (2016/17)

Correspondent: Clerk to the Trustees, Burton & Dyson Solicitors, 22 Market Place, Gainsborough, Lincolnshire DN21 2BZ (tel: 01427 010761; email: mb@burtondyson.com)

 www.burtondyson.com

CC number: 527691

Eligibility

People under the age of 21 who live in the parishes of Morton and Thornock and are in need.

Types of grant

Grants are available towards educational needs.

Applications

Apply in writing to the correspondent or download the application form from the Burton & Dyson Solicitors' website.

Financial information

Year end	30/11/2017
Income	£6,000
Total expenditure	£8,200

Further financial information

The 2016/17 accounts were the latest available at the time of writing (December 2019).

Sources of information

Burton & Dyson website; Charity Commission record.

Northamp-tonshire

Edmund Arnold's Charity

£ £11,500 (2018)

Correspondent: Marina Eaton, Grange Park Court, Roman Way, Grange Park, Northampton, Northamptonshire NN4 5EA (tel: 01604 876697; email: meaton@wilsonbrowne.co.uk)

CC number: 260589

Eligibility

Students under the age of 25 who are resident in, or educated in, the parishes of Nether Heyford, Stony Stratford or St Giles, Northampton, for a minimum of one year are also eligible for support.

Types of grant

The charity makes grant for educational purposes. One-off welfare grants are available for 'extra comforts'.

Applications

Apply in writing to the correspondent.

Financial information

Year end	31/12/2018
Income	£46,800
Total expenditure	£38,400

Further financial information

During 2018 the charity also awarded £17,800 in welfare grants.

Other information

The Charity Commission record states: 'The Apprenticing and Education Branch has been amalgamated with Arnold's Educational Foundation.'

Sources of information

Accounts; annual report; Charity Commission record.

Horne Foundation

£ £12,000 (2017/18)

Correspondent: The Trustees, PO Box 6165, Newbury, Berkshire RG14 9FY (email: hornefoundation@googlemail.com)

CC number: 283751

Eligibility

Students from Northampton who are in higher education.

Types of grant

Bursaries to students for costs associated with higher education.

Applications

Apply in writing to the correspondent.

Financial information

Year end	05/04/2018
Income	£116,200
Total expenditure	£61,600

Further financial information

In 2017/18, grants were awarded to six individuals.

Other information

The foundation also gives support to organisations for educational projects that involve new buildings and through regular smaller donations to local projects in the Northampton and Oxfordshire areas. The trustees' policy is to distribute an amount approximately equal to the investment income received.

Sources of information

Accounts; annual report; Charity Commission record.

The Dorothy Johnson Charitable Trust

£ £6,500 (2017/18)

Correspondent: The Trustees, Hybank, 12 Old Road, Walgrave, Northampton, Northamptonshire NN6 9QW (tel: 01604 780662; email: zinaida@zinaidasilins.com)

CC number: 298499

Eligibility

People under the age of 25 who were born and are living, have lived or were educated at some time in Northamptonshire.

Types of grant

Grants are made to college students, undergraduates, vocational students, postgraduates and people with special educational needs, towards clothing/uniforms, fees, study/travel abroad, books, equipment/instruments, maintenance/living expenses and excursions.

Applications

Apply in writing to the correspondent.

Financial information

Year end	05/04/2018
Income	£22,200
Total expenditure	£28,900

Further financial information

Full accounts were not available to view on the Charity Commission's website due to the charity's low income. We have therefore estimated the grant total based on the charity's total expenditure.

Other information

The trust also awards grants to educational organisations.

Sources of information

Charity Commission record.

Parson Latham's Educational Foundation

£ £1,900 (2018/19)

Correspondent: The Trustees, 1 Main Street, Cotterstock, Peterborough, Cambridgeshire PE8 5HD (tel: 01832 226025; email: grahamsands@btconnect.com)

 www.parsonlathamscharity.org.uk

CC number: 309843

Eligibility

Students in further or higher education who live in the urban district of Oundle.

Types of grant

One-off and recurrent grants according to need.

Exclusions

Our research indicates that grants are not given to overseas students studying in the UK or for student exchange.

Applications

Apply in writing to the correspondent.

Financial information

Year end	28/02/2019
Income	£5,600
Total expenditure	£4,100

Further financial information

Full accounts were not available to view on the Charity Commission's website due to the charity's low income. We have therefore estimated the grant total based on the charity's total expenditure.

Sources of information

Charity Commission record.

The Lillingstone Trust

£ £28,600 (2018)

Correspondent: Julie Powell, Trustee, Bridge House, Brookside, Lillingstone Lovell, Buckingham MK18 5BD (tel: 07944 460582; email: julie.powell@lillingstonetrust.co.uk)

 www.lillingstonetrust.co.uk/home

CC number: 1151686

Eligibility

Individuals attending schools in North Buckinghamshire, Northampton and South Northamptonshire, who are from low-income backgrounds and are continuing into higher education.

Preference is given to those studying subjects relating to science, technology, engineering or mathematics, at research-based universities.

Types of grant

Scholarships of up to £4,000 are awarded over the three years of the degree course. During the first year, individuals will receive £1,500 to contribute to the cost of required equipment and books. A small amount of funding is available to assist with the costs of travel to university interviews.

Applications

Application forms are available to download from the trust's website. Completed forms should be returned by post to the correspondent or, if the application was obtained from a sixth form college, it should be returned to the head of sixth form. Applications should be returned by the end of November and applicants will be informed of the outcome of their application by the end of December. Assistance towards travel costs for interviews should be discussed directly with the applicant's head of sixth form.

Financial information

Year end	31/12/2018
Income	£91,700
Total expenditure	£74,600

Further financial information

In 2018, the trust continued to fund 18 scholars and funding to a further ten scholars was awarded.

Other information

The trust also supports a community laboratory in a science centre at a local school, as well as supporting its outreach program of monthly science lectures and sports science seminar room. The trust also funds the Lillingstone Trust STEM Scholarship in conjunction with the University of Nottingham.

Sources of information

Accounts; annual report; funder's website.

The Poors Allotment

£ £510 (2018)

Correspondent: Pam Hicks, Trustee, 1 Edwards Close, Byfield, Daventry, Northamptonshire NN11 6XP (tel: 01327 261257; email: pamhicks@uwclub.net)

CC number: 220321

Eligibility

Residents in the parish of Byfield who are in need.

Types of grant

Educational grants have been awarded previously to undergraduates for books and study/travel overseas.

Applications

Apply in writing to the correspondent.

Financial information

Year end	31/12/2018
Income	£1,100
Total expenditure	£1,100

Further financial information

Full accounts were not available to view on the Charity Commission's website due to the charity's low income. We have therefore estimated the grant total based on the charity's total expenditure.

Sources of information

Charity Commission record.

Foundation of Thomas Roe

£ £1,000 (2017)

Correspondent: The Trustees, Highfield Grange, Highfield Park, Creaton, Northampton, Northamptonshire NN6 8NT (tel: 01604 505554; email: ursula@ursulamorris.co.uk)

CC number: 309801

Eligibility

Young people in need under the age of 25 who live in the parishes of Brixworth and Scaldwell, Northamptonshire.

Types of grant

One-off and recurrent grants according to need.

Applications

Application forms are available from the correspondent or can be obtained from the library in Brixworth. They are normally considered in March and September each year.

Financial information

Year end	31/12/2017
Income	£2,600
Total expenditure	£2,200

Further financial information

Full accounts were not available to view on the Charity Commission's website due to the charity's low income. We have therefore estimated the grant total based on the charity's total expenditure.

Other information

Assistance is also provided to schools in the local area.

Sources of information

Charity Commission record.

The Scaldwell Charity

£ £2,700 (2017)

Correspondent: The Trustees, The Hollies, High Street, Scaldwell, Northampton, Northamptonshire NN6 9JS (tel: 01604 881950; email: d. doddssmith@me.com)

CC number: 277208

Eligibility
People in need who live in the parish of Scaldwell.

Types of grant
One-off and recurrent grants according to need.

Applications
Apply in writing to the correspondent.

Financial information
Year end	31/12/2017
Income	£3,600
Total expenditure	£3,000

Further financial information
Full accounts were not available to view on the Charity Commission's website due to the charity's low income. We have therefore estimated the grant total based on the charity's total expenditure.

Sources of information
Charity Commission record.

Daventry

The Chauntry Estate

£ £2,400 (2017/18)

Correspondent: The Trustees, 2 The Pond, Great Brington, Northampton, Northamptonshire NN7 4JQ (tel: 01604 770613; email: chauntryestateclerk@ gmail.com)

CC number: 200795

Eligibility
Educational grants are made to students from Brington of any age.

Types of grant
Educational grants have been made previously to students in higher/further education, and to those studying apprenticeships, towards the cost of books and equipment.

Applications
Apply in writing to the correspondent.

Financial information
Year end	31/03/2018
Income	£11,500
Total expenditure	£10,600

Further financial information
Full accounts were not available to view on the Charity Commission's website

due to the charity's low income. We have therefore estimated the grant total based on the charity's total expenditure.

Other information
This charity also makes grants to organisations.

Sources of information
Charity Commission record.

Kettering

The Burton Latimer United Educational Foundation

£ £1,700 (2017)

Correspondent: The Trustees, 11 Manor Road, Rothwell, Kettering, Northamptonshire NN14 6JE

CC number: 309818

Eligibility
People who live in Burton Latimer.

Types of grant
Grants are awarded for costs associated with further/ higher education.

Applications
Apply in writing to the correspondent.

Financial information
Year end	31/12/2017
Income	£5,000
Total expenditure	£3,600

Further financial information
Full accounts were not available to view on the Charity Commission's website due to the charity's low income. We have therefore estimated the grant total based on the charity's total expenditure.

Sources of information
Charity Commission record.

Northampton

Beckett's and Sergeant's Educational Foundation

£ £120,500 (2018)

Correspondent: Angela Moon, Hewitsons LLP, Elgin House, Billing Road, Northampton, Northamptonshire NN1 5AU (tel: 01604 233233; email: angelamoon@hewitsons.com)

CC number: 309766

Eligibility
People under the age of 25 who live and are being educated in the borough of Northampton. The trustees have discretion to award grants to further/

higher education students who live in Northampton during holidays but attend an institution elsewhere.

Types of grant
Grants of £800 for the initial year then £500 for each ensuing year for educational purposes.

Applications
Apply in writing to the correspondent.

Financial information
Year end	31/12/2018
Income	£239,100
Total expenditure	£211,100

Other information
Grants are also awarded to local schools and organisations.

Sources of information
Accounts; annual report; Charity Commission record.

Blue Coat Educational Charity

£ £4,300 (2017/18)

Correspondent: The Trustees, 41 Thorburn Road, Northampton, Northamptonshire NN3 3DA (tel: 01604 408710; email: pestells@btinternet.com)

CC number: 309764

Eligibility
Schoolchildren, students and people entering work who are under the age of 25 and live in the borough of Northampton.

Types of grant
One-off and recurrent grants according to need.

Exclusions
Grants are not available to mature students or overseas students studying in Britain.

Applications
Apply in writing to the correspondent. Our research suggests that applications are usually considered in February, July and November.

Financial information
Year end	24/01/2018
Income	£9,400
Total expenditure	£9,500

Further financial information
Full accounts were not available to view on the Charity Commission's website due to the charity's low income. We have therefore estimated the grant total based on the charity's total expenditure.

Other information
Grants are also made to the Church of England schools in Northampton.

Sources of information

Charity Commission record.

The Charity of Hervey and Elizabeth Ekins

£ £2,100 (2017/18)

Correspondent: Richard Pestell, Clerk, 41 Thorburn Road, Northampton, Northamptonshire NN3 3DA (tel: 01604 408712; email: pestells@btinternet.com)

CC number: 309858

Eligibility

Children and young people who have lived in the borough of Northampton or the parish of Great Doddington for no less than three years, attended a state school for no less than one year, and attended a Church of England church on a regular basis. Preference will be given to those residing in the ecclesiastical parishes of: St Peter Weston Favell, St Peter and St Paul Abington, and Emmanuel Northampton.

Types of grant

Grants are awarded to young people for university and college education.

Exclusions

Grants are not given for school fees.

Applications

Application forms can be obtained from the local parish churches or from writing to the correspondent.

Financial information

Year end	30/09/2018
Income	£37,800
Total expenditure	£28,600

Other information

The charity also awards grants to schools and organisations in the parishes.

Sources of information

Accounts; annual report; Charity Commission record; Weston Favell Primary School website.

South Northamptonshire

Brackley United Feoffee Charity

£ £2,000 (2017/18)

Correspondent: Irene Bennett, 24 Broad Lane, Evenley, Brackley, Northamptonshire NN13 5SF (tel: 01280 703904; email: brackleyunitedfeoffee. charity@gmail.com)

CC number: 238067

Eligibility

People in need who live in the ecclesiastical parish of Brackley (which consists of the town of Brackley and the village of Halse only).

Types of grant

Grants are made to undergraduates for stationery and equipment.

Applications

Applications can be made in writing to the correspondent by the individual or through a social worker, Citizens Advice or other welfare agency. The trustees meet every three to four months.

Financial information

Year end	30/09/2018
Income	£37,300
Total expenditure	£29,700

Other information

The charity also awards grants to local organisations and helps with the upkeep of St Peter's Church.

Sources of information

Accounts; annual report; Charity Commission record.

Nottingham-shire

The Francis Bernard Caunt Education Trust

£ £41,000 (2017/18)

Correspondent: The Trustees, 10 Lombard Street, Newark, Nottinghamshire NG24 1XE (tel: 01636 703333; email: info@larken.co.uk)

 www.larken.co.uk/about/in-the-community.html

CC number: 1108858

Eligibility

People aged between 16 and 25 who are, or whose parents/guardians are, resident within a 12-mile radius of Newark on Trent parish church. Applicants should have attended or attend Newark schools or colleges or Southwell or Tuxford schools in the previous eight years for at least two years, and be intending to study part-time or full-time for at least one year on a recognised academic or vocational course.

Types of grant

Grants, scholarships and loans between £500 and £2,000 to assist with the cost of further/higher education.

Applications

Application forms can be downloaded from the trust's website and should be submitted along with a letter of reference from a headteacher, employer or other appropriate person, such as a career adviser.

Financial information

Year end	05/04/2018
Income	£58,600
Total expenditure	£59,600

Sources of information

Accounts; annual report; Charity Commission record; funder's website.

Faith Clerkson's Exhibition Foundation

£ £3,700 (2017/18)

Correspondent: The Trustees, 68 Hillside Road, Beeston, Nottingham, Nottinghamshire NG9 3AY (tel: 07771 978622; email: colinp.mckay@btinternet. com)

CC number: 528240

Eligibility

People going to university or entering further education who have lived in the borough of Mansfield or the urban district of Mansfield Woodhouse for at least two years.

Types of grant

Grants are available for those going into university or further education to assist with general educational costs.

Applications

Apply in writing to the correspondent.

Financial information

Year end	31/03/2018
Income	£3,500
Total expenditure	£4,000

Further financial information

Full accounts were not available to view on the Charity Commission's website due to the charity's low income. We have therefore estimated the grant total based on the charity's total expenditure.

Sources of information

Charity Commission record.

The Nottingham Roosevelt Memorial Travelling Scholarship Fund

£ £2,500 (2018)

Correspondent: The Trustees, 8 The Corner, Lowdham, Nottingham, Nottinghamshire NG14 7AE (email: secretary@rooseveltscholarship.org)

 www.rooseveltscholarship.org

CC number: 512941

Eligibility

People between the ages of 21 and 35 (cut-off date is 1 August of the current year) who work and/or live in the city or county of Nottingham and are primarily engaged in trade, commerce or 'the professions'.

Types of grant

A scholarship to enable an individual to visit the USA for a period of between one and three months. Scholars are expected to fulfil an ambassadorial role while travelling widely throughout the USA and learning about the American way of life.

Applications

Detailed guidelines, application forms and submission deadlines can be found on the fund's website. Applications are usually invited in spring and the fund prefers to receive them via email. Shortlisted candidates are required to attend interviews.

Financial information

Year end	31/12/2018
Income	£5,000
Total expenditure	£2,900

Further financial information

Full accounts were not available to view on the Charity Commission's website due to the charity's low income. We have therefore estimated the grant total based on the charity's total expenditure.

Other information

Applicants do not need to have any formal qualifications. Further queries can be submitted online on the fund's website.

Sources of information

Charity Commission record.

Read's Exhibition Foundation

£600 (2017/18)

Correspondent: The Trustees, Sandyacre, Eagle Road, Spalford, Newark, Nottinghamshire NG23 7HA (tel: 01522 778250)

CC number: 528238

Eligibility

Students who live in the parish of Tuxford.

Types of grant

Support is given towards the cost of education and training for people at school, university or other further education institutions and people undertaking apprenticeships.

Applications

Apply in writing to the correspondent.

Financial information

Year end	29/03/2018
Income	£3,300
Total expenditure	£1,200

Further financial information

Full accounts were not available to view on the Charity Commission's website due to the charity's low income. We have therefore estimated the grant total based on the charity's total expenditure.

Other information

The foundation may also award grants to organisations.

Sources of information

Charity Commission record.

Newark and Sherwood

The Farnsfield Trust

£3,900 (2018/19)

Correspondent: David Harvey, Chair, Wayside, Tippings Lane, Farnsfield, Newark, Nottinghamshire NG22 8EP (tel: 07949 246380; email: thefarnsfieldtrust@gmail.com)

CC number: 1078367

Eligibility

People in need who live in Farnsfield in Nottinghamshire and the surrounding area.

Types of grant

One-off and recurring grants according to need.

Applications

Applications should be made in writing to the correspondent.

Financial information

Year end	31/03/2019
Income	£27,500
Total expenditure	£24,000

Other information

The trust was formerly known as The John and Nellie Brown Farnsfield Trust. It also awards grants to organisations in the area.

Sources of information

Accounts; annual report; Charity Commission record.

Nottingham

Arnold Educational Foundation

£13,300 (2017/18)

Correspondent: Brian West, Clerk to the Trustees, 73 Arnot Hill Road, Arnold, Nottingham, Nottinghamshire NG5 6LN (tel: 0115 920 6656; email: b.west909@yahoo.co.uk)

 www.stmarysarnold.org.uk/arnold_parochial_charities.html

CC number: 528191

Eligibility

People under the age of 25 who live in (or whose parents live in) the ancient parish of Arnold (which includes Daybrook and Woodthorpe) and who require financial assistance.

Types of grant

Grants are awarded to specifically help with the purchase of books and equipment for education, or to assist with contributions towards courses and educational trips associated with studies. The amount of available money for grants can vary each year. Repeat applications can be made throughout the duration of a course up to the age 25.

Applications

Applications can be obtained from the correspondent or downloaded from the foundation's website.

Financial information

Year end	30/06/2018
Income	£16,800
Total expenditure	£14,700

Further financial information

Full accounts were not available to view on the Charity Commission's website due to the charity's low income. We have therefore estimated the grant total based on the charity's total expenditure.

Sources of information

Charity Commission record; funder's website.

Audrey Harrison Heron Memorial Fund

£3,300 (2017/18)

Correspondent: The Trustees, 6th Floor, Trinity Quay 2, Avon Street, Bristol BS2 0PT (tel: 0345 304 2424)

CC number: 504494

Eligibility

Women and girls under the age of 25, living in the city of Nottingham.

Types of grant

One-off and recurrent grants to help with the cost of books, equipment/ instruments, clothing, travel in the UK and overseas, as well as school, college or university fees.

Applications

Apply in writing to the correspondent.

Financial information

Year end	29/05/2018
Income	£4,700
Total expenditure	£3,700

Further financial information

Full accounts were not available to view on the Charity Commission's website due to the charity's low income. We have therefore estimated the grant total based on the charity's total expenditure.

Other information

Grants may also be awarded to organisations which share the fund's objectives.

Sources of information

Charity Commission record.

Nottingham Gordon Memorial Trust for Boys and Girls

£ £7,400 (2017)

Correspondent: Anna Chandler, Cumberland Court, 80 Mount Street, Nottingham, Nottinghamshire NG1 6HH (tel: 0115 901 5562; email: anna. chandler@freeths.co.uk)

CC number: 212536

Eligibility

Children and young people under the age of 25, living in Nottingham, who are in need. Children and young people under the age of 25 who are currently in, or plan to be in, education or training are also eligible for support. Preference is given in both instances to old boys of the former Gordon Memorial Home.

Types of grant

Educational grants are made to help with costs associated with studying such as books, tools and equipment.

Applications

Apply in writing to the correspondent.

Financial information

Year end	31/12/2017
Income	£47,800
Total expenditure	£57,200

Other information

This charity also makes grants to organisations.

Sources of information

Accounts; annual report; Charity Commission.

Rutland

The Sir John Sedley Educational Foundation

 £2,800 (2017/18)

Correspondent: Elaine Everington, 39 Digby Drive, Oakham, Rutland LE15 6LJ (tel: 07884 235974; email: ellemai@btinternet.com)

https://www.whissendine.net/news/ sir-john-sedley-educational- foundation

CC number: 527884

Eligibility

People under the age of 25 who live in the parish of Wymondham and the peripheral areas and are in further/ higher education.

Types of grant

Grants are available to support the costs of further/higher education and can be used towards the cost of tuition fees, travel, books, equipment, clothing and so on.

Applications

Application forms can be requested from the correspondent.

Financial information

Year end	31/03/2018
Income	£11,200
Total expenditure	£9,200

Further financial information

Full accounts were not available to view on the Charity Commission's website due to the charity's low income. We have therefore estimated the grant total based on the charity's total expenditure.

Other information

The foundation also provides support to schools and other charitable organisations as well as maintaining a hall and recreational field.

Sources of information

Charity Commission record; funder's website.

West Midlands Region

General

The W. E. Dunn Trust

 £1,500 (2018/19)

Correspondent: Mary Touhy, Secretary to the Trustees, 30 Bentley Heath Cottages, Tilehouse Green Lane, Knowle, Solihull, West Midlands B93 9EL (tel: 01564 773407; email: wedunn@tiscali.co.uk)

CC number: 219418

Eligibility
People living in the West Midlands who are undertaking education.

Types of grant
Grants are awarded towards education and training.

Exclusions
Grants will not be awarded towards debts already incurred.

Applications
Apply in writing to the correspondent. Applications for educational grants should be submitted through the individual's parent/guardian, school or welfare agency. Mature students may apply directly. Applications are considered weekly.

Financial information

Year end	05/04/2019
Income	£249,300
Total expenditure	£235,400

Further financial information
In 2018/19 a total of £59,700 was awarded to 309 individuals. Within this, grants for social welfare purposes totalled £58,200 and were distributed as follows:

Clothing and furniture	144	£24,800
Domestic equipment	109	£23,000
Radio, TV and licences	23	£5,800
Social welfare	23	£4,000
Convalescence and holidays	3	£600

Education grants to seven individuals totalled £1,500.

Other information
The trust also makes grants to organisations.

Sources of information
Accounts; annual report; Charity Commission record; Holiday Grants leaflets.

Sir Josiah Mason Trust

Correspondent: The Trustees, Alexandra House, Hillborough Road, Birmingham, West Midlands B27 6PF (tel: 0121 245 1002; email: enquiries@sjmt.org.uk)

 https://www.sjmt.org.uk

CC number: 1179890

Eligibility
People under the age of 25 who live or study in the West Midlands area and are in financial hardship.

Types of grant
Funding is available for looked-after young people for individual tuition to enable them to access higher level qualifications and training.

Bursaries are available to students at the University of Birmingham, studying degrees such as Social Policy and Social Work, through its Access to Birmingham Scholarships Programme. Apprenticeships can also be funded in several areas including catering, painting and decorating, care and customer service.

Applications
Contact the correspondent by phone for more information.

Further financial information
As the trust was newly registered at the time of writing (December 2019) there was no financial information available.

Other information
The Sir Josiah Mason Trust was created as an umbrella charity to administer the almshouse charity (which is one of its main services), the relief-in-need and educational charity, and the care charity.

Sources of information
Charity Commission record; funder's website.

The Norton Foundation

 £2,700 (2018/19)

Correspondent: The Correspondent, The Paddock, Bwlch Y Gwynt Road, Llysfaen, Colwyn Bay, Clwyd LL29 8DQ (tel: 01492 512079; email: correspondent@nortonfoundation.org)

 www.nortonfoundation.org

CC number: 702638

Eligibility
Young people under the age of 25 who live in Birmingham, Coventry, Solihull and Warwickshire and are in need.

Types of grant
Grants are awarded towards education and training. Grants of up to a maximum of £500 can be awarded, although they are usually within the range of £50 to £250.

Applications
Applications should be made through a third party sponsor such as a social worker, Citizens Advice, probation service, scouts and guides groups or a religious group using the form available from the foundation's website. Applications are considered on a

monthly basis. Further guidance notes can also be found on the website.

Financial information

Year end	05/04/2019
Income	£209,000
Total expenditure	£213,600

Further financial information

In 2018/19 a total of £15,000 was awarded to 141 individuals. Welfare grants totalled £12,300 and were distributed as follows:

Household	95	£10,700
Clothing	19	£1,600

A a further £2,700 was awarded to 27 individuals towards education and training. In addition, £21,700 was paid in block discretionary grants to 13 sponsors for redistribution to individuals. However, this is not included in the grant total.

Other information

The foundation also makes grants to organisations.

Sources of information

Accounts; annual report; Charity Commission record; funder's website.

Sebrights Educational Foundation

Correspondent: P. Copsey, Clerk to the Governors, Adam House, Birmingham Road, Kidderminster, Worcestershire DY10 2SH (tel: 01562 820181; email: clerk@sebrights.org.uk)

 https://www.sebrights.org.uk

CC number: 527523

Eligibility

Young people under the age of 25 (in exceptional cases, the foundation may consider people up to the age of 30) who live in the area of benefit described as 'most of the Wyre Forest area and parts of the Dudley metropolitan borough'. A map of eligible areas is available to view on the foundation's website. Preference is given to those resident in Wolverly and Cookley. Support is given to university and postgraduate students and those who are studying or intending to study for a BTEC, higher national certificate (HNC) or similar skill based courses. Students whose home address is in the area of benefit but who live elsewhere during term time are still eligible to apply.

Support is also given to such people, resident in the area of benefit who are undertaking music, art and sport activities. Except for in very exceptional circumstances, the foundation will not normally consider applications from children under the age of ten.

Types of grant

Grants are awarded towards the cost of specialist clothing, equipment or fees for activities relating to music, sport or art. Support is also given for travel that delivers educational benefits as long as it is provided by the applicant's place of education or a recognised organisation. Previously, consideration has been given to applications for Operation Raleigh, Rotary exchanges and scouts/guides jamborees.

Grants are awarded for a range of educational purposes:

- Post-16 education – grants are awarded to those studying a BTEC, HNC or similar skill based courses towards books, tools, special equipment, software, field trips and in some cases the cost of course fees and rail/bus travel. Assistance may also be given towards the cost of a high spec laptop if it is appropriate to the course
- University – grants are awarded to people studying for a degree towards books, tools, equipment, software, field trips and electives. In some cases, support may be given towards the cost of travel and high spec laptops (if appropriate to the course)
- Postgraduate – grants are awarded towards the fees of a master's course. Interest-free loans may also be offered
- Travel abroad – grants are awarded to assist with the cost of educational travel. Previously, consideration has been given to applications from students taking medical electives and year abroad degrees

Exclusions

Support will not be given towards the cost of running a car.

Applications

Applications for each category of grant can be made after creating an account on the foundation's website. Applications for children under the age of 16 should be made by the child's parent or guardian. Those who are studying music, art or sports at college or university should instead apply through the foundation's post-16 education or university application, details of which can be found on the website. Applications for travel should be submitted along with evidence from the organising body.

Applications for further/higher education travel will be required to provide evidence of the relationship between the travel and course. Those applying for help towards a postgraduate course should submit their application before June/July for consideration in the following year.

Financial information

Year end	31/08/2018
Income	£179,600
Total expenditure	£179,600

Further financial information

In 2017/18 a total of £107,800 was awarded to 145 individuals. Bursaries totalled £2,300 and further education grants totalled £105,500. We were unable to determine the split between grants for social welfare purposes, grants for educational purposes and loans, and have therefore not provided a grant total.

Other information

The foundation also gives grants to organisations.

Sources of information

Accounts; annual report; Charity Commission record; funder's website.

The Wessex Young Musicians Trust

£ £5,400 (2017/18)

Correspondent: Sandrey Date, Trustee, 7 Southbourne Coast Road, Bournemouth BH6 4BE (tel: 01202 423429; email: sandreydate1234@gmail.com W)

CC number: 1100905

Eligibility

Young musicians who live in Dorset and Hampshire, particularly, but not exclusively, the participants and supporters of the Centre for Wessex Young Musicians.

Types of grant

Grants towards equipment and facilities, and loans, scholarships, bursaries and prizes, not usually provided by the statutory authorities.

Applications

Apply in writing to the correspondent.

Financial information

Year end	31/03/2018
Income	£9,000
Total expenditure	£12,000

Further financial information

Full accounts were not available to view on the Charity Commission's website due to the charity's low income. We have therefore estimated the grant total based on the charity's total expenditure.

Sources of information

Charity Commission record; funder's website.

Margaret Westwood Memorial Charity

(£) £4,200 (2018/19)

Correspondent: The Trustees, Higgs & Sons, Unit 3, Waterfront Business Park, Dudley Road, Brierley Hill, West Midlands DY5 1LX (tel: 01384 327322; email: kirsty.mcewen@higgsandsons.co.uk)

CC number: 500125

Eligibility

Children and young people who live in the former county of Worcestershire (as constituted on 18 August 1946). This includes the current county of Worcestershire and parts of the West Midlands.

Types of grant

Grants for the furtherance of education.

Applications

Apply in writing to the correspondent.

Financial information

Year end	05/04/2019
Income	£84,700
Total expenditure	£53,200

Other information

Grants are also awarded to organisations.

Sources of information

Accounts; annual report; Charity Commission record.

Hereford-shire

The Elmley Foundation

(£) £23,500 (2017/18)

Correspondent: The Trustees, West Aish, Morchard Bishop, Crediton, Devon EX17 6RX (tel: 01363 877433; email: foundation@elmley.org.uk)

 www.elmley.org.uk

CC number: 1004043

Eligibility

Students born and schooled in Herefordshire and Worcestershire taking up places on nationally recognised specialist arts courses. Preference will be given to postgraduates and to young people offered exceptional opportunities such as membership of the National Youth Orchestra or the National Youth Theatre.

Types of grant

Grants are available to support a small number of students to take up places on arts courses at a higher level, especially those on postgraduate courses.

Exclusions

The foundation will not support non-arts projects, general appeals or retrospective applications.

Applications

The foundation requests that applicants contact the correspondent prior to making an application. Applications can be submitted as a letter, explaining how much is required and what it will be used for. Alternatively application forms may be downloaded from the foundation's website, although there is no obligation to use them. It is recommended that those who choose to apply with a letter look at the application form to see what details to include. Applications can be made at any time and an answer will usually be given within two months.

Financial information

Year end	05/04/2018
Income	£444,200
Total expenditure	£392,200

Other information

The foundation primarily makes grants to arts organisations.

Sources of information

Accounts; annual report; Charity Commission record; funder's website.

Hereford Municipal Charities

(£) £5,500 (2018)

Correspondent: Clerk, 147 St Owen Street, Hereford, Herefordshire HR1 2JR (tel: 01432 354002; email: herefordmunicipal@btconnect.com)

CC number: 218738

Eligibility

People in need who live in the city of Hereford.

Types of grant

One-off grants are awarded to help with the cost of education and starting work.

Exclusions

Grants are not given towards debts or nursery fees.

Applications

Application forms are available from the correspondent and should be submitted directly by the individual or through a relevant third party. Applications are considered five times a year but can be authorised within meetings if they are very urgent. Applicants are normally interviewed as part of the application process.

Financial information

Year end	31/12/2018
Income	£403,600
Total expenditure	£336,500

Further financial information

Note: the grant total has been estimated.

Other information

The charity also offers almshouse accommodation. There are two separate funds (eleemosynary and educational) administered by the Grants Committee.

Sources of information

Accounts; annual report; Charity Commission record; University of Worcester website.

The Hereford Society for Aiding the Industrious

(£) £600 (2017/18)

Correspondent: Sally Robertson, 18 Venns Close, Bath Street, Hereford, Herefordshire HR1 2HH (tel: 01432 274014; email: info@hsfai.co.uk)

CC number: 212220

Eligibility

People in need who live in Herefordshire and are considered as 'industrious' by the trustees.

Types of grant

One-off and recurring grants according to need.

Exclusions

Postgraduate studies are not usually assisted.

Applications

Apply in writing to the correspondent.

Financial information

Year end	05/04/2018
Income	£130,200
Total expenditure	£194,300

Further financial information

The grant total has been estimated from the 2017/18 accounts.

Other information

The charity's main activity is providing and maintaining almshouses. It also awards to local organisations active in the community.

Sources of information

Accounts; annual report; Charity Commission record.

The Jarvis Educational Foundation

£ £12,600 (2018)

Correspondent: Rachel Jones, Clerk to the Charities, Flintsham Court, Titley, Kington, Herefordshire HR3 3RG (tel: 07929 650290)

CC number: 526881

Eligibility

People who are under the age of 25 and live in the county of Herefordshire; preference is given to those living in Staunton-on-Wye, Bredwardine and Letton.

Types of grant

Grants of either £500 or £1,000 to support people undertaking higher education courses and apprenticeships.

Applications

Apply in writing to the correspondent.

Financial information

Year end	31/12/2018
Income	£30,700
Total expenditure	£43,600

Other information

The foundation also owns land and property and contributed to the cost of building a new school which it continues to support. The foundation is associated with Jarvis Eleemosynary Charity (Charity Commission no. 1167024) and Jarvis Recreational Charity (Charity Commission no. 513356).

Sources of information

Accounts; annual report; Charity Commission record; Kinnersley and District Group Parish Council website.

Ross Educational Foundation

£ £4,000 (2017)

Correspondent: The Trustees, 5 Old Stables, Glewstone, Ross-on-Wye, Herefordshire HR9 6AW

CC number: 527229

Eligibility

People under the age of 25 who live (or whose parents live) in the town of Ross-on-Wye and the civil parish of Ross Rural and who, in the opinion of the trustees, are in need of financial assistance.

Types of grant

Grants are awarded towards the cost of books, equipment and other educational needs for students in higher education and those learning professional or skilled trades. People studying music and other arts may also apply.

Applications

Apply in writing to the correspondent.

Financial information

Year end	31/12/2017
Income	£2,900
Total expenditure	£4,500

Further financial information

Full accounts were not available to view on the Charity Commission's website due to the charity's low income. We have therefore estimated the grant total based on the charity's total expenditure.

Sources of information

Charity Commission record.

Walwyn's Educational Foundation

£ £3,400 (2017/18)

Correspondent: Charles Walker, Clerk to the Trustees, 29 Brookmill Close, Colwall, Malvern, Worcestershire WR13 6HY (tel: 01684 541995; email: cdw1810@btinternet.com)

 https://www.colwall.net/wp-content/uploads/2018/07/Walwyn-Trust-2018-Application-Notice.pdf

CC number: 527152

Eligibility

People under the age of 25 who live in the parishes of Colwall and Little Malvern and are pursuing a degree or an equivalent further education course at a recognised institution (including vocational training).

Types of grant

Small annual grants are available towards general educational expenses as well as support for those leaving an institution of education to assist entry into a trade or profession.

Applications

Application forms are available from Colwall library or can be requested by email from the correspondent. Completed applications must be returned to the correspondent's address. The deadline for applications is usually in September.

Financial information

Year end	05/04/2018
Income	£4,500
Total expenditure	£3,800

Further financial information

Full accounts were not available to view on the Charity Commission's website due to the charity's low income. We have therefore estimated the grant total based on the charity's total expenditure.

Sources of information

Charity Commission record; funder's website.

Shropshire

Bowdler's Educational Foundation

£ £1,600 (2017)

Correspondent: Tim Collard, Shropshire Council, Shirehall, Abbey Foregate, Shrewsbury, Shropshire SY2 6ND (tel: 01743 252756; email: tim.collard@shropshire.gov.uk)

CC number: 528366

Eligibility

People under the age of 25 who live in the county of Shropshire. Priority is given to those living in the Shrewsbury area, in particular the parishes of St Julian and Holy Cross with St Giles.

Types of grant

Grants can be awarded towards the cost of education such as fees, supplementing existing grants, apprenticeships, training and equipment and clothing for those starting work.

Applications

Application forms are available from the correspondent.

Financial information

Year end	31/12/2017
Income	£3,000
Total expenditure	£1,800

Further financial information

Full accounts were not available to view on the Charity Commission's website due to the charity's low income. We have therefore estimated the grant total based on the charity's total expenditure.

Sources of information

Charity Commission record; Shrewsbury Colleges Group website.

The Careswell Foundation

£ £6,900 (2017/18)

Correspondent: The Trustees, Talbot House, 11–15 Market Street, Shrewsbury, Shropshire SY1 1LG (tel: 01743 218450; email: terri.gill@lindermyers.co.uk)

CC number: 528393

Eligibility

People under the age of 25 who live in Shropshire, the parish of Bobbington or

Staffordshire and have attended any of the following schools: Adam's Grammar School (Newport), Bridgnorth Endowed School, Idsall School (Shifnal), Shrewsbury School, Thomas Adam's School (Wem) or any secondary school in the Donnington area.

Types of grant

Grants are available to support students in further education.

Applications

Apply in writing to the correspondent.

Financial information

Year end	31/03/2018
Income	£13,000
Total expenditure	£7,700

Further financial information

Full accounts were not available to view on the Charity Commission's website due to the charity's low income. We have therefore estimated the grant total based on the charity's total expenditure.

Sources of information

Charity Commission record.

Charity of Charles Clement Walker (The Walker Trust)

£ £64,500 (2017/18)

Correspondent: Edward Hewitt, 2 Breidden Way, Bayston Hill, Shrewsbury, Shropshire SY3 0LN (tel: 01743 873866; email: edward. hewitt@btinternet.com)

CC number: 215479

Eligibility

People who live in Shropshire. Applicants should have been resident in the area for at least 12 months prior to application. Preference is given to individuals who are on low incomes or state benefits, people estranged from their families, single parents and young people leaving care.

Types of grant

Grants can be given towards further/ higher education and training courses undertaken within or outside the area of benefit, also for gap-year projects, music, drama and arts costs and expeditions or travel. Individual grants range from £100 up to about £5,000.

Applications

Apply in writing to the correspondent. Applications are considered four times a year, normally in January, April, July and October. They must reach the correspondent at least one month before help is required. Decisions on urgent cases can be made between meetings.

Financial information

Year end	31/03/2018
Income	£451,900
Total expenditure	£548,600

Other information

The trust's registered name is the Charity of Charles Clement Walker.

Sources of information

Accounts; annual report; Charity Commission record.

Ercall Magna Education Endowment

£ £620 (2018/19)

Correspondent: The Trustees, 35 Talbot Fields, High Ercall, Telford, Shropshire TF6 6LY (tel: 01952 770353; email: geoff@gloyderdrome.com)

CC number: 505544

Eligibility

People between the ages of 16 and 25 who are in full-time education and have been living in the civil parish of Ercall Magna for at least one year.

Types of grant

Financial assistance is available for students at university or in other forms of higher education and people entering a trade or profession. Grants can be used towards the cost of books, tools, instruments, clothing and so on.

Applications

Apply in writing to the correspondent.

Financial information

Year end	30/06/2019
Income	£1,300
Total expenditure	£680

Further financial information

Full accounts were not available to view on the Charity Commission's website due to the charity's low income. We have therefore estimated the grant total based on the charity's total expenditure.

Other information

The charity also awards grants to organisations.

Sources of information

Charity Commission record.

The Gorsuch, Langley and Prynce Charity

£ £8,500 (2018)

Correspondent: The Trustees, 116 Underdale Road, Shrewsbury, Shropshire SY2 5EF (email: vicar@ shrewsburyabbey.com)

CC number: 247223

Eligibility

Educational grants are available to students whose usual home address is within the parishes of Holy Cross (The Abbey and St Peter's Monkmoor) and St Giles.

Types of grant

Educational grants are to students for costs associated with pursuing post-16 education (i.e. vocational training and higher/further education).

Applications

Applications should be made by email, using 'Gorsuch, Langley and Prynce Application' as the subject line. All applicants are visited by the Trust Secretary who will conduct a 'means test' and complete an application form with the applicant, which is then submitted for consideration at the trustees' next meeting. The trustees meet on eleven occasions each year.

Financial information

Year end	31/12/2018
Income	£44,300
Total expenditure	£38,200

Further financial information

During 2018, the charity awarded grants to 139 individuals and families for welfare and educational purposes. Note: the grant total for educational grants has been estimated.

Other information

This charity also makes grants to organisations, particularly to local schools to help fund school trips for pupils and their families who are in need.

Sources of information

Accounts; annual report; Charity Commission record; Shrewsbury Abbey website.

Millington's Charity (Millington's Hospital)

£ £3,000 (2018)

Correspondent: The Trustees, Admiral Rodney Inn, Criggion, Shrewsbury SY5 9AU (tel: 01743 360904; email: clerk@millingtons.org.uk)

CC number: 213371

Eligibility

Further/higher education students under the age of 25 who live or have been educated in Shropshire and who, or whose parents/guardians, are members of the Church of England.

Types of grant

Grants are awarded to help people in further/higher education (including religious instruction). Support is given towards general educational expenses associated with college or university attendance, including equipment, books, maintenance/living costs, study/travel abroad. Help can also be given for a specific educational project, musical instruments or extra activities within the chosen course.

Exclusions

Grants are not normally given towards fees.

Applications

Apply in writing to the correspondent.

Financial information

Year end	31/12/2018
Income	£177,300
Total expenditure	£203,700

Other information

The charity also provides almshouse accommodation for older and vulnerable people.

Sources of information

Accounts; annual report; Charity Commission record.

The St Chad's and St Alkmund's Charity
See record on page 128

Telford and Wrekin

The Careswell Foundation
See record on page 154

Maxell Educational Trust

£ £17,600 (2017/18)

Correspondent: The Trustees, Oaktree Place, Hortonwood 35, Telford, Shropshire TF1 7FR (tel: 01952 522207; email: hr@maxell.eu)

CC number: 702640

Eligibility

Students whose family home is within the boundaries of Telford, or who attend schools or colleges in the area.

Types of grant

Grants are available towards educational costs.

Applications

Apply in writing to the correspondent.

Financial information

Year end	05/04/2018
Income	£4,700
Total expenditure	£39,100

Further financial information

Full accounts were not available to view on the Charity Commission's website due to the charity's low income. We have therefore estimated the grant total based on the charity's total expenditure.

Other information

Grants are also made towards research in electronics and technology in Telford, and may also be made to organisations.

Sources of information

Charity Commission record.

Staffordshire

Lady Dorothy Grey's Foundation

£ £30,500 (2017/18)

Correspondent: Richard E. Jones, Trustee, Batfield House, Batfield Lane, Enville, Stourbridge, West Midlands DY7 5LF (tel: 07939 978777; email: enville.trusts@btopenworld.com)

CC number: 508900

Eligibility

Children and young people under the age of 25 who live in (or whose parent/parents live in) the parishes of Bobbington, Enville or Kinver, with a preference for Enville and who, in the opinion of the trustees, are in need of financial assistance.

Types of grant

Grants are awarded towards the general educational expenses of individuals who are in need of financial assistance.

Applications

Apply in writing to the correspondent.

Financial information

Year end	31/03/2018
Income	£374,000
Total expenditure	£308,100

Further financial information

In 2018 a total of £30,500 was awarded in grants to individuals. The charity's large expenditure is due to the purchase of investments.

Sources of information

Accounts; annual report; Charity Commission record.

East Staffordshire

Consolidated Charity of Burton upon Trent

£ £57,200 (2018)

Correspondent: Mr J. Southwell, Clerk to the Trustees, Dains LLP, 1st Floor, Gibraltar House, Crown Square, First Avenue, Burton-on-Trent, Staffordshire DE14 2WE (tel: 01283 527067; email: clerk@consolidatedcharityburton.org.uk)

 www.consolidatedcharityburton.org.uk

CC number: 239072

Eligibility

People who live in Burton-on-Trent and the neighbouring parishes of Branston, Outwoods and Stretton and are in need.

Types of grant

The charity offers a number of schemes:

- Bursaries of up to £1,500 (£500 per year for three years) are given to undergraduate students resident in the area of benefit to assist with the costs associated with a university degree. The schools and colleges included in the scheme are Abbot Beyne School, Burton and South Derbyshire College, De Ferrers Specialist Technology College, John Taylor High School, Paget High School, Paulet High School, Blessed Robert Sutton Catholic Sports College and Derby Grammar School
- Education and personal development grants offer up to £300 per year towards further education, vocational training, overseas travel for personal development, sports activities and arts scholarships

Exclusions

Grants are not awarded for the relief of debt or towards postgraduate courses.

Applications

Applications for bursaries must be submitted through the applicant's school or college and must be accompanied by a personal statement from the individual and a supporting statement from the school or college. Application forms for the education and personal development grant can be downloaded from the charity's website to be returned by post, or can be completed online. Applicants are required to provide evidence that they have been accepted onto the course or project for which they are seeking assistance.

Financial information

Year end	31/12/2018
Income	£626,200
Total expenditure	£857,400

Further financial information

In 2018 a total of £114,300 was awarded to individuals. Relief-in-need grants totalling £57,100 were awarded to 124 individuals. Three individuals received education and personal development grants totalling £900 and £56,300 was awarded as bursaries to 40 individuals.

Other information

The charity also runs 29 almshouses in the local area, and provides grants for organisations.

Sources of information

Accounts; annual report; Charity Commission record; funder's website.

Stafford
Stafford Educational Endowment Charity

£ £850 (2017/18)

Correspondent: The Trustees, Treasury & Pensions, 2 Staffordshire Place, Tipping Street, Stafford, Staffordshire ST16 2LP (tel: 01785 276330; email: melanie.stokes@staffordshire.gov.uk)

 www.sirgrahambalfour.co.uk/ Stafford-Educational-Endowment-Charity

CC number: 517345

Eligibility

Pupils and former pupils of one of the six Stafford high schools, who are under the age of 25. Applicants can apply up until their 26th birthday.

Types of grant

Grants in the past have been in the region of £100 to £500 and can be used for a range of educational purposes such as apprentice schemes, residential courses, scientific field work, overseas travel and so on.

Applications

Applications can be completed on the Sir Graham Balfour School website or can be requested from the correspondent. Applications are usually considered in October, February and June when the trustees meet.

Financial information

Year end	31/03/2018
Income	£16,900
Total expenditure	£16,700

Further financial information

Grants are also made to individuals for welfare purposes and to schools. Full accounts were not available to view on the Charity Commission's website due to the charity's low income. We have therefore estimated the grant total based on the charity's total expenditure.

Sources of information

Accounts; annual report; Charity Commission record; funder's website; Staffordshire County Council website.

Tamworth
The Rawlet Trust

£ £6,000 (2017/18)

Correspondent: The Trustees, 47 Hedging Lane, Wilnecoate, Tamworth, Staffordshire B77 5EX (tel: 07850 614410; email: rawlettrust@ mail.com)

CC number: 221732

Eligibility

Educational grants are available to young people in Tamworth aged under 25.

Types of grant

One-off and recurring grants according to need.

Applications

Apply in writing to the correspondent. The trustees meet quarterly in January, April, July and October to consider grant applications.

Financial information

Year end	09/03/2018
Income	£25,900
Total expenditure	£27,100

Other information

As part of its welfare grant-making, the charity also distributes bibles to beneficiaries.

Sources of information

Accounts; annual report; Charity Commission record.

Warwick-shire
William Edwards Educational Charity

£ £31,900 (2017/18)

Correspondent: Mr J. M. P. Hathaway, Clerk to the Charity, Heath & Blenkinsop Solicitors, 42 Brook Street, Warwick, Warwickshire CV34 4BL (tel: 01926 492407; email: law@ heathandblenkinsop.com)

CC number: 528714

Eligibility

People under the age of 25 who live, or whose parents live in the town of Kenilworth, or those who have attended a school in the town.

Types of grant

Bursaries are available for postgraduate students towards tuition fees and living expenses as well as financial assistance for undergraduates.

Applications

Apply in writing to the correspondent.

Financial information

Year end	30/06/2018
Income	£266,900
Total expenditure	£311,300

Further financial information

In 2017/18 the total sum of grants to individuals was £67,400. Grants were broken down as follows: school uniforms/trips (£35,500); bursaries (£25,900); awards to undergraduates (£6,000).

Other information

In 2017/18 the charity received 115 applications. It made 101 awards towards the cost of school uniforms/school trips, two bursaries were made to postgraduate students, (in addition to ongoing bursaries), and one award was made to an undergraduate student. The charity also supports local schools.

Sources of information

Accounts; annual report; Charity Commission record.

The Leigh Educational Foundation

£ £17,000 (2018)

Correspondent: James Johnson, Clerk to the Trustees, 3 Barford Woods, Barford Road, Warwick, Warwickshire CV34 6SZ (tel: 01926 419300; email: admin@ leigheducationalfoundation.org.uk)

 leigheducationalfoundation.org.uk

CC number: 701462

Eligibility

People under the age of 25 and who (or whose parents) are resident in the parishes of Stoneleigh, Ashow, Leek Wootton and Guy's Cliffe and Burton Green.

Types of grant

Grants are awarded to schoolchildren, college students, higher/further education students and apprentices for any educational purpose. Grants can assist towards the costs of school trips both home and abroad, school uniform, equipment of all kinds, tuition fees, etc. The trustees are much more willing to consider making a contribution to fees or charges.

Exclusions

The trustees are unlikely to fund applications for computers or other equipment that is for wider use.

Applications

Application forms and full guidelines are available on the foundation's website along with the current deadlines. The trustees meet four times a year to allocate grants – in February, May, August and November. For an application to be considered at a meeting, a completed application form must have been received by the Clerk by the start of the prior month. There is no limit to the number of times an applicant may apply for a grant; however, it is unlikely the trustees will make more than one award to any one applicant in each year. Illegible handwriting, poor grammar and spelling, and lack of clarity may reduce your chances of a successful application.

Financial information

Year end	31/12/2018
Income	£193,000
Total expenditure	£230,700

Further financial information

We estimate that around £17,000 is available towards higher/further education costs and approximately £17,000 available towards school trips and uniforms for schoolchildren.

Other information

The foundation also supports local youth groups and organisations such as scouts, guides, brownies, cubs and local teams.

Sources of information

Accounts; annual report; Charity Commission record; funder's website.

Newfield Charitable Trust

£ £14,700 (2018/19)

Correspondent: Eli Williams, Admin Assistant, Rotherham & Co., 8–9 The Quadrant, City Centre, Coventry, Warwickshire CV1 2EG (tel: 024 7622 7331; email: e.williams@ rotherham-solicitors.co.uk)

 https://cid.coventry.gov.uk/kb5/ coventry/directory/service. page?id=O52HR2XgnIs

CC number: 221440

Eligibility

Girls and women under the age of 40 living in Coventry or Leamington Spa who are in need.

Types of grant

Grants are awarded towards college fees, textbooks, educational equipment and educational trips.

Exclusions

Grants are not awarded for the following purposes:

- Repayment of loans from purchasing non-essential items
- Rent/community charge arrears (except in exceptional circumstances)
- Utility bills
- Private school fees
- Holidays (except in exceptional circumstances)
- Postgraduate education or second degrees

Applications

Application forms can be downloaded from the Coventry Information Directory website and should be completed by hand and returned to Rotherham and Co. Solicitors (addressed 'FAO Mrs Mary Allanson – Clerk to Trustees' if returning by post). Applications must be submitted along with a supporting letter from a professional which details the applicant's domestic situation and need. Applications can be submitted directly from the individual or through a third party such as social services, a teacher or health worker. See the Coventry Information Directory website for current deadlines. Grants can be awarded to an individual up to three times but cannot be applied for more than once in a year.

Financial information

Year end	31/03/2019
Income	£62,200
Total expenditure	£66,600

Further financial information

Grants were awarded to 125 individuals for both welfare and educational purposes. Grants are also made to organisations including schools.

Sources of information

Accounts; annual report; Charity Commission record; Coventry Information Directory website.

Perkins's Educational Foundation

£ £29,000 (2018)

Correspondent: The Clerk to the Governors, c/o Lodders Solicitors LLP, 10 Elm Court, Arden Street, Stratford-upon-Avon, Warwickshire CV37 6PA (tel: 01789 293259; email: info@ williamperkinscharity.org)

 www.williamperkinscharity.org

CC number: 528678

Eligibility

People aged between 16 and 25 who have been living in Bidford-on-Avon, Broom, Cleeve Prior, Harvington or Salford Priors for at least two years immediately prior to their application. Applicants must be thinking about pursuing some form of further/higher education or vocational training.

Types of grant

Grants are available towards the costs of further/higher education and vocational training in the form of scholarships, bursaries or maintenance allowances.

Exclusions

Awards are not usually made to students under the age of 18 doing GCSE or A-level courses, or to candidates who have reached the age of 25.

Applications

Application forms can be requested in writing from the correspondent or downloaded from the foundation's website. Only official application forms will be considered and forms must be signed by the applicant personally. First-time applicants should also provide a statement of recommendation from their headteacher, college principal or employer. Completed forms should be returned to the clerk by post or email by 15th October each year. Late submissions are not accepted.

Financial information

Year end	31/12/2018
Income	£67,600
Total expenditure	£48,900

Further financial information

In 2018, grants totalling £29,000 were awarded to young individuals in higher education. Grants are also awarded to local schools and youth organisations.

Sources of information

Accounts; annual report; Charity Commission record; funder's website.

The Marc Smith Educational Charity
See record on page 138

North Warwickshire

Educational Foundation of Simon Lord Digby and Others

£ £600 (2018)

Correspondent: Clerk, The Vicarage, High Street, Coleshill, Birmingham B46 3BP (tel: 01675 462188; email: clerk.sldigby@yahoo.com)

CC number: 528710

Eligibility
Students who live or attend school in the parish of Coleshill who are in financial need.

Types of grant
Grants and scholarships to advance education.

Applications
Application forms are available from the correspondent. The trustees usually meet twice a year to consider applications. Applicants may be required to undergo an interview prior to grants being awarded.

Financial information
Year end	31/12/2018
Income	£33,600
Total expenditure	£32,700

Further financial information
In 2018, one individual grant of £600 was awarded.

Other information
The foundation also makes grants to organisations and supports local schools.

Sources of information
Accounts; annual report; Charity Commission record.

Nuneaton and Bedworth

Exhall Educational Foundation

£ £490 (2018)

Correspondent: Carol Gough, Secretary, c/o Parish Office, St Giles' Church Hall, St Giles Road, Ash Green, Coventry, Warwickshire CV7 9GZ (tel: 024 7631 8219; email: cagough@sky.com)

 www.exhalleducationalfoundation. blogspot.co.uk

CC number: 528663

Eligibility
People under the age of 25 who live, or whose parents live, in the parish of Exhall or Keresley End.

Types of grant
Grants of around £200 for educational purposes; past examples include books for degree courses, field trips/expeditions, travel to educational courses and more.

Applications
Application forms are available from the foundation's website or can be requested from the correspondent. Applications are considered twice a year, in mid-March and mid-October. They can be submitted by post or by email in advance of the trustees' meeting.

Financial information
Year end	31/12/2018
Income	£2,600
Total expenditure	£2,200

Further financial information
Full accounts were not available to view on the Charity Commission's website due to the charity's low income. We have therefore estimated the grant total based on the charity's total expenditure.

Other information
The foundation also supports local schools.

Sources of information
Charity Commission record; funder's website.

Rugby

The Bilton Poors' Land and Other Charities

£ £5,100 (2017/18)

Correspondent: The Trustees, 9 Critchley Drive, Rugby, Warwickshire CV22 6PJ (tel: 01788 811030; email: biltoncharities@outlook.com)

CC number: 215833

Eligibility
Residents of Bilton who are preparing for entry into any trade or profession are eligible for support.

Types of grant
Educational grants are awarded according to need. Grants have previously been made for the cost of tools/equipment, books, travel expenses and any fees for instruction or examination.

Applications
Apply in writing to the correspondent.

Financial information
Year end	28/02/2018
Income	£23,600
Total expenditure	£17,000

Further financial information
Full accounts were not available to view on the Charity Commission's website due to the charity's low income. We have therefore estimated the grant total based on the charity's total expenditure.

Other information
Grants are made predominantly for welfare purposes, as well as to organisations whose work benefits the residents of Bilton.

Sources of information
Charity Commission record.

Dunchurch and Thurlaston Educational Foundation

£ £1,700 (2017/18)

Correspondent: Paul Smith, Clerk to the Governors, 11 Bilton Lane, Dunchurch, Rugby, Warwickshire CV22 6PY (tel: 01788 810635; email: pppsmith80@hotmail.com)

 https://www.stpeters-dunchurch. org/children-in-church

CC number: 528738

Eligibility
People under the age of 25 who live or whose parents live in the parishes of Dunchurch and Thurlaston.

Types of grant
Grants are available to further/higher education students and people entering a trade/occupation for general educational needs including travel to pursue education and the study of music and art.

Applications
Application forms can be obtained from the correspondent.

Financial information
Year end	26/10/2018
Income	£2,700
Total expenditure	£3,800

Further financial information
Full accounts were not available to view on the Charity Commission's website due to the charity's low income. We have therefore estimated the grant total based on the charity's total expenditure.

Other information
This foundation also awards grants to local schools for repairs and supports voluntary organisations that provide assistance to young people.

Sources of information

Charity Commission record; funder's website.

Stratford

The Shipston-on-Stour Educational Charity

£ £1,900 (2018)

Correspondent: The Trustees, 49 Telegraph Street, Shipston-on-Stour, Warwickshire CV36 4DA (tel: 01608 664065; email: ds@pinnegards.com)

CC number: 507400

Eligibility

People under the age of 25 who live, or have a parent/parents living in the parish of Shipston-on-Stour who are in need of financial assistance.

Types of grant

Small grants for students undertaking further education.

Applications

Apply in writing to the correspondent.

Financial information

Year end	31/12/2018
Income	£3,000
Total expenditure	£2,100

Further financial information

Full accounts were not available to view on the Charity Commission's website due to the charity's low income. We have therefore estimated the grant total based on the charity's total expenditure.

Sources of information

Charity Commission record.

Warwick

Arlidge's Charity

£ £980 (2017/18)

Correspondent: The Trustees, 10 Inverary Close, Kenilworth, Warwickshire CV8 2NZ (tel: 01926 512507; email: cjritchie3@hotmail.co.uk)

CC number: 528758

Eligibility

People under the age of 25 who live in the county of Warwick and who are, or whose parent/s are, members of the United Reformed Church. Preference is given to those living in Kenilworth.

Types of grant

Grants are awarded to support general educational needs.

Applications

Apply in writing to the correspondent.

Financial information

Year end	31/03/2018
Income	£2,600
Total expenditure	£2,600

Further financial information

Full accounts were not available to view on the Charity Commission's website due to the charity's low income. We have therefore estimated the grant total based on the charity's total expenditure.

Other information

The charity's Charity Commission record states that a seventh of its income is paid to the minister for Abbey Hill United Reform Church to further religious and other charitable work of the congregation, or in augmentation of his/her stipend. The residual income is applied for the benefit of United Reform congregation members in Kenilworth, and/or promoting education for United Reform members in Warwick and Kenilworth who need financial assistance.

Sources of information

Charity Commission record.

Barford Relief-in-Need Charity

£ £3,400 (2017)

Correspondent: The Trustees, 14 Dugard Place, Barford, Warwick, Warwickshire CV35 8DX (tel: 01926 624153)

CC number: 256836

Eligibility

People in need who live in the parish of Barford.

Types of grant

Grants can also be made to individuals who are attending school, college or university. Occasional financial assistance is provided for specific purposes such as Raleigh International and Outward Bound-type courses.

Applications

Applications can be made in writing to the correspondent, directly by the individual or a family member. One of the trustees will then visit the applicant to obtain all necessary information. Applications are usually considered in May and October.

Financial information

Year end	31/12/2017
Income	£11,800
Total expenditure	£15,000

Further financial information

Full accounts were not available to view on the Charity Commission's website due to the charity's low income. We

have therefore estimated the grant total based on the charity's total expenditure.

Other information

Grants are also made to organisations.

Sources of information

Charity Commission record.

Austin Edwards Charity

£ £4,400 (2017/18)

Correspondent: Jackie Newton, 26 Mountford Close, Wellesbourne, Warwick, Warwickshire CV35 9QQ (tel: 01789 840135; email: jackie. newton114@gmail.com)

 www.austinedwards.org.uk

CC number: 225859

Eligibility

People living in the old borough of Warwick (generally the CV34 postcode). Our research indicates that support is normally provided to students at college or university (including mature students) or people starting work.

Types of grant

Grants, generally of no more than £300, are awarded for relief-in-need. Grants can be given for clothing, equipment, books, travel, course fees and study/travel overseas.

Exclusions

Grants cannot be provided for follow-on courses, postgraduate courses or additional degrees. The charity's website also states that 'where grants are applied for in respect of study courses, the trustees will only consider providing funding for one course per applicant'.

Applications

Application forms can be downloaded from the charity's website and should be returned to the correspondent stating the purpose of the grant and the amount required, as well as details of any other charities approached with the same request. The individual's name and address must be supplied with the application. The trustees usually hold one meeting annually in July but will consider applications throughout the year.

Financial information

Year end	05/04/2018
Income	£11,400
Total expenditure	£9,700

Further financial information

Full accounts were not available to view on the Charity Commission's website due to the charity's low income. We have therefore estimated the grant total based on the charity's total expenditure.

Sources of information

Charity Commission record; funder's website.

Hatton Consolidated Fund (Hatton Charities)

 £2,300 (2017/18)

Correspondent: David Thompson, The Clerk, 1 Gardner Way, Kenilworth, Warwickshire CV8 1QW (tel: 01926 864943; email: david@dmbfs.com)

CC number: 250572

Eligibility

Students and apprentices who live in the parishes of Hatton, Beausale and Shrewley.

Types of grant

Grants are awarded to students, apprentices and people starting work towards fees, books, equipment, outfits, travel expenses and so on.

Applications

Apply in writing to the correspondent.

Financial information

Year end	31/03/2018
Income	£13,300
Total expenditure	£10,200

Further financial information

Full accounts were not available to view on the Charity Commission's website due to the charity's low income. We have therefore estimated the grant total based on the charity's total expenditure.

Other information

Grants are awarded to both organisations and individuals for educational and social welfare purposes. Note: the fund may also provide loans which may be included in the grant total.

Sources of information

Charity Commission record; Shrewley Parish website.

The Lucy Price Relief-in-Need Charity

 £34,400 (2018)

Correspondent: D. Thomas, Clerk, Holly House, 13 Holly Walk, Baginton, Coventry, Warwickshire CV8 3AE (tel: 07884 182904)

CC number: 516967

Eligibility

Young people aged between 5 and 25 who live in the parish of Baginton and are in need.

Types of grant

Grants are awarded mainly to students in college or university for general educational/living costs. Grants are paid in instalments on a termly basis.

Exclusions

Grants cannot be used for the relief of rates or taxes. Once a grant is awarded, it cannot be repeated or renewed.

Applications

Apply in writing to the correspondent.

Financial information

Year end	31/12/2018
Income	£301,000
Total expenditure	£36,400

Sources of information

Accounts; annual report; Charity Commission record.

Charity of Sir Thomas White, Warwick

Correspondent: The Trustees, 12 High Street, Warwick, Warwickshire CV34 4AP (tel: 01926 350555; email: connect@sirthomaswhite.org.uk)

 www.sirthomaswhite.org.uk

CC number: 1073331

Eligibility

People between the ages of 18 and 35 who live, or whose parents live in the town of Warwick, and who are establishing a business or undertaking tertiary education or vocational training.

Types of grant

Interest-free loans for young people undertaking tertiary education courses or vocational training. Candidates can borrow up to £1,500 per year for each year of their course (depending on the length of their course). The charity also provides interest-free loans to young people wishing to establish a business, or assist them to improve their existing business in the town of Warwick. These interest-free loans are available up to £10,000 (for five years).

Applications

Application forms and further guidelines can be downloaded from the charity's website or requested from the correspondent. Those applying for student loans should return the application together with details of the course and its financial requirements. Two adults must complete the Guarantor Questionnaire attached to the form; guarantors will be required to sign a deed of guarantee.

Those applying for business loans should return the application form together with their business plan; details of what to include can be find on the website.

Applicants for both category of loan will have to attend an interview with a small panel of trustees to discuss the applicant's requirements/business plan. Successful applicants will be required to sign a loan agreement. Repayment of loans will begin 12 months after the final loan instalment has been paid for student loans and one month after the loan has been released for business loans, both to be repaid over a period of up to five years.

Financial information

Year end	31/12/2018
Income	£253,100
Total expenditure	£249,700

Further financial information

During 2018 the charity advanced 24 loans to new and continuing higher education students and one business loan. Total loans advanced was £36,000.

Other information

There is no grant total given for this charity as it provides interest-free loans rather than grants to individuals. The charity also makes grants to local schools.

Sources of information

Accounts; annual report; Charity Commission record; funder's website.

Warwick Apprenticing Charities

 £41,700 (2018)

Correspondent: Mr C. E. R. Houghton, Clerk to the Trustees, c/o Moore & Tibbits, 34 High Street, Warwick, Warwickshire CV34 4BE (tel: 01926 491181; email: choughton@moore-tibbits.co.uk)

 www.warwickapprenticingcharities.org.uk

CC number: 528745

Eligibility

People under the age of 25 who live in Warwick.

Types of grant

Grants are also available for students who wish to pursue further education after leaving school and can help towards a range of educational pursuits including apprenticeships, college or university. Grants can assist towards the costs of fees, clothing, tools, books, travel and maintenance expenses.

Applications

Applications for each type of grant can be found on the charity's website. Application forms should be printed, completed and returned by post together with a letter giving further details of the applicant, the course of study/project and the costs.

Financial information

Year end	31/12/2018
Income	£94,700
Total expenditure	£62,000

Further financial information

In 2018, £41,700 was paid in 'advancement in life' grants to 62 individuals. A further £9,600 was paid for outward bound places for individuals.

Sources of information

Accounts; annual report; Charity Commission record; funder's website.

West Midlands Metropolitan Area

The Birmingham and Three Counties Trust for Nurses

£ £9,200 (2017/18)

Correspondent: The Trustees, 19 Hanover Gardens, Upper Holly Walk, Leamington Spa, Warwickshire CV32 4JW (tel: 07711 794049; email: bham3counties@hotmail.co.uk)

CC number: 217991

Eligibility

Nurses in Warwickshire, Worcestershire and Staffordshire who are in need. Preference is given to older nurses.

Types of grant

One-off and recurring grants according to need.

Applications

Apply in writing to the correspondent.

Financial information

Year end	31/03/2018
Income	£13,700
Total expenditure	£20,500

Further financial information

Full accounts were not available to view on the Charity Commission's website due to the charity's low income. We have therefore estimated the grant total based on the charity's total expenditure.

Sources of information

Charity Commission record.

Grantham Yorke Trust

£ £6,200 (2018/19)

Correspondent: Christine Norgrove, Clerk to the Trustees, The Estate Office, Wharf Cottage, Broombank, Newnham Bridge, Tenbury Wells, Worcestershire WR15 8NY (tel: 07799 784019; email: chrissy@granthamyorketrust.org.uk)

CC number: 228466

Eligibility

People under the age of 25 who were born in the former West Midlands metropolitan county area (comprising Birmingham, Coventry, Dudley, Redditch, Sandwell, Solihull, Tamworth, Walsall or Wolverhampton).

Types of grant

Grants are available for people in education, apprenticeships and those starting work, towards books, tools, clothing and equipment.

Applications

Application forms are available from the correspondent and can be submitted either directly by the individual or via a relevant third party such as a social worker. The trustees meet four times a year to consider applications.

Financial information

Year end	05/04/2019
Income	£282,200
Total expenditure	£347,400

Further financial information

Grants were awarded to 33 individuals for education and welfare purposes.

Other information

The trust also promotes education and training for the prevention of anti-social behaviour and addiction as well as education focusing on family planning and parenting. It also makes grants to organisations and provides facilities for recreational activities.

Sources of information

Accounts; annual report; Charity Commission record; University of Worcester website.

Birmingham

Building Birmingham Scholarship

Correspondent: Joy Anibaba and Carl Bradley   (tel: 0121 675 4685 or 0121 675 3282; email: bbs@birmingham.gov.uk)

 https://www.birmingham.gov.uk/info/20139/support_for_business/447/building_birmingham_scholarship

Eligibility

UK citizens (or EU citizens with indefinite leave to remain in the UK) aged between 16 and 24 who want to study for a career in the construction and built environment sector at higher education level. Applicants must have been resident in Birmingham for at least three years, living in Birmingham or having settled in the UK within the meaning of the UK immigration act. An applicant's annual household income must not exceed £35,000.

Types of grant

Scholarships of up to £9,000 per student towards tuition fees or a paid internship each year in between studies. A further £500 is given for expenses such as a travel pass, books, essential materials, a laptop/PC or essential childcare.

Exclusions

Applicants who already have a degree will not be accepted.

Applications

Application forms are available to download from the Birmingham City Council website. Completed forms should be returned by email. Short-listed applicants will be required to attend an interview.

Further financial information

We were unable to determine the financial details of the scholarship.

Sources of information

Birmingham City Council website.

The George Fentham Birmingham Charity

£ £23,500 (2018)

Correspondent: Jaime Hobday, Secretary, c/o Veale Wasbrough Vizards LLP, Second floor, 3 Brindley Place, Birmingham, West Midlands B1 2JB (tel: 0121 227 3703; email: GeorgeFentham@vwv.co.uk)

www.georgefenthamcharity.org.uk

CC number: 214487

Eligibility

Long-term residents of the city of Birmingham who are under the age of 25 and studying at college or university.

Types of grant

Support with study at college or university.

Applications

Application forms can be downloaded from the charity's website, once completed they can be returned by post or email. Students must supply evidence that they are in receipt / have applied for a student loan.

Financial information

Year end	31/12/2018
Income	£203,800
Total expenditure	£203,700

Other information

Grants are also awarded to organisations.

Sources of information

Accounts; annual report; Charity Commission record; funder's website.

The King's Norton United Charities

 £6,100 (2017)

Correspondent: Revd Larry Wright, The Rectory, 273 Pershore Road, Kings Norton, Birmingham, West Midlands B30 3EX (tel: 0121 459 0560; email: parishoffice@kingsnorton.org.uk)

www.knuc.org.uk

CC number: 202225

Eligibility

The charity is able to assist only those who live within the boundary of the ancient parish of Kings Norton, now in the city of Birmingham and Worcestershire and much larger than the current parish of Kings Norton. This area includes the current Church of England parishes of Kings Norton, Cotteridge, Stirchley, parts of Bournville, Balsall Heath, Kings Heath, Moseley (St Anne's and St Mary's), Brandwood, Hazelwell, Highters Heath, Wythall, West Heath, Longbridge, Rubery and Rednal. There is a helpful map on the charity's website which shows the area of benefit.

Types of grant

Grants of £50 to £350 for educational needs such as help with fees.

Applications

The trustees prefer to receive referrals for help through a GP or a relevant agency. However, there is a form available on the charity's website for self-referrals. The trustees will then contact applicants to discuss the situation.

Financial information

Year end	31/12/2017
Income	£9,500
Total expenditure	£13,600

Further financial information

Full accounts were not available to view on the Charity Commission's website due to the charity's low income. We have therefore estimated the grant total based on the charity's total expenditure.

Sources of information

Charity Commission record; funder's website.

Yardley Educational Foundation

 £56,200 (2017/18)

Correspondent: Derek Hackett, Clerk to the Trustees, Yardley Great Trust, 31 Brookside, Yardley Fields Road, Birmingham, West Midlands B36 8QL (tel: 0121 784 7889; email: karen.grice@ygtrust.org.uk)

www.ygt.org.uk/yef_21674.html

CC number: 528918

Eligibility

Children and young people between the ages of 11 and 19 who have lived in the ancient parish of Yardley for at least two years and have a low household income.

Types of grant

The foundation provides grants to individuals for items such as sports kits, school uniforms and books. It also awards grants for individuals to undertake vocational training or apprenticeships.

Applications

Application forms can be obtained from the individual's school or college or downloaded from The Yardley Great Trust Group's website.

Financial information

Year end	31/03/2018
Income	£200,900
Total expenditure	£153,800

Further financial information

In 2018 a total of £100,800 was awarded in grants. We have estimated that around £44,600 was awarded towards the cost of school uniforms, school trips and sports equipment for schoolchildren, £44,600 towards further education, and the remaining £11,611 was awarded as book tokens.

Other information

The foundation also awards grants to 'educational establishments for students aged 11 years and over'.

Sources of information

Accounts; annual report; Charity Commission record; funder's website.

Coventry

General Charity (Coventry)

£ £79,900 (2018)

Correspondent: Susan Hanrahan, Clerk to the Trustees, General Charities Office, Old Bablake, Hill Street, Coventry, Warwickshire CV1 4AN (tel: 024 7622 2769; email: cov.genchar@outlook.com)

CC number: 216235

Eligibility

People in need living in the city of Coventry.

Types of grant

Grants are awarded towards the advancement of education and research. Funding is given towards books, music education and to support individuals studying for a medical PhD.

Applications

Apply in writing to the correspondent.

Financial information

Year end	31/12/2018
Income	£1,650,000
Total expenditure	£1,660,000

Further financial information

Grants awarded for educational purposes totalled £79,900 and were broken down as follows:

Medical PhD Students	3	£56,400
Books and equipment	108	£13,500
Music	1	£10,000

Other information

The charity consists of the charities formerly known as The Relief in Need Charity, Sir Thomas White's Pension Fund and Sir Thomas White's Educational Foundation. The trustees are also responsible for the administration of Lady Herbert's Homes (Charity Commission no. 232066) and Eventide Homes Ltd (Charity Commission no. 246570) providing accommodation for older people in the city of Coventry. Support is also given to organisations.

Sources of information

Accounts; annual report; Charity Commission record.

Learner Support Fund

Correspondent: The Administrator

 https://www.coventry.gov.uk/info/
58/adult_education/219/learner_
support_fund

Eligibility

People in Coventry aged 19 and over who are attending an accredited course with the Adult Education Service. Applicants must either have a disability and need help with travel to and from their course, or have an annual household income of less than £22,600 and need help with fees.

Types of grant

Grants can be made to help with travel costs or tuition and examination fees.

Exclusions

The fund cannot reimburse petrol costs and is unable to help with the cost of private childcare.

Applications

Request an application form from your tutor or course organiser.

Other information

Applicants are entitled to free places in crèche facilities while they attend their class (subject to a £5 registration fee). Applicants should contact staff at the centre where they are studying for more information. Note: the fund is no longer able to cover 100% of taxi/travel costs. This fund is administered by Coventry City Council and we were unable to determine a grant total, specific postal address or telephone number. Please visit the council's website for further information.

Sources of information

Coventry City Council (website).

Soothern and Craner Educational Foundation

£ £2,900 (2017/18)

Correspondent: The Clerk, The Hollies, Priory Road, Wolston, Coventry, Warwickshire CV8 3FX (tel: 024 7655 4255; email: admin@soothernandcraner. org.uk)

 www.soothernandcraner.org.uk

CC number: 528838

Eligibility

Girls and young women who live in the city of Coventry or who are connected to Coventry Quaker Meeting. Studies may be undertaken away from Coventry, but the connection with the city is crucial to eligibility.

Types of grant

Grants are awarded towards the furtherance of education or vocational training for young women over 16 and can be used towards trips, specialist equipment and other educational needs. In some cases grants for daily travel or computer equipment will be considered.

Exclusions

Support will rarely be given to people studying beyond first degree level.

Applications

The foundation's website provides two application forms – one for those still in school and one for school leavers. Applications can be made at any time of year and can be submitted either electronically or by paper, along with two references to support the application. Applications are usually considered in July and again in October and January providing there are funds available. The foundation asks that application forms be submitted via ordinary post rather than recorded delivery as this may result in delays.

Financial information

Year end	30/04/2018
Income	£14,200
Total expenditure	£9,500

Further financial information

Full accounts were not available to view on the Charity Commission's website due to the charity's low income. We have therefore estimated the grant total based on the charity's total expenditure.

Other information

Support may also be given to schools.

Sources of information

Charity Commission record; funder's website.

Dudley

Baylies' Educational Foundation

£ £35,600 (2017/18)

Correspondent: D. F. Hughes, Clerk to the Trustees, 53 The Broadway, Dudley, West Midlands DY1 4AP (tel: 01384 259277; email: bayliesfoundation@ hotmail.co.uk)

 www.dudleyrotary.org.uk/baylies.
html

CC number: 527118

Eligibility

Children and young people under the age of 25 living in the borough of Dudley. A limited number of special awards may also be available, depending on funds, to students over the age of 25

or students taking a second degree. All candidates must demonstrate genuine financial need and show they have attempted to secure funding elsewhere.

Types of grant

Grants that are tenable at any secondary school, training college for teachers, university, or other institution of further education approved by the trustees. In addition the foundation offers financial assistance, clothing, equipment or books for those leaving school, university or other educational establishment to assist entry into a trade, profession or calling as well as help towards travel, educational trips and the encouragement of music, arts or sport. Grants are also made to help unemployed candidates retrain, or who face barriers in their access to education.

Applications

Application forms are available on the foundation's website or can be requested from the correspondent.

Financial information

Year end	28/02/2018
Income	£102,400
Total expenditure	£51,100

Other information

Local schools and organisations are also supported.

Sources of information

Accounts; annual report; Charity Commission record; funder's website.

The Palmer and Seabright Charity

£ £5,900 (2018)

Correspondent: Susannah Griffiths, Clerk to the Trustees, c/o Wall James Chappell Solicitors, 15–23 Hagley Road, Stourbridge, West Midlands DY8 1QW (tel: 01384 371622; email: sgriffiths@ wjclaw.co.uk)

CC number: 200692

Eligibility

Students under the age of 25 living in the borough of Stourbridge.

Types of grant

One-off and recurrent grants are awarded towards fees, books, equipment, instruments and living expenses.

Applications

Apply in writing to the correspondent.

Financial information

Year end	31/12/2018
Income	£46,400
Total expenditure	£23,200

Further financial information

In 2018 grants totalling £13,500 were made (including £1,700 in Christmas grants). We estimate that welfare grants to individuals totalled £7,600 and education grants to individuals totalled £5,900.

Sources of information

Accounts; annual report; Charity Commission record; Schumacher College website.

Daniel Parsons Educational Charity

£ £11,700 (2017)

Correspondent: The Trustees, 53 The Broadway, Dudley, West Midlands DY1 4AP (tel: 01384 259277; email: parsonscharity@hotmail.com)

 www.dudleyrotary.org.uk/parsons. html

CC number: 1068492

Eligibility

People under the age of 25 who (or whose parents) live in Dudley and the surrounding neighbourhood or who have, at any time, attended school in the area.

Types of grant

Grants are available for educational purposes, including to gain or develop any type of academic, artistic or athletic skill.

Exclusions

Grants are not available to those who could obtain the same support from the state or any other source.

Applications

Application forms can be downloaded from the Dudley Rotary website or obtained by writing to the correspondent. Applications are more likely to be successful if they are returned along with a supporting letter giving information on the proposed course of study or project and the reasons for wanting to take part.

Financial information

Year end	31/12/2017
Income	£15,000
Total expenditure	£13,000

Further financial information

Full accounts were not available to view on the Charity Commission's website due to the charity's low income. We have therefore estimated the grant total based on the charity's total expenditure.

Sources of information

Charity Commission record; funder's website.

The Sedgley Educational Trust

£ £1,300 (2018)

Correspondent: Secretary to the Trustees, 12 Larkswood Drive, Sedgley, Dudley, West Midlands DY3 3UQ (tel: 01902 672880)

CC number: 1091563

Eligibility

People who live in the ecclesiastical parishes of All Saints Sedgley, St Mary the Virgin Sedgley and St Chad Coseley.

Types of grant

Grants are available towards advancing education, including religious education.

Applications

Apply in writing to the correspondent.

Financial information

Year end	31/12/2018
Income	£2,900
Total expenditure	£2,800

Further financial information

Full accounts were not available to view on the Charity Commission's website due to the charity's low income. We have therefore estimated the grant total based on the charity's total expenditure.

Other information

The trust also awards grants to organisations.

Sources of information

Charity Commission record.

Sandwell

The Fordath Foundation

£ £2,000 (2018)

Correspondent: The Trustees, 33 Thornyfields Lane, Stafford, Staffordshire ST17 9YS (tel: 01785 247035; email: fordath-foundation@ ntlworld.com)

CC number: 501581

Eligibility

People in need who live in the metropolitan borough of Sandwell.

Types of grant

Grants are available for educational needs.

Applications

Application forms can be requested from the correspondent and should usually be submitted through a recognised social care, welfare rights or education organisation such as social services, Citizens Advice and so on. Applications can be submitted at any time.

Financial information

Year end	31/12/2018
Income	£7,600
Total expenditure	£9,000

Further financial information

Full accounts were not available to view on the Charity Commission's website due to the charity's low income. We have therefore estimated the grant total based on the charity's total expenditure.

Sources of information

Charity Commission record.

Palmer Educational Charity (The Palmer Trust)

£ £3,700 (2017)

Correspondent: The Trustees, The Church of England, 1 Colmore Row, Birmingham, West Midlands B3 2BJ (tel: 0121 426 0400)

CC number: 508226

Eligibility

Young people under the age of 25 who live in the Warley deanery and young people who are in need of financial assistance.

Types of grant

Grants are prioritised to support religious education. However, grants are also given to individuals who are in need of financial assistance to promote education including social and physical training.

Applications

Apply in writing to the correspondent.

Financial information

Year end	31/12/2017
Income	£9,300
Total expenditure	£16,400

Further financial information

Full accounts were not available to view on the Charity Commission's website due to the charity's low income. We have therefore estimated the grant total based on the charity's total expenditure.

Other information

Primarily grants are made to the Church of England schools in the Warley deanery. Local churches and organisations may also be supported.

Sources of information

Charity Commission record.

George and Thomas Henry Salter Trust

£ £26,500 (2018)

Correspondent: Mrs J. Styler, Clerk to the Trustees, 8 Yarnborough Hill, Stourbridge, West Midlands DY8 2EB (tel: 01384 316344; email: gthsaltertrust@outlook.com)

CC number: 216503

Eligibility
Students who have lived in the borough of Sandwell for at least three years and are undertaking further or higher education. Students must have already obtained a place on a course to be eligible.

Types of grant
Cash grants of up to £350 are given to students to enable them to pursue their education either in the UK or abroad.

Applications
To apply for a relief-in-need grant, apply in writing to the correspondent.

Applications for student grants can be requested from the correspondent or downloaded from the Phoenix Sixth Form website. Application forms must be supported by evidence of enrolment and attendance on the course from the educational organisation that also confirms the applicant's home address. Applicants must also obtain a copy of their passport/ID photo certified as a true copy by the educational organisation.

Financial information
Year end	31/12/2018
Income	£44,900
Total expenditure	£72,000

Other information
The trust also supports local schools and organisations.

Sources of information
Accounts; annual report; Charity Commission record; Phoenix Collegiate website.

Walsall

The Fishley Educational and Apprenticing Foundation

£ £3,600 (2017/18)

Correspondent: Clerk to the Trustees, Democratic Services, PO Box 23, Walsall, West Midlands WS1 1TW (tel: 01922 654764; email: charities@walsall.gov.uk)

 www.walsall.gov.uk/charities

166

CC number: 529010

Eligibility
Young people in need who are under the age of 25 and live, work or study in Walsall.

Types of grant
Grants are awarded for general educational needs including scholarships, tuition fees, maintenance allowances, travel abroad in pursuance of education, books and the study of music and the arts.

Applications
Application forms can be downloaded from the foundation's website or requested from the correspondent. Grants are considered at least twice a year. Applications must be supported by a member of the educational establishment's teaching staff. Note that applications for grants towards educational trips should be made through the educational establishment.

Financial information
Year end	31/03/2018
Income	£23,000
Total expenditure	£11,900

Further financial information
Full accounts were not available to view on the Charity Commission's website due to the charity's low income. We have therefore estimated the grant total based on the charity's total expenditure.

We estimate that in 2017/18 a total of £3,600 was awarded for welfare purposes, a further £3,600 was awarded for educational expenses and the remaining income was awarded to organisations.

Sources of information
Charity Commission record; funder's website.

C. C. Walker Charity

£ £4,400 (2017/18)

Correspondent: Clerk to the Trustees, Democratic Services, Walsall Council, Lichfield Street, Walsall, West Midlands WS1 1TW (tel: 01922 654764; email: charities@walsall.gov.uk)

 https://go.walsall.gov.uk/charities

CC number: 528898

Eligibility
People who are under the age of 25 and live or study in the borough of Walsall. Preference is given to applicants whose parent/parents have died and who were either born in Walsall and/or whose parents or surviving parent has lived in Walsall at any time since the birth of the applicant.

Types of grant
Grants are available in the form of scholarships and financial assistance for higher education students towards tuition fees and other course costs.

Applications
Application forms are available to download from the charity's website or can be requested from the correspondent. The trustees meet at least twice a year.

Financial information
Year end	31/03/2018
Income	£22,300
Total expenditure	£9,800

Further financial information
Full accounts were not available to view on the Charity Commission's website due to the charity's low income. We have therefore estimated the grant total based on the charity's total expenditure.

Sources of information
Charity Commission record; funder's website.

Worcester-shire

Perkins's Educational Foundation
See record on page 158

Worcester Municipal Charities (CIO)

£ £2,400 (2018)

Correspondent: Office Administration, Kateryn Heywood House, Berkeley Court, The Foregate, Worcester, Worcestershire WR1 3QG (tel: 01905 317117; email: admin@wmcharities.org.uk)

 www.wmcharities.org.uk

CC number: 1166931

Eligibility
People of any age who live in the city of Worcester or the parishes of Powick, Bransford and Rushwick, and the ancient parish of Leigh who are undertaking education. Applications from people living outside these areas but who have attended school in the city of Worcester for at least two years may be considered. Further information on eligibility can be found on the charity's website.

Types of grant

Grants are awarded towards equipment, supplies and other educational items to help an individual to complete their course.

Exclusions

Grants will not be awarded for school uniforms due to the government's pupil premium payments to schools.

Grants towards fees, travel abroad and awards beyond first degree level are normally excluded.

Applications

Individuals should first apply to the Worcester City Council's 'Discretionary Welfare Assistance Scheme' (details can be found on Worcester Municipal Charities' website). Those who are unsuccessful in that application should then apply to this charity. Application forms can be downloaded from the charity's website and returned via email – handwritten forms will not be accepted. Applications must be made through a support worker from a statutory or voluntary organisation. Guidance, other sources of support and deadlines are also available on the charity's website.

Application forms can be downloaded from the charity's website and returned via email – handwritten forms will not be accepted. Consult the charity's website for current deadlines.

Financial information

Year end	31/12/2018
Income	£1,180,000
Total expenditure	£821,100

Further financial information

In 2018 welfare grants totalled £36,700 with £32,100 given for relief-in-need and £4,600 for white goods. Educational grants totalling £2,400 were awarded to four individuals.

Other information

This CIO is the successor of the Worcester Municipal Exhibitions Foundation and the Worcester Consolidated Municipal Charity, whose assets and liabilities were transferred to this CIO on 30 June 2016. The charity owns a number of properties and affordable almshouses for retired people and young people who are currently homeless. In addition, the charity provides support to organisations and helps to administer the Worcester City Council's 'Discretionary Welfare Assistance Scheme' which gives grants to individuals in need for white goods and food.

Sources of information

Accounts; annual report; Charity Commission record; funder's website.

Bromsgrove

Alvechurch Grammar School Endowment

 £10,500 (2017/18)

Correspondent: Richard Keen, Clerk to the Trustees, c/o The Highlands, Hollow Tree Lane, Vigo, Bromsgrove, Worcestershire B60 1PR (tel: 0121 445 3594; email: enquiries@alvechurchgst.org.uk)

🌐 www.alvechurchgst.org.uk

CC number: 527440

Eligibility

People under the age of 25 who (or whose parents) live in the old parish of Alvechurch, which includes Alvechurch, Hopwood, Rowney Green, Bordesley and those parts of Barnt Green 'only up to the railway line'. Applicants must be able to demonstrate they are in need of financial assistance.

Types of grant

Funding is available for a wide range of purposes to enable the applicant to continue their education. This includes help towards course fees, living costs, travel in the pursuance of education, clothing, tools, instruments, IT equipment, books and educational trips both in the UK and abroad and worthwhile projects that may not otherwise be afforded.

Exclusions

Assistance is only available where support cannot be received from the local education authority.

Applications

Application forms can be downloaded from the charity's website or requested from the correspondent. Completed applications should be returned by post. The deadlines for applications are 1 January, 1 May, and 1 September each year.

Financial information

Year end	31/03/2018
Income	£29,300
Total expenditure	£15,700

Further financial information

In 2017/18 a total of £10,500 was paid in grants to individuals.

Other information

Grants are also given to local organisations that support young people in the area.

Sources of information

Accounts; annual report; Charity Commission record; funder's website.

William James Reeve's Charity

£ £900 (2017/18)

Correspondent: The Trustees, Worcestershire County Council, County Hall, Spetchley Road, Worcester, Worcestershire WR5 2NP (tel: 01905 845224; email: fmorgan@worcestershire.gov.uk)

CC number: 527426

Eligibility

Boys who were born or who ordinarily reside in the parishes of Stoke Prior, Stoke Works and Aston Fields.

Types of grant

Grants are available to assist with the cost of full-time university education. Preference is given to those studying for degrees in science and medicine.

Applications

Apply in writing to the correspondent.

Financial information

Year end	31/03/2018
Income	£160
Total expenditure	£1,000

Further financial information

Full accounts were not available to view on the Charity Commission's website due to the charity's low income. We have therefore estimated the grant total based on the charity's total expenditure.

Sources of information

Charity Commission record.

Malvern Hills

Alfrick Educational Charity

£ £5,800 (2017/18)

Correspondent: Andrew Duncan, Trustee, Bewell, Alfrick, Worcestershire WR6 5EY (tel: 01905 731731; email: a.duncan@wwf.co.uk)

CC number: 517760

Eligibility

People under the age of 25 who live in the parish of Alfrick, Lulsley and Suckley.

Types of grant

Grants are aimed at further and higher education students to be used towards books, maintenance/living expenses and educational outings in the UK.

Applications

Applications can be made in writing to the correspondent and can be submitted at any time.

Financial information

Year end	30/06/2018
Income	£9,700
Total expenditure	£12,900

Further financial information

Full accounts were not available to view on the Charity Commission's website due to the charity's low income. We have therefore estimated the grant total based on the charity's total expenditure.

Other information

Support is also given to Suckley primary school and other educational establishments in Alfrick, Lulsley and Suckley.

Sources of information

Charity Commission record.

Redditch

The Feckenham Educational Foundation

£ £2,900 (2017/18)

Correspondent: Judy Bate, Clerk to the Trustees, Wychway, Droitwich Road, Hanbury, Bromsgrove B60 4DB (tel: 01527 821285; email: judy.bate@hotmail.co.uk)

CC number: 527565

Eligibility

Young people under the age of 25 in the pursuit of further education and training who live, or whose parents live, in the borough of Redditch, with a preference for those in the ancient parish of Feckenham. Grants are divided on the basis that 4/5 of the funds are allocated to individuals in Feckenham and the remaining 1/5 to those in Redditch.

Types of grant

The foundation awards grants that are tenable at any school, college, university or further education institution that has been approved by the trustees. Financial assistance is also offered for apprentices and people preparing to enter a trade or profession, to assist towards the cost of clothing, tools, instruments or books.

Applications

Apply in writing to the correspondent. Application deadlines are usually at the end of August, however, contact the correspondent for current deadlines. Individuals may apply a maximum of three times.

Financial information

Year end	30/04/2018
Income	£3,500
Total expenditure	£3,200

Further financial information

Full accounts were not available to view on the Charity Commission's website due to the charity's low income. We have therefore estimated the grant total based on the charity's total expenditure.

Sources of information

Charity Commission record.

Wychavon

John Martin's Charity

£ £262,400 (2018/19)

Correspondent: John Daniels, Clerk to the Trustees, 16 Queen's Road, Evesham, Worcester, Worcestershire WR11 4JN (tel: 01386 765440; email: enquires@johnmartins.org.uk)

 www.johnmartins.org.uk

CC number: 527473

Eligibility

People resident in Evesham, Worcestershire, who are in need.

Individuals between the ages of 16 and state retirement age, may apply for educational grants to support study in a wide variety of courses at local colleges in addition to universities and colleges throughout the country and also, the Open University. Qualifying courses include Higher National Diplomas (HND) and degree, postgraduate and part-time vocational courses. Applicants must have been a permanent resident or (if living away from home during term time) have maintained a residential address in the town for a minimum of twelve months immediately prior to 1 September in the year of application.

Types of grant

Educational grants for further and higher education are typically up to £1,050 a year (although students living at home will receive less than this) to cover living expenses while studying.

There is a miscellaneous Education Grant of up to £175 available to students aged from 4 to 18 for activities including school trips, music lessons/instrument hire and sporting activities. Applications are assessed based on the number of children and adults in the household, and housing costs are also taken into consideration. There is an easy-to-use eligibility calculator on the charity's website.

Standards of Excellence awards are for students aged from 4 to 18 for achieving a 'standard of excellence' in a sporting or arts/music area. Applications are not subject to a financial assessment, however, suitable evidence of the achievement must be provided.

Exclusions

The charity cannot replace statutory benefits or supply equipment that is normally available from statutory sources, nor can it pay council tax bills or fines.

The charity does not currently provide grants for full-time courses below HND/degree level.

Applications

Application forms are available from the correspondent or as a download from the charity's website, where criteria is also posted. Applications can be submitted directly by the individual or through a social worker, Citizens Advice or other welfare agency. All applications are subject to a financial assessment and evidence of income and housing costs must be provided. The charity's office can be contacted to discuss an individual's request and circumstances. The website publishes upcoming application deadlines.

Financial information

Year end	31/03/2019
Income	£800,000
Total expenditure	£887,000

Other information

Grants are also made to organisations.

Sources of information

Accounts; annual report; Charity Commission record; funder's website.

Wyre Forest

The Bewdley Old Grammar School Foundation

£ £17,700 (2017/18)

Correspondent: The Administrator, The Bewdley School, Stourport Road, Bewdley DY12 1BL (tel: 01299 403277; email: office@bewdley.worcs.sch.uk)

CC number: 527429

Eligibility

People under the age of 25 living in Bewdley or the parishes of Rock and Ribbesford, Worcestershire.

Types of grant

Grants are available for schoolchildren and further/higher education students to assist with general educational costs including books, equipment, clothing, maintenance and other educational needs. Support is also available for candidates to study music and art.

Applications

Apply in writing to the correspondent.

Financial information

Year end	10/10/2018
Income	£16,100
Total expenditure	£19,600

Further financial information

Full accounts were not available to view on the Charity Commission's website due to the charity's low income. We have therefore estimated the grant total based on the charity's total expenditure.

Sources of information

Charity Commission record.

East of England

General

Kentish's Educational Foundation

 £11,600 (2018/19)

Correspondent: Margery Roberts, Clerk to the Trustees, 7 Nunnery Stables, St Albans, Hertfordshire AL1 2AS (tel: 01727 856626)

https://directory.hertfordshire.gov. uk/Services/9920

CC number: 313098

Eligibility

Young people between the ages of 11 and 25 who are in need. Applicants must be permanently resident in Hertfordshire or Bedfordshire. Preference is given to people with the family name Kentish or people related to the foundation's founder, Thomas Kentish.

Types of grant

Grants are available for those undertaking a first degree, further education, apprenticeships and for people leaving education to enter a profession or trade. Grants can be used towards associated costs including travel in pursuance of education, the study of music and the arts, books, outfits, tools and instruments. Grants for postgraduates may be considered in special circumstances. Grants usually range from £150 to £1,000 but this may change.

Exclusions

Support is not usually given for postgraduate courses or second first degrees.

Applications

Application forms and further information can be requested from the correspondent. Applications should usually be submitted in September for consideration in November. However, contact the correspondent for current deadlines.

Financial information

Year end	31/03/2019
Income	£28,700
Total expenditure	£17,600

Further financial information

In 2018/19 the total amount awarded in grants to 14 individuals was £11,600. This is broken down in the charity's 2018/19 accounts as follows:

Postgraduate	£8,000
Higher/further education	£3,100
Secondary Education	£500

Other information

The 2018/19 accounts state that the cut-off age for beneficiaries is currently around 25 and that the trustees prefer to make awards to apprentices, those on vocational courses and those undertaking first degrees.

Sources of information

Accounts; annual report; Charity Commission record; funder's website.

Rand's Educational Foundation

 £66,500 (2018)

Correspondent: Katrina Henshaw, Clerk to the Governers, Rand's Educational Foundation, Devonshire Business Centre, Works Road, Letchworth Garden City SG6 1GJ (tel: 07817 104734; email: randsclerk@gmail.com)

https://rands.org.uk

CC number: 311022

Eligibility

Students who live in the villages of Ickleford, Holwell, Pirton or Stondon, are between the ages of 16 and 25 and are undertaking a further or higher education course.

Types of grant

Grants for educational purposes. A separate application should be made for each year of study. The foundation also makes grants towards personal development activities.

Applications

Application forms can be downloaded from the charity's website and submitted by either post or email. Documentary evidence of the course from the educational institution must also be provided.

Financial information

Year end	31/12/2018
Income	£144,900
Total expenditure	£140,000

Other information

The foundation also makes grants to organisations in the area of benefit.

Sources of information

Accounts; annual report; Charity Commission record; funder's website.

SPRET (The Sir Philip Reckitt Educational Trust Fund)

 £21,400 (2018)

Correspondent: Christine Atherton, c/o Rollits LLP, Forsyth House, Alpha Court, Monks Cross, York, North Yorkshire YO32 9WN (tel: 01904 688506; email: spretrust@googlemail.com OR christine. atherton@rollits.com)

www.spret.org

CC number: 529777

Eligibility

People who live in Kingston upon Hull, the former county of East Riding of Yorkshire, or the county of Norfolk.

Types of grant

Contributions towards the costs of travel, residence and attendances at conferences, lectures and educational courses, held nationally or internationally, for individuals and groups of individuals.

Applications

An application form can be completed and submitted online or can be downloaded and posted to the appropriate address after completion. A reference from the head of the institution of study, an employer or other suitable referee is required. Applications should be received by the trust more than six weeks before the intended departure date. Those submitted later are not normally considered. Successful applicants must complete a report to be returned to the trustees within three months of the end of the project or period of study.

Financial information

Year end	31/12/2018
Income	£38,100
Total expenditure	£60,400

Other information

East Riding of Yorkshire correspondent: Christine Atherton (christine.atherton@rollits.com), Sir Philip Reckitt Educational Trust, c/o Rollits LLP, Forsyth House, Alpha Court, Monks Cross, York YO32 9WN

County of Norfolk correspondent: Sir Philip Reckitt Educational Trust, c/o Mrs J Pickering, 99 Yarmouth Road, Ellingham. Bungay, NR35 2PH; spretrust@googlemail.com.

Grants were also made to individuals for welfare purposes.

Sources of information

Accounts; annual report; Charity Commission record; funder's website.

Bedfordshire

Ashton Schools Foundation

 £3,900 (2017/18)

Correspondent: Julie Tipler, Clerk, Grove House, 76 High Street North, Dunstable, Bedfordshire LU6 1NF (tel: 01582 660008; email: dunstablecharity@yahoo.com)

www.associationofdunstable charities.co.uk

CC number: 307526

Eligibility

Children and young people under the age of 25 living in Dunstable. Proof of receipt of housing benefit is required. If an applicant is *not* in receipt of housing benefit, they must contact the Clerk to arrange an interview and complete a finance form.

Types of grant

Grants, scholarships, bursaries and maintenance allowances are awarded to students in any school, university, college or any other place of further education. Grants for clothing, equipment, books and more general

financial assistance are available to students to assist in their studies (including the study of music and the arts.) The charity also awards grants to cover the cost of undertaking travel upon leaving education and preparing to enter a trade or profession.

Exclusions

Grants are limited to a maximum of four per child. Those who have applied for a Chews Foundation (Charity Commission no. 307500) grant are not eligible for a grant from this charity.

Applications

Contact the correspondent to request an application form. All forms should be signed by the applicant and their school or college. Applications usually close at the beginning of May and are sent out in July.

Financial information

Year end	31/03/2018
Income	£2,220,000
Total expenditure	£731,300

Other information

The trust also makes annual grants to Manshead Academy and Ashton St Peter's Primary School, to enlarge their current schools and allow for additional places for children.

Sources of information

Accounts; annual report; Charity Commission record; funder's website.

Oakley Educational Foundation

 £10,000 (2017/18)

Correspondent: Louise Tunley, c/o Steve Monico Ltd, 19 Goldington Road, Bedford MK40 3JY (tel: 01234 402040; email: louise.tunley@monico.co.uk)

CC number: 307464

Eligibility

Young people between the ages of 16 and 25 who live in Oakley.

Types of grant

Grants are made towards books and equipment/tools.

Applications

Apply in writing to the correspondent.

Financial information

Year end	31/10/2018
Income	£10,300
Total expenditure	£11,200

Further financial information

Full accounts were not available to view on the Charity Commission's website due to the charity's low income. We have therefore estimated the grant total based on the charity's total expenditure.

Sources of information

Charity Commission record.

Bedford

The Harpur Trust

 £77,600 (2017/18)

Correspondent: Lucy Bardner, Princeton Court, The Pilgrim Centre, Brickhill Drive, Bedford, Bedfordshire MK41 7PZ (tel: 01234 369503; email: grants@ harpurtrust.org.uk)

www.harpurtrust.org.uk

CC number: 1066861

Eligibility

Adults living in the borough of Bedford who left formal education at least five years ago, are returning to work/ planning a career change, and are on a low income. In addition, students aged 19 or under who are wishing to undertake an undergraduate or foundation degree course. To be eligible students must meet all of the following criteria:

- Be the age of 19 or under
- Have lived in the borough of Bedford for at least two years and attended one of the schools listed on the trust's website
- Have already been offered a place on a full-time course
- Have already applied for other forms of support

And at least two of the following conditions:

- Be from the first generation in their family to attend university
- Come from a low-income family
- Live independently
- Have additional financial difficulties arising from personal circumstances

Students who have received the trust's undergraduate bursary may be eligible to apply for a postgraduate bursary providing they graduated between 2013 and 2018 with a 2:1 or above, still have a permanent Bedford address and have been accepted onto a full-time postgraduate course (details of eligible courses can be found on the trust's website).

Types of grant

University bursary programme

Grants of £1,200 per year for up to three years are available to students to assist with costs associated with their course.

Postgraduate bursary programme

Grants are available to support postgraduate students who also received the trust's undergraduate bursary. The maximum grant is £4,000.

Exclusions

Grants will not be given for: PGCE courses or recreational courses. People who are part way through a course will only be supported in exceptional circumstances.

Applications

Grants to individuals

All application forms and detailed guidelines can be found on the trust's website. Potential applicants should contact the trust for guidance before submitting the application. Forms should be submitted by the end of May for courses beginning in September/ October and shortlisted candidates will be invited for an interview. Applicants must determine their entitlement to statutory funding before making an application.

University and postgraduate bursaries

Application forms, guidelines and current deadlines are available on the trust's website.

Financial information

Year end	30/06/2018
Income	£54,360,000
Total expenditure	£52,040,000

Further financial information

In 2017/18 £57,600 was awarded as part of the university bursary programme, £20,000 for college bursaries and £2,100 was awarded to one individual.

Other information

Most grants are awarded to registered charities, voluntary organisations and other groups. The trust also runs four independent schools (Bedford School, Bedford Modern School, Bedford Girls' School, Pilgrims Pre-Preparatory School), sponsors Bedford Academy, and provides almshouse accommodation in Bedford.

Sources of information

Accounts; annual report; Charity Commission record; funder's website.

Ursula Taylor Charity

£ £1,100 (2017)

Correspondent: Mavis Nicholson, Secretary to the Trustees, 39 George Street, Clapham, Bedford MK41 6AZ (tel: 01234 405141; email: mavis. nicholson1@ntlworld.com)

CC number: 307520

Eligibility

Children and young people between the ages of 11 and 25 who live in the parish of Clapham and are in full-time education or training.

Types of grant

Grants are made to people starting work, individuals undertaking apprenticeships and students in further/higher education. Support can be given for books, course fees, equipment/instruments, tools, clothing and other educational needs.

Applications

Apply in writing to the correspondent.

Financial information

Year end	31/12/2017
Income	£2,400
Total expenditure	£2,500

Further financial information

Full accounts were not available to view on the Charity Commission's website due to the charity's low income. We have therefore estimated the grant total based on the charity's total expenditure.

Sources of information

Charity Commission record.

Central Bedfordshire

Flitwick Combined Charities

£ £5,100 (2017/18)

Correspondent: Revd Lucy Davis, Trustee, The Vicarage, 26 Dew Pond Road, Flitwick, Bedfordshire MK45 1RT (tel: 01525 712369; email: Lucy@ flitwickchurch.org)

 www.flitwickcombinedcharities.org. uk

CC number: 233258

Eligibility

Grants are available for students who are about to start their second year of university or are in an apprenticeship and whose home is the parish of Flitwick.

Types of grant

One-off and recurring grants according to need.

Applications

Application forms are available from the charity's website or the correspondent. The trustees' meetings are held three times a year and the dates are publicised on the website.

Financial information

Year end	31/08/2018
Income	£11,600
Total expenditure	£11,400

Further financial information

Full accounts were not available to view on the Charity Commission's website due to the charity's low income. We have therefore estimated the grant total based on the charity's total expenditure.

Other information

Grants are also awarded to individuals for welfare purposes.

Sources of information

Charity Commission record.

Potton Consolidated Charity

£ £39,150 (2018/19)

Correspondent: Dean Howard, Clerk, 69 Stotfold Road, Arlesey, Bedfordshire SG15 6XR (tel: 01462 735220; email: clerk@potton-consolidated-charity.co. uk)

 www.potton-consolidated-charity. co.uk

CC number: 201073

Eligibility

Educational grants are available for children and young people under the age of 25 who are residents of Potton. Applicants must be in further or higher education. Full guidelines can be found on the funder's website.

Types of grant

Educational grants are made to support those in full-time education. This includes assistance with the cost of transport.

Applications

Application forms for educational grants are available to download from the funder's website. Alternatively, application forms can be collected from the Potton post office.

For welfare grants, apply in writing to the correspondent.

The trustees meet between five and six times each year to consider grant applications.

Financial information

Year end	31/03/2019
Income	£150,500
Total expenditure	£172,200

Other information

This charity also makes grants to organisations, mainly to local schools and other welfare organisations assisting residents of Potton.

Sources of information

Accounts; annual report; Charity Commission record; funder's website.

Cambridge-shire

The Downham Feoffee Charity

£ £2,000 (2018/19)

Correspondent: J. E. Howard, Clerk to the Trustees, 35 Fieldside, Ely, Cambridgeshire CB6 3AT (tel: 01353 665774; email: downhamfeoffeescharity@outlook.com)

CC number: 237233

Eligibility

Residents of the ancient parish of Downham who are in need.

Types of grant

Educational grants are made to students in higher education.

Welfare grants are awarded according to need.

Applications

Apply in writing to the correspondent.

Financial information

Year end	05/04/2019
Income	£125,600
Total expenditure	£42,900

Other information

The charity also makes grants to local schools and other organisations.

Sources of information

Accounts; annual report; Charity Commission record.

Town Lands Educational Foundation

£ £11,000 (2017/18)

Correspondent: The Trustees, 78 High Road, Gorefield, Wisbech, Cambridgeshire PE13 4NB (tel: 01945 870454; email: leveoffees@aol.com)

CC number: 311325

Eligibility

People in further/higher education who live in Leverington, Parson Drove and Gorefield.

Types of grant

One-off and recurrent grants according to need.

Applications

Apply in writing to the correspondent.

Financial information

Year end	30/06/2018
Income	£13,900
Total expenditure	£12,200

Further financial information

Full accounts were not available to view on the Charity Commission's website due to the charity's low income. We have therefore estimated the grant total based on the charity's total expenditure.

Other information

Grants are also made to local schools.

Sources of information

Charity Commission record.

East Cambridgeshire

Bishop Laney's Charity

£ £33,600 (2017/18)

Correspondent: Richard Tyler, Clerk to the Trustees, George Court, Bartholomew's Walk, Ely, Cambridgeshire CB7 4JW (tel: 01353 662595; email: secretary@bishoplaneyscharity.org.uk)

 https://www.bishoplaneyscharity.org.uk

CC number: 311306

Eligibility

People under the age 25 who live in the parishes of Soham and Ely. Consideration might be given to people under the age of 25 who live in other parts of Cambridgeshire where funds permit.

Types of grant

Grants are awarded to students going to university for the purchase of books and equipment. Grants are considered for other items based on need and supporting information should be provided. The usual grant is £250 for the first year and £150 for the next two years of a three year course. Apprentices (long and short-term) can apply for grants which are paid in instalments upon a satisfactory report from the employer each year. For a three year apprenticeship the apprentice would receive £1,000 over the three years and the employer would receive £250 at the start and end of the period.

Applications

Application forms are available from the charity's website or can be requested from the correspondent. They can be submitted directly by the individual. Applications should include a copy of the applicant's birth certificate, proof of attendance at college/university/training and details of the items needed. Full details are available from the charity's website.

Financial information

Year end	25/03/2018
Income	£136,900
Total expenditure	£70,400

Other information

The charity can also give grants to educational organisations.

Sources of information

Accounts; annual report; Charity Commission record; funder's website.

Fenland

The Whittlesey Charity

£ £16,000 (2017)

Correspondent: The Trustees, 33 Bellamy Road, Oundle, Peterborough, Cambridgeshire PE8 4NE (tel: 01832 273085)

CC number: 1005069

Eligibility

People in need who live in the ancient parishes of Whittlesey Urban and Whittlesey Rural.

Types of grant

One-off and recurring grants according to need.

Applications

Apply in writing to the correspondent.

Financial information

Year end	31/12/2017
Income	£74,300
Total expenditure	£57,700

Other information

The charity makes grants to organisations and individuals, for relief-in-need, educational purposes and general charitable purposes. It also awards grants to churches.

Sources of information

Annual report; Charity Commission record.

Elizabeth Wright's Charity

£ £2,000 (2017)

Correspondent: Iain Mason, Trustee, 13 Tavistock Road, Wisbech, Cambridgeshire PE13 2DY (tel: 01945 588646; email: i.h.mason60@gmail.com)

CC number: 203896

Eligibility

People who live in the ancient parish of Wisbech St Peter, Cambridgeshire.

Types of grant

Grants are awarded towards education and training including the study of music, art and religious education.

Applications

Apply in writing to the correspondent.

Financial information

Year end	31/12/2017
Income	£43,400
Total expenditure	£35,900

Other information

The charity also makes grants to organisations.

Sources of information

Accounts; annual report; Charity Commission record.

Huntingdonshire

Huntingdon Freemen's Trust

 £56,400 (2017/18)

Correspondent: Karen Clark, Grants Officer, 37 High Street, Huntingdon, Cambridgeshire PE29 3AQ (tel: 01480 414909; email: info@huntingdonfreemen. org.uk)

 www.huntingdonfreemen.org.uk

CC number: 1044573

Eligibility

Students undertaking vocational or higher education, who live in the area covered by Huntingdon Town Council, including Oxmoor, Hartford, Sapley, Stukeley Meadows and Hinchingbrooke Park. Applicants should have lived in the area for at least 12 months, although exceptions can be made depending on the circumstances.

Types of grant

Grants of up to £1,000 per student per year. Financial assistance is available for students over 16 undertaking vocational courses towards course fees, equipment and in some cases, travel costs. Grants are also available to students leaving home to attend university or further education colleges to cover half of their accommodation fees.

Exclusions

The trust will not usually give grants towards council tax, debts, fines or funerals.

Applications

Individuals applying for grants should apply in writing to the correspondent including their name, contact details and a brief description of the type of help required. Most applications will require a home visit from a grants officer who will assess the applicant's needs and financial circumstances.

Applications for student grants can be downloaded from the trust's website.

Financial information

Year end	30/04/2018
Income	£670,800
Total expenditure	£479,700

Further financial information

Note: the grant total has been estimated.

Other information

The trust supports local organisations that cater for a wide variety of recreational activities for all ages as well as local nurseries and primary schools. It also provides specialist equipment on long-term loan, including over 100 electric scooters.

Sources of information

Accounts; annual report; Charity Commission record; funder's website.

South Cambridgeshire

Girton Town Charity

 £12,500 (2017/18)

Correspondent: The Administrator, 22 High Street, Girton, Cambridge CB3 0PU (tel: 01223 276008; email: gtc@ girtontowncharity.co.uk)

 www.girtontowncharity.co.uk

CC number: 1130272

Eligibility

Students living in Girton who are undertaking further or higher education.

Types of grant

Grants of up to £300 per year are given towards books, equipment, tools and other costs related to the student's course through the charity's Educational Grant Scheme.

Applications

Contact the correspondent via email, telephone or post. Application guidelines are available on the charity's website.

Financial information

Year end	30/06/2018
Income	£1,030,000
Total expenditure	£642,000

Further financial information

In 2017/18, grants were awarded to 37 individuals.

Other information

The charity also supports local organisations and gives funding towards village infrastructure The charity manages a number of almshouses and runs a variety of schemes for the benefit of Girton residents, details of which can be found on its website. The charity administers the Care Plus Scheme which aims to support independent living, provides short-term additional care and helps residents leaving hospital to return home as quickly as possible.

Sources of information

Accounts; annual report; Charity Commission record; funder's website.

Essex

The Tom Acton Memorial Trust

 £4,300 (2017/18)

Correspondent: The Trustees, Hamilton House, Cobblers Green, Felsted, Dunmow, Essex CM6 3LX (tel: 01371 820382; email: tim.gage. annessandpartners@ukgateway.net)

 https://tomactonorg.wordpress. com/home

CC number: 1088069

Eligibility

Young musicians under the age of 25 who live in Essex, or were born or educated there. Applicants must have already reached an advanced standard of musical education.

Types of grant

Bursaries are available towards the cost of musical education. In the past, grants of up to £750 have been made towards course fees, instrument purchase, tuition and travel expenses.

Applications

Apply in writing to the correspondent. Applicants will be required to provide a reference from a music teacher to support the application. Candidates may be invited to audition.

Financial information

Year end	31/03/2018
Income	£5,100
Total expenditure	£4,800

Further financial information

Full accounts were not available to view on the Charity Commission's website due to the charity's low income. We have therefore estimated the grant total based on the charity's total expenditure.

Sources of information

Charity Commission record; Help Musicians UK website.

Tom Amos Charity

 £14,800 (2018)

Correspondent: J. Salmon, Secretary, Springlands, Main Road, Little Waltham, Chelmsford CM3 3PA (tel: 01245 360314; email: enquiries@ tomamoscharity.org)

www.tomamoscharity.org

CC number: 1080954

Eligibility

Residents of Little Waltham, Essex, Chelmsford, Uttlesford and Braintree who are in need.

Types of grant

Grants are made for the advancement of education.

Applications

Application forms, deadlines and guidance notes are available to download from the charity's website. Completed forms should be sent to the charity via email, as a PDF document.

Financial information

Year end	31/12/2018
Income	£227,300
Total expenditure	£228,500

Further financial information

During 2018, the charity awarded grants to 16 beneficiaries. Note: the grant total for education has been estimated.

Other information

The charity makes grants to organisations whose work coincides with the charity's objectives (i.e. the relief of poverty and the advancement of religion and education). Grants are also made for the provision of recreational facilities in Little Waltham.

Sources of information

Accounts; annual report; Charity Commission record; funder's website.

The Cranfield Charitable Trust

 £2,000 (2017/18)

Correspondent: The Trustees, 44 Lowestoft Road, Worlingham, Beccles NR34 7DY (tel: 01502 712462)

CC number: 263518

Eligibility

Our research indicates that students in higher/further education (i.e. university or vocational training) are supported.

Types of grant

One-off and recurring grants according to need.

Applications

Apply in writing to the correspondent.

Financial information

Year end	15/02/2018
Income	£15,500
Total expenditure	£8,700

Further financial information

Full accounts were not available to view on the Charity Commission's website due to the charity's low income. We have therefore estimated the grant total based on the charity's total expenditure.

Other information

The trust also makes grants to organisations.

Sources of information

Charity Commission record.

Earls Colne and Halstead Educational Charity

 £5,200 (2018/19)

Correspondent: Clerk to the Trustees, 4 Mill Chase, Halstead, Essex C09 2DQ (tel: 07539 489477; email: earlscolnehalstead.edcharity@yahoo.co.uk)

www.echec.org.uk

CC number: 310859

Eligibility

Children and young people between the ages of 5 and 25 who have lived for at least one year or attended school in the charity's beneficial area in North Essex. The charity's area of benefit covers most of the northern part of Braintree District and a small part of the borough of Colchester. A helpful map is available on the charity's website.

Types of grant

Project grants are available for various educational purposes including educational outings for schoolchildren. For example, small grants for students undertaking their Duke of Edinburgh Award.

Exclusions

Tuition fees are not normally supported and grants towards the purchase of books cannot be awarded to students in further (not higher) education e.g. A-levels.

Applications

Application forms can be found on the charity's website or requested from the correspondent. The trustees normally meet to consider grant applications during February, July and November. See the charity's website for details of closing dates for applications.

Financial information

Year end	28/02/2019
Income	£48,300
Total expenditure	£53,500

Other information

The charity also gives grants to local schools for educational travel or other purposes and supports voluntary bodies working for the benefit of young people in its beneficial area.

Sources of information

Accounts; annual report; Charity Commission record; funder's website.

Essex Community Foundation

 £217,300 (2017/18)

Correspondent: Grants Team, 121 New London Road, Chelmsford CM2 0QT (tel: 01245 356018; email: grants@ essexcf.org.uk)

www.essexcommunity foundation.org.uk

CC number: 1052061

Eligibility

Children and young people. Visit the foundation's website for additional criteria specific to each grant.

Types of grant

A number of funds are available to individuals to contribute towards educational and sporting opportunities. Visit the foundation's website for further information on the grants available.

Applications

Applications should be made to the foundation who will match the application to the appropriate fund. Contact the grants team via telephone or email to request an application form.

Financial information

Year end	30/06/2018
Income	£3,270,000
Total expenditure	£3,600,000

Further financial information

Grants were made to 66 individuals for education and welfare purposes.

Other information

This is one of the 46 community foundations, which distribute funding for a wide range of purposes. Grant schemes tend to change frequently; therefore, consult the foundation's website for details of current programmes and upcoming deadlines.

Sources of information

Accounts; annual report; Charity Commission record; funder's website.

Sir Robert Hitcham's Exhibition Foundation

£ £6,900 (2017/18)

Correspondent: Nicholas Johnson, Clerk to the Governors, 75 Queen Street, Coggeshall, Colchester CO6 1UE (tel: 01376 562915; email: nicjo@btinternet.com)

CC number: 1095014

Eligibility

People under the age of 25 who live in Coggeshall, have left school and are moving on to higher education or training.

Types of grant

Grants are awarded towards outfits, tools, instruments or books to assist people who are pursuing further or higher education or preparing to enter work.

Applications

Application forms can be requested from the correspondent. Applications are normally considered in early September and should be submitted by the end of August.

Financial information

Year end	31/07/2018
Income	£7,700
Total expenditure	£7,700

Further financial information

Full accounts were not available to view on the Charity Commission's website due to the charity's low income. We have therefore estimated the grant total based on the charity's total expenditure.

Sources of information

Charity Commission record.

Lord Maynard's Charity

£ £930 (2017/18)

Correspondent: Daniel Fox, Trustee, Moulton, Vicarage Lane, Thaxted, Dunmow, Essex CM6 2QP (tel: 01371 830470; email: thaxtedfox@gmail.com)

CC number: 278579

Eligibility

Educational grants are made to people aged 25 or younger, living in the parish of Thaxted.

Types of grant

Educational grants are awarded to young people towards the cost of college or university expenses or for tools/equipment required for work.

Applications

Apply in writing to the correspondent.

Financial information

Year end	31/08/2018
Income	£3,900
Total expenditure	£4,100

Further financial information

Full accounts were not available to view on the Charity Commission's website due to the charity's low income. We have therefore estimated the grant total based on the charity's total expenditure.

Other information

The charity also makes donations to the vicar of Thaxted, for repairs and improvements to the church and for 'performing the requisitions contained in the Testator's will'.

Sources of information

Charity Commission record.

David Randall Foundation

£ £3,800 (2017/18)

Correspondent: Sue Randall, Secretary, 7 Browning Road, Maldon, Essex CM9 6BU (email: info@davidrandallfoundation.org)

 www.davidrandallfoundation.org

CC number: 1151121

Eligibility

Individuals aged between 12 and 25 who live in Essex, Suffolk or the London borough of Havering and can demonstrate exceptional dedication to the interest they wish to pursue.

Types of grant

The David Randall Scholarship offers financial support to individuals towards pursuing their ambitions in music or sport including career development, education and training, overseas placements and assistance with kit and equipment.

Applications

Application forms for the David Randall Scholarship are available to download from the foundation's website. All applications should be supported by a referee, who knows the applicant well and can vouch for their dedication and passion in their chosen field. Applications open at the beginning of October and must be submitted by 31 December. A decision will be made by 23 February. In exceptional circumstances applications may be considered outside of this time scale. Please contact the correspondent by email if you need to apply outside of the normal application time. There are opportunities for applicants to receive lesser awards and these can be submitted at any time to the trustees and will be reviewed quarterly by the trustees. All applications will only be accepted on the official David Randall Foundation application form.

Financial information

Year end	31/03/2018
Income	£39,000
Total expenditure	£25,800

Further financial information

A total of £23,100 was awarded to individuals. Outings for over 130 families totalled £19,300 and scholarships were awarded to two individuals totalling £3,800.

Sources of information

Accounts; annual report; Charity Commission record; funder's website.

Basildon

Great Bursthead Exhibition Foundation (Billericay Educational Trust)

£ £10,200 (2017/18)

Correspondent: The Trustees, The Billericay School, School Road, Billericay, Essex CM12 9LH (tel: 01277 655191; email: info@billericayeducationaltrust.co.uk)

 www.billericayeducationaltrust.co.uk

CC number: 310836

Eligibility

Young people under the age of 25 who live within a six-mile radius of Billericay (including Noak Bridge, Ramsden Bellhouse, Ramsden Heath and Stock) and are in need.

Types of grant

One-off or recurring grants may be given for up to three years to further/higher education students and people in vocational training or those starting work. Help is given towards general educational necessities, including clothing, tools, instruments and equipment, books, also tuition fees, travel for educational purposes in the UK or abroad, study of music or other arts, recreational activities or physical training. The trustees can make awards for:

- University or college education
- Vocational grants for help to enter a trade or profession
- Travel grants in furtherance of education

▶ Recreational grants for recreation and social and physical training not provided by a local educational authority

▶ Cultural grants to enable beneficiaries to study music or other arts

Applications

Application forms can be downloaded from the foundation's website and should be submitted by May and returned via post or email.

Financial information

Year end	31/08/2018
Income	£16,300
Total expenditure	£11,300

Further financial information

Full accounts were not available to view on the Charity Commission's website due to the charity's low income. We have therefore estimated the grant total based on the charity's total expenditure.

Other information

Previously grants have also been given to schools to help with specific educational projects.

Sources of information

Charity Commission record; funder's website.

Chelmsford

The Butler Educational Foundation

£ £5,100 (2017/18)

Correspondent: The Trustees, Duffield Stunt, 71 Duke Street, Chelmsford, Essex CM1 1JU (tel: 01245 262351; email: butlereducational@outlook.com)

 www.borehamparishcouncil.co.uk/ breaking-news/butler-trust-applications

CC number: 310731

Eligibility

Children and young people living in the parishes of Boreham and Little Baddow and are at primary or secondary school.

Types of grant

Grants are available for expenses related to higher and further education costs such as travel and books. Grants are generally between £50 and £250 and the student will usually get a grant for every year of their course if they make a yearly application.

Exclusions

Grants are not made for the cost of school uniforms.

Applications

Application forms are available on the Boreham Parish Council website. The trustees meet three times a year to review applications, usually in October, January and April.

Financial information

Year end	31/08/2018
Income	£10,400
Total expenditure	£10,100

Further financial information

Full accounts were not available to view on the Charity Commission's website due to the charity's low income. We have therefore estimated the grant total based on the charity's total expenditure.

Sources of information

Charity Commission record; Boreham parish council website.

Chelmsford Educational Foundation (CEF)

£ £20,700 (2018)

Correspondent: Richard Emsden, 19 Rushleydale, Chelmsford CM1 6JX (tel: 07941 958652; email: remsden@gmail.com)

CC number: 310815

Eligibility

People who live or have been educated in the borough and former rural district of Chelmsford.

Types of grant

Grants can be awarded for the purchase of books, fees and other equipment to help individuals achieve qualifications of employment.

Applications

Apply in writing to the correspondent.

Financial information

Year end	31/12/2018
Income	£27,700
Total expenditure	£24,100

Further financial information

A total of 22 grants were awarded in 2018.

Sources of information

Accounts; annual report; Charity Commission record.

Ann Johnson's Educational Foundation

£ £35,300 (2017/18)

Correspondent: Administrator, 58 New London Road, Chelmsford, Essex CM2 0PA (tel: 01245 493939; email: contactajef@yahoo.com)

 www.cchs.co.uk/sixth-form/ann-johnsons-educational-foundation

CC number: 310799

Eligibility

People living or educated in Chelmsford and the surrounding parishes, who are under the age of 25 and in need of financial assistance.

Types of grant

Grants are awarded to help young people further their education to pursue a job, career or trade. It may cover or contribute towards such things as tools, equipment, specialised clothing or costs associated with following a course at any recognised college or university.

Applications

Contact the correspondent for an application form or further information. Applications may be made at any time of the year but it is advisable to allow three months for the process.

Financial information

Year end	30/09/2018
Income	£123,400
Total expenditure	£147,500

Further financial information

In 2017/18 grants were awarded to 31 individuals and were broken down in the annual report as follows:

Girls	£21,700
Boys	£13,600

Other information

The trust also gives funding to local schools.

Sources of information

Accounts; annual report; Charity Commission record; funder's website.

Colchester

The Hervey Benham Charitable Trust

£ £5,700 (2017/18)

Correspondent: Clerk to the Trustees, c/o Sparling Benham & Brough, 3 West Stockwell Street, Colchester CO3 8ZB (tel: 01255 429594; email: admin@herveybenhamtrust.org.uk)

 herveybenhamtrust.org.uk

CC number: 277578

Eligibility

People who live in Colchester or North East Essex and wish to further their artistic talents, particularly musical, but are prevented by physical, environmental or financial difficulties. A map of the beneficial area is available on the trust's website.

Types of grant

One-off and recurrent musical scholarships ranging from £150 to £2,000. Support is given towards equipment/instruments, fees, study or travel abroad, album launches and other expenses.

Exclusions

Applications are only accepted within the trust's beneficial area and grants are not given for mainstream education.

Applications

Application forms are available from the correspondent. The trustees meet quarterly and the clerk will advise the applicant of the submission time scales for the next two meetings. Applicants will need to provide references and the trustees may decide to interview the applicant and/or the family before issuing any grant.

Financial information

Year end	28/02/2018
Income	£35,600
Total expenditure	£43,100

Further financial information

In 2017/18, grants were awarded to six individuals.

Other information

The trust also makes grants to organisations.

Sources of information

Accounts; annual report; Charity Commission record; funder's website.

Epping Forest

Joseph King Trust

£ £28,500 (2017)

Correspondent: Mrs C. E. R. Kenny, Secretary, 36 Coopers Hill, Ongar, Essex CM5 9EF (tel: 01277 366167; email: JKT1678@btinternet.com)

CC number: 810177

Eligibility

People between the ages of 16 and 25 who live in the civil parish of Chipping Ongar, Marden Ash, Greensted and Shelley.

Types of grant

Grants are available to students at college, university and other institutions of further education and towards other educationally beneficial activities outside the scope of mainstream education.

Applications

Apply in writing to the correspondent.

Financial information

Year end	31/12/2017
Income	£81,900
Total expenditure	£55,300

Further financial information

In 2017, a total of £28,500 was awarded in grants to around 50 students undertaking further education or educational activities.

Other information

The majority of applications received are for financial support for university students. The trust also supports local schools for specific projects and music facilities as well as local churches for youth activities.

Sources of information

Accounts; annual report; Charity Commission record.

Harlow

The Fawbert and Barnard's Educational Foundation

£ £540 (2018)

Correspondent: Christine Baxter, Trustee, Fawbert and Barnards Primary School, London Road, Harlow, Essex CM17 0DA (tel: 01279 429427; email: admin@fawbert-barnards.essex.sch.uk)

CC number: 310757

Eligibility

People who live in Harlow and surrounding areas.

Types of grant

Scholarships are awarded for secondary schools, universities or any other educational institution. Grants can also be given for equipment, clothing, books and such like to assist entry into, or advancement in a profession or trade on leaving education.

Applications

Apply in writing to the correspondent.

Financial information

Year end	31/12/2018
Income	£1,700
Total expenditure	£1,200

Further financial information

Full accounts were not available to view on the Charity Commission's website due to the charity's low income. We have therefore estimated the grant total based on the charity's total expenditure.

Sources of information

Charity Commission record.

Rochford

The Canewdon Educational Foundation

£ £1,500 (2018)

Correspondent: Clerk to the Trustees, Trust House, Anchor Lane, Canewdon, Rochford, Essex SS4 3PA (tel: 07706 877437; email: clerktotrustees@gmail.com)

CC number: 310718

Eligibility

People living in the old parish of Canewdon who are under the age of 25.

Types of grant

Grants are made to assist with general expenses associated with education or if the applicant is entering a trade. Past examples are tuition fee grants, travel expenses and nursing course fees.

Applications

Apply in writing to the correspondent.

Financial information

Year end	31/12/2018
Income	£39,900
Total expenditure	£36,300

Other information

The trustees use a proportion of the income to maintain Canewdon Endowed Primary School and 20% of the unrestricted fund income (after the deduction of the trustees' expenses) is paid to the Canewdon Poor's Charity (Charity Commission number: 210406). Grants are also made to organisations.

Sources of information

Accounts; annual report; Charity Commission record.

Hertfordshire

Robert Dewhurst's School Foundation

£ £4,300 (2017/18)

Correspondent: The Trustees, 215 Northbrooks, Harlow, Essex CM19 4DH (tel: 01279 425251; email: jillhempleman@yahoo.co.uk)

CC number: 310972

Eligibility

Children and young people under the age of 25 who live within the ancient parish of Cheshunt. Preference is given to people who have attended Dewhurst St Mary's Church of England Primary School for at least two years.

Types of grant

One-off and recurrent grants according to need.

Applications

Apply in writing to the correspondent.

Financial information

Year end	31/03/2018
Income	£14,000
Total expenditure	£9,600

Further financial information

Full accounts were not available to view on the Charity Commission's website due to the charity's low income. We have therefore estimated the grant total based on the charity's total expenditure.

Other information

The foundation also provides support to Dewhurst St Mary's Church of England Primary School.

Sources of information

Charity Commission record.

Fawbert and Barnard School's Foundation

£ £5,200 (2018)

Correspondent: The Trustees, 22 South Brook, Sawbridgeworth, Hertfordshire CM21 9NS (tel: 01279 724670)

CC number: 310965

Eligibility

People between the ages of 16 and 25 who live within a three-mile radius of Great St Mary's Church in Sawbridgeworth or who attend/have attended school in that area for at least three years.

Types of grant

One-off grants, scholarships and bursaries to assist further/higher education students.

Applications

Apply in writing to the correspondent.

Financial information

Year end	31/12/2018
Income	£9,600
Total expenditure	£11,600

Further financial information

Full accounts were not available to view on the Charity Commission's website due to the charity's low income. We have therefore estimated the grant total based on the charity's total expenditure.

Sources of information

Charity Commission record.

The Follett Trust

£ £5,000 (2017/18)

Correspondent: The Trustees, The Follett Office, Follett House, Primett Road, Stevenage SG1 3EE (tel: 01438 810400; email: folletttrust@ thefollettoffice.com)

CC number: 328638

Eligibility

Students undertaking higher education. Preference may be given to students who live in Hertfordshire.

Types of grant

Small grants and scholarships to support higher education.

Applications

To apply, contact the correspondent via email. Applicants should include information about their past studies, reasons for applying for funding and their home address.

Financial information

Year end	30/06/2018
Income	£164,800
Total expenditure	£160,000

Further financial information

In 2017/18 a total of £5,000 was awarded to five individuals.

Other information

The trust also supports local charities and organisations.

Sources of information

Accounts; annual report; Charity Commission record; further information provided by the funder.

Hertfordshire Community Nurses' Charity

£ £12,000 (2017/18)

Correspondent: Louise Landman, Trustee, 11 High Street, Barkway, Royston, Hertfordshire SG8 8EA (tel: 01763 848888; email: louise@ hertscommunitynursescharity.co.uk)

 hertscommunitynurses charity.co.uk

CC number: 1158593

Eligibility

Nurses working or retired from working in the community in Hertfordshire (including nurses working in the following settings: community; practice; school; community – children; community – mental health and learning disabilities; hospice; as well as community midwives and health

visitors). To be eligible, applicants must have worked in the community in Hertfordshire for at least six months. Groups of nurses can also apply for a grant to help develop a project or to fund particular equipment which will aid their development and improve the quality of care for patients in the area.

Types of grant

Grants are awarded to enable nurses to undertake professional development. Applicants must be able to demonstrate how the grant will benefit the quality of care to patients. A wide range of courses and levels can be funded, including part-time and full-time degree courses – for example: counselling, palliative care, mental health, learning disabilities, and pain management. Grants are awarded for one year only and those undertaking longer courses must reapply.

Applications

Applications can be made using the form on the charity's website.

Financial information

Year end	31/03/2018
Income	£79,600
Total expenditure	£62,800

Other information

The charity was previously known as Hertfordshire County Nursing Trust (Charity Commmission no. 207213). It was incorporated in 2014. The charity occasionally makes major grants of up to £20,000 for projects which will benefit patients in Hertfordshire. The charity also provides subsidised accommodation for retired nurses who previously worked in the community in Hertfordshire.

Sources of information

Accounts; annual report; Charity Commission record; funder's website.

The Hertfordshire Educational Foundation

£ £10,400 (2017/18)

Correspondent: The Trustees, c/o County Hall, Post Point CHO 126, Pegs Lane, Hertford, Hertfordshire SG13 8DF (tel: 01438 843319; email: hertfordshireeducationalfoundation@ hertfordshire.gov.uk)

https://www.hertfordshire.gov.uk/ services/schools-and-education/ at-school/financial-help/ hertfordshire-educational-foundation.aspx

CC number: 311025

Eligibility

Pupils and students up to the age of 25 who have a home address in Hertfordshire.

Types of grant

The foundation administers a number of different grant schemes, which are detailed on its website.

Travel scholarships

Grants of between £100 and £500 to individuals aged between 12 and 21 to undertake approved courses of study, expeditions, voluntary work and other projects in overseas countries. The usual duration is for a minimum of one month and individuals should be able to demonstrate how their project will benefit the local community they are visiting.

The Sir George Burns Fund

Grants of between £50 and £500 to enable young people aged between 16 and 21 who have a disability or who are disadvantaged, to purchase special equipment, take part in recreational or educational activities or to participate in expeditions, educational visits, short courses or conferences

Donald Mackean Trust

Grants of between £50 and £1,000 to enable young people aged between 14 and 25 to participate in learning or careers in the areas of science, technology, engineering, maths or health and environment-related subjects. Grants can be used for purposes such as equipment, personal development, additional support or other costs. This funding particularly targets those who are disadvantaged – for example, orphans, care-leavers, people who have offended, refugees, young parents, people with mental health problems or other circumstances.

Applications

Application forms are available to download from the foundation's website. Applications should be submitted at least eight weeks before the activities (for which the grant is required) take place. The foundation will not consider any applications that are received less than six weeks in advance. The closing dates for applications and guidance notes for each fund are provided on the foundation's website.

Financial information

Year end	31/01/2018
Income	£34,700
Total expenditure	£54,600

Other information

The foundation may also provide grants to organisations.

Sources of information

Accounts; annual report; Charity Commission record; funder's website.

Broxbourne
Wormley Parochial Charity

£ £2,000 (2018)

Correspondent: The Trustees, 43 The Oval, Broxbourne, Hertfordshire EN10 6DQ (tel: 01992 464764)

CC number: 218463

Eligibility

People who are in need and live in the parish of Wormley as it was defined before 31 March 1935. There is a preference for supporting students over the age of 18, older people and people who have been recently bereaved.

Types of grant

Grants are made to students towards essential clothing, equipment, instruments or books. The charity also distributes food vouchers through local stores, contributes to utility bills and awards bereavement grants.

Applications

Applications can be made in writing to the charity, either directly by the individual, or through a social worker, Citizens Advice, welfare agency or a third party such as a friend who is aware of the situation.

Financial information

Year end	31/12/2018
Income	£12,500
Total expenditure	£7,400

Further financial information

Full accounts were not available to view on the Charity Commission's website due to the charity's low income. We have therefore estimated the grant total based on the charity's total expenditure.

Other information

Grants are also made to local community organisations and to support the Royal Voluntary Service hospital transport scheme.

Sources of information

Charity Commission record.

East Hertforshire
Newton Exhibition Foundation

£ £16,500 (2017/18)

Correspondent: The Trustees, 117 Ladywood Road, Hertford, Hertfordshire SG14 2TA (tel: 01992 550121; email: clerk@ newtonexhibitionfoundation.co.uk)

CC number: 311021

Eligibility

Young people under the age of 25 who are attending/have attended school in the town of Hertford. Preference is given to members of the Church of England.

Types of grant

One-off and recurrent grants according to need.

Applications

Apply in writing to the correspondent.

Financial information

Year end	31/03/2018
Income	£14,000
Total expenditure	£18,300

Further financial information

Full accounts were not available to view on the Charity Commission's website due to the charity's low income. We have therefore estimated the grant total based on the charity's total expenditure.

Sources of information

Charity Commission record.

The Ware Charities

£ £5,500 (2018/19)

Correspondent: Susan Newman, Clerk, 3 Scotts Road, Ware, Hertfordshire SG12 9JG (tel: 01920 461629; email: suedogs@hotmail.com)

CC number: 225443

Eligibility

Residents in the town of Ware and the parishes of Wareside and Thundridge who are in need due to ill-health or financial hardship.

Types of grant

Educational grants are awarded to schoolchildren, college students, people with special educational needs, people starting work and overseas students for fees, books and equipment. Grants are also made to undergraduates and vocational students for uniforms/ clothing.

Applications

Apply in writing to the correspondent. All applications must be supported by a health professional, social worker, school headteacher, support worker at a children's centre or person in a similar role. If successful, grants are paid directly to the supplier or supporter and not to the individual.

Financial information

Year end	31/03/2019
Income	£46,800
Total expenditure	£24,500

Further financial information

During 2018/19, the charity awarded grants to 21 beneficiaries. Note: the grant total has been estimated.

Other information

The charity also awards grants to individuals for welfare purposes. In addition, it owns and operates two almshouses, which are available to older residents in the area of benefit.

Sources of information

Accounts; annual report; Charity Commission record.

North Hertfordshire

The Letchworth Civic Trust

 £57,800 (2018/19)

Correspondent: Sally Jenkins, Secretary, Broadway Chambers, Letchworth Garden City, Hertfordshire SG6 3AD (tel: 01462 686919; email: letchworthct@gmail.com)

🌐 letchworthct.org.uk

CC number: 273336

Eligibility

Students undertaking higher or further education who have lived in Letchworth Garden City for at least two years.

Types of grant

Grants of up to £500 are awarded towards the cost of books and learning materials for university and further education students (diploma, HND, apprenticeships and so on).

Applications

Separate application forms for each type of grant are available to download from the trust's website. Applications from schoolchildren need to be supported by their headteacher. If applying for medical assistance or for a particular social need, the form must be completed by a relevant professional or social worker on behalf of the individual. Applications should be returned by the end of December, February, May, August, September, and November, for consideration the following month. Applications are not usually acknowledged before the trustees' meeting.

Separate application forms for each type of grant are available to download from the trust's website. University students must not apply before receiving their successful A-level results in August. Applications are not usually acknowledged before the trustees' meeting.

Financial information

Year end	30/06/2019
Income	£89,400
Total expenditure	£84,600

Further financial information

Educational grants totalling £57,800 were awarded to 162 university students.

Other information

Around 200 individuals are supported each year, particularly young people. The trust also makes awards to around 20 local organisations per year.

Sources of information

Accounts; annual report; Charity Commission record; funder's website.

St Albans

The James Marshall Foundation

 £82,200 (2018/19)

Correspondent: Fran Brown, Freepost RTLS-TAUS-TBHT, Unit 6, 17 Leyton Road, Harpenden, Hertfordshire AL5 2HY (tel: 01582 760735; email: grants@jamesmarshallfoundation.co.uk)

🌐 https://www.jamesmarshall foundation.co.uk

CC number: 312127

Eligibility

People under the age of 25 who live in Harpenden and Wheathampstead and are in financial need. Priority is given to individuals over the age of 16.

Types of grant

Grants are awarded to pay for or contribute to educational and career development purposes. Financial support has been granted for items including: work tools, clothing, books, study materials and laptops. University-related (including postgraduate study) costs have been met, such as accommodation, travel and books or equipment, extracurricular sport, music or dance tuition, course or examination fees. The foundation's website states that this is not an exhaustive list and that potential applicants can contact the foundation to see if their cause may be eligible. Where funds are limited priority will be given to those seeking apprenticeships, then work related applications, then university applications, and lastly, postgraduate applications.

Applications

Application forms and guidance on supporting documents that need to be submitted can be found on the foundation's website. Alternatively write to the correspondent at the Freepost address provided.

Financial information

Year end	31/03/2019
Income	£3,528,200
Total expenditure	£237,000

Further financial information

300 awards were made in 2018/19. Note: the totals below include grants for both welfare and educational purposes:

Purpose	Amount for Wheat-hampstead	Amount for Harpenden
School uniform	43	37
School trips	28	38
Degree	11	25
Computer	15	19
Music/drama/ sport	15	19
Travel	12	7
Educational equipment	5	3
Other	4	3
Master's degree	2	4
Diploma	4	1
Educational course	3	2
Total	**142**	**158**

Sources of information

Accounts; annual report; Charity Commission record; funder's website.

Norfolk

The Bunting's Fund

£ £2,100 (2017/18)

Correspondent: Christopher Padley, Hedges, Creake Road, Burnham Thorpe, King's Lynn, Norfolk PE31 8HW (tel: 07881 364245; email: padleychris@ btinternet.com)

CC number: 311175

Eligibility

Children and young people in need who are under the age of 25 and live in the parish of Burnham Thorpe.

Types of grant

Financial assistance is available towards the cost of clothing, school uniforms, books, equipment/instruments, tools, educational outings, travel/study abroad, student exchange and other educational necessities or expenses.

Applications

Apply in writing to the correspondent.

Financial information

Year end	04/08/2018
Income	£4,700
Total expenditure	£4,700

Further financial information

Full accounts were not available to view on the Charity Commission's website due to the charity's low income. We have therefore estimated the grant total based on the charity's total expenditure.

Other information

The foundation can give financial assistance towards the provision of facilities for recreation, social or physical training for students in primary, secondary or further education, where these are not normally provided by the local authorities.

Sources of information

Charity Commission record.

The Cranfield Charitable Trust

See record on page 176

Norfolk Community Foundation

Correspondent: Grants Team, 5th Floor, St James Mill, Whitefriars, Norwich, Norfolk NR3 1TN (tel: 01603 623958; email: grants@norfolkfoundation.com)

 www.norfolkfoundation.com

CC number: 1110817

Eligibility

People living in Norfolk. Individual funds have their own specific eligibility criteria – see the community foundation's website for details.

Types of grant

The foundation manages The South Norfolk Council Community Sports Fund which aims to support young people to excel in their chosen sport. It has two schemes:

▶ The Community Coach Development Bursary Scheme offers volunteer coaches over the age of 16 living in South Norfolk financial assistance to undertake National Governing Body Level 1, 2 and 3 coaching qualifications. Grants are awarded up to £300 or 75% of the course costs or can be given towards travel costs associated with the course.
▶ The Elite Athletes Support Scheme offers a 12-month free gym member ship and selected local gyms to athletes aged between 14 and 25 who are currently competing at national and international level.

Applications

The application process varies for each scheme, visit the foundation's website for further information or contact the correspondent to request an application form.

Financial information

Year end	31/12/2018
Income	£2,750,000
Total expenditure	£3,010,000

Further financial information

In 2018 a total of £41,900 was awarded to 180 individuals, mainly through small funds including the carers grants available from the Norfolk Millennium Trust for Carers. We were unable to determine the split between social welfare grants and educational grants.

Other information

The foundation also works with the Nelsonspirit Future Leaders Fund which awards grants to young people who are engaged in community or adventure projects to help them grow as leaders. Organisations are also supported. This is one of the 46 community foundations, which distribute funding for a wide range of purposes. Grant schemes tend to change frequently; therefore, consult the foundation's website for details of current programmes and upcoming deadlines.

Sources of information

Accounts; annual report; Charity Commission record; funder's website.

Norwich French Church Charity

£ £14,500 (2019)

Correspondent: Andrea Bell, Clerk, Hansells Solicitors, 13–14 The Close, Norwich, Norfolk NR1 4DS (tel: 01603 275814; email: AndreaBell@hansells.co.uk)

 www.norwichfrenchchurch charity.org.uk

CC number: 212897

Eligibility

Children and young people up to the age of 25 who are resident in Norwich. Priority is given to those who are of Huguenot descent and then to those whose education or training is threatened by financial difficulty.

Types of grant

Students embarking on apprenticeships, college or undergraduate courses, or equivalent, where tools or equipment are needed. While tertiary education programmes are not disregarded completely, they are considered very carefully to see whether they fit with the theme of an apprenticeship.

Applications

Applications can be submitted using the online form on the charity's website or by downloading a printable application form. Applications should be

accompanied by a covering letter outlining the applicant's circumstances as well as evidence of the education to be undertaken.

Financial information

Year end	31/12/2019
Income	£14,900
Total expenditure	£16,100

Further financial information

Full accounts were not available to view on the Charity Commission's website due to the charity's low income. We have therefore estimated the grant total based on the charity's total expenditure.

Sources of information

Charity Commission record; funder's website.

The Charity of Sir John Picto and Others

£ £2,200 (2017/18)

Correspondent: Stephen Pipe, Beam End, Mill Street, Buxton, Norwich, Norfolk NR10 5JE (tel: 01603 279823; email: stephenpipe@live.co.uk)

CC number: 208896

Eligibility

Residents in parishes of Buxton Lamas, Little Hautbois, Brampton and Oxmead who are in need.

Types of grant

Educational grants have been made previously to college students, undergraduates, vocational students, mature students and people starting work towards the cost of books.

Applications

Apply in writing to the correspondent.

Financial information

Year end	31/03/2018
Income	£40,700
Total expenditure	£25,400

Other information

A large portion of the charity's income is used to maintain and administer property and land owned by the charity.

Sources of information

Accounts; annual report; Charity Commission record.

Town Lands Educational Foundation

See record on page 174

Breckland

The Garboldisham Parish Charities

£ £3,800 (2018/19)

Correspondent: The Trustees, Sandale, Smallworth Common, Garboldisham, Diss, Norfolk IP22 2QW (tel: 01953 681646; email: pandw6@btinternet.com)

CC number: 210250

Eligibility

People in need who live in the parish of Garboldisham.

Types of grant

Grants are awarded to young people leaving school and continuing their education or entering work.

Applications

Apply in writing to the correspondent.

Financial information

Year end	28/02/2019
Income	£10,400
Total expenditure	£8,400

Further financial information

Full accounts were not available to view on the Charity Commission's website due to the charity's low income. We have therefore estimated the grant total based on the charity's total expenditure.

Sources of information

Charity Commission record.

Kings Lynn and West Norfolk

The Brancaster Educational and Almshouse Charity

£ £6,100 (2018)

Correspondent: J. Gould, Brette Cottage, Cross Lane, Brancaster, King's Lynn, Norfolk PE31 8AE (tel: 01485 210721; email: jjgould10@gmail.com)

CC number: 311128

Eligibility

Children and young people who live, or whose parents live, in the ancient parishes of Brancaster, Titchwell, Thornham, and Burnham Deepdale.

Types of grant

Grants are made for educational necessities.

Applications

Apply in writing to the correspondent.

Financial information

Year end	31/12/2018
Income	£16,500
Total expenditure	£13,600

Further financial information

Full accounts were not available to view on the Charity Commission's website due to the charity's low income. We have therefore estimated the grant total based on the charity's total expenditure.

Other information

The charity also awards grants to local schools for benefits not provided by the local authority and uses income for the running and maintenance of their owned almshouses, and the care of its residents.

Sources of information

Charity Commission record.

Hall's Exhibition Foundation

£ £39,500 (2017/18)

Correspondent: Christopher Holt, Administrator, 4 Bewick Close, Snettisham, King's Lynn, Norfolk PE31 7PJ (tel: 01485 541534; email: mail@chrisholtphotographic.co.uk)

 www.hallsfoundation.co.uk

CC number: 325128

Eligibility

People between the ages of 11 and 25 (as of 1 September in the year of the course) who have been resident in the village of Snettisham for at least one year and are in need of financial assistance.

Types of grant

Grants of up to £250 are available to students over the age of 11 moving on to secondary education. Grants can be used towards books, uniforms, travel costs, materials or whatever the individual feels necessary. Funding can also be given for extracurricular activities.

Grants are available to higher/further education students in the following categories:

- Young people over the age of 16 going on to further education/ undertaking A-levels can be awarded grants of up to £250 for each year of the course
- Students over the age of 18 undertaking higher education at universities or equivalent can receive grants of up to £1,600 each year of the course (this payment will be awarded in two £800 grants at the start and the end of the academic year)
- Postgraduate students can be awarded a one-off grant of up to £1,000

Grants can be used towards the cost of accommodation or whatever purpose the individual requires.

Exclusions

No additional grants are made for word processors, computers, normal travelling expenses or work experience costs. Grants must be returned if any year of the course is not completed.

Applications

Application forms and further guidelines are available from the foundation's website or can be requested from the correspondent.

Financial information

Year end	31/03/2018
Income	£80,800
Total expenditure	£50,100

Further financial information

In 2017/2018 a total of £45,200 was awarded to individuals. The grants were distributed in the following categories:

Pupils moving from primary to secondary school	21	£5,300
Sixth form/16+ further education	26	£6,500
University/higher education	25	£33,000
Extracurricular activities	-	£430

Other information

The foundation will support university students in their 4th and 5th years. Following the awards to individuals each year, the foundation may consider providing support to group projects and organisations if they have an educational benefit and involve the young people of Snettisham.

Sources of information

Accounts; annual report; Charity Commission record; funder's website.

Hilgay United Charities (Non-Ecclesiastical Branch)

£ £860 (2018)

Correspondent: Anthony Hall, Windrush, Church Road, Ten Mile Bank, Downham Market, Norfolk PE38 0EJ (tel: 07900 518153; email: hilgay. feoffees@aol.com)

CC number: 208898

Eligibility

People who live in the parish of Hilgay and are undertaking an apprenticeship or training.

Types of grant

Grants are awarded towards the cost of apprenticeships and training.

Applications

Apply in writing to the correspondent. Applications are usually considered in June each year.

Financial information

Year end	31/12/2018
Income	£30,700
Total expenditure	£28,700

Further financial information

In 2018 a total of £6,000 was awarded to individuals with £5,100 given towards welfare purposes and £860 for apprenticeships and training.

Other information

The charity also supports the maintenance of two village halls and provides grants to local schools.

Sources of information

Accounts; annual report; Charity Commission record; Making Money Count website.

Sir Edmund Moundeford Charity

£ £3,100 (2018)

Correspondent: The Trustees, The Estate Office, 15 Lynn Road, Downham Market, Norfolk PE38 9NL (tel: 01366 387180; email: info@barryhawkins.co.uk)

CC number: 1075097

Eligibility

People who live in Feltwell.

Types of grant

Grants are awarded towards the purchase of books for university students and to school leavers.

Applications

Apply in writing to the correspondent. Applications are considered at meetings held quarterly.

Financial information

Year end	31/12/2018
Income	£166,900
Total expenditure	£194,400

Other information

The main purpose of this charity is the provision of almshouse accommodation.

Sources of information

Accounts; annual report; Charity Commission record.

Town Lands Educational Foundation (Outwell Town Lands Educational Foundation)

£ £1,900 (2017)

Correspondent: The Trustees, 90 Wisbech Road, Outwell, Wisbech, Cambridgeshire PE14 8PF (tel: 01945 774327; email: outwellpc@btinternet.com)

CC number: 311211

Eligibility

People who live in the ancient parish of Outwell.

Types of grant

Grants are available each year for students in higher education.

Applications

Applications can be made on a form available from the correspondent.

Financial information

Year end	31/12/2017
Income	£7,100
Total expenditure	£4,300

Further financial information

Full accounts were not available to view on the Charity Commission's website due to the charity's low income. We have therefore estimated the grant total based on the charity's total expenditure.

Sources of information

Charity Commission record.

West Norfolk and King's Lynn Girls' School Trust

£ £11,400 (2017/18)

Correspondent: Miriam Aldous, Clerk, Woodstock Cottage, 2 School Lane, Little Dunham, King's Lynn, Norfolk PE32 2DQ (tel: 01760 720617)

 www.wnklgirlsschoolstrust.org.uk

CC number: 311264

Eligibility

Girls and young women over the age of 11 who are at a secondary school or in their first year after leaving school or further education, who live in the borough of King's Lynn and West Norfolk. Awards to older candidates will be made in exceptional circumstances.

Types of grant

One-off and recurrent grants. Grants are provided for a range of educational needs including living expenses.

Exclusions

Primary schoolchildren.

Applications

Apply on a form available on the trust's website. Application forms should be completed together with a supporting letter outlining the proposed venture or study course, and include two independent references, one of which must be from a teacher or tutor who can vouch for the suitability of the course.

Financial information

Year end	30/06/2018
Income	£29,500
Total expenditure	£27,600

Further financial information

Grant totals were estimated from the 2017/18 accounts. Grants to 21 people totalling £22,800 were made that year.

Sources of information

Accounts; annual report; Charity Commission record; funder's website.

Norwich

Anguish's Educational Foundation

£ £256,900 (2018/19)

Correspondent: David Hynes, Chief Executive, 1 Woolgate Court, St Benedicts Street, Norwich, Norfolk NR2 4AP (tel: 01603 621023; email: david.hynes@norwichcharitabletrusts.org.uk)

 www.anguisheducational foundation.org.uk

CC number: 311288

Eligibility

Individuals under the age of 25 who have been residents of the city of Norwich and the parishes of Costessey, Hellesdon, Catton, Sprowston, Thorpe and Corpusty for at least two years. Household income should not exceed £600 per week. A further allowance is made to families of up to ten children in total.

Types of grant

Grants are made for university maintenance, further education and college fees.

Exclusions

Postgraduates are not supported.

Applications

There is no formal application form to complete. Applicants should contact the correspondent. They will then be given an interview with a grants officer and will be required to detail their personal or family income. Applicants must provide copies of evidence of their income, e.g. letters, wage slips, etc.

Financial information

Year end	31/03/2019
Income	£970,600
Total expenditure	£1,130,000

Further financial information

School clothing	1,697	£167,700
Educational travel	542	£90,600
Other grants	13	£4,441
University maintenance	126	£153,585
Further education	147	£72,241
College fees	16	£31,033

Other information

The foundation also made grant payments to 24 organisations across Norwich.

Sources of information

Accounts; annual report; Charity Commission record; funder's website.

Educational Foundation of Alderman John Norman

£113,700 (2018/19)

Correspondent: Nick Saffell, Clerk, The Atrium, St George's Street, Norwich, Norfolk NR3 1AB (tel: 01603 629871; email: nick.saffell@brown-co.com)

 wp.normanfoundation.org.uk

CC number: 313105

Eligibility

Descendants of Alderman John Norman. Grants are available from the age of 6 to 24 for compulsory and tertiary education. This includes higher and further education, as well as work-based learning, apprenticeships and vocational training. If funds permit, grants are awarded in the following order of preference: young people living in the parish of Old Catton; young residents in the city of Norwich.

Types of grant

One-off and recurrent grants according to need.

Exclusions

There must be a blood relationship between the applicant and Alderman John Norman. Stepchildren and adopted children are not eligible for support. Grants cannot be made for postgraduate study.

Applications

Apply in writing to the Clerk. Before applying, applicants must obtain a 'pedigree' proving their direct descendancy from the beneficiaries listed in the first schedule of the will of Alderman John Norman. For more information on how to apply for a pedigree, contact the charity.

Financial information

Year end	31/03/2019
Income	£249,000
Total expenditure	£245,400

Further financial information

During 2018/19, the charity awarded £95,700 in grants to descendants of Alderman John Norman and £18,000 to residents in Old Catton. No grants were made to residents in Norfolk.

Other information

This charity also makes grants to organisations.

Sources of information

Accounts; annual report; Charity Commission record; funder's website.

Norwich Town Close Estate Charity

£52,300 (2018/19)

Correspondent: Grants Officer, 1 Woolgate Court, St Benedicts Street, Norwich, Norfolk NR2 4AP (tel: 01603 621023; email: info@ norwichcharitabletrusts.org.uk)

 www.norwichtowncloseestate charity.org.uk

CC number: 235678

Eligibility

Freemen of the city of Norwich, and their dependants, who are in need.

Types of grant

Educational grants are awarded toward the cost of pursuing further education or vocational training (including necessary equipment), university maintenance (including support for doctorates) and personal tuition in music, the arts and sport where the beneficiary is likely to reach professional status.

Applications

Initial enquiries should be made by contacting the charity directly. The charity will then arrange to meet the applicant to discuss their application. When applying for household items, the charity will seek the applicant's permission to conduct a home visit. Applicants should provide evidence of their income from employment, savings and/or benefits including housing benefit

or council tax benefit. If successful, grants are valid for six months from the date on which the trustees agree the grant. The trustees meet quarterly (in February, April, June and October) to consider grant applications.

Financial information

Year end	31/03/2019
Income	£1,070,000
Total expenditure	£1,130,000

Further financial information

Educational grants are broken down as follows: eight university maintenance grants totalling £14,900; 13 grants for college/further education fees totalling £35,000; four grants of £987 for educational travel; two miscellaneous educational grants totalling £1,400.

Other information

This charity is one of three amalgamated charities and part of the Norwich Charitable Trusts. All of the charity's activity is devoted to making educational and welfare grants.

Sources of information

Accounts; annual report; Charity Commission record; funder's website.

The Foundation of Joanna Scott and Others

£35,600 (2017/18)

Correspondent: Secretary to the Trustees, 21a Colegate, Norwich, Norfolk NR3 1BN (tel: 01603 224800; email: secretary@foundationofjoannascott.org. uk)

 www.foundationofjoanna scott.org.uk

CC number: 311253

Eligibility

People under the age of 25 who are being educated or live within five miles of Norwich City Hall and whose families are in financial need.

Types of grant

Grants are awarded for a wide range of educational expenses including towards fees, maintenance/living expenses and study or travel abroad.

Applications

Application forms are available from the foundation's website and can be posted or sent via email.

Financial information

Year end	31/03/2018
Income	£78,200
Total expenditure	£80,600

Further financial information

The grant total has been estimated from the 2017/18 accounts.

Other information

Small grants are also given to organisations and schools.

Sources of information

Accounts; annual report; Charity Commission record; funder's website.

Sir Peter Seaman's Charity

 £18,600 (2017/18)

Correspondent: The Trustees, Great Hospital, Bishopgate, Norwich, Norfolk NR1 4EL (tel: 01603 622022; email: andrewbarnes@greathospital.org)

www.greathospital.org.uk/charities/ peter-seaman-charity.htm

CC number: 311101

Eligibility

People under the age of 21 who live in Norwich.

Types of grant

Grants can be given towards all kinds of educational purposes. There is no upper limit for the grant amount, but funding for more than £1,500 is unlikely.

Exclusions

Applications for salaries and/or general costs will not be considered.

Applications

Application forms can be accessed on the charity's web page. Applications can be submitted at any time, the trustees meet four times a year to consider them. Applications for a specific project are more likely to be supported by the trustees. Applicants must wait one year before applying again.

Financial information

Year end	31/03/2018
Income	£6,900
Total expenditure	£20,700

Further financial information

Full accounts were not available to view on the Charity Commission's website due to the charity's low income. We have therefore estimated the grant total based on the charity's total expenditure.

Other information

Awards may also be made 'to charitable organisations which support the educational and other needs of young people living in Norwich'.

Sources of information

Charity Commission record; funder's website.

South Norfolk

The Town Estate Educational Foundation (Hempnall)

 £8,400 (2018)

Correspondent: Alison Harris, Clerk to the Trustees, 1 Freemasons Cottage, Mill Road, Hempnall, Norwich, Norfolk NR15 2LP (tel: 01508 498258; email: hteefclerk@gmail.com)

CC number: 311218

Eligibility

People under the age of 25 who live in Hempnall.

Types of grant

Grants are made for educational, training, sport and recreational needs.

Applications

Grant application forms can be obtained from Hempnall Village Hall, Hempnall Mill, Hempnall Surgery, 34 Roland Drive or by emailing the clerk.

Financial information

Year end	31/12/2018
Income	£20,700
Total expenditure	£18,700

Further financial information

Full accounts were not available to view on the Charity Commission's website due to the charity's low income. We have therefore estimated the grant total based on the charity's total expenditure.

Sources of information

Charity Commission record; The Hempnall Trust website.

Suffolk

Calthorpe and Edwards Educational Foundation

 £9,300 (2017/18)

Correspondent: Mrs R. Boswell, Clerk, Chegwidden, Beauford Road, Ingham, Bury St Edmunds IP31 1NW (tel: 01284 728199; email: rgboswell@care4free.net)

CC number: 310464

Eligibility

Young people between the ages of 16 and 25, who are attending a further or higher educational institution, including NVQ study. The applicant must live in one of the parishes of Ampton, Great/ Little Livermere, Ingham, Timworth, Troston, Ixworth, Culford, Great Barton, West Stow, Wordwell, Fornham St Genevieve or Fornham St Martin.

Types of grant

An annual grant is paid in three termly instalments to help students buy books and equipment for a course in further education. It is usually limited to three years but may be extended at the discretion of the trustees.

Applications

Application forms can be requested from the correspondent or are available to download from the Thurston Community College website.

Financial information

Year end	30/06/2018
Income	£10,300
Total expenditure	£10,300

Further financial information

Full accounts were not available to view on the Charity Commission's website due to the charity's low income. We have therefore estimated the grant total based on the charity's total expenditure.

Sources of information

Charity Commission record; Thurston Community College Website.

The Cranfield Charitable Trust
See record on page 176

Kirkley Poor's Land Estate

 £6,400 (2017/18)

Correspondent: Lucy Walker, Clerk to the Trustees, 4 Station Road, Lowestoft, Suffolk NR32 4QF (tel: 01502 514964; email: kirkleypoors@gmail.com)

 www.kirkleypoorslandestate.co.uk

CC number: 210177

Eligibility

Educational grants are available for students undertaking their first degree who live in the parish of Kirkley and are in need.

Types of grant

One-off grants of about £100 per term to help towards university degree expenses throughout the course of the degree.

Applications

Applications can be made writing to the correspondent.

Financial information

Year end	30/04/2018
Income	£98,000
Total expenditure	£82,700

Other information

The boundaries of the parish are fully defined on the charity's website. The charity also awards grants to local organisations.

Sources of information

Accounts; annual report; Charity Commission record; funder's website.

Lowestoft Church and Town Educational Foundation

£ £5,900 (2017/18)

Correspondent: The Trustees, Norton Peskett Solicitors, 148 London Road North, Lowestoft, Suffolk NR32 1HF (tel: 01493 849200)

CC number: 310460

Eligibility

Children and young people under the age of 25 who live (or whose parents live) in the parish of Lowestoft and have attended school in the area for at least three years.

Types of grant

Preference is given to applications for scholarships, bursaries and maintenance allowances to help students attend an institution of further education. Grants are also awarded for items such as books, clothing and tools that allow applicants to further their education or enter a profession after finishing their education.

Applications

Apply in writing to the correspondent.

Financial information

Year end	05/04/2018
Income	£23,700
Total expenditure	£13,200

Further financial information

Full accounts were not available to view on the Charity Commission's website due to the charity's low income. We have therefore estimated the grant total based on the charity's total expenditure.

Other information

Up to a third of the foundation's funds can be awarded to schools in the area.

Sources of information

Charity Commission record.

The Mendlesham Education Foundation

£ £24,000 (2017)

Correspondent: Mike Favager, Clerk, Beggars Roost, Church Road, Mendlesham, Stowmarket, Suffolk IP14 5SF (tel: 01449 767770)

CC number: 271762

Eligibility

Students under the age of 25 living in Mendlesham.

Types of grant

Grants for costs associated with further/ higher education at college or university.

Applications

Apply in writing to the correspondent.

Financial information

Year end	31/12/2017
Income	£30,200
Total expenditure	£28,800

Further financial information

In 2017, grants were awarded to ten individuals.

Other information

Grants are also made to organisations and schools.

Sources of information

Accounts; annual report; Charity Commission record.

The Mills Educational Foundation

£ £2,800 (2017/18)

Correspondent: The Trustees, PO Box 1703, Framlingham, Woodbridge, Suffolk IP13 9WW (tel: 01728 685031; email: themillscharity@btconnect.com)

 www.themillscharity.co.uk

CC number: 310475

Eligibility

Children and young people who live in Framlingham and the surrounding district, or attend a school there.

Types of grant

Grants are provided for a wide range of educational needs.

Applications

Apply in writing to the correspondent.

Financial information

Year end	31/01/2018
Income	£6,900
Total expenditure	£12,600

Further financial information

Full accounts were not available to view on the Charity Commission's website

due to the charity's low income. We have therefore estimated the grant total based on the charity's total expenditure.

Other information

The charity also contributes directly to the Thomas Mills High School.

Sources of information

Charity Commission record; funder's website.

Old School Fund

£ £1,300 (2017)

Correspondent: Natalie Stoter, Greene & Greene, 80 Guildhall Street, Bury St Edmunds IP33 1QB (tel: 01284 717420; email: nataliestoter@ greene-greene.com)

CC number: 310348

Eligibility

People under the age of 25 who live in, or whose parents live in, Bury St Edmunds.

Types of grant

One-off and recurrent grants according to need.

Applications

Apply in writing to the correspondent.

Financial information

Year end	31/12/2017
Income	£3,600
Total expenditure	£2,500

Further financial information

Full accounts were not available to view on the Charity Commission's website due to the charity's low income. We have therefore estimated the grant total based on the charity's total expenditure.

Other information

The fund also awards grants to state schools in the area.

Sources of information

Charity Commission record.

Pakenham Educational Trust

£ £4,700 (2017)

Correspondent: The Trustees, 13 Manor Garth, Pakenham, Bury St Edmunds, Suffolk IP31 2LB (tel: 01359 239431)

CC number: 310364

Eligibility

Residents of the parish of Pakenham who are undertaking post-school education or training and require financial assistance.

Types of grant
One-off and recurrent grants according to need.

Applications
Contact the correspondent for further information.

Financial information
Year end	31/12/2017
Income	£5,000
Total expenditure	£5,200

Further financial information
Full accounts were not available to view on the Charity Commission's website due to the charity's low income. We have therefore estimated the grant total based on the charity's total expenditure.

Other information
Grants are also given to local schools and organisations for educational causes.

Sources of information
Charity Commission record.

The Seckford Foundation

£7,000 (2017/18)

Correspondent: Graham Watson, Seckford Springboard, Marryott House, Burkitt Road, Woodbridge, Suffolk IP12 4JJ (tel: 01394 615173; email: enquiries@seckford-foundation.org.uk)

 www.seckford-foundation.org.uk

CC number: 1110964

Eligibility
Young people under the age of 25 who live in Suffolk.

Types of grant
The Seckford Springboard scheme supports access to education, employment and training. Grants of up to £500 are available for a range of purposes including travel to training/work, course costs, equipment/tools and essential equipment for an apprenticeship.

Exclusions
The foundation will not support:
- Overseas projects or gap-years
- Retrospective funding
- Activities which should be funded by statutory bodies
- Building projects or refurbishments/adaptations
- Loan or debt repayments, or budget shortfalls
- Tuition fees
- Medical treatment
- Postgraduate study
- Those who have received a grant in the last 12 months
- Individuals living outside Suffolk

The foundation is unlikely to provide funding if their grant only forms a small contribution to the funding required.

Applications
Applications should be made in a letter, stating: the age of the individual; where they live; what the funding is required for; and why they are unable to provide the funds themselves. Potential applicants are welcome to contact the foundation by telephone to ascertain their eligibility. Guidance notes are provided on the foundation's website and should be read before applying. In most cases, the foundation can make a decision within three weeks of receiving an application. Applications for large amounts may take longer, in which case the foundation will notify applicants of a likely timescale.

Financial information
Year end	31/08/2018
Income	£19,600
Total expenditure	£21,600

Further financial information
In 2017/18 a total of £14,000 was awarded to 19 individuals. We estimate that around £7,000 was given as grants for education and £7,000 was awarded for social welfare purposes.

Other information
Seckford Springboard is part of the Seckford Foundation, and also provides apprenticeships and mentoring opportunities, as well as making grants to organisations. The Seckford Foundation runs Woodbridge School and two free schools, and the 16th century Seckford almshouses.

Sources of information
Accounts; annual report; Charity Commission record; funder's website.

Felix Thornley Cobbold Agricultural Trust

£33,600 (2017/18)

Correspondent: The Administrator, The Willows, Lackford, Bury St Edmunds, Suffolk IP28 6HL (tel: 01284 728316; email: office@felixcobboldtrust.org.uk)

 www.felixcobboldtrust.org.uk

CC number: 211245

Eligibility
Education and training grants: People from Suffolk or the adjoining counties who have lived in the area for a minimum of three years (excluding time spent in further or higher education). Students must be accepted (or provisionally accepted) for a course in agriculture or a related subject at a college, university or research centre.

Priority may be given to people from disadvantaged backgrounds.

Research and development grants: applicants do not need to have lived in Suffolk or the adjoining counties, but preference will be given to residents/former residents in the area of benefit. Research projects must be of a definable benefit to farming in Suffolk and the surrounding area and all trials must take place within the area of benefit. Applicants must be under the supervision of a senior research leader at an appropriate centre in the UK.

John Forrest Award: agriculturalists, including scientists and farmers, for whom clear communication skills are integral to their careers.

For further information on eligibility, see the trust's website.

Types of grant
Grants are made for costs associated with training or further/higher education and for research projects. The John Forrest Memorial Award is made to eight agriculturalists annually for professional training courses in public communication skills.

Exclusions
Students applying for education and training grants should not be eligible for state funding.

Applications
Applications should be made to the Administrator by email. Applications should include the following information:
- Full name, address, telephone number and email address
- The category of grant applied for and confirmation that all the conditions within the category are fulfilled
- Name of course, project or activity proposed
- Brief statement in support of the application (i.e. why it should be funded)
- Total grant requested
- The amount of any grants applied for, or awarded by any other body (including state funding)

Applications for the John Forrest Award should also be made by email and should include: full contact details along with a personal statement outlining their link with East Anglia; why they wish to attend the course; how they will utilise the training; how it will benefit farming in East Anglia; and what difference it will make to their future. Applicants should also include details of their education, career and current position. Applications should be submitted in September, for consideration in October.

Financial information

Year end	31/03/2018
Income	£249,200
Total expenditure	£239,100

Further financial information

During 2017/18, the charity awarded 21 educational grants. Of this figure, eight grants were made for higher education, another eight grants were made in the form of John Forrest Awards and five were made for agricultural research projects.

Other information

Grants are also made to local teaching and/or training centres for building and equipment projects, and to organisations for educational activities aimed at improving public understanding of farming, food and food production.

Sources of information

Accounts; annual report; Charity Commission record; funder's website.

Babergh

Ann Beaumont's Educational Foundation

£ £9,000 (2018/19)

Correspondent: Rose Welham, 55 Castle Road, Hadleigh, Ipswich, Suffolk IP7 6JP (tel: 01473 823565; email: rosewelham55@aol.com)

CC number: 310397

Eligibility

Students under the age of 25 who are in need of financial assistance to support their further education and who live in the parish of Hadleigh.

Types of grant

One-off and recurrent grants according to need.

Applications

Applications are to be requested from the correspondent.

Financial information

Year end	31/03/2019
Income	£55,700
Total expenditure	£34,300

Further financial information

In 2018/19, grants were made to 55 individuals.

Other information

The foundation also awards grants to organisations.

Sources of information

Accounts; annual report; Charity Commission record.

East Suffolk

The Dennington Consolidated Charities

£ £1,700 (2018)

Correspondent: Peter Lamb, 2 The Coach House, The Square, Dennington, Woodbridge, Suffolk IP13 8AB (tel: 01728 638897; email: peterlamb54@googlemail.com)

CC number: 207451

Eligibility

Educational grants are made to students in the village of Dennington who are in higher education.

Types of grant

Educational grants are awarded according to need.

Applications

Apply in writing to the correspondent. The trustees meet twice each year in March/April and October/November.

Financial information

Year end	31/12/2018
Income	£18,100
Total expenditure	£7,600

Further financial information

Full accounts were not available to view on the Charity Commission's website due to the charity's low income. We have therefore estimated the grant total based on the charity's total expenditure.

Other information

The charity also makes grants to local organisations and supports the maintenance and repair of the parish church (St Mary).

Sources of information

Charity Commission record; Dennington Parish Council website.

Ipswich

Hope House and Gippeswyk Educational Trust

£ £4,200 (2017/18)

Correspondent: The Trustees, 4 Church Meadows, Henley, Ipswich, Suffolk IP6 0RP (email: clements4henley@aol.com)

CC number: 1068441

Eligibility

Young people in need who are under the age of 21 and live in Ipswich or the surrounding area.

Types of grant

Grants are available to promote the education of young people in Ipswich and the surrounding area, who are in need.

Applications

Apply in writing to the correspondent.

Financial information

Year end	30/04/2018
Income	£12,400
Total expenditure	£9,300

Further financial information

Full accounts were not available to view on the Charity Commission's website due to the charity's low income. We have therefore estimated the grant total based on the charity's total expenditure.

Other information

Financial assistance may also be given to organisations.

Sources of information

Charity Commission record.

Mid Suffolk

Gislingham United Charity

£ £4,800 (2018)

Correspondent: Sheila Eade, Clerk, Woodberry, High Street, Gislingham, Suffolk IP23 8JD (tel: 01379 783541; email: gislinghamunitedcharity@gmail.com)

 https://gislinghamparishcouncil.com/organisations/gislingham-united-charity

CC number: 208340

Eligibility

People in need who live in Gislingham.

Types of grant

Grants are awarded for educational purposes through the charity's Education Branch.

Applications

Apply in writing to the correspondent.

Financial information

Year end	31/12/2018
Income	£15,100
Total expenditure	£21,400

Further financial information

Full accounts were not available to view on the Charity Commission's website due to the charity's low income. We have therefore estimated the grant total based on the charity's total expenditure.

Other information

The charity also supports the upkeep and maintenance of the St Mary's Church in Gislingham.

Sources of information

Charity Commission record.

The Stowmarket Educational Foundation

(£) £2,600 (2017/18)

Correspondent: Clerk, 9 Temple Road, Stowmarket, Suffolk IP14 1AX (tel: 07414 504513; email: clerk. relieftrust@gmail.com)

CC number: 802573

Eligibility

People in need who are under the age of 25 and live (or whose parents live) or attend a school or other educational establishment in the town of Stowmarket and the civil parishes of Badley, Combs, Greeting St Peter, Great Finborough, Haughley, Old Newton with Dagworth, Onehouse and Stowupland, all in the county of Suffolk.

Types of grant

One-off grants according to need.

Applications

Apply in writing to the correspondent.

Financial information

Year end	30/09/2018
Income	£2,200
Total expenditure	£5,700

Further financial information

Full accounts were not available to view on the Charity Commission's website due to the charity's low income. We have therefore estimated the grant total based on the charity's total expenditure.

Other information

Organisations may also be supported.

Sources of information

Charity Commission record.

West Suffolk

George Goward and John Evans

(£) £19,800 (2018)

Correspondent: Laura Williams, Clerk to the Trustees, 8 Woodcutters Way, Lakenheath, Brandon, Suffolk IP27 9JQ (tel: 07796 018816; email: laurawill@ btinternet.com)

CC number: 253727

Eligibility

Students that live in the parish of Lakenheath, Suffolk.

Types of grant

Grants are awarded to 16 to 18-year-olds, further/higher education students and other young people towards educational costs.

Applications

Apply in writing to the correspondent.

Financial information

Year end	31/12/2018
Income	£35,600
Total expenditure	£38,600

Other information

The charity also supports local schools, colleges, Sunday schools and organisations. One eighth of the charity's income is allocated to Soham United Charities.

Sources of information

Accounts; annual report; Charity Commission record.

Hundon Educational Foundation

(£) £3,600 (2018)

Correspondent: The Trustees, Beauford Lodge, Mill Road, Hundon, Sudbury, Suffolk CO10 8EG (tel: 01440 786942; email: beaufordlodge@hotmail.com)

CC number: 310379

Eligibility

Young people under the age of 25 living in the parish of Hundon.

Types of grant

Grants are awarded towards the costs of course fees and for general educational purposes, including books, clothing and equipment.

Applications

Apply in writing to the correspondent.

Financial information

Year end	31/12/2018
Income	£5,200
Total expenditure	£4,000

Further financial information

Full accounts were not available to view on the Charity Commission's website due to the charity's low income. We have therefore estimated the grant total based on the charity's total expenditure.

Sources of information

Charity Commission record.

Greater London

General

The Aldgate and Allhallows Foundation

 £49,800 (2018)

Correspondent: Richard Foley, Clerk, 31 Jewry Street, London EC3N 2EY (tel: 020 7488 2489; email: aldgateandallhallows@sirjohncass.org)

www.aldgateallhallows.org.uk

CC number: 312500

Eligibility

Grants are made to individuals who meet the following criteria:

- Are under the age of 30 on the day their course is due to begin
- Permanently reside in Tower Hamlets or the City of London and have done so for the last three years
- Are from a low-income background
- Are studying full time in further, higher or postgraduate education for at least one year, which will result in a recognised qualification

Individuals with refugee status are eligible to apply as long as they have been granted indefinite leave to remain, or full refugee status.

Types of grant

Most of the grants made are through undergraduate bursaries at Queen Mary University. However, grants for students at other universities are considered, and can be used for payment of tuition fees, living expenses, and educational costs.

Exclusions

Grants are not normally given for courses at private colleges, independent schools, or courses less than a year in length. Grants are not given towards the cost of repeated years of study, a qualification that is lower than the individual already holds (even if the subject/s or module/s are different), medical electives, or fees for higher education courses, unless they relate to a second degree and a student loan is unavailable. Individuals with limited leave to remain in the UK cannot apply.

Applications

Applications can be made in writing to the correspondent, specifying the applicant's name, address, phone number, email address, age, course, how long they have lived in the City of London or Tower Hamlets, how they heard about the foundation, and what they need a grant for. Eligible candidates will then be sent an application form which should include full details of their financial circumstances. Applications can be made throughout the year.

Financial information

Year end	31/12/2018
Income	£242,300
Total expenditure	£274,800

Other information

The foundation also makes grants to educational institutions within the area.

Sources of information

Accounts; annual report; Charity Commission record.

Sir John Cass's Foundation

 £32,500 (2017/18)

Correspondent: John Hall, Chair of Grants, Sir John Cass's Foundation, 31 Jewry Street, London EC3N 2EY (tel: 020 7480 5884; email: contactus@sirjohncass.org)

www.sirjohncassfoundation.com/grants-to-individuals

CC number: 312425

Eligibility

Individuals must:

- Be under the age of 25
- Be from a low-income background
- Be studying full time or part time on a course that is at least one year in length
- Permanently live in London, or have lived there for at least one year

The London boroughs supported are: Camden; Greenwich; Hackney; Hammersmith and Fulham; Islington; Kensington and Chelsea; Lambeth; Lewisham; Newham; Southwark; Tower Hamlets; Wandsworth; Westminster and the City of London.

Types of grant

Grants are for educational costs, such as books and equipment, travel costs, living costs, tuition fee payments, second qualifications at the same level, or repeated year of study. Many of the foundation's grants are for one year, but can cover activities lasting two or three years. There is no minimum or maximum grant size – the amount requested should be the amount needed.

Applications

The application process is in two stages. Applicants should download an initial enquiry form from the foundation's website, to be completed and sent back with the requested supporting documents via post. The trustees will consider the application, and applicants will be notified of the outcome within three weeks.

Financial information

Year end	31/03/2018
Income	£7,240,000
Total expenditure	£5,320,000

Other information

The foundation also awards funding to organisations and institutes bearing the founder's name, for example the Sir John Cass Faculty of Art, Architecture, and Design at London Metropolitan University.

Sources of information

Accounts; annual report; Charity Commission record.

The Castle Baynard Educational Foundation

£ £2,400 (2017/18)

Correspondent: Catherine McGuiness, Members' Room, PO Box 270, Guildhall, London EC2P 2EJ (tel: 020 7606 3030)

CC number: 312502

Eligibility

People in need under the age of 25 who are (or whose parents are) resident or employed in the Castle of Baynard Ward of the City of London or in the former county of Middlesex, or who are/have been in full-time education at any educational establishment closely connected with the City of London Corporation. Preference may be given to the City of London School and The City of London School for Girls or to people with special educational needs.

Types of grant

Grants are awarded for books, equipment/instruments, tools, materials, events for students in further or higher education.

Exclusions

Support is not normally available for the course fees or general maintenance.

Applications

Apply in writing to the correspondent. Applicants should provide an sae and include the following details: the purpose of the grant; a CV; evidence of financial need; and a reference of support to confirm their current educational status and financial circumstances. Applications are normally considered in March, June, September and December.

Financial information

Year end	31/03/2018
Income	£4,100
Total expenditure	£5,300

Further financial information

Full accounts were not available to view on the Charity Commission's website due to the charity's low income. We have therefore estimated the grant total based on the charity's total expenditure.

Other information

The foundation also supports a Sunday school at St Andrew by the Wardrobe, as well as exhibitions at any secondary school, teacher training college, university, or other further education institute.

Sources of information

Charity Commission record.

The Cutler Trust

£ £2,800 (2017/18)

Correspondent: The Trustees, Teacher Support Network, 40A Drayton Park, London N5 1EW (tel: 020 7697 2772; email: grantscaseworker@edsupport.org.uk)

CC number: 279271

Eligibility

Young people between the ages of 16 and 25 who are on low income and whose one or both parents are current or former teachers of the Inner or Greater London Area, which includes City of London, Camden, Enfield, Greenwich, Hackney, Hammersmith and Fulham, Islington, Kensington and Chelsea, Lambeth, Lewisham, Southwark, Tower Hamlets, Wandsworth and Westminster. Preference is given to applicants whose one or both parents are deceased.

Types of grant

Small grants or bursaries towards continuing education or undertaking apprenticeships and support for educational necessities, including books, clothing, equipment and tools or instruments to people in training and those entering a profession/trade. Travel expenses are also covered.

Applications

Applications should be made by registering on the Teacher Support website and following the online procedure. Alternatively, a form can be downloaded from the website and emailed.

Financial information

Year end	31/03/2018
Income	£3,700
Total expenditure	£3,100

Further financial information

Full accounts were not available to view on the Charity Commission's website due to the charity's low income. We have therefore estimated the grant total based on the charity's total expenditure.

Sources of information

Charity Commission record.

The Hornsey Parochial Charities (Educational and Vocational Foundation)

£ £33,600 (2018)

Correspondent: Lorraine Fincham, The Clerk to the Trustees, PO Box 22985, London N10 3XB (tel: 020 8352 1601; email: hornseypc@blueyonder.co.uk)

 www.hornseycharities.com

CC number: 312810

Eligibility

People under the age of 25 who live in Hornsey, including the parish of Clerkenwell in Haringey and Hackney. Applicants must have resided in the area for at least 12 months. The charity's website has helpful maps showing the area of benefit.

Types of grant

Grants are available to assist with costs incurred through education and beginning work. Assistance can be given in a number of areas including bursaries, maintenance allowances, clothing, instruments and books.

Exclusions

Applications are not accepted if the applicant was not educated or does not reside during academic holidays within the areas defined by the maps.

Applications

Application forms are available to download from the charity's website to be completed and returned to the trustees via post. There is also a schedule of upcoming trustee meetings available.

Financial information

Year end	31/12/2018
Income	£69,700
Total expenditure	£43,900

Further financial information

Grants were awarded to 36 young people in 2018 ranging from £300 to £2,000 with and average grant of £820.

Other information

The charity also awards grants to organisations. Note: the Hornsey Parochial Charities (Charity Commission no. 229410) awards grants for educational purposes to both individuals and organisations.

Sources of information

Accounts; annual report; Charity Commission record; funder's website.

The Sheriffs' and Recorders' Fund

 £16,200 (2018/19)

Correspondent: Secretary, 16 Cowley Street, London SW1P 3LZ (tel: 020 7192 2734 (Tuesdays and Wednesdays, 11am until 4:45pm) or 020 7248 2739; email: secretary@srfund.net)

www.srfund.org.uk

CC number: 221927

Eligibility

People who are on probation in the Greater London area. Support is also available to the families of people who are currently serving prison sentences in Greater London.

Types of grant

Educational grants are awarded to deter people on probation from re-offending. Grants have been made towards vocational training courses (such as fork-lift truck driving courses) and IT courses.

Applications

Contact the correspondent for information on how to apply.

Financial information

Year end	31/03/2019
Income	£368,100
Total expenditure	£378,100

Further financial information

During 2018/19, the charity awarded 1,314 grants to individuals. Grants were broken down as follows:

Clothing	£88,800
Furnishings	£60,500
Tools	£20,100
Training	£16,200
White goods	£9,200

Other information

This charity also makes grants to organisations, particularly to other voluntary organisations that work with ex-offenders and to prisons for mentoring projects and training/job opportunities.

Sources of information

Accounts; annual report; Charity Commission record; funder's website.

St Andrew Holborn and Stafford's Charity

 £21,300 (2018)

Correspondent: Anna Paterson, Grants Officer, 5 St Andrew Street, London EC4A 3AF (tel: 020 7583 7394; email: charities@standrewholborn.org.uk)

www.standrewholborn.org.uk

CC number: 1095045

Eligibility

People in need who live in a defined area of Holborn (a map of eligible areas is available on the charity's website).

Types of grant

One-off grants of up to £500 are awarded for a range of educational purposes including books, computers, travel and general maintenance.

Exclusions

Grants will not be given towards rent or utility arrears, credit card debt, rental deposits, holidays, school fees or for goods and services already bought.

Grants will not be given towards second degrees or postgraduate courses.

Applications

Application forms can be downloaded from the charity's website. Once the application is received, a home visit will be arranged with the grants officer. Applicants must be able to provide proof of income and expenditure. Only one application per individual will be considered in any 12 month period and only two applications over three years.

Financial information

Year end	31/12/2018
Income	£586,600
Total expenditure	£562,600

Other information

Grants are also given to organisations. In 2018 the St Andrew Holborn Charity and Stafford's Charity came together to form St Andrew Holborn and Stafford's Charity.

Sources of information

Accounts; annual report; Charity Commission record; funder's website.

Mary Trevelyan Fund

 £15,000 (2017/18)

Correspondent: S. Bolton, Secretary, International Students House, 1 Park Crescent, Regents Park, London W1B 1SH (tel: 020 7631 8309; email: s.bolton@ish.org.uk)

www.ish.org.uk/the-mary-trevelyan-hardship-fund

CC number: 294448–1

Eligibility

Students who are studying full-time at a recognised higher education organisation and find themselves in unexpected financial difficulty. They must either be an International Student House (ISH) resident of any nationality or a non-British student at an organisation that holds a membership with ISH. See the fund's website for a list of higher education organisations that hold ISH membership. Preference will be given to those in their final year studies.

Types of grant

Grants or loans of up to £1,000 (in exceptional circumstances up to £2,000) are available to those who experience difficulties due to unexpected financial hardship.

Exclusions

The grant cannot normally be used to pay tuition fees.

Applications

Application forms are available from the fund's website or can be requested from the correspondent. The fund has stated that the application will have a greater chance of success if it is supported by the student's own college/university advice or welfare service.

Financial information

Year end	30/09/2018
Income	£11,200
Total expenditure	£16,000

Other information

This fund is a subsidiary charity of The International Students Trust.

Sources of information

Accounts; annual report; Charity Commission record; funder's website.

Truro Fund

£9,000 (2018/19)

Correspondent: Lt Col. Richard Martin, Clerk to the Trustees, St Margaret's Church, Lothbury, London EC2R 7HH (email: lm800aat@hotmail.com)

CC number: 312288

Eligibility

Children and young people under the age of 21 living or attending an educational establishment in Greater London.

Types of grant

One-off bursaries, scholarships and maintenance allowances are available to schoolchildren, further/higher education students, people entering a trade/profession, people starting work/businesses or apprenticeships. Support is given towards the cost of outfits/clothing, books, equipment/instruments, materials, tools, travel/study abroad, also for music and arts studies.

Exclusions

Our previous research suggests that grants are not intended to cover fees.

Applications

Apply in writing to the correspondent. Applications should include three references (at least one of which should be from the applicant's educational establishment), evidence of the date of birth (either a photo page from a British passport or a birth certificate), full financial details and any information concerning the immigration status (if applicable). The trustees meet twice a year in April and September to consider applications.

Financial information

Year end	04/04/2019
Income	£10,200
Total expenditure	£10,600

Further financial information

Full accounts were not available to view on the Charity Commission's website due to the charity's low income. We have therefore estimated the grant total based on the charity's total expenditure.

Other information

The fund is an amalgamation of three small charities – The Rt Hon. The Dowager Baroness Truro's Fund (The Truro Fund), The East London Industrial School Fund and the Regent's Park Boy's Home Fund.

Sources of information

Charity Commission record.

Barnet

Elizabeth Allen Trust

 £20,600 (2016/17)

Correspondent: Clerk, PO Box 1180, St Albans, Hertfordshire AL1 9XP (tel: 01727 823206; email: clerk@ elizabethallentrust.org.uk)

www.elizabethallentrust.org.uk

CC number: 310968

Eligibility

People in need under the age of 25 who live, are employed, or in education in the borough of Barnet.

Types of grant

One-off grants are offered to those in education and people starting work/ entering a trade. Financial assistance is given for general educational expenses, including books, fees, maintenance expenses, and travel for education. For apprentices or those preparing for entry into employment, funding can be provided for tools, clothing/outfits, uniforms, and other necessary equipment.

Applications

Application forms can be requested by emailing the clerk. The trustees meet around four times per year to consider

applications. Genuine financial hardship must be established.

Financial information

Year end	31/08/2017
Income	£32,700
Total expenditure	£39,100

Further financial information

The 2016/17 accounts were the latest available at the time of writing (January 2020).

Sources of information

Accounts; annual report; Charity Commission record; funder's website.

The Hyde Foundation

£ £25,000 (2018)

Correspondent: Mr C. E. R. Marson, Clerk to the Trustees, 1 Hillside, Codicote, Hitchin, Hertfordshire SG4 8XZ (tel: 01438 820409; email: clerkhyde@btinternet.com)

CC number: 302918

Eligibility

Young people in education up to (and including) university level in the parishes of Chipping Barnet, Arkley and Monken Hadley.

Types of grant

Grants are awarded towards travel abroad (for those studying musics or the arts), books, equipment and maintenance/living expenses.

Applications

Apply in writing to the correspondent. The trustees meet quarterly to consider grant applications.

Financial information

Year end	31/12/2018
Income	£40,600
Total expenditure	£40,900

Other information

The charity also makes grants to organisations.

Sources of information

Accounts; annual report; Charity Commission record.

Bromley

The Hayes (Kent) Trust

£ £2,000 (2018/19)

Correspondent: The Trustees, 2 Warren Wood Close, Bromley, Kent BR2 7DU (tel: 020 8462 1915; email: hayes.kent. trust@gmail.com)

CC number: 221098

Eligibility

People in need who live in the parish of Hayes.

Types of grant

One-off and recurring grants according to need.

Applications

Apply in writing to the correspondent. The trustees meet six times a year to review applications.

Financial information

Year end	31/03/2019
Income	£54,716
Total expenditure	£61,165

Other information

The trust is an amalgamation of the following charities: The Poors Land Cottage Charity; The Poors Land Eleemosynary Charity; The Hayes (Kent) Educational Foundation. It also awards grants to organisations.

Sources of information

Accounts; annual report; Charity Commission record.

Camden

Philological Foundation

 £22,900 (2017/18)

Correspondent: Ms S. Hallin, Clerk, 8 Southcliffe', Lewes, East Sussex BN7 2BZ (email: thephilological@gmail. com)

www.philological.org.uk

CC number: 312692

Eligibility

Individual recipients of grants must be under the age of 26 and be or have been pupils at a secondary school in the City of Westminster or London borough of Camden.

Types of grant

Grants can be awarded for pursuing apprenticeships, further or higher education at colleges or universities, attendance at schools of art, music dancing or drama, travel for educational purposes or preparation for entering a profession, trade, occupation or service.

Exclusions

Support will not be given to individuals who could be assisted by a statutory loan or for postgraduate research degrees. Retrospective funding cannot be given.

Applications

Application forms can be downloaded from the foundation's website. Applicants must provide proof of acceptance on the course, documents showing evidence of income and evidence of proposed expenditure such as a current price list for any equipment or travel.

Financial information

Year end	31/03/2018
Income	£74,600
Total expenditure	£62,900

Further financial information

The grant total has been estimated from the 2017/18 accounts.

Other information

Grants are also given to state-funded primary and secondary schools in Westminster or Camden for the provision of recreation or leisure activities such as playground equipment and educational visits.

Sources of information

Accounts; annual report; Charity Commission record; funder's website.

City of London

Bromfield's Educational Foundation

 £10,000 (2018)

Correspondent: Anna Paterson, Grants Officer, 5 St Andrew Street, London EC4A 3AB (tel: 020 7583 7394; email: info@standrewholborn.org.uk)

www.standrewholborn.org.uk

CC number: 312795

Eligibility

People in need under the age of 25 who for at least the past two years have lived (or whose parents or guardians lived) in the area of the former parish of St Andrews Holborn and whose socio-economic circumstances mean that they are restricted in their ability fully to benefit from educational opportunities.

Types of grant

Grants are awarded for further and higher educational purposes such as for laptops, travel and books.

Exclusions

No grants are awarded for school, college or university fees. Applications for postgraduate studies will not be considered.

Applications

Apply on a form available from the foundation's website. Details of income, expenditure and personal information are required, supported by documentary evidence. When the application is

received, the grants officer will be in touch to arrange a home visit. Applications usually take about 20 working days to process.

Financial information

Year end	31/12/2018
Income	£78,700
Total expenditure	£82,500

Further financial information

The grant totals have been estimated from the 2018 accounts. During 2018, 51 grants were awarded for welfare and educational purposes.

Other information

Priority is given to families of children with disabilities. Grants totalling £43,900 were awarded to organisations in 2018.

Sources of information

Accounts; annual report; Charity Commission record; funder's website.

The Thomas Carpenter Educational and Apprenticing Foundation (Thomas Carpenter's Trust)

 £30,800 (2017/18)

Correspondent: Lt Col. Richard Martin, St Margaret's Church, Lothbury, London EC2R 7HH (email: lm800aat@hotmail.com)

CC number: 312155

Eligibility

People under the age of 25 who have (or whose parents have) lived or worked for three years in Bread Street and adjoining wards in the City of London, or who attend an educational establishment in that area.

Types of grant

General course-related costs, including outfits for entering a trade, fees, books, equipment/tools, study of music or other arts, travel/study abroad and so on. People in schools, universities/colleges or those starting work/entering trades can be supported.

Exclusions

Grants are not normally given towards electives or field trips which are not part of a full-time study course.

Applications

Application forms can be requested from the correspondent. They should normally be submitted before 31 July by the individual's parent or guardian, details of whose financial circumstances should be included.

Financial information

Year end	30/06/2018
Income	£40,800
Total expenditure	£35,400

Other information

Applications from local groups for recreational, social and physical training or equipment will also be considered.

Sources of information

Accounts; annual report; Charity Commission record.

The City of London Corporation Combined Education Charity

Correspondent: Central Grants Team, Community and Children's Services, City of London, PO Box 270, Guildhall, London EC2P 2EJ (tel: 020 7332 3712; email: grants@cityoflondon.gov.uk)

www.cityoflondon.gov.uk/about-the-city/community-work/Pages/central-grants-programme.aspx

CC number: 312836

Eligibility

People who are undertaking secondary, further or higher education. Applicants must have been either born in the City of London, be living in the City of London or have attended a place of education in the City of London or other London boroughs. Preference may be given to those studying cultural arts, science and technology related subjects. Support is also given to teachers working at maintained schools and academies in the City of London and other London boroughs who are wishing to develop in their role.

Types of grant

Grants range between £5,000 (which must be spent in one year) and £10,000 (which must be spent in two years). Grants are awarded to enable students to continue their education. Support can be given towards travel, equipment and maintenance costs. In addition, grants are awarded to teachers to undertake further study in order to develop as teachers.

Applications

Individuals seeking support should contact the correspondent to request an application form. See the charity's website for current deadlines.

Financial information

Year end	31/03/2018
Income	£37,500
Total expenditure	£7,100

Further financial information

No grants were awarded in 2017/18; however, 24 grants totalling £66,200 were made the previous year.

Other information

The charity primarily awards grants to organisations and organisations applying on behalf of an individual. Applications that benefit groups of individuals will take priority over applications that benefit just one.

Sources of information

Accounts; annual report; Charity Commission record; funder's website.

The Mitchell City of London Educational Foundation

 £31,800 (2017/18)

Correspondent: Lucy Jordan, Clerk to the Trustees, 24 Station Lane, Holme-on-Spalding Moor, York, North Yorkshire YO43 4AL (tel: 0845 600 1558; email: mitchellcityoflondon@gmail.com)

CC number: 312499

Eligibility

People aged 11 to 19 who are either attending school in the City of London or whose parents have lived or worked there for at least five years. The 'city' is classified as almost all EC3 and EC4 postcodes and small areas of EC1 and EC2.

Types of grant

Bursaries are awarded to students studying for their A-level or International Baccalaureate qualifications. The foundation grants Diploma Awards of £2,500 to students in need.

Applications

Apply in writing to the correspondent.

Financial information

Year end	31/03/2018
Income	£96,400
Total expenditure	£79,200

Other information

Grants were also made to individuals for welfare purposes.

Sources of information

Accounts; annual report; Charity Commission record.

City of Westminster

The Sir Simon Milton Foundation

 £55,000 (2018)

Correspondent: Matthew Sykes, Chief Executive, Westminster City Hall (16th Floor), 5 Strand, London WC2N 5HR (tel: 020 7641 1396; email: info@sirsimonmiltonfoundation.com)

🌐 www.sirsimonmilton foundation.com

CC number: 1174405

Eligibility

Applicants must be under the age of 30 and former attendees of a school or college in Westminster or living or have lived in Westminster and come from a household with an income below £25,000. They must be undertaking their first year of their first undergraduate degree in either engineering, construction, politics, history, or a combined course that includes one of these subjects. In 2019 the foundation prioritised the following groups: women with registered disabilities, young women, first generation attendees of university in a family and young people leaving care.

Types of grant

Scholarships of £10,000 over the course of the degree. The grant can cover accommodation and living costs or tuition fees. Bursaries are available to students at Gonville and Caius College Cambridge and are to cover the living costs of students from low-income backgrounds.

Applications

Application forms can be downloaded and completed on the foundation's website, where deadlines, further guidance and the terms and conditions of the scholarship can also be found. The application period generally opens from July to September, in advance of the start of the course.

Financial information

Year end	31/12/2018
Income	£456,000
Total expenditure	£418,000

Other information

The foundation's objects are focused on getting young people in Westminster into work through education and training and reducing loneliness and isolation amongst older people in the city and across the country. Grants are also awarded to organisations. The foundation also holds events including the annual Westminster Tea Dance and provides Christmas hampers to older citizens.

Sources of information

Accounts; annual report; Charity Commission record; funder's website.

Paddington Charitable Estates Educational Fund

£ £22,400 (2017/18)

Correspondent: Caroline Headley-Barton, Voluntary Section Officer/Clerk to the Trustees, Westminster City Council, Westminster City Hall, 64 Victoria Street, London SW1E 6QP (tel: 020 7641 1859; email: cheadley-barton@westminster.gov.uk or scraddock@westminster.gov.uk)

🌐 https://www.westminster.gov.uk/ paddington-charities

CC number: 312347

Eligibility

Young people under the age of 25 who are living in Paddington. Preference is given to students who are 'particularly gifted' or those in need of further tuition.

Types of grant

Grants are made towards educational/vocational course fees, special tuition, and towards the education of those wanting to study music or other arts.

Applications

Prospective applicants should contact the correspondent for further information.

Financial information

Year end	31/10/2018
Income	£23,800
Total expenditure	£96,400

Further financial information

Full accounts were not available to view on the Charity Commission's website due to the charity's low income. We have therefore estimated the grant total based on the charity's total expenditure.

Other information

The charity makes grants to voluntary-aided schools in Paddington for repairs or physical alterations and to organisations in the area of benefit.

Grants may also be given towards school uniforms and educational trips. The educational fund operates in conjunction with the Paddington Relief in Need Charity (Charity Commission no. 810132), referred to as the Paddington Charities. The two organisations are distinct in terms of their beneficiaries but organisationally, function as one body.

Sources of information
Charity Commission record; funder's website.

Philological Foundation
See record on page 196

Croydon

The Frank Denning Memorial Charity

 £3,900 (2017/18)

Correspondent: Stephanie Davis, Democratic Services and Governance Officer, Bernard Weatherill House, 8 Mint Walk, Croydon CR0 1EA (tel: 020 8726 6000 ext 84384; email: Stephanie.Davis@croydon.gov.uk or cliona.may@croydon.gov.uk)

www.croydon.gov.uk/advice/grants/frankdenning

CC number: 312813

Eligibility
Students between the ages of 19 and 25 who are (or whose parents are) resident in the London borough of Croydon and who want to carry out an educational project overseas.

Types of grant
One-off travelling scholarships are available to full-time university or college students for undertaking a specific project abroad as a part of their course of study. Grants are awarded for journeys starting between 1 May and 30 April following the year of the application. See the charity's website for further details.

Applications
Apply in writing to the correspondent.

Financial information
Year end	31/03/2018
Income	£4,900
Total expenditure	£4,400

Further financial information
Full accounts were not available to view on the Charity Commission's website

due to the charity's low income. We have therefore estimated the grant total based on the charity's total expenditure.

Sources of information
Charity Commission record; funder's website.

Ealing

Acton (Middlesex) Educational Charity

 £14,400 (2017)

Correspondent: Clerk to the Trustees, c/o St Mary's Parish Office, 1 The Mount, Acton High Street, London W3 9NW (email: clerk@actoncharities.co.uk or acton.charities@virgin.net)

www.actoncharities.co.uk

CC number: 312312

Eligibility
Students whose home residence is in the former ancient parish of Acton in West London (their term-time address does not have to be in Acton). Candidates must be over the age of 18 (and normally up to the age of 25) and have entered a full-time course in the UK, usually of at least three years, which will lead to a recognised qualification. If there is a high demand, priority will be given to students who have spent some part of their education in an Acton school.

Types of grant
Grants of £300 per year to assist with books or equipment.

A small amount of available funds will be reserved for applicants undertaking vocational courses of less than three years at local colleges, who will be considered for grants of £100 to £200.

Exclusions
Anyone outside the area of benefit cannot apply (there is a helpful map on the charity's website). Grants are not given for courses in private schools or institutions.

Applications
Application forms are available online or can be obtained from the correspondent. Applications must be accompanied by written proof of attendance from the applicant's educational institute.

All applications received during the period 1 September to 30 November will be considered for grants and successful applicants will receive their grant in December.

Financial information
Year end	31/12/2017
Income	£10,100
Total expenditure	£16,900

Further financial information
Full accounts were not available to view on the Charity Commission's website due to the charity's low income. We have therefore estimated the grant total based on the charity's total expenditure.

Other information
This charity is one of four organisations that make up the Acton (Middlesex) Charities group. Also included are Relief in Need Charity, John Perryn Relief in Need Fund, and the Athawes Art Gallery. In 2017, the combined charities donated a total of £22,500 in grants.

Sources of information
Charity Commission record; funder's website.

The Educational Foundation of Francis Courtney

£2,700 (2018/19)

Correspondent: The Trustees, Housing Pathways, 33 Dean Court, London W13 9YU (tel: 020 8579 7411; email: info@yourpathways.org.uk)

CC number: 312547

Eligibility
People under the age of 25 who live in the London borough of Ealing.

Types of grant
Scholarships, bursaries and maintenance allowances are given to assist with fees, living expenses and travel abroad. Grants can also be given to people leaving any educational organisation and entering a trade or profession for clothing, tools, instruments or books.

Applications
Apply in writing to the correspondent.

Financial information
Year end	31/03/2019
Income	£3,400
Total expenditure	£3,000

Further financial information
Full accounts were not available to view on the Charity Commission's website due to the charity's low income. We have therefore estimated the grant total based on the charity's total expenditure.

Sources of information
Charity Commission record.

Enfield

The Old Enfield Charitable Trust

 £123,400 (2017/18)

Correspondent: The Trust Team, 22 The Town, Enfield, Middlesex EN2 6LT (tel: 020 8367 8941; email: enquiries@ thetrustenfield.org.uk)

https://www.thetrustenfield.org.uk

CC number: 207840

Eligibility

People living in the ancient parish of Enfield who are undertaking education or training. An eligibility checker is available to use on the trust's website. In exceptional circumstances, the trustees may award a grant to an applicant living outside the ancient parish of Enfield.

Types of grant

Grants are awarded to assist with living costs, equipment, childcare, travel and other educational expenses to help the individual complete their course. The trust will support a wide range of courses including degrees, access courses, driving instructor training, counselling training and so on.

Exclusions

The trust will not provide support where local authority or central government should be assisting.

Applications

Applications can be submitted directly from the individual or through a third party professional. A home visit may be required. The trustees consider applications once a month.

Application forms and further guidance can be found on the trust's website. Applicants may be invited to an interview.

Financial information

Year end	31/03/2018
Income	£662,600
Total expenditure	£684,600

Further financial information

In 2017/18 a total of £241,900 was awarded to individuals. Welfare grants to 160 individuals totalled £118,400, this includes four quarterly grants totalling £3,200. Educational grants were awarded to 67 individuals and totalled £123,400.

Other information

The charity makes community grants to local organisations and manages Enfield Market Place. The charity also administers Ann Crowe's and Wright's Almshouse Charity (Charity Commission no. 279346) and administers two sets of almshouses.

Sources of information

Accounts; annual report; Charity Commission record; funder's website.

Greenwich

Sir William Boreman's Foundation

 £12,500 (2017/18)

Correspondent: Clerk to the Trustees, The Drapers' Company, Drapers' Hall, Throgmorton Avenue, London EC2N 2DQ (tel: 020 7588 5001; email: charities@thedrapers.co.uk)

www.thedrapers.co.uk/Charities/ Grant-making-trusts/Sir-William- Boremans-Foundation.aspx

CC number: 312796

Eligibility

The foundation makes grants to young people who are resident in Greenwich and Lewisham, are full or part-time students, aged below 25 and from low-income/disadvantaged backgrounds. Preference to practising members of the Church of England and to sons and daughters of seamen, watermen and fishermen, particularly those who have served in the armed forces.

Types of grant

Grants of up to £1,000 per year are normally awarded and can be used to help cover living expenses while continuing studying, including:

- Daily living costs such as rent and food
- Travel costs to and from college or university
- Educational materials, books and equipment
- Childcare costs

Exclusions

Grants are not made for:

- A-level studies (except for students over the age of 19)
- Students aged over 25 or pre-schoolchildren
- Non-UK citizens and asylum seekers (only those with full refugee status may apply)
- Postgraduate students who have attained a 2.2 or lower
- Overseas study/travel or exchange visits
- Retrospective appeals
- Tuition fees
- Loans or debts not related to education
- Setting up business ventures

- Performing arts courses (acting, dance or drama)
- Private school fees

Applications

To apply for a grant for a primary or secondary school student contact the local (Greenwich/Lewisham) Attendance and Welfare Services. Details can be found on the foundation's website.

Application forms for young people aged between 16 and 25 can be found on the website alongside the guidelines for applicants. Applications can be submitted at any time. The trustees meet three times a year, check the website to see the next meeting dates. Applications should be submitted at least three weeks before the meeting.

Financial information

Year end	31/07/2018
Income	£136,000
Total expenditure	£134,400

Further financial information

Grants of £12,500 were awarded to 12 individuals studying at further or higher education institutions.

Other information

The foundation also supports organisations with similar objectives. In 2017/18 grants to 23 organisations totalling £105,600 were made.

Sources of information

Accounts; annual report; Charity Commission record; funder's website; guidelines for applicants.

Greenwich Blue Coat Foundation

 £16,400 (2017/18)

Correspondent: Mr M. Baker, Clerk to the Trustees, 136 Charlton Lane, London SE7 8AB (tel: 020 8858 7575; email: bluecoat@baker5.co.uk)

www.bluecoathistory.co.uk/ page829.html

CC number: 312407

Eligibility

Young people up to the age of 25 who have lived or have been educated in the London borough of Greenwich for at least two years prior to their application. Preference is given to individuals with limited means.

Types of grant

One-off and recurrent grants, normally of around £500, are given to help individuals to further their education, develop life skills or enter a chosen career path. Financial assistance can be given for the course fees, equipment/

instruments or other course-related expenses.

Exclusions

Maintenance or travel costs are not normally supported.

Applications

Application forms can be downloaded from the foundation's website or requested from the correspondent. Candidates are required to provide the name of a referee. The trustees usually meet four times a year to consider applications. The trustees may ask applicants to attend an interview to help determine their suitability for an award.

Financial information

Year end	31/03/2018
Income	£35,200
Total expenditure	£35,000

Other information

The website states that the foundation only has 'a relatively small sum of money available annually and does not therefore usually make large individual awards'.

Sources of information

Accounts; annual report; Charity Commission record.

Hammersmith and Fulham

Dr Edwards and Bishop King's Fulham Charity

 £800 (2018/19)

Correspondent: Jonathan Martin, Clerk to the Trustees, Percy Barton House, 33–35 Dawes Road, Fulham, London SW6 7DT (tel: 020 7386 9387; email: clerk@debk.org.uk)

www.debk.org.uk

CC number: 1113490

Eligibility

People in need who live in the old metropolitan borough of Fulham. A full list of eligible addresses is available to view on the charity's website.

Types of grant

Grants are awarded towards education and training. Recent examples of funding include a phlebotomy course, fitness instructor training and educational trips.

Exclusions

The charity will not provide support for the following:
- Applications from people who are homeowners
- Applications from those not in the area of benefit
- Cash grants (unless they are to be administered by an agency)
- Retrospective requests or arrears on utility bills
- Funding for funerals
- Wheelchairs or electric scooters
- Computer equipment of any sort, unless for an applicant that is housebound
- Dishwashers or laminate flooring
- Equipment where the local or central government, or any other agency is required to provide that equipment by law

Applications

Application forms are available to download from the charity's website and can be submitted directly from the individual or through a supporting agency such as Social Services.

Financial information

Year end	31/03/2019
Income	£468,400
Total expenditure	£537,700

Further financial information

In 2018/19 a total of £152,600 was awarded to 190 individuals. Welfare grants totalled £151,800 and educational grants totalled £800.

Other information

The charity also gives grants to organisations and runs summer schemes whereby funding is given to projects that allow children to enjoy a break during the summer holidays that they would otherwise not have access to.

Sources of information

Accounts; annual report; Charity Commission record; funder's website.

Haringey

The Tottenham Grammar School Foundation

 £428,700 (2017/18)

Correspondent: Graham Chappell, Clerk to the Foundation, PO Box 34098, London N13 5XU (tel: 020 8882 2999; email: info@tgsf.info or trustees@tgsf.org.uk)

www.tgsf.org.uk

CC number: 312634

Eligibility

Young people under the age of 25 who live/whose parents live in the borough of Haringey and who have attended a state maintained school in the borough.

Types of grant

The foundation has different types of awards and there are different eligibility criteria for each:
- The Somerset Award – generally a one-off grant to students on full-time vocational courses at colleges of further education or equivalent
- The Somerset Undergraduate Award – recurrent payments (£1,050 payable in annual instalments of £250 for the first year, £350 for the second year and £450 for the third year) for university students following a full-time degree or an equivalent higher education course of at least two years' duration
- The Somerset Special Award – a wide range of grants are awarded to postgraduate students, young sportspeople at a county standard or higher, musicians at a conservatoire standard and individuals with special needs
- The foundation also makes a limited number of Somerset Scholarships and Sponsorships each year. Generally, these are made in partnership with Mountview Academy of Theatre Arts, the Harrington scheme, and The College of Haringey, Enfield and North East London

Further information on each type of award is given on the foundation's website.

Exclusions

Grants are not made to young people who do not live in the London borough of Haringey (unless they attend/attended a school in the borough). Somerset Awards/Undergraduate Awards are not given for:
- A or AS levels, GCSEs or any courses at a school or sixth form college
- Part-time courses
- Apprenticeships

Applications

Separate application forms for the Somerset Awards and the Somerset Undergraduate Awards can be downloaded from the foundation's website. Applications can also be made through a fast-track online system on the website. Candidates are invited to apply from 1 May each year (for the academic year commencing the following September). The closing date for applications for each academic year is 31 January. Applications for The Somerset Special Award must be made in writing to the correspondent providing the date of birth, relevant documentation, letters of support and other information specific for different categories (see the website for details). For children with special needs, there is an application form for use by the parent, guardian or other appropriate person applying for assistance on their behalf (which can be downloaded from the website).

Financial information

Year end	31/08/2018
Income	£553,600
Total expenditure	£1,370,000

Other information

Grants are also made to charities, voluntary groups, schools and other organisations which work with young people in the borough of Haringey for purposes such as trips, special educational needs, sports and art activities, etc. In 2017/18, £815,816 was awarded to institutions.

Sources of information

Accounts; annual report; Charity Commission record; funder's website.

Hillingdon

Uxbridge United Welfare Trust

Correspondent: Grants Officer, Woodbridge House, New Windsor Street, Uxbridge, Middlesex UB8 2TY (tel: 01895 232976; email: universal@ uuwt.org)

 www.uuwt.org

CC number: 1181683

Eligibility

People who are in need and live in, or has a parent who lives in, or have a very strong connection with, the Uxbridge area. The area of benefit covers Cowley, Harefield, Hillingdon, Ickenham and Uxbridge.

Types of grant

Educational grants to individuals are primarily for school trips, books, course fees, and similar items.

Exclusions

Our research suggests that grants are not normally given for school fees. Funding is not intended to be provided where statutory support is available.

Applications

Application forms can be requested from the correspondent. They can be submitted directly by the individual or through a social worker, Citizens Advice or educational welfare agency, if applicable. Awards are considered each month. A trained member of staff will

visit applicants for an interview to better assess their case.

Further financial information

At the time of writing (August 2019), the trust's most recent accounts were not available to view on the Charity Commission's website as it re-registered in January 2019.

Other information

The trust also runs almshouses and makes grants to local organisations.

Sources of information

Charity Commission record; funder's website.

Islington

Worrall and Fuller Exhibition Fund

 £10,800 (2017/18)

Correspondent: Clerk, St Luke's Community Centre, 90 Central Street, London EC1V 8AJ (tel: 020 7549 8181; email: worrall&fuller@slpt.org.uk)

 www.worrallandfuller.org

CC number: 312507

Eligibility

Children and young people between the ages of 5 and 25 who are resident in the old borough of Finsbury (now part of Islington). Preference is given to those who live in the parish of St Luke, Old Street, or whose parents have had their business or employment there in previous years.

Types of grant

Students in further and higher education can be supported with grants towards study materials including laptops and IT equipment, but not course fees. Grants are typically between £250 and £750.

Applications

Application forms can be found on the charity's website. The trustees meet four times a year to consider applications but can also take urgent requests.

Financial information

Year end	31/03/2018
Income	£19,800
Total expenditure	£24,100

Further financial information

Full accounts were not available to view on the Charity Commission's website due to the charity's low income. We have therefore estimated the grant total based on the charity's total expenditure.

Other information

The charity is administered by St Luke's Community Centre and Trust. They

carry out all aspects of the grants and financial administration.

Sources of information

Charity Commission record; funder's website.

Kensington and Chelsea

The Campden Charities

 £610,000 (2018/19)

Correspondent: Christopher Stannard, Chief Executive/Company Secretary, Studios 3&4, 27A Pembridge Villas, London W11 3EP (tel: 020 7243 0551; email: chris-stannard@campdencharities. org.uk)

 www.campdencharities.org.uk

CC number: 1104616

Eligibility

Residents of Kensington, London, who are:
- A British or European Union citizen (or have Indefinite Leave to Remain)
- Living in rented accommodation
- In low-paid work or receiving benefits

Types of grant

Campden Scholarships are awarded to young people studying at university, towards the cost of accommodation, books and materials. Vocational training grants are also available to young people who wish to gain qualifications via Employment Routes.

Applications

Initial enquiries should be made by contacting the charity by telephone.

Financial information

Year end	31/03/2019
Income	£4,060,000
Total expenditure	£34,600,000

Further financial information

During 2018/19, the charity awarded 389 educational grants.

Other information

In 2018/19 the charity contributed to the Grenfell response. It also awards grants to organisations and to individuals for welfare purposes.

Sources of information

Accounts; annual report; Charity Commission record; funder's website.

The Pocklington and the Thomas Huggett Apprenticeship Aid Fund Trust

 £16,200 (2017/18)

Correspondent: Glen Peache, Director for Family Services, The Royal borough of Kensington and Chelsea Town Hall, Hornton Street, London W8 7NX (tel: 020 7361 3317; email: glen.peache@rbkc.gov.uk)

https://www.rbkc.gov.uk

CC number: 312943

Eligibility

Young people aged 21 or younger (occasionally up to the age of 25) who were either born in the Royal borough of Kensington and Chelsea or whose parent(s) has/have lived there for at least ten years. Preference is given to looked-after young people including those who are in the care of, or under the supervision of the Royal borough.

Types of grant

One-off and recurrent grants are awarded for people undertaking apprenticeships, those preparing to enter work and students at university or another educational institution. Financial assistance can be given for a range of educational purposes; previous examples include living expenses, equipment, clothing, course fees, costs arising from the course, accommodation costs, study of music/the arts and travel in pursuance of education in the UK or abroad.

Applications

Application forms are available from the correspondent.

Financial information

Year end	31/03/2018
Income	£6,500
Total expenditure	£18,000

Further financial information

Full accounts were not available to view on the Charity Commission's website due to the charity's low income. We have therefore estimated the grant total based on the charity's total expenditure.

Other information

In 2018 the Pocklington Apprenticeship Trust merged with the Thomas Huggett Aid Fund to form The Pocklington and the Thomas Huggett Apprenticeship Aid Fund Trust.

Sources of information

Charity Commission record; report of the Director for Family Services.

Lambeth

Walcot Educational Foundation

 £238,400 (2018/19)

Correspondent: Daniel Chapman, Grants Manager, 127 Kennington Road, London SE11 6SF (tel: 020 7735 1925; email: grants@walcotfoundation.org.uk)

www.walcotfoundation.org.uk

CC number: 312800

Eligibility

People, normally under the age of 30, who are on a low income and live in the borough of Lambeth. According to the foundation's guidance notes, eligible applicants must:

- Have been living in Lambeth for at least one year at the time of application
- Be turning at least 19 in the academic year that they are applying for
- Come from a low-income household, that is applicants (or their parents/carers if if the applicant is under the age of 25 and living with them) need to be in receipt of one of the following income-based benefits: Universal Credit; income-based Job Seekers' Allowance; income-related Employment and Support Allowance (Work Related Activity Group); support under Part VI of the Immigration and Asylum Act 1999; the Guaranteed element of State Pension Credit

Applicants who are currently eligible for free school meals or are on a very low income (even if they or their parents/carers do not receive any of the above listed benefits) may still be eligible. The foundation encourages applicants to use the online eligibility checker if in doubt.

Types of grant

The foundation's guidance notes state that grants are aimed to help with the cost of a first-degree or vocational qualification that is likely to lead to employment. According to the guidance, students can apply for support with:

- **A degree course:** For students starting their degree in September/October 2019, successful applicants receive a grant of £1,500 per year (split termly) for every year of their course (up to a maximum of four years). For students who are already in Years 2, 3 or 4 of their course, successful applicants receive a single grant of £1,500 grant split termly into 3 x £500 payments. Grants can be used towards general living expenses at university (e.g. travel, accommodation fees), course-related items (e.g. books, laptop, specialist equipment) and childcare.

- **A vocational/non-degree course up to NVQ level 4 or an apprenticeship:** Students can apply for a grant of up to £1,500 towards travel costs; books; special clothing; equipment; study/field trips, childcare and course fees.
- **A degree course at a Russell Group university:** Each year the Foundation offers three 'Townsend Scholarships' to Lambeth-resident Black and Minority Ethnic pupils from low-income homes who gain a place at a Russell Group University. Each scholarship is worth £1,000 a term for three years (£9,000 in total).

The guidance notes further state:

Moving into employment:

If you've been out of work for much of the last five years and haven't gained a degree or NVQ-4 (or equivalent) vocational qualification in the last ten years, we could make a grant to help you move into employment. Grants can be made for costs associated with:

- a further education or vocational training course that has a strong likelihood of leading to work
- costs associated with gaining work experience that will strengthen your chances of getting paid work
- costs associated with making the transition from long-term unemployment to employment, such as suitable work clothes and equipment

If you are applying for a grant for the above, it is very likely that we'll refer you to the Walcot-funded careers advisor for 1:1 support and guidance to help you to transition into employment.

Grants can be made up to £1,500. The foundation can also make a grant for up to £4,000 to cover childcare costs.

Exclusions

Grants are not given for:
- Postgraduate studies
- Second degrees
- Personal development courses
- Studies at private institutions
- Repayment of debts
- Career changes
- Course fees in cases where it is not clear that the applicant will be able to raise the balance of funds to complete the entire course
- Childcare applications which include a child who is too young to receive the 15 hours free childcare from the Government
- Childcare costs linked to distance-learning courses (e.g. Open University)
- The cost of goods/services already purchased or those provided by the central/local government
- Council tax, rent or other taxes
- Household goods, furnishing, clothing, unless directly related to work or education progress

If the applicant already has significant work experience with a reasonable level of responsibility, or a vocational qualification (at NVQ-4 or equivalent), the trust will not fund further study.

Applications

Application forms are available on the foundation's website. Supporting documents are required and include ID, proof of residence, bank statements, proof of student enrolment, student finance letter (if applicable), immigration status (if applicable), childcare costs (if applicable). The foundation aims to respond to applications from individuals within six weeks.

Financial information

Year end	31/03/2019
Income	£2,430,000
Total expenditure	£3,060,000

Further financial information

Grants were awarded to 249 individuals.

Other information

The foundation provides additional services to beneficiaries including careers advice, debt and budgeting advice, capacity building and low-cost psychotherapy. Various projects, schools and organisations working for individuals can also be supported.

Sources of information

Accounts; annual report; Charity Commission record; funder's website; guidelines for applicants.

Lewisham

Sir William Boreman's Foundation

See record on page 200

The Lee Education Charity of William Hatcliffe

£7,100 (2017/18)

Correspondent: Anne Wilson, Clerk, PO Box 7041, Bridgnorth, Shropshire WV16 9EL (tel: 07517 527849; email: annewilsontc@hotmail.co.uk)

CC number: 312801

Eligibility

Young people under the age of 25 living in Lewisham.

Types of grant

Grants were awarded for a wide range of educational needs.

Applications

Apply in writing to the correspondent.

Financial information

Year end	31/03/2018
Income	£40,100
Total expenditure	£10,800

Further financial information

Grants to 14 individuals totalled £7,100.

Other information

Grants may also be made to local charities.

Sources of information

Accounts; annual report; Charity Commission record.

Lewisham Educational Charity

 £680 (2017/18)

Correspondent: Finance and Administration Manager, Clerk's Office, Lloyd Court, Slagrove Place, London SE13 7LP (tel: 020 8690 8145; email: admin@lpcharities.co.uk)

www.lpcharities.co.uk

CC number: 1025785

Eligibility

Students under the age of 25 who live, or have parents who live, in the ancient parish of Lewisham, excluding Deptford and Lee (a map of eligible areas can be found on the charity's website).

Types of grant

Grants of up to £500 can be made towards course costs, travel, outfits, instruments and books to assist individuals who are pursuing education or preparing to enter a profession or trade.

Applications

Application forms and further information, including current deadlines, are available from the charity's website.

Financial information

Year end	31/03/2018
Income	£1,300
Total expenditure	£760

Further financial information

Full accounts were not available to view on the Charity Commission's website due to the charity's low income. We have therefore estimated the grant total based on the charity's total expenditure.

Other information

Support may also be given to organisations.

Sources of information

Charity Commission record; funder's website.

Richmond upon Thames

The Barnes Workhouse Fund

 £7,700 (2018)

Correspondent: Katy Makepeace-Gray, Director, PO Box 347, Hampton, Middlesex TW12 9ED (tel: 07484 146802; email: kmakepeacegray@ barnesworkhousefund.org.uk)

www.barnesworkhousefund.org.uk

CC number: 200103

Eligibility

Residents in the parish of Barnes (roughly SW13 postal district) who are in need as a result of ill-health, age or financial hardship.

Types of grant

Educational grants are awarded towards the cost of fees, maintenance, equipment, travel and childcare.

Exclusions

The charity does not normally award educational grants for postgraduate study, unless an applicant can demonstrate that their current employment will benefit.

Applications

Applications for both welfare and educational grants must be made on the individual's behalf by referral agencies such as Citizens Advice, social services, housing associations, etc. The charity is unable to accept applications from individuals directly. For welfare grants, two trustees from the charity may suggest visiting the applicant in their home to fully assess their needs. For educational grants, all applicants will be interviewed by a representative of the trustees.

Financial information

Year end	31/12/2018
Income	£690,000
Total expenditure	£592,600

Further financial information

The charity awarded grants to 133 individuals for both welfare and educational purposes.

Other information

The charity operates and maintains a sheltered housing facility, Walsingham Lodge, which provides accommodation for approximately 40 residents. The charity also makes grants to local voluntary organisations.

Sources of information

Accounts; annual report; Charity Commission record; funder's website.

The Hampton Wick United Charity

 £2,200 (2017/18)

Correspondent: Paul Barnfield, The Clerk, 258 Hanworth Road, London TW3 3TY (tel: 020 8737 0371; email: info@hwuc.org.uk)

hwuc.org.uk

CC number: 1010147

Eligibility

People under the age of 25 who are in need and have lived in the parishes of St John the Baptist in Hampton Wick, St Mark in Teddington, and St Mary with St Alban in Teddington for at least 12 months.

Types of grant

Grants can be awarded for educational costs such as books and travel expenses.

Applications

Contact the Clerk for an informal discussion regarding applying. The trustees meet three times a year but special arrangements can be made to consider emergency requests without delay.

Financial information

Year end	31/03/2018
Income	£46,300
Total expenditure	£27,500

Further financial information

The grant total has been estimated from the 2017/18 accounts.

Other information

Grants are also awarded to organisations.

Sources of information

Accounts; annual report; Charity Commission record; funder's website.

The Petersham United Charities

 £2,300 (2017)

Correspondent: The Trustees, The Vicarage, Bute Avenue, Richmond, Surrey TW10 7AX (tel: 020 8940 8435)

CC number: 200433

Eligibility

Residents in the ecclesiastical parish of Petersham who are in need.

Types of grant

Grants are made for welfare and educational purposes.

Applications

Apply in writing to the correspondent.

Financial information

Year end	31/12/2017
Income	£10,400
Total expenditure	£10,100

Further financial information

Full accounts were not available to view on the Charity Commission's website due to the charity's low income. We have therefore estimated the grant total based on the charity's total expenditure.

Other information

This charity also makes grants to organisations.

Sources of information

Charity Commission record.

Richmond Parish Lands Charity (RPLC)

 £75,500 (2017/18)

Correspondent: Sharon La Ronde, Grants Director, The Vestry House, 21 Paradise Road, Richmond, Surrey TW9 1SA (tel: 020 8948 5701; email: grants@rplc.org.uk)

 www.rplc.org.uk

CC number: 200069

Eligibility

People over the age of 18, living in the areas covered by the TW9, TW10, SW14 and SW13 postcodes, who are studying at a state-run school, college, university or training provider are eligible to apply. Support may be extended to students aged between 16 and 18. Support is available to students under the age of 16 only in very exceptional cases. Non-residents who have worked for a charitable organisation/social enterprise within the borough, or non-residents who have at one time been educated in the borough, may also be eligible for funding.

Types of grant

Educational grants, usually of up to £750, are made to help with the cost of any additional qualifications or training needed for employment. The charity has previously funded courses in: literacy, gas fitting, plumbing, beauty therapy, hairdressing, first aid, IT, HGV driving, nursing, teaching, accounting. Other fees associated with studying for a course (such as transport, childcare, books/equipment, general living costs) are also covered. Support is also available for undergraduate programmes.

Exclusions

Welfare grants can only be made in cases where there are either no statutory funds

or all statutory sources have been exhausted.

Educational grants can only be awarded for study at private institutions when courses or training programmes are unavailable within the state sector. The charity does not usually support postgraduate degrees.

Applications

For educational grants, applications can be made using an online form on the funder's website. Note: there are two different forms for applicants requesting grants of up to £750, and those requesting grants greater than £750.

Application forms for welfare grants are available to download from the funder's website. Applications must be made on the individual's behalf by a local agency such as Richmond borough support teams, Citizens Advice, social services, Age UK Richmond or the community mental health teams. Completed forms should be sent to the charity by email.

Financial information

Year end	30/06/2018
Income	£2,190,000
Total expenditure	£3,280,000

Further financial information

During 2017/18, the charity awarded 396 grants to individuals for both welfare and educational needs.

Other information

The charity also provides regular funding to local charities (currently assisting 38 organisations) for support with administration costs/core operation activities. The charity also makes grants to schools and various non-statutory educational initiatives that promote learning opportunities for children and adults in the area of benefit.

Sources of information

Accounts; annual report; Charity Commission record; funder's website.

Thomas Wilson Educational Trust

 £71,800 (2017)

Correspondent: Marianne Malam, Secretary to the Trust, 94 Oldfield Road, Hampton, Richmond upon Thames TW12 2HR (email: marianne.malam.flp@gmail.com)

CC number: 1003771

Eligibility

People under the age of 25 who live in the neighbourhood of Teddington.

Types of grant

Grants are available to schoolchildren for educational purposes such as school trips. The trust also provides grants to those undertaking university and higher education courses.

Applications

Application forms are available from the correspondent. Applications can be submitted directly by the individual, by a parent or guardian, or by a school or case worker.

Financial information

Year end	31/12/2017
Income	£112,700
Total expenditure	£114,600

Further financial information

In 2017, a total of £71,800 was paid in educational grants to 38 students. Out of the 38 grants, 11 were given to school age children for trips and other educational needs. The majority of the awards were given to students attending university or higher education courses.

Other information

The trust also makes grants towards the upkeep of a local school.

Sources of information

Accounts; annual report; Charity Commission record.

Southwark

Newcomen Collett Foundation

 £44,700 (2017/18)

Correspondent: Ms C. de Cintra, Clerk to the Trustees, Marshall's House, 66 Newcomen Street, London SE1 1YT (tel: 020 7407 2967; email: grantoffice@newcomencollett.org.uk)

 www.newcomencollett.org.uk

CC number: 312804

Eligibility

People under the age of 25 who have lived in the London borough of Southwark for at least two years and are pursuing post-16 education. Priority is given to those born in Southwark, and to those embarking on their first post-school qualification. Grants are sometimes given to individuals under the age of 16 in cases of exceptional talent or need.

Types of grant

The majority of grants are awarded towards the living costs of those attending tertiary or higher education or undertaking an apprenticeship.

Applications

Applications can be made through the foundation's website. The closing date for applications and the corresponding

meeting they will be considered at are available on the foundation's website.

Financial information

Year end	30/09/2018
Income	£183,700
Total expenditure	£203,900

Further financial information

Grants were awarded to 26 individuals over the year. The grant total was estimated from the 2017/18 accounts.

Other information

Grants are also given to schools and organisations.

Sources of information

Accounts; annual report; Charity Commission record; funder's website.

Southwark Scholarship Scheme

Correspondent: Jas Dhell, 160 Tooley Street, London SE1 2QH (email: jas.dhell@southwark.gov.uk)

 https://localoffer.southwark.gov.uk/youth-offer/money/19-25-education-money

Eligibility

Students under the age of 25 who are about to begin their first degree. Applicants must:

- Have lived in Southwark for the last three years
- Have a good academic record of achievement
- Have made a positive contribution to the community of Southwark
- Have a household income of less than £25,000 per annum

Types of grant

Scholarships are made to cover the cost of university tuition fees.

Exclusions

Current university students are not eligible for funding.

Applications

Applicants must first express their interest in the scholarship scheme via the Southwark Council website. Those who have expressed their interest will then be sent an email asking them to upload evidence of provisional offers received from prospective universities. After this stage, applicants will be asked to provide further evidence, including:

- Details of the sixth form/college they attended
- Academic qualifications achieved
- Proof of income
- A community statement
- Details of academic and community references

Once final A-level results have been received, evidence of these must be uploaded too. After all information has been sent, a panel will evaluate applications and successful applicants will be invited to attend an interview at Southwark Council's offices in Tooley Street in late August/early September.

Sources of information

Funder's website.

St Olave, St Thomas and St John United Charity

Correspondent: The Trustees, 6–8 Druid Street, London SE1 2EU (tel: 020 7407 2530; email: st.olavescharity@btconnect.com)

CC number: 211763

Eligibility

People living in the in the former metropolitan borough of Bermondsey in the London borough of Southwark who are in need.

Types of grant

Grants are awarded for educational purposes.

Applications

Apply in writing to the correspondent.

Financial information

Year end	31/03/2019
Income	£581,600
Total expenditure	£666,100

Further financial information

No educational grants were made to individuals in 2018/19; however, in the previous year grants totalled £27,300.

Other information

Grants are also given to organisations.

Sources of information

Accounts; annual report; Charity Commission record.

St Olave's and St Saviour's Schools Foundation CIO

 £23,400 (2017/18)

Correspondent: Mr R. Walters, Clerk to the Governors, St Olave's and St Saviour's Schools Foundation, Europoint Centre, 5–11 Lavington Street, London SE1 0NZ (tel: 020 7401 2871; email: grants@stolavesfoundation.co.uk)

 www.stolavesfoundationfund.org.uk

CC number: 1181857

Eligibility

Students under the age of 25, who live in the London borough of Southwark and are undertaking higher, further or vocational education courses or direct educational activities. Consideration will also be given to young people looking to pursue courses in the arts, crafts, music, dance and sports.

Types of grant

Grants of up to £2,000 per year for three years (average is between £500 and £700) for specific educational costs can be awarded. Past examples include laptops, printers, books, materials, travel and instruments. Grants may be split termly if appropriate. Grants are awarded for a maximum of three years although longer term support may be considered in exceptional cases.

Exclusions

Grants are not awarded for individual salaries, school/college fees, university loan fees, postgraduate students, domestic bills, childcare, food or payment of debts. Grants are also not awarded for items that have already been purchased.

Applications

Application forms and guidance notes are available on the foundation's website. Applications must include the following:

▷ A supporting reference on official headed paper or emailed from an official email address from the student's tutor or other qualified person
▷ A personal statement explaining the reasons for applying
▷ Copy of course enrolment/acceptance letter
▷ Copy of government student loan/ grant award/bursary/refusal letter
▷ Details of current financial circumstances (e.g. last two bank statements)
▷ Proof of address

Applications can be made at any time of year; however, consult the foundation's website for cut-off dates to be considered for specific meetings. The trustees meet four times a year to consider applications. Applicants will receive a letter/email informing them of the decision and an interview either in person or on the telephone may be required. Grants must be claimed within 12 months or they will be cancelled.

Financial information

Year end	31/03/2018
Income	£1,750,000
Total expenditure	£1,600,000

Further financial information

In 2017/18 a total of £23,400 was awarded to 25 individuals.

Other information

Grants are also awarded to organisations. The foundation was previously registered as St Olave's and St Saviour's Schools Foundation (Charity Commission no. 312987).

Sources of information

Accounts; annual report; Charity Commission record; funder's website.

Waltham Forest

Henry Green Scholarships in Conection with Council Schools

£ £9,000 (2017/18)

Correspondent: Strategic Financial Advisor, Waltham Forest Town Hall, Forest Road, Walthamstow, London E17 4JF (tel: 020 8496 3502; email: duncan.pike@walthamforest.gov.uk)

 https://walthamforest.gov.uk/ content/education-trust-funds

CC number: 310918

Eligibility

People under the age of 25 and who are residents of either Leyton or Leytonstone and are attending a full-time course at the universities of Oxford, Cambridge or London. They must also have attended one or more of the following schools for at least two years: Buxton All-through School Secondary Phase; Connaught School for Girls; George Mitchell Secondary Phase All-through School; Leyton Sixth Form College; Leytonstone School; Norlington School for Boys; or The Lammas School.

In making their decision, the trustees may give consideration to the results of any examinations passed by the applicants, their school record, the headteacher's report, financial needs and their ability to profit by further education.

Types of grant

Small annual grants.

Applications

Application forms can be found on the charity's website. Each grant will be made for one year only. Applications for grants for further years must be the subject of a separate application each year.

Financial information

Year end	31/03/2018
Income	£4,500
Total expenditure	£10,000

Further financial information

Full accounts were not available to view on the Charity Commission's website due to the charity's low income. We have therefore estimated the grant total based on the charity's total expenditure.

Sources of information

Charity Commission record; funder's website.

Sir William Mallinson Scholarship Trust

£ £2,100 (2018/19)

Correspondent: The Trustees, Waltham Forest College, 707 Forest Road, London E17 4JB (tel: 020 8501 8118)

CC number: 312489

Eligibility

People under the age of 25 who live in the former metropolitan borough of Walthamstow.

Types of grant

Grants for equipment for students in further education.

Applications

Application forms are available from the correspondent.

Financial information

Year end	31/03/2019
Income	£2,000
Total expenditure	£2,400

Further financial information

Full accounts were not available to view on the Charity Commission's website due to the charity's low income. We have therefore estimated the grant total based on the charity's total expenditure.

Sources of information

Charity Commission record.

Sir George Monoux Exhibition Foundation

£ £4,900 (2017/18)

Correspondent: Tammy Hanna, Meetings and Events Team, Business Support, Education Charity Trusts, London borough of Waltham Forest, Sycamore House, Town Hall Complex, Forest Road, London E17 4SU (email: tammy.hanna@walthamforest.gov.uk)

 https://walthamforest.gov.uk/ content/education-trust-funds

CC number: 310903

Eligibility

Students who are undertaking a full-time course at a university or college of higher education, are in need of financial assistance, are under the age of 25, live in the London borough of Waltham Forest and are pupils or former pupils of the following schools: Frederick Bremer School, Leyton Sixth Form College, Walthamstow Academy, Connaught School For Girls, Leytonstone School, Buxton All-through School Secondary Phase, George Mitchell Secondary Phase All-through School, Norlington School For Boys, Walthamstow School For Girls, Highams Park School, Rushcroft Foundation School, Willowfield School, Holy Family Catholic School and Sixth Form, Sir George Monoux Sixth Form College, Waltham Forest College, Kelmscott School, The Lammas School, Chingford Foundation School, Heathcote School and Science College, Belmont Park School, Brookfield House School, Whitefield Academy, William Morris School.

In making their decision the trustees may take into consideration results of any examinations taken by the applicants, their school record, the headteacher's report, their financial needs and their ability to profit by further education.

Types of grant

One-off awards ranging from £500 to £2,000 are available towards the costs associated with higher education.

Applications

Application forms are available from the foundation's website or can be requested from the correspondent. The application must be accompanied with a supporting statement and signature of a referee from the applicant's school/college/ university. Applications open in April and should be submitted before the end of May. Candidates who are successful in their initial application are invited for an interview which is normally held in September.

Financial information

Year end	31/03/2018
Income	£4,000
Total expenditure	£5,400

Further financial information

Full accounts were not available to view on the Charity Commission's website due to the charity's low income. We have therefore estimated the grant total based on the charity's total expenditure.

Sources of information

Charity Commission record; funder's website; guidelines for applicants.

Wandsworth

Battersea United Charities

 £4,400 (2017/18)

Correspondent: Stephen Willmett, Clerk to the Trustees, Battersea United Charities, Battersea District Library, Lavender Hill, London SW11 1JB (tel: 07960 483842)

https://batterseaunitedcharities.org. uk

CC number: 247377

Eligibility

People in need who live in the former metropolitan borough of Battersea.

Types of grant

Grants are available for the advancement of education.

Applications

Contact the charity via a form available on the charity's website with an initial enquiry and a request for an application form.

Financial information

Year end	31/03/2018
Income	£23,600
Total expenditure	£19,600

Other information

Grants are also given to organisations.

Sources of information

Charity Commission record; funder's website.

North East

General

The Christina Aitchison Trust

See record on page 249

Lord Crewe's Charity

 £306,600 (2018)

Correspondent: Mr C. Smithers, Clerk to the Trustees, The Miners' Hall, Durham, County Durham DH1 4BD (tel: 0191 384 7736; email: enquiries@lordcrewescharity.co.uk)

www.lordcrewescharity.org.uk

CC number: 1155101

Eligibility
The children of clergy members are eligible for educational grants.

Types of grant
Educational grants are awarded to support the children of clergy members through their studies, up to postgraduate level.

Exclusions
The charity is unable to make grants to individuals who are not clergy members, nor dependants of clergy, in the two dioceses. The charity is also unable to support applications for church buildings or church projects, except in a very small number of parishes in which the charity holds property or has rights of presentation.

Applications
Apply in writing to the correspondent.

Financial information
Year end	31/12/2018
Income	£1,480,000
Total expenditure	£1,330,000

Further financial information
The charity made 120 educational grants to children of clergy members, totalling £176,700 in 2018. The charity makes annual payments to Lincoln College Oxford to fund various bursaries and scholarships at the university: Grants are broken down as follows:

Junior Research Fellow in Music	1	£40,000
Postgraduate scholarships	8	£36,000
Undergraduate Crewe Territories bursaries	6	£31,500
Postgraduate Crewe Territories scholarships	2	£14,000
Undergraduate Lord Crewe scholarships	12	£8,400

Other information
This charity is linked to the Lord Crewe's Library and Archives Trust (Charity Commission no. 1155101–3). The charity makes a small annual grant to the Lord Crewe's Durham Apprenticeship Fund, to assist young people in learning a trade or occupation. The charity also makes grants to the diocese of Newcastle and Durham for projects designed to support clergy members such as pastoral care and counselling, mentoring and continuing ministerial development.

Sources of information
Accounts; annual report; Charity Commission record; funder's website.

S. Y. Killingley Memorial Trust

 £9,300 (2017/18)

Correspondent: Katie Stamps, 9 Rectory Drive, Newcastle upon Tyne, Tyne and Wear NE3 1XT (tel: 0191 285 8053; email: trust@grevatt.f9.co.uk)

syktrust.org.uk

CC number: 1111891

Eligibility
People aged 18 or over who live in north east England (Northumberland, Tyne and Wear, County Durham and Teesside), or who are wishing to take a course based in the area. Courses must be part-time and wholly or mainly based in arts or humanities subjects (e.g. languages, literature, music, history, philosophy, creative and expressive arts).

Types of grant
Grants are available for course fees, books, equipment, materials, travel or childcare and similar expenses.

Exclusions
Grants will not cover living costs.

Applications
Application forms and guidance notes can be downloaded from the trust's website or requested from the correspondent. Applications can be submitted by post at any time of year and should include a letter of support from a referee. Handwritten applications are preferred, although typewritten are acceptable. Applications sent by email will not be accepted. Applicants may be asked to attend an informal interview. The selection panel meets about three times a year, usually in January, April and September.

Financial information
Year end	05/04/2018
Income	£8,500
Total expenditure	£10,400

Further financial information
Full accounts were not available to view on the Charity Commission's website due to the charity's low income. We have therefore estimated the grant total based on the charity's total expenditure.

Other information
Successful applicants are assigned a mentor to provide them with informal support and advice during the course.

Sources of information
Charity Commission record; funder's website.

The Gus Robinson Foundation

 £6,400 (2017/18)

Correspondent: Jeanette Henderson, Gus Robinson Developments Ltd, Stranton House, West View Road, Hartlepool, County Durham TS24 0BW (tel: 01429 234221)

🌐 www.gusrobinson.com/foundation

CC number: 1156290

Eligibility
Individuals in need under the age of 25 living in the Tees Valley.

Types of grant
Grants are available to support individuals with education, training, sport, music, art and entrepreneurship.

Applications
Apply in writing to the correspondent.

Financial information
Year end	30/11/2018
Income	£106,200
Total expenditure	£37,500

Further financial information
The grant total has been estimated from the 2017/18 accounts.

Other information
In May 2018 Hartlepool Youth became linked to the foundation and funds were transferred across. The total expenditure for 2017/18 includes amounts for fundraising activities and sponsorship.

Sources of information
Accounts; annual report; Charity Commission record; funder's website.

Tees Valley Community Foundation

 £53,800 (2018/19)

Correspondent: Peter Rowley, Secretary, Tees Valley Community Foundation, Wallace House, Falcon Court, Preston Farm Industrial Estate, Stockton-on-Tees, County Durham TS18 3TX (tel: 01642 260860; email: info@ teesvalleyfoundation.org)

🌐 www.teesvalleyfoundation.org

CC number: 1111222

Eligibility
Students in local authority areas of Hartlepool, Stockton-on-Tees, Redcar and Cleveland, Middlesbrough and Teesside wide – see separate funds on the foundation's website for specific criteria as they will vary.

Types of grant
The John Bloom Law Bursary supports students intending to study for a full-time undergraduate degree in law at a UK university. The successful candidate for the bursary will be expected to obtain good A-level grades and will be from a background of modest means. A bursary of £6,000 (over three years) will be awarded to a student who might otherwise struggle to find the necessary funding to pursue their chosen career.

Applications
Application forms and guidelines for separate funds can be found on the foundation's website, once the application round begins.

Financial information
Year end	31/03/2019
Income	£758,800
Total expenditure	£909,800

Further financial information
Grants were awarded 221 individuals in 2018/19.

Other information
This is one of the 46 community foundations, which distribute funding for a wide range of purposes. Grant schemes tend to change frequently; therefore, consult the foundation's website for details of current programmes and upcoming deadlines.

Sources of information
Accounts; annual report; Charity Commission record; funder's website.

County Durham

County Durham Community Foundation

Correspondent: Grants Team, Victoria House, Whitfield Court, St John's Road, Meadowfield Industrial Estate, Durham, County Durham DH7 8XL (tel: 0191 378 6340; email: info@cdcf.org.uk)

 www.cdcf.org.uk

CC number: 1047625

Eligibility
People in need who live in County Durham and Darlington. The community foundation manages a number of different funds each with their own specific eligibility criteria – see the foundation's website for details.

Types of grant
A number of funds are available to individuals providing support towards education and training for young people.

Visit the foundation's website for further information on the grants available.

Applications
Each scheme has a different application process, see the foundation's website for further details. Applications must be submitted on behalf of the individual by a referee such as a parent, guardian, care professional or social worker.

Financial information
Year end	31/03/2019
Income	£4,140,000
Total expenditure	£3,520,000

Further financial information
In 2018/19 a total of £241,000 was awarded to 508 individuals, the average grant being £480. We were unable to determine the split between grants for welfare and grants for education.

Other information
This is one of the 46 community foundations, which distribute funding for a wide range of purposes. Grant schemes tend to change frequently; therefore, consult the foundation's website for details of current programmes and upcoming deadlines.

Sources of information
Accounts; annual report; Charity Commission record; funder's website.

Frosterley Exhibition Foundation

£ £1,500 (2017/18)

Correspondent: Judith Bainbridge, Trustee, 6 Osborne Terrace, Frosterley, Bishop Auckland DL13 2RD (tel: 07801 054917; email: judith.bainbridge1@ btinternet.com)

CC number: 527338

Eligibility
People over the age of 11 who are in full-time further or higher education and who live in the parish of Frosterley.

Types of grant
The 'John Hinks Exhibitions' grants are awarded to support students in higher/ further education towards books and equipment.

Exclusions
Children under the age of 11 are not eligible.

Applications
Apply in writing to the correspondent. Applications should be submitted by the applicant's parent. Grants are distributed in September.

Financial information

Year end	28/02/2018
Income	£3,100
Total expenditure	£1,600

Further financial information

Full accounts were not available to view on the Charity Commission's website due to the charity's low income. We have therefore estimated the grant total based on the charity's total expenditure.

Sources of information

Charity Commission record.

The Hartwell Educational Foundation

 £500 (2018/19)

Correspondent: Jayne Dobson, Hillfield, Cotherstone, Barnard Castle DL12 9PG (tel: 07738 873152; email: jayned11@hotmail.com)

https://democracy.durham.gov.uk/mgOutsideBodyDetails.aspx?ID=487

CC number: 527368

Eligibility

People aged between 11 and 21 who live in the civil parish of Stanhope. Eligibility is dependent on parental income.

Types of grant

Recurrent grants are available for students who are attending university or college towards the cost of fees, living expenses and books.

Applications

Application forms can be requested from the correspondent.

Financial information

Year end	31/03/2019
Income	£1,500
Total expenditure	£1,000

Further financial information

Full accounts were not available to view on the Charity Commission's website due to the charity's low income. We have therefore estimated the grant total based on the charity's total expenditure.

Sources of information

Charity Commission record; funder's website.

Johnston Educational Foundation

 £1,100 (2018/19)

Correspondent: Grants Team, County Durham Community Foundation, Victoria House, 2 Whitfield Court, St John's Road, Meadowfield Industrial Estate, Durham, County Durham

DH7 8XL (tel: 0191 378 6340; email: info@cdcf.org.uk)

https://www.cdcf.org.uk

CC number: 1047625

Eligibility

People under the age of 24 who have lived in Durham City for at least two years. Those whose live elsewhere for university but have parents residing in Durham may still apply. Applicants must have attended one of the following schools at any time for at least two years: Belmont Community School, Durham Community Business College, Durham Johnston Comprehensive School, Durham Sixth Form Centre, Durham Trinity School and Sports College, Framwellgate School, St Leonard's RC Comprehensive School.

Types of grant

Grants between £100 and £250 are available to college and university students towards equipment, educational trips, research trips, books, instruments and so on.

Applications

Application forms and guidelines are available on the County Durham Community Foundation website and can be submitted at any time. Applicants will be asked to provide the name of a referee to support their application. The foundation will be in touch within six weeks of submission with their decision.

Financial information

Year end	31/03/2019

Other information

This charity is administered by the County Durham Community Foundation (1047625).

Sources of information

Accounts; annual report; Charity Commission record; funder's website.

The Sedgefield District Relief in Need Charity (The Sedgefield Charities)

 £3,000 (2018)

Correspondent: John Hannon, Clerk to the Trustees, East House, Mordon, Stockton-on-Tees, County Durham TS21 2EY (tel: 01740 622512; email: east.house@btinternet.com)

CC number: 230395

Eligibility

Students in higher education (any course beyond A-levels) who are under the age of 25 and live in Bishop Middleham,

Bradbury, Cornforth, Fishburn, Mordon, Sedgefield and Trimdon are eligible for support.

Types of grant

Educational grants are awarded to help with costs related to higher education.

Applications

Apply in writing to the correspondent. Applications are usually made via social services, Citizen Advice or by professionals on the applicant's behalf.

Financial information

Year end	31/12/2018
Income	£30,100
Total expenditure	£24,400

Further financial information

During 2018, the charity awarded 33 welfare grants and six educational grants.

Other information

Grants are also made to local organisations.

Sources of information

Accounts; annual report; Charity Commission record; Durham Locate website.

The Sedgefield Educational Foundation

 £1,400 (2018)

Correspondent: John Hannan, Clerk to the Trustees, East House, Mordon, Stockton-on-Tees, County Durham TS21 2EY (tel: 01740 622512; email: east.house@btinternet.com)

CC number: 527317

Eligibility

People under the age of 25 who live (or whose parents live) in the parishes of Fishburn, Sedgefield, Bradbury and Morden, and are in full-time higher/further education.

Types of grant

Grants are available for people in full-time further/higher education and training (higher than A-level) to assist with educational costs.

Applications

Application forms can be requested from the correspondent and should be submitted by 30 September each year.

Financial information

Year end	31/12/2018
Income	£2,600
Total expenditure	£3,100

Further financial information

Full accounts were not available to view on the Charity Commission's website due to the charity's low income. We have therefore estimated the grant total based on the charity's total expenditure.

Other information

Local schools may also be assisted.

Sources of information

Charity Commission record; Durham Locate website.

Hartlepool

The Preston Simpson and Sterndale Young Musicians Trust

£ £6,800 (2017/18)

Correspondent: Judith Oliver, Hartlepool Borough Council, Civic Centre, Victoria Road, Hartlepool, County Durham TS24 8AY (tel: 01429 523914; email: Judith.oliver@hartlepool. gov.uk)

 https://www.hartlepool.gov.uk/ youngmusicianstrust

CC number: 512606

Eligibility

Young musicians who are between the ages of 14 and 25 on 31 July the year the award is made. Applicants must have either been born in the borough of Hartlepool or have/had a parent who has lived in the area for at least five years. The grant is designed to support those who have already achieved a good standard in their musical studies and wish to pursue a career in music. Applicants' achievements should be demonstrated by participation in concerts, membership in bands or orchestras, a minimum standard of Grade V in the Associated Board Examination or equivalent qualification from Trinity College London, and have genuine intentions to use musical abilities in their future career (such as commitment to GCSE Music).

Types of grant

Scholarships are awarded to young musicians enabling them to study music in any institution providing courses in musical education.

Applications

Application forms and guidance notes can be downloaded from the Hartlepool borough council's website. Application deadlines are usually mid-December with auditions taking place in February; however, consult the website for the current deadline. Applications will require two references and must be completed electronically prior to printing and signing. Handwritten applications will not be accepted.

Financial information

Year end	31/03/2018
Income	£8,400
Total expenditure	£7,600

Further financial information

Full accounts were not available to view on the Charity Commission's website due to the charity's low income. We have therefore estimated the grant total based on the charity's total expenditure.

Other information

The trust holds an annual awards event at which some of the award winners are invited to perform.

Sources of information

Charity Commission record; funder's website.

Northumber-land

Allendale Exhibition Endowment

£ £6,800 (2017/18)

Correspondent: Norman Robinson, Secretary, Amberlea, Catton, Hexham, Northumberland NE47 9QS (tel: 01434 683586)

CC number: 505515

Eligibility

People under the age of 25 who live, or whose parents live, in the parishes of Allendale and West Allen.

Types of grant

Financial assistance is available to support students in their further/higher education studies.

Applications

Apply in writing to the correspondent.

Financial information

Year end	30/09/2018
Income	£8,900
Total expenditure	£8,900

Further financial information

We have estimated the grant total for 2017/18.

Sources of information

Charity Commission record.

Coates Educational Foundation

See record on page 213

The Eleemosynary Charity of Giles Heron

£ £5,600 (2017/18)

Correspondent: George Benson, Trustee, Walwick Farmhouse, Humshaugh, Hexham, Northumberland NE46 4BJ (tel: 01434 681203; email: office@ chestersestate.co.uk)

CC number: 224157

Eligibility

People in need who live in the parish of Wark and Simonburn.

Types of grant

Grants to those in need for apprenticeships.

Applications

Apply in writing to the correspondent.

Financial information

Year end	31/03/2018
Income	£14,900
Total expenditure	£24,700

Further financial information

Full accounts were not available to view on the Charity Commission's website due to the charity's low income. We have therefore estimated the grant total based on the charity's total expenditure.

Sources of information

Charity Commission record.

Rothbury Educational Trust

£ £6,700 (2017/18)

Correspondent: Susan Rogerson, Clerk, 1 Gallow Law, Alwinton, Morpeth, Northumberland NE65 7BQ (tel: 01669 650390)

CC number: 505713

Eligibility

Higher education students between the ages of 18 and 25 who live or have attended school in the parishes of Cartington, Hepple, Hesleyhurst, Rothbury, Snitter, Thropton and Tosson; and the parts of Brinkburn, Hollinghill and Netherton that lie within the ancient parish of Rothbury.

Types of grant

Bursaries are available to assist students pursuing a course of higher education.

Applications

Apply in writing to the correspondent.

Financial information

Year end	31/08/2018
Income	£8,300
Total expenditure	£7,400

Further financial information

Full accounts were not available to view on the Charity Commission's website due to the charity's low income. We have therefore estimated the grant total based on the charity's total expenditure.

Sources of information

Charity Commission record.

Shaftoe Educational Foundation

 £16,200 (2017/18)

Correspondent: Mr P. Fletcher, Clerk to the Trustees, The Office, Shaftoe Terrace, Haydon Bridge, Northumberland NE47 6BW (tel: 01434 684239 or 07979 602896; email: clerkshaftoecharities@outlook.com)

www.shaftoecharities.org.uk

CC number: 528101

Eligibility

People who live, or have a parent living, in the parish of Haydon.

Types of grant

Grants are available to support higher/further education students for the full duration of their course. In addition, students undertaking apprenticeships or vocational training can apply for a support grant and/or financial assistance with the cost of tools.

Applications

Application forms can be downloaded from the foundation's website or requested from the correspondent. The trustees meet three times a year, normally in March, July and November.

Financial information

Year end	31/03/2018
Income	£207,300
Total expenditure	£237,600

Further financial information

A total of £16,200 was paid in grants to 38 individuals in 2017/18.

Other information

The foundation owns nine almshouses on Shaftoe Terrace, where the Almshouse Charity of John Shaftoe can assist people aged over 60 who are in need of housing.

Sources of information

Accounts; annual report; Charity Commission record; funder's website.

Tyne and Wear

Newcastle upon Tyne

Coates Educational Foundation

 £2,600 (2018)

Correspondent: Andrew Morgan, Trustee, 14 Bell Villas, Ponteland, Newcastle upon Tyne, Tyne and Wear NE20 9BE (tel: 01661 871012; email: amorgan@nicholsonmorgan.co.uk)

CC number: 505906

Eligibility

People under the age of 25 who live in the parishes of Ponteland, Stannington, Heddon-on-the-Wall, and the former district of Newburn. Current/former pupils of the Richard Coates Church of England Voluntary Aided Middle School may also apply.

Types of grant

Grants and bursaries are available to students at college or university towards the costs of materials, travel, clothing, books, maintenance, educational trips, equipment and fees.

Applications

Application forms are available from the correspondent and should be submitted directly by the applicant.

Financial information

Year end	31/12/2018
Income	£23,600
Total expenditure	£5,800

Further financial information

Full accounts were not available to view on the Charity Commission's website due to the charity's low income. We have therefore estimated the grant total based on the charity's total expenditure.

Other information

The foundation may also support organisations.

Sources of information

Charity Commission record; Uni Grants website.

The Town Moor Money Charity

 £16,900 (2017/18)

Correspondent: The Trustees, Moor Bank Lodge, Claremont Road, Newcastle upon Tyne, Tyne and Wear NE2 4NL

(tel: 0191 261 5970; email: admin@freemenofnewcastle.org)

 www.freemenofnewcastle.org

CC number: 227620-1

Eligibility

Freemen of Newcastle upon Tyne and their spouses who are in need. The widows of deceased Freemen are also eligible for support. Educational grants are available to the children of Freemen who are in further education.

Types of grant

Financial assistance for the children of Freemen who are aged between 18 and 20 and are in full-time further education.

Applications

Application forms are available in April and October from the Senior Steward of the Company through which the applicant's family hail. Contact the correspondent for further information. Grants are awarded twice each year in June and December.

Financial information

Year end	29/09/2018
Total expenditure	£72,400

Further financial information

Note: the grant total has been estimated. The charity does not disclose its income in their accounts.

Other information

This charity is linked to The Town Moor Charity. According to the 2017/18 annual report: 'The trustees are currently reviewing its costs and funding stream.

Sources of information

Accounts; annual report; Charity Commission record; funder's website.

South Tyneside

Westoe Educational Charity

 £1,900 (2017/18)

Correspondent: Ian Burden, South Tyneside Council, Town Hall, Westoe Road, South Shields, County Durham NE33 2RL (tel: 0191 424 4222; email: ian.burden@southtyneside.gov.uk)

CC number: 1074869

Eligibility

People under the age of 25 who live, or whose parents live in the borough of South Teeside and who are in need of financial assistance.

Types of grant

Grants are available to schoolchildren, further/higher education students and people preparing to enter work or a trade. Financial assistance is given, for example, towards the cost of books, travel in pursuance of education, maintenance costs and clothing.

Applications

Apply in writing to the correspondent.

Financial information

Year end	31/03/2018
Income	£1,400
Total expenditure	£2,800

Further financial information

Full accounts were not available to view on the Charity Commission's website due to the charity's low income. We have therefore estimated the grant total based on the charity's total expenditure.

Other information

The charity also provides support to local schools, where the need is not already addressed by the local authority.

Sources of information

Charity Commission record.

Sunderland

The Sunderland Orphanage and Educational Foundation

£ £17,000 (2017/18)

Correspondent: Peter Taylor, 19 John Street, Sunderland, Tyne and Wear SR1 1JG (tel: 0191 567 4857; email: petertaylor@mckenzie-bell.co.uk)

CC number: 527202

Eligibility

Young people under the age of 25, who live in or around Sunderland and have one or two parents who are deceased, separated, divorced, or who have a disability, and attend a school, college or university approved by the trustees.

Types of grant

Grants are awarded for the following purposes:
- Provision of tools, equipment, books, and other physical necessities for education
- Purchasing school uniforms or job-related clothing
- Scholarships, bursaries, and maintenance allowances teneable at any place of learning approved by the trustees
- Financial assistance for people leaving school and about to enter employment or trade

- Provision and tutoring of musical instruments
- Travelling abroad for study
- Coaching and training in sports and athletics
- Financial assistance to study music and the arts

The foundation also provides grants in the form of boarding and 'pocket money' to young people in financial need.

Applications

Applications should be made in writing to the correspondent.

Financial information

Year end	05/04/2018
Income	£22,900
Total expenditure	£19,200

Further financial information

Full accounts were not available to view on the Charity Commission's website due to the charity's low income. We have therefore estimated the grant total based on the charity's total expenditure.

Sources of information

Charity Commission record.

North West

General

The Bishop Sheppard Tenth Anniversary Trust

£ £6,700 (2017)

Correspondent: Margaret Sadler, 5 Hazel Grove, Crosby, Liverpool, Merseyside L23 9SH (tel: 01744 623238; email: margaret.sadler@hotmail.co.uk)

 https://www.sthelens.ac.uk/adults/extra-financial-support-for-adults/1131-additional-learner-support-funds

CC number: 517368

Eligibility
People between the ages of 21 and 49 who live in the Anglican diocese of Liverpool (which includes Southport, Kirkby, Ormskirk, Skelmersdale, Wigan, St Helens, Warrington and Widnes) and who are undertaking second-chance learning at a college or training centre.

Types of grant
Grants are provided for books, equipment, stationery and any other expenses that could arise related to the course.

Exclusions
Grants are not available to those who have already graduated.

Applications
Information on how to apply is available on the St Helens College website or by contacting the correspondent.

Financial information

Year end	31/12/2017
Income	£6,900
Total expenditure	£7,400

Further financial information
Full accounts were not available to view on the Charity Commission's website due to the charity's low income. We have therefore estimated the grant total based on the charity's total expenditure.

Sources of information
Charity Commission record; funder's website.

Community Foundations for Lancashire and Merseyside

£ £68,600 (2017/18)

Correspondent: The Trustees, Community Foundations for Lancashire and Merseyside, Third Floor, Stanley Building, 43 Hanover Street, Liverpool, Merseyside L1 3DN (tel: 0330 440 4900; email: applications@cflm.email)

 www.cfmerseyside.org.uk

CC number: 1068887

Eligibility
Refer to the charity's website for eligibility details for the various current funds.

Types of grant
A number of funds are available to individuals. Refer to the charity's website for details of current and open grants.

Applications
See the foundation's website for further details and information on how to apply to the specific grants.

Financial information

Year end	31/03/2018
Income	£5,400,000
Total expenditure	£3,030,000

Further financial information
In 2017/18 we estimate that a total of £77,300 was awarded to individuals with around £9,300 being awarded for social welfare purposes and £68,600 for educational purposes.

Other information
This is one of the 46 community foundations, which distribute funding for a wide range of purposes. Grant schemes tend to change frequently; therefore, consult the foundation's website for details of current programmes and upcoming deadlines.

Sources of information
Accounts; annual report; Charity Commission record; funder's website.

The Winwick Educational Foundation

£ £950 (2017/18)

Correspondent: The Trustees, Forshaws Davies Ridgway LLP, 17–21 Palmyra Square South, Warrington, Cheshire WA1 1BW (tel: 01925 230000)

CC number: 526499

Eligibility
Further education students who live in the parishes of Winwick, Emmanuel Wargrave, Lowton St Luke's, Lowton St Mary's, Newton All Saints, Newton St Peter's and St John's Earlestown.

Types of grant
Small grants are available to further education students towards general educational needs.

Applications
Apply in writing to the correspondent.

Financial information

Year end	30/06/2018
Income	£2,800
Total expenditure	£2,100

Further financial information
Full accounts were not available to view on the Charity Commission's website due to the charity's low income. We have therefore estimated the grant total based on the charity's total expenditure.

Other information
The foundation also supports four specific Church of England primary schools in north Warrington.

Sources of information
Charity Commission record.

Cheshire

Audlem Educational Foundation

£ £7,100 (2017/18)

Correspondent: Judy Evans, Clerk to the Trustees, 1 Shropshire Street, Audlem, Crewe, Cheshire CW3 0AE (tel: 01270 811210)

 www.audlem.org/directories/ groups/audlem-education-foundation.html

CC number: 525810

Eligibility

Students and young people undergoing training who are under the age of 25 and resident in the ancient parish of Audlem, including Buerton and Hankelow and part of Dodcott-cum-Wilkesley and Newhall. Preference is given to those who attend or have attended a maintained school (those funded and run by the local education authority) for at least two years.

Types of grant

Financial assistance in the form of grants, bursaries and maintenance allowances to enhance education including educational courses, equipment and trips.

Applications

Application forms are available from local schools and colleges or can be downloaded from the foundation's website. Applications are only considered for completed trips, purchases or after commencing a higher education course or apprenticeship. Copies of receipts or proof of expenditure must be attached to the application form. Applications are usually considered in November, February and July.

Financial information

Year end	31/03/2018
Income	£21,200
Total expenditure	£11,800

Further financial information

Full accounts were not available to view on the Charity Commission's website due to the charity's low income. We have therefore estimated the grant total based on the charity's total expenditure.

Other information

The foundation allocates a third of its income and interest from the investments to support schools in the area of benefit. The remainder is used to award grants to individuals.

Sources of information

Charity Commission record; funder's website.

Cheshire East

Alsager Educational Foundation

£ £2,000 (2017/18)

Correspondent: Catherine Lovatt, Secretary, 6 Pikemere Road, Alsager, Stoke-on-Trent, Staffordshire ST7 2SB (tel: 01270 873680; email: colovatt@ hotmail.com)

CC number: 525834

Eligibility

Children and young people who live in the parish of Alsager.

Types of grant

Scholarships, bursaries and maintenance allowances for educational purposes, such as books, travel abroad in pursuance of education, the study of music and travel costs.

Applications

Apply in writing to the correspondent.

Financial information

Year end	30/06/2018
Income	£28,400
Total expenditure	£22,500

Further financial information

In 2017/18 the grants to individuals totalled £4,100. We have estimated that £2,000 was awarded to individuals for welfare purposes and £2,000 was given to individuals for education.

Other information

The foundation also supports organisations. Special benefits are provided to the Alsager Church of England Junior School.

Sources of information

Accounts; annual report; Charity Commission record.

The Consolidated Charity of the Parish of Wrenbury

£ £2,500 (2017)

Correspondent: Helen Smith, Trustee, Peckforton House, Sheppenhall Lane, Aston, Nantwich, Cheshire CW5 8DE (tel: 01270 780262; email: helen@ peckfortonhouse.co.uk)

CC number: 241778

Eligibility

People in need who live in the parishes of Chorley, Sound, Broomhall, Newhall, Wrenbury and Dodcott-cum-Wilkesley. There is a preference for supported older people and students.

Types of grant

One-off and recurring grants according to need.

Applications

Apply in writing to the correspondent.

Financial information

Year end	31/12/2017
Income	£10,000
Total expenditure	£11,100

Other information

Grants are also given to churches, the village hall and to local schools. Full accounts were not available to view on the Charity Commission's website due to the charity's low income. We have therefore estimated the grant total based on the charity's total expenditure.

Sources of information

Charity Commission record.

Cheshire West and Chester

Chester Municipal Charities

Correspondent: The Trustees, The Bluecoat, Upper Northgate Street, Chester, Cheshire West and Chester CH1 4EE (tel: 01244 403277; email: administration@chestermc.org.uk)

 www.thebluecoat-chester.org.uk/ about

CC number: 1077806

Eligibility

Residents of Chester who are in need. The charity also awards educational grants to young people under the age of 25 who are attending or have attended a school in Chester and who are resident in the city.

Types of grant

Mainly one-off grants for relief-in-need purposes. Grants may come in the form of bursaries or grants paid directly to schools, colleges or universities. Grants are made for education to help with the costs of equipment, educational trips and other expenses. The charity also provides a limited number of bursaries and a programme of funding support in Early Years education.

Applications

An application form is available from the correspondent.

Financial information

Year end	31/12/2017
Income	£567,400
Total expenditure	£392,600

Further financial information

The 2017 accounts note that £218,700 was awarded to organisations and individuals during that year; however, a breakdown of grants was not provided.

Other information

The charity also manages almshouses in Chester.

Sources of information

Accounts; annual report; Charity Commission record.

The Sir Thomas Moulson Trust

£ £2,600 (2017)

Correspondent: The Trustees, Meadow Barn, Cow Lane, Hargrave, Chester CH3 7RU

CC number: 214342

Eligibility

Students under the age of 25 who live in the villages of Huxley and Tarvin.

Types of grant

One-off grants to students in further/higher education towards books, fees/living expenses and study or travel abroad.

Applications

Apply in writing to the correspondent.

Financial information

Year end	31/12/2017
Income	£19,300
Total expenditure	£8,700

Further financial information

Full accounts were not available to view on the Charity Commission's website due to the charity's low income. We have therefore estimated the grant total based on the charity's total expenditure.

Other information

A third of the trust's income is awarded for educational purposes to people under the age of 25.

Sources of information

Charity Commission record.

Dr Robert Oldfield Charity

£ £23,700 (2017/18)

Correspondent: P. J. Anderson, Clerk, c/o Jolliffe & Co. LLP, 6 St John Street, Chester CH1 1DA (tel: 01244 310022; email: admin@drrobertoldfield.co.uk)

 https://www.drrobertoldfield.co.uk

CC number: 525969

Eligibility

Students born or living in Chester who are in tertiary, further and higher education, or students looking to travel for educational purposes. Preference may be given to students from independent schools.

Types of grant

Grants are made towards school fees at the King's and Queen's Schools in Chester and for educational trips in the UK or abroad. Grants can also be made for costs such as fees, general maintenance, books/equipment and travel incurred while studying a course at college or university. Grants for travel and equipment are also available for apprentices.

Applications

Application forms are available to download from the charity's website. Completed forms should be sent to the Clerk at the charity's postal address. Students who were born in Chester but are not currently residing in the area must include a photocopy of their birth certificate with their application. All applicants should include photocopies of any grants/loans they currently receive. Decisions are usually made within four to six weeks.

Financial information

Year end	31/03/2018
Income	£276,300
Total expenditure	£228,800

Further financial information

Note: the grant total has been estimated.

Other information

This charity also makes grants to further education colleges and other voluntary organisations operating for educational purposes.

Sources of information

Accounts; annual report; Charity Commission record; funder's website.

Cumbria

Burton-in-Kendal Educational Foundation

£ £2,900 (2016/17)

Correspondent: The Trustees, 45 Pear Tree Park, Holme, Carnforth LA6 1SD (tel: 01524 784918; email: mvrob23@gmail.com)

CC number: 526953

Eligibility

People under the age of 25 who are studying at a sixth form or university/college and living in the parishes of Arnside, Beetham and Burton-in-Kendal, in Cumbria. Applicants must have attended a county or voluntary primary school for at least two years.

Types of grant

The foundation offers scholarships and bursaries as well as financial assistance towards study/travel abroad, maintenance expenses and facilities for social and physical training.

Applications

Apply in writing to the correspondent.

Financial information

Year end	31/03/2017
Income	£3,600
Total expenditure	£3,200

Further financial information

The 2016/17 accounts were the latest available at the time of writing (December 2019). Full accounts were not available to view on the Charity Commission's website due to the charity's low income. We have therefore estimated the grant total based on the charity's total expenditure.

Sources of information

Charity Commission record.

Cumbria Community Foundation

Correspondent: Grants Team, Cumbria Community Foundation, Dovenby Hall, Dovenby, Cockermouth CA13 0PN (tel: 01900 825760; email: grants@cumbriafoundation.org)

 www.cumbriafoundation.org

CC number: 1075120

Eligibility

People in need who live in Cumbria. Individual funds have their own specific eligibility criteria – see the foundation's website for details.

Types of grant

There can be several funds open to applications with varying criteria and amount of grant available. See the foundation's website for further details.

Applications

An application form can be downloaded from the foundation's website and the foundation will then decide which fund best meets the candidate's needs. For further information, visit the website.

Financial information

Year end	31/03/2018
Income	£3,360,000
Total expenditure	£4,760,000

Further financial information

In 2017/18 a total of £1,180,000 was awarded to 746 individuals. We were unable to determine the split between social welfare grants and education grants.

Other information

This is one of the 46 community foundations, which distribute funding for a wide range of purposes. Grant schemes tend to change frequently; therefore, consult the foundation's website for details of current programmes and upcoming deadlines.

Sources of information

Accounts; annual report; Charity Commission record; funder's website.

Kelsick's Educational Foundation

 £94,700 (2017/18)

Correspondent: Peter Frost, Clerk to the Trustees, The Kelsick Centre, St Mary's Lane, Ambleside, Cumbria LA22 9DG (tel: 01539 431289; email: john@kelsick. plus.com)

🌐 www.kelsick.org.uk

CC number: 526956

Eligibility

Young people under the age of 25 who have been resident in the Lakes parish, including Ambleside, Grasmere, Langdale and Troutbeck north of Trout Beck, for at least four years.

Types of grant

The foundation offers grants towards extra assistance for pupils with special needs, music/drama/art lessons and the hire of instruments, travel costs for certain educational trips, tools, equipment and extra training for apprentices or working trainees and books for A-level, college and university courses. First year higher education students are eligible for the purchase of computers and all eligible students attending universities or colleges of further education can apply for subsistence grants. Financial help is available for apprentices and those on vocational and training courses at colleges of further education as well as any other activities the trustees deem to be of educational benefit.

Exclusions

Tuition fees and residency expenses cannot be paid by the trust.

Applications

Application forms and further guidelines can be found on the foundation's website. Grants are considered in February, May, August and November each year. The deadlines for applications are 31 January, 30 April, 31 July and 31 October respectively.

Financial information

Year end	31/03/2018
Income	£409,200
Total expenditure	£463,600

Further financial information

The total grants for individuals can be broken down as follows: primary school (£6,500); secondary and further education (£30,800); higher education (£49,700); and special and other (£7,800). In 2017/18, 47 higher education students (including degree and HND) applied for a grant.

Other information

Grants totalling £151,200 were awarded to schools and organisations in the area of benefit (2017/18). The foundation provides support for those in their 4/5th years of higher education.

Sources of information

Accounts; annual report; Charity Commission record; funder's website.

The Mary Grave Trust

 £24,500 (2017/18)

Correspondent: Gary Higgs, Cumbria Community Foundation, Dovenby Hall, Dovenby, Cockermouth, Cumbria CA13 0PN (tel: 01900 825760; email: gary@cumbriafoundation.org)

🌐 https://www.cumbriafoundation. org/fund/mary-grave-trust-fund

CC number: 1075120

Eligibility

Young people aged between 11 and 21 who live in the old county of Cumberland (excluding Carlisle, unless the applicants mother was resident outside Carlisle at the time of birth). Applicants must have attended full-time education within the last two years. Priority will be given to people living in the areas of Workington, Maryport and Whitehaven. The grant is means tested, to be eligible the applicant's household income must be less than £590 per week.

Types of grant

Grants up to a maximum of £1,200 are available towards the cost of activities that are part of a higher or further education course.

Exclusions

The trust will not fund:
- Individuals born outside the old county of Cumberland
- Individuals born in Carlisle (unless their mother was resident outside Carlisle at the time of birth)
- Trips in the UK of less than three nights' duration
- Family holidays

Applications

Application forms and guidelines are available from the Cumbria Community Foundation's website. Applications are considered three times a year usually in January, June and November and application deadlines fall a month before each meeting. Applicants are required to submit a full copy of their birth certificate along with the application form.

Financial information

Year end	31/03/2018
Income	£59,600
Total expenditure	£50,700

Further financial information

In 2017/18 the trust made grants totalling £48,900 to 60 individuals. We have estimated that around £24,500 was awarded to individuals for welfare purposes and £24,500 for education.

Other information

The fund is administered by the Cumbria Community Foundation.

Sources of information

Accounts; annual report; Charity Commission record; funder's website.

Robinson's Educational Foundation

£ £5,000 (2017/18)

Correspondent: The Trustees, Milne Moser, 100 Highgate, Kendal, Cumbria LA9 4HE (tel: 01539 729786; email: solicitors@milnemoser.co.uk)

CC number: 529897

Eligibility

Young people who live in the parish of Sedbergh, with a preference for those who live in Howgill.

Types of grant

Grants are available for the advancement of education in the form of scholarships, bursaries and maintenance allowances.

Applications

Apply in writing to the correspondent.

Financial information

Year end	05/04/2018
Income	£14,000
Total expenditure	£11,200

Further financial information

Full accounts were not available to view on the Charity Commission's website due to the charity's low income. We have therefore estimated the grant total based on the charity's total expenditure.

Other information

The foundation also supports local schools.

Sources of information

Charity Commission record.

Silecroft School Educational Charity

£1,000 (2018)

Correspondent: The Trustees, Hestham Hall Farm, Millom LA18 5LJ (tel: 01229 774851; email: cathjopson@yahoo.co.uk)

CC number: 509580

Eligibility

People who live in the parishes of Whicham, Millom, Millom Without and Ulpha. Preference is given to people under the age of 25.

Types of grant

Grants are awarded towards the cost of further education including books, study aids and equipment (not including sixth form).

Applications

Application forms can be requested from the correspondent. Applications can usually be submitted in September and again by the end of February. Meetings are held twice a year to consider applications.

Financial information

Year end	31/12/2018
Income	£2,500
Total expenditure	£2,300

Further financial information

Full accounts were not available to view on the Charity Commission's website due to the charity's low income. We have therefore estimated the grant total based on the charity's total expenditure.

Other information

The charity also provides grants to schools and organisations.

Sources of information

Charity Commission record; Millom Town Council Facebook page.

Carlisle

Carlisle Educational Charity

£9,500 (2017/18)

Correspondent: The Trustees, Carlisle City Council, Civic Centre, Rickergate, Carlisle, Cumbria CA3 8QG (tel: 01228 817557; email: cec@carlisle.gov.uk)

 https://www.carlisle.gov.uk/ Council/Council-and-Democracy/Carlisle-Educational-Charity

CC number: 509357

Eligibility

Students in full-time further education (not including sixth form) and graduates who are wishing to pursue higher education/professional qualifications; who (or whose parents) live within the Carlisle district may be eligible to apply. Applicants must be under the age of 25 at the time of the application. Financial circumstances of the individual's parents and the extent to which they can support the applicant will be taken into account. Generally, preference is given to students with a joint family income below £21,000.

Types of grant

Grants are available to students in higher or further education and young graduates undertaking higher studies or professional qualifications. Support is given for general educational costs including books and equipment; or for students travelling in the UK or abroad for educational purposes associated with their course of study.

Applications

Hard-copy application forms are available from the Civic Centre, Carlisle, or can be requested by telephone. The deadline for applications is usually 20 September; however, check the charity's website for current deadlines. The trustees meet twice a year to consider applications; the majority of applications will be considered in October, the rest in March.

Financial information

Year end	31/03/2018
Income	£9,500
Total expenditure	£10,500

Further financial information

Full accounts were not available to view on the Charity Commission's website due to the charity s low income. We have therefore estimated the grant total based on the charity s total expenditure.

During 2018, the charity awarded 22 grants with a total of £9,500 to local students.

Sources of information

Charity Commission record; funder's website.

South Lakeland

Cartmel Old Grammar School Foundation

£4,600 (2017/18)

Correspondent: Colin Milner, Clerk to the Trustees, Quintaine, Cardrona Road, Grange-over-Sands, Cumbria LA11 7EW (tel: 01539 535043; email: mrcolinmilner@gmail.com)

CC number: 526467

Eligibility

Young people between the ages of 18 and 25 who live in the ancient parish of Cartmel, Cartmel Fell, Field Broughton, Grange-over-Sands, Staveley, Lower Allithwaite, Upper Allithwaite, Cark, Flookburgh, Lindale and that part of Haverthwaite east of the River Leven, who are continuing their education at university or other institutes of further/higher education, i.e post-A-level.

Types of grant

Small grants of around £150 for a maximum of three years are awarded to help with the cost of further/higher education. Grants may also be available for music/art students, educational travel and financial help for students on apprenticeship schemes.

Applications

Further information and application forms are available from the correspondent by writing to the address given (enclose an sae to hold an A4 document) or, preferably, by email. Small supplies of application forms are also distributed in local churches, educational establishments and to parish/town council clerks. Applications should be submitted by the end of September at the latest.

Financial information

Year end	31/03/2018
Income	£12,100
Total expenditure	£10,100

Further financial information

Full accounts were not available to view on the Charity Commission's website due to the charity's low income. We have therefore estimated the grant total based on the charity's total expenditure.

Other information

The foundation also makes payments to the Cartmel Poor Charity and Brow

Edge Foundation. Local schools are also supported to meet expenditure not covered by the local authority.

Sources of information

Charity Commission record; Lower Holker Parish Council website.

Greater Manchester

Bolton

James Eden's Foundation

£ £10,400 (2017/18)

Correspondent: The Trustees, R. P. Smith and Co, Hamill House, 112–116 Chorley New Road, Bolton, Lancashire BL1 3AJ (tel: 01204 534421; email: info@rpsmithbolton.co.uk)

CC number: 526265

Eligibility

Young people resident in the metropolitan borough of Bolton who are in need of financial assistance, in particular those in further education. Preference is given to people who have lost either or both parents, or whose parents are separated or divorced.

Types of grant

Grants are awarded to assist those undergoing further education.

Applications

Application forms are available from the correspondent.

Financial information

Year end	16/07/2018
Income	£14,500
Total expenditure	£23,100

Further financial information

Full accounts were not available to view on the Charity Commission's website due to the charity's low income. We have therefore estimated the grant total based on the charity's total expenditure.

Other information

Grants are also awarded to local charitable institutions who support the care and benefit of deprived children in Bolton.

Sources of information

Charity Commission record.

Manchester

Ann Butterworth and Daniel Bayley Charity

£ £1,000 (2017/18)

Correspondent: The Trustees, Gaddum Centre, Gaddum House, 6 Great Jackson Street, Manchester M15 4AX (tel: 0161 834 6069; email: info@gaddum.org.uk)

CC number: 526055

Eligibility

Young people under the age of 21 who are studying the arts.

Types of grant

Grants are awarded towards the costs associated with a course of study including tuition fees, educational materials or field trips.

Applications

Apply in writing to the correspondent. Applications are accepted throughout the year.

Financial information

Year end	31/03/2018
Income	£0
Total expenditure	£1,200

Further financial information

Full accounts were not available to view on the Charity Commission's website due to the charity's low income. We have therefore estimated the grant total based on the charity's total expenditure.

Other information

The charity is administered by the Gaddum Centre (Charity Commission no. 507162).

Sources of information

Charity Commission record; further information provided by the funder.

Mynshull's Educational Foundation

£ £8,900 (2016/17)

Correspondent: Trust Administration, Gaddum Centre, Gaddum House, 6 Great Jackson Street, Manchester M15 4AX (tel: 0161 834 6069; email: info@gaddum.co.uk)

 www.gaddumcentre.co.uk/trust-funds-more-info

CC number: 532334

Eligibility

Students aged 25 and under. Applicants must be resident in the city of Manchester or its adjoining districts.

Types of grant

Financial assistance in the form of scholarships, bursaries and maintenance allowances for any school, university or place of learning as well as for training and apprenticeships. Grants are considered towards the costs of books, clothing, equipment, one-off educational travel, maintenance and any other expenses that may arise.

Exclusions

Funding is not given for course fees, ongoing expenditure or postgraduate studies.

Applications

Application forms and guidance notes can be requested from the correspondent and must be submitted by a professional such as a teacher or social worker. Potential applicants should also contact the correspondent to check the current application deadlines.

Financial information

Year end	30/11/2017
Income	£14,500
Total expenditure	£9,900

Further financial information

Full accounts were not available to view on the Charity Commission's website due to the charity's low income. We have therefore estimated the grant total based on the charity's total expenditure. The 2016/17 accounts were the latest available at the time of writing (October 2019).

Other information

The foundation is administered by the Gaddum Centre (Charity Commmission no. 507162).

Sources of information

Charity Commission record; funder's website.

Rochdale

The Heywood Educational Trust

£ £2,500 (2017/18)

Correspondent: The Trustees, c/o 4 Chaffinch Close, Thornton-Cleveleys, Lancashire FY5 2UR (email: phoenixtrust@outlook.com)

 www.rochdale.gov.uk/the_council/more_about_the_council/charitable_trusts.aspx

CC number: 526690

Eligibility

People who live in either the Heywood area or the village of Birch, or those attending or who have attended a school in the area. There is no age limit for applicants.

Types of grant

Grants are awarded to promote the education, training and development of the applicant and to assist with financial barriers. This includes: awarding scholarships grants, or maintenance allowances, tenable at any education provider approved by the trustees; financial assistance towards clothing, tools, instruments or books enabling people to enter a profession, trade or calling; and help with travel expenses associated with pursuing education.

Exclusions

The trust is unable to cover the full cost of fees or expenses, unless exceptional hardship is shown on the application.

Applications

Application forms are available from the Rochdale Borough Council website and further information can be requested by either emailing or writing to the trust.

Financial information

Year end	31/03/2018
Income	£1,600
Total expenditure	£3,700

Further financial information

Full accounts were not available to view on the Charity Commission's website due to the charity's low income. We have therefore estimated the grant total based on the charity's total expenditure.

Other information

The trust also supports organisations.

Sources of information

Charity Commission record; funder's website.

Middleton Educational Trust (The Emerson Educational Trust for Middleton)

 £4,400 (2017/18)

Correspondent: The Trustees, c/o 4 Chaffinch Close, Thornton-Cleveleys, Lancashire FY5 2UR (email: middletoneducationaltrust@outlook. com)

www.rochdale.gov.uk/the_council/ more_about_the_council/ charitable_trusts.aspx

CC number: 510495

Eligibility

People who live or attend/have attended any school in the area of the former municipal borough of Middleton. There is no age limit for applicants.

Types of grant

Grants are offered to promote education and development. In particular, grants are awarded for scholarships, bursaries and maintenance allowances tenable at any school, university, college/institution of further (including professional and technical) education approved by the trustees. Grants are available to assist with travel costs associated with education including travel both in the UK and abroad. Grants are also given towards providing financial assistance, clothing, equipment or books for school/ university leavers to assist with their entry into a profession/trade.

Exclusions

Grants do not cover the full cost of fees or expenses, unless exceptional hardship is shown on the application.

Applications

Application forms can be downloaded from the Rochdale Borough Council website or requested from the correspondent.

Financial information

Year end	31/03/2018
Income	£9,100
Total expenditure	£5,800

Further financial information

Full accounts were not available to view on the Charity Commission's website due to the charity's low income. We have therefore estimated the grant total based on the charity's total expenditure.

Other information

This trust also offers grants to organisations, such as awards for schoolchildren.

Sources of information

Charity Commission record; funder's website.

Herbert Norcross Scholarship Fund

 £5,100 (2017/18)

Correspondent: The Clerk, Governance and Committee Services, Floor 2, Number One Riverside, Smith Street, Rochdale OL16 1XU (tel: 01706 924872 or 01706 647474; email: committee. services@rochdale.gov.uk)

https://www.rochdale.gov.uk/the_ council/more_about_the_council/ charitable_trusts.aspx

CC number: 526666

Eligibility

Young people under the age of 30 who have completed a course of study at any university, college or any other place of further education. Preference is given to

residents in Middleton or those who have attended a school in Middleton. Grants are then given more generally to residents in Rochdale and the county of Lancaster.

Types of grant

Grants are made towards course fees, travel expenses, books/equipment and any other expenses incurred when undertaking postgraduate study, research or a similar course in the UK or abroad.

Exclusions

Grants are not awarded for first/ undergraduate degree courses or for general living expenses. Repeat applications will be not considered.

Applications

Application forms are available to download from the Rochdale Borough Council website. Completed forms should be returned to the Clerk by post. The trustees meet annually to consider grant applications, usually in August.

Financial information

Year end	31/03/2018
Income	£6,100
Total expenditure	£5,600

Further financial information

Full accounts were not available to view on the Charity Commission's website due to the charity's low income. We have therefore estimated the grant total based on the charity's total expenditure.

Sources of information

Charity Commission record; Rochdale Borough Council website.

Rochdale Ancient Parish Educational Trusts

 £13,000 (2017/18)

Correspondent: The Trustees, Park House, 200 Drake Street, Rochdale, Lancashire OL16 1PJ (tel: 01706 655117; email: info@e-wmg.co.uk)

rapet.org.uk/index.html

CC number: 526318

Eligibility

People who live in the ancient parish of Rochdale (which includes: Rochdale, Littleborough, Milnrow, Wardle, Whitworth, Todmorden, Saddleworth, Newhey and Bacup) or attend, or have attended a school in the area. There is no age limit for applicants, but preference will be given to those under the age of 25.

Types of grant

Grants are awarded for a range of purposes including scholarships, grants, maintenance allowances and bursaries tenable at any school, college, university or institution of further education that has been approved by the trustees. In addition, grants are available to help with the cost of travel in the UK or abroad in order to pursue education as well as financial assistance for clothing, books and equipment to assist entry into a trade, profession or calling.

Applications

Application forms and further information on eligibility are available to download from the trust's website. Applications are considered by the trustees three times a year. Completed application forms should be returned by 20 February, 20 May or 31 August each year.

Financial information

Year end	31/03/2018
Income	£28,400
Total expenditure	£26,000

Further financial information

In 2017/18 the trust agreed to pay grants between £80 and £3,400 to individuals, totalling £16,000. Of this, £3,000 is still due to be paid once the conditions of the grant have been met.

Sources of information

Accounts; annual report; Charity Commission record; funder's website.

Salford

The Salford Foundation Trust

 £9,800 (2017/18)

Correspondent: Peter Collins, Company Secretary, Foundation House, 3 Jo Street, Salford, Greater Manchester M5 4BD (tel: 0161 787 3834; email: mail@ salfordfoundationtrust.org.uk)

🌐 www.salfordfoundationtrust.org.uk

CC number: 1105303

Eligibility

Young people in need between the ages of 5 and 25 who have lived in Salford for at least three years. Priority is given to applicants under the age of 21.

Types of grant

Grants of up to £500 are made towards training, vocational courses, performing arts qualifications and so on. The trust also provides apprenticeship tool-kits and college resources for young people living on their own or for people who are solely responsible for dependants.

Exclusions

Funding will not be considered for the following:

- Driving lessons and associated items
- Childcare costs
- Course fees or living expenses
- Membership fees
- Remedial intervention (speech/ language/occupational therapies)
- Retrospective funding
- Standard school/college and sports trips or residential excursions
- Activities with political or religious focus
- Needs that should be financed by statutory services
- Activities that are for the benefit of a group of people

Applications

Application forms and further guidance notes can be downloaded from the trust's website. Applications can be made: directly by the individual; through a parent/legal guardian; through a third party such as a teacher, youth worker or mentor; or through an agency. Applications open four times a year and up-to-date details of opening times can be found on the website. Applicants who may have difficulty completing application forms may apply with an acoustic or visual recording in which the answers to the questions on the application form are spoken rather than written. Applications must be supported by two referees and returned by post.

Financial information

Year end	31/03/2018
Income	£38,300
Total expenditure	£49,100

Further financial information

In 2017/18, 60 grants were awarded to individuals. Grants totalled £19,500; this included some individuals who were still receiving staged or continuous payments from the previous years. We estimate that around £9,800 was awarded for welfare purposes and £9,800 was awarded for educational purposes.

Other information

The trust also offers advice services and organises/delivers programmes to 'enhance personal and learning development opportunities'. The trust has recently entered into a partnership with the Charles Camilleri Foundation to joint fund a part-time post to develop and manage the Business Start-Up programme and increase the number of applications.

Sources of information

Accounts; annual report; Charity Commission record; funder's website.

Stockport

The Barrack Hill Educational Charity (Barrack Hill Trust)

£ £5,000 (2018)

Correspondent: The Trustees, 7 Henbury Drive, Woodley, Berkshire SK6 1PY (tel: 0161 494 2521; email: jgreen.barrackhilltrust@virginmedia. com)

CC number: 525836

Eligibility

People under the age of 21 who live or whose parents live in Bredbury and Romiley.

Types of grant

Grants are awarded to promote the education, including social and physical training of young people under the age of 21.

Applications

Application forms can be requested from the correspondent.

Financial information

Year end	31/12/2018
Income	£17,600
Total expenditure	£11,200

Further financial information

Full accounts were not available to view on the Charity Commission's website due to the charity's low income. We have therefore estimated the grant total based on the charity's total expenditure.

Other information

The charity also makes grants to schools in the local area.

Sources of information

Charity Commission record.

The Ephraim Hallam Charity

£ £5,900 (2018)

Correspondent: The Trustees, 3 Highfield Road, Poynton, Stockport, Cheshire SK12 1DU (tel: 01625 874445; email: SMTcharities@outlook.com)

CC number: 525975

Eligibility

People who are resident in the metropolitan borough of Stockport and are in need.

Types of grant

The charity awards scholarships, maintenance allowances or grants tenable at any university, college or institution of higher/further education.

In addition, grants are awarded towards the cost of travel associated with furthering education as well as to assist with entry into any occupation, profession or trade for those leaving an educational establishment.

Applications
Apply in writing to the correspondent.

Financial information

Year end	31/12/2018
Income	£15,600
Total expenditure	£13,000

Further financial information
Full accounts were not available to view on the Charity Commission's website due to the charity's low income. We have therefore estimated the grant total based on the charity's total expenditure.

Other information
Grants are also made to local charities whose aims include advancing the education of young people.

Sources of information
Charity Commission record.

Wigan

The Leigh Educational Endowment

£ £12,900 (2017/18)

Correspondent: The Trustees, Fairhouse Farm, Pocket Nook Lane, Lowton, Warrington, Cheshire WA3 1AL (tel: 07831 501129; email: walter.glen@ hotmail.com)

CC number: 526469

Eligibility
Children and young people under the age of 25 who live in the former borough of Leigh and are attending any institution of education approved by the trustees.

Types of grant
Grants and scholarships tenable at any institution of education approved by the trustees.

Applications
Apply in writing to the correspondent.

Financial information

Year end	31/03/2018
Income	£15,100
Total expenditure	£14,300

Further financial information
Full accounts were not available to view on the Charity Commission's website due to the charity's low income. We have therefore estimated the grant total based on the charity's total expenditure.

Sources of information
Charity Commission record.

Lancashire

Baines's Charity

£ £4,000 (2018)

Correspondent: Duncan Waddilove, 2 The Chase, Normoss Road, Blackpool, Lancashire FY3 0BF (tel: 01253 893459; email: duncanwaddilove@hotmail.com)

CC number: 224135

Eligibility
People in need who live in the areas of Blackpool, Fylde and Wyre, specifically Carleton, Hardhorn-with-Newton, Marton, Poulton-Le-Fylde and Thornton. If there are surplus funds available, people who are temporarily resident in the beneficial area can be supported. Educational grants are awarded to those about to start vocational or further education.

Types of grant
The trustees award small grants according to need. Occasionally they purchase equipment, books or other goods on behalf of the applicant.

Applications
Application forms are available from the correspondent. They can be submitted either directly by the individual or through a social worker, Citizens Advice or other welfare agency. Applications are considered upon receipt.

Financial information

Year end	31/12/2018
Income	£19,100
Total expenditure	£16,900

Further financial information
Full accounts were not available to view on the Charity Commission's website due to the charity's low income. We have therefore estimated the grant total based on the charity's total expenditure.

Other information
Grants can be made to individuals and organisations for both welfare and educational purposes, including support to schools. The charity works in conjunction with John Sykes Dewhurst Bequest (Charity Commission no. 224133).

Sources of information
Charity Commission record.

The Harris Charity

£ £2,200 (2017/18)

Correspondent: David Ingram, Secretary, c/o Moore and Smalley, Richard House, 9 Winckley Square, Preston, Lancashire PR1 3HP (tel: 01772 821021; email: harrischarity@ mooreandsmalley.co.uk)

 theharrischarity.co.uk

CC number: 526206

Eligibility
People in need under the age of 25 who live in the 'old' Lancashire boundaries as defined in 1972, with a preference for the Preston district.

Types of grant
One-off grants for training and education, including apprenticeships, and for associated costs such as books and equipment.

Applications
Application forms are available to download from the charity's website. The half-yearly dates by which the applications must be submitted are 31 March and 30 September. Successful applicants are notified in July and January respectively.

Financial information

Year end	05/04/2018
Income	£165,900
Total expenditure	£93,600

Further financial information
In 2017/18, £3,800 was awarded to individuals in the Preston area and £500 in the Lancashire area for both welfare and educational purposes. The grant total has been estimated from the 2017/18 accounts.

Other information
The original charity known as the Harris Orphanage Charity dates back to 1883. A new charitable scheme was established in 1985 following the sale of the Harris Orphanage premises in Garstang Road, Preston. The charity also supports charitable organisations that benefit individuals, recreation and leisure and the training and education of individuals.

Sources of information
Accounts; annual report; Charity Commission record; funder's website.

John Parkinson (Goosnargh and Whittingham United Charity)

£ £2,200 (2017)

Correspondent: The Trustees, Lower Stanalea Farm, Stanalea Lane, Goosnargh, Preston, Lancashire PR3 2EQ (tel: 01995 640224)

CC number: 526060

Eligibility
People under the age of 25 who live in the parishes of Goosnargh, Whittingham and part of Barton.

Types of grant
Grants towards fees, books, tools, outfits, travel and maintenance expenses for people entering a profession, trade or service.

Applications
Apply in writing to the correspondent.

Financial information

Year end	31/12/2017
Income	£4,500
Total expenditure	£2,400

Further financial information
Full accounts were not available to view on the Charity Commission's website due to the charity's low income. We have therefore estimated the grant total based on the charity's total expenditure.

Sources of information
Charity Commission record.

Swallowdale Children's Trust

£ £19,700 (2018/19)

Correspondent: The Trustees, 13 Newlands Avenue, Blackpool FY3 9PG (tel: 07984 539657; email: secswallowdale@hotmail.co.uk)

CC number: 526205

Eligibility
People who live in the boroughs of Blackpool, Wyre and Fylde area who are under the age of 25.

Types of grant
The trust provides grants for general educational purposes such as fees for training and educational courses.

Exclusions
Grants are not awarded where the benefit is available from family or community sources.

Applications
Apply in writing to the correspondent.

Financial information

Year end	31/03/2019
Income	£37,400
Total expenditure	£80,800

Further financial information
Grants were made to 281 individuals.

Other information
The trust also assists charities working with young people in its operating area.

Sources of information
Accounts; annual report; Charity Commission record; further information provided by the funder.

Blackburn with Darwen

The W. M. and B. W. Lloyd Trust

£ £28,900 (2018/19)

Correspondent: John Jacklin, Trustee/Secretary, Gorse Barn, Rock Lane, Tockholes, Darwen, Lancashire BB3 0LX (tel: 01254 771367; email: johnjacklin@homecall.co.uk)

CC number: 503384

Eligibility
People who live in, or have been educated in, the borough of Darwen and are in need.

Types of grant
Educational grants are made for 'the advancement of education', according to the trust's annual report.

Applications
Apply in writing to the correspondent. Applications should be sponsored by a third party such as a social worker, doctor, minister or someone known to the applicant who can support their application.

Financial information

Year end	05/04/2019
Income	£123,300
Total expenditure	£117,300

Further financial information
Note: the grant total has been estimated.

Other information
The trust also makes grants to organisations for medical equipment, sports equipment, church repairs and improvements to public parks. In 2019, the trust awarded £8,000 to purchase a mobile bladder scanner for the Royal Blackburn Teaching Hospital.

Sources of information
Accounts; annual report; Charity Commission record; East Lancashire Hospitals NHS Trust website; Lancashire Telegraph website.

Burnley

Edward Stocks-Massey Bequest Fund

£ £7,600 (2017/18)

Correspondent: Sam Gorton, Burnley Borough Council, Town Hall, Manchester Road, Burnley BB11 9SA (tel: 01772 532471; email: democracy@burnley.gov.uk)

 https://www.burnley.gov.uk/about-council/other-information/charities

CC number: 526516

Eligibility
People who live in the borough of Burnley and higher education students who have gone into further education in the borough, and who have achieved a place at a higher education institution.

Types of grant
Grants are awarded towards the provision of education and the advancement of science, learning, music and other arts. In addition, two higher education scholarships are available each year to assist those who have gone into further education.

Applications
An advertisement will be published in the Burnley Express inviting applications in late April. Application forms will then be made available to download from the Burnley Borough Council website. Scholarship applicants must have been nominated by their previous school or college and have demonstrated academic achievement, contribution to school/college life, or have difficulty in financing their higher education. The application deadline is usually towards the end of May.

Financial information

Year end	31/03/2018
Income	£34,000
Total expenditure	£58,600

Further financial information
In 2017/18 the total allocation of funding approved was £46,500, which was awarded to Burnley Borough Council, Lancashire County Council, individuals and voluntary organisations and higher education student scholarships. The fund awarded two scholarships at £1,000 per annum over three years, resulting in a total of £7,000 in grants to individuals.

Other information

Support is also given to organisations and groups.

Sources of information

Accounts; annual report; Charity Commission record; funder's website.

Lancaster

Herbert Norcross Scholarship Fund

See record on page 221

Preston

Educational Foundation of John Farrington

£3,100 (2017/18)

Correspondent: The Trustees, 35 Ribblesdale Drive, Grimsargh, Preston, Lancashire PR2 5RJ (tel: 01772 703050; email: dvicj@talktalk.net)

CC number: 526488

Eligibility

People under the age of 25 who live, or have a parent who lives, in any of the following areas: the city of Preston, Ribbleton, the former urban district of Fulwood, the parishes of Goosnargh, Grimsargh, Haighton, Longridge and Whittingham.

Types of grant

Grants are available to advance the education, including social and physical training, of young people under the age of 25.

Exclusions

Grants are not available to postgraduate students.

Applications

Apply in writing to the correspondent.

Financial information

Year end	31/03/2018
Income	£2,900
Total expenditure	£3,400

Further financial information

Full accounts were not available to view on the Charity Commission's website due to the charity's low income. We have therefore estimated the grant total based on the charity's total expenditure.

Sources of information

Charity Commission record.

The Shepherd Street Trust

£10,300 (2017/18)

Correspondent: Judith Turner, Secretary, PO Box 658, Longridge, Preston, Lancashire PR3 2WJ (tel: 01200 427625; email: enquiries@ shepherdstreettrust.co.uk)

 www.shepherdstreettrust.co.uk

CC number: 222922

Eligibility

People under the age of 21 residing within a radius of 50 miles around Preston Town Hall.

Types of grant

The trustees will award funds for outfits, clothing, tools, instruments and equipment, which will help to further education or entry into a profession, trade or calling.

Applications

Application forms can be downloaded from the trust's website or requested from the correspondent. Candidates are required to provide supporting references from their school, college, social worker, religious authority or other professional. Applications for grants of less than £500 will be decided by the trustees within four weeks of receipt. Applications for grants exceeding £500 will be discussed at the trustee meetings unless there is a pressing need for funds, in which case, earlier consideration can be made. The trustees meet every two months, in January, March, May, July, September and November.

Financial information

Year end	30/06/2018
Income	£57,800
Total expenditure	£60,900

Other information

The trustees also award grants to organisations and to individuals for health and other leisure occupations in the interests of social welfare.

Sources of information

Accounts; annual report; Charity Commission record; funder's website.

West Lancashire

Peter Lathom's Charity (including the Lathom Educational Foundation)

£1,600 (2018)

Correspondent: Christine Aitken, Clerk, 13 Mallard Close, Aughton, Ormskirk, Lancashire L39 5QJ (tel: 0151 520 2717; email: c.aitken@brighouse-wolff.co.uk)

CC number: 228828

Eligibility

Educational grants are available to children and young people under the age of 25 living in Chorley and West Lancashire.

Types of grant

One-off and recurring grants according to need.

Applications

Apply in writing to the correspondent.

Financial information

Year end	31/12/2018
Income	£59,400
Total expenditure	£54,100

Other information

The charity also makes grants to local schools.

Sources of information

Accounts; annual report; Charity Commission record.

Merseyside

Girls Welfare Fund

Correspondent: Mrs S. O'Leary, Trustee, West Hey, Dawstone Road, Heswall, Wirral CH60 4RP (email: gwf_charity@ hotmail.co.uk)

CC number: 220347

Eligibility

Girls and young women, usually those aged between 15 and 25, who were born, educated and are living in Merseyside.

Types of grant

The following information has been taken from Sefton Council's website: 'One-off and recurrent grants for leisure and creative activities, sports, welfare and the relief of poverty. Grants may be given to schoolchildren and mature students for uniforms/clothing, college students and undergraduates for uniforms/clothing, study/travel overseas and books, vocational students for uniforms/clothing and equipment/ instruments. The fund is particularly interested in helping individual girls and young women of poor or deferred education to establish themselves. Grants range from £50 to £750.'

Exclusions

Grants are not made to charities that request funds to pass on and give to individuals.

Applications

Apply in writing to the correspondent or by e-mail. Applications can be submitted directly by the individual or through a social worker, Citizens Advice, other welfare agency or college/educational establishment. Applications are considered quarterly in March, June, September and December, and should include full information about the college, course and particular circumstances.

Financial information

Year end	31/12/2017
Income	£11,400
Total expenditure	£11,700

Other information

The fund also makes grants to organisations.

Sources of information

Accounts; annual report; Charity Commission record; Sefton Council website.

Halsall Educational Foundation

£900 (2017)

Correspondent: Hugh Hollinghurst, Clerk to the Trustees, 37 St Michaels Road, Crosby, Liverpool, Merseyside L23 7UJ (tel: 0151 924 7889)

 https://hughhollinghurst.wordpress. com/organisations

CC number: 526236

Eligibility

Girls and young women under the age of 25 who live or have parents living in the ancient township of Crosby, who are undertaking higher/further education. The ancient township of Crosby comprises of Great Crosby, Blundellsands and Waterloo.

Types of grant

Grants are available to higher education students for educational purposes such as purchasing books.

Applications

Apply in writing to the correspondent.

Financial information

Year end	31/12/2017
Income	£2,000
Total expenditure	£2,000

Further financial information

Full accounts were not available to view on the Charity Commission's website due to the charity's low income. We have therefore estimated the grant total based on the charity's total expenditure.

Sources of information

Charity Commission record; funder's website.

Sheila Kay Fund

£3,700 (2017/18)

Correspondent: Mr T. Murphy, Secretary, c/o LCVS, 151 Dale Street, Liverpool, Merseyside L2 2AH (tel: 0151 237 2689; email: enquiries@skfund.org. uk)

 sheilakay.org.uk

CC number: 1021378

Eligibility

People in need living in the Liverpool region who are intending to enter a career in the social care/welfare sector. Applicants must be aged 18 and over and have indefinite leave to remain or permanent residency. Applicants should be able to demonstrate a commitment to their community (for example, through volunteering).

Types of grant

Grants of up to £200 are available to enable access to learning and development up to level four and in some cases towards a social work degree. Grants can be used for study related expenses such as travel, equipment and books.

Exclusions

The fund will not support MA/ postgraduate courses.

Applications

Apply in writing to the correspondent, a contact form is available to use on the fund's website.

Financial information

Year end	31/03/2018
Income	£61,400
Total expenditure	£86,600

Other information

The fund also provides a range of other services and support including advice sessions, workshops, mentoring for young people who have been in care, support for individuals to overcome barriers to employment and volunteering opportunities.

Sources of information

Accounts; annual report; Charity Commission record; funder's website.

John James Rowe's Foundation for Girls

£2,800 (2016/17)

Correspondent: The Trustees, 18–28 Seel Street, Liverpool, Merseyside L1 4BE (tel: 0151 702 5555)

CC number: 526166

Eligibility

Girls and young women between the ages of 11 and 25 who live in Merseyside who have lost either one or both of their parents, whose parents are separated/ divorced or whose home conditions are especially difficult.

Types of grant

Grants are also available to promote the education of young women in secondary and further education, apprenticeships and to assist those preparing to enter a profession, trade or calling.

Applications

Apply in writing to the correspondent.

Financial information

Year end	30/09/2017
Income	£17,400
Total expenditure	£6,200

Further financial information

Full accounts were not available to view on the Charity Commission's website due to the charity's low income. We have therefore estimated the grant total based on the charity's total expenditure. The 2016/17 accounts were the latest available at the time of writing (October 2019).

Sources of information

Charity Commission record.

The Rushworth Trust

£3,700 (2017/18)

Correspondent: The Trustees, Liverpool Charity and Voluntary Services, 151 Dale Street, Liverpool, Merseyside L2 2AH (tel: 0151 227 5177; email: grants@lcvs. org.uk)

www.lcvs.org.uk/grants/rushworth- trust

CC number: 1076702

Eligibility

Young musicians living within a 60-mile radius of Liverpool Town Hall. Grants are available to a wide range of musicians, including composers, young conductors, young performers, student singers and instrumentalists, and choral singers.

Types of grant

One-off grants of up to £500 are given towards musical education and performance. Examples of what could be supported include: support towards study, tuition or practical work for young composers; specialist training and the purchase of instruments for young performers; assistance with publication and performance for composers; coaching for a scholarship and maintenance costs (but not towards higher education) for student singers/ instrumentalists; training, travel and concerts for choral singers.

Exclusions

Grants are not available towards course fees or for maintenance during higher education.

Applications

Application forms can be requested from the correspondent or downloaded from the trust's website. Completed forms should be submitted in advance of the trustee meetings which are normally held in March, June, September and December.

Financial information

Year end	30/09/2018
Income	£74,400
Total expenditure	£7,900

Further financial information

We estimate that around £3,700 was awarded as grants to individuals in 2017/18.

Other information

The trust has been formed by the merging of The William Rushworth Trust, The Thew Bequest and The A K Holland Memorial Award.

Sources of information

Accounts; annual report; Charity Commission record; funder's website.

Liverpool

The Liverpool Council of Education (Incorporated)

£ £11,600 (2017/18)

Correspondent: The Trustees, 4 St Anne's Road, Aigburth, Liverpool, Merseyside L17 6BW (tel: 0151 427 1766)

CC number: 526714

Eligibility

Schoolchildren and adults in Liverpool.

Types of grant

Grants are awarded to enable individuals to undertake educational opportunities.

Applications

Apply in writing to the correspondent.

Financial information

Year end	31/07/2018
Income	£19,900
Total expenditure	£25,700

Further financial information

Full accounts were not available to view on the Charity Commission's website due to the charity's low income. We have therefore estimated the grant total based on the charity's total expenditure.

Other information

The charity acts as a trustee to various charitable funds providing educational support to schools, pupils and teachers in Liverpool. The charity is linked to the Liverpool Educational Foundation 526714–1.

Sources of information

Charity Commission record.

World Friendship

£ £29,000 (2018)

Correspondent: The Trustees, 15 Dudlow Lane, Liverpool, Merseyside L18 0HH (tel: 0151 722 9700; email: worldfriendship@hotmail.co.uk)

 www.worldfriendship.merseyside. org

CC number: 513643

Eligibility

International students studying at universities in the diocese of Liverpool. Priority is given to students from outside the European Union and eligibility is not restricted by faith. International students from the following universities can apply for a grant; Liverpool Hope University, Liverpool Institute of Performing Arts, Liverpool John Moores University, Liverpool School of Tropical Medicine, University of Liverpool. In some cases, students from Chester University and Edge Hill University may also apply for grants.

Types of grant

The charity offers one-off grants of about £500 to assist with education and hardships for international students in need of financial assistance. Grants are also offered to assist people from overseas who temporarily reside in the UK but wish to undertake study within the diocese of Liverpool.

Applications

Application forms are available from the chaplains at the listed universities or by applying in writing to the correspondent.

Financial information

Year end	31/12/2018
Income	£20,900
Total expenditure	£32,200

Further financial information

Full accounts were not available to view on the Charity Commission's website due to the charity's low income. We have therefore estimated the grant total based on the charity's total expenditure.

Sources of information

Charity Commission record; funder's website.

South East

General

Ewelme Exhibition Endowment

 £96,900 (2018)

Correspondent: James Oliver, Clerk and Trust Manager, c/o HMG-Law, 126 High Street, Oxford, Oxfordshire OX1 4DG (tel: 01865 244661; email: clerk@ewelme-education-awards.info)

www.ewelme-education-awards.info

CC number: 309240

Eligibility

Young people (both in state and independent education) aged between 11 and 25 who live in Berkshire, Buckinghamshire, Conock in Wiltshire, Oxfordshire or Ramridge in Hampshire and demonstrate exceptional talent or need. The combined family income must be less than £75,000 a year.

Types of grant

Bursaries are awarded to young people with exceptional talent, specific educational needs or unexpected financial crises or bereavement. In 2018 grants ranged between £2,400 and £5,000 per year. They are usually made on first entry into secondary education, although later applications are considered. Some awards are aimed towards gifted young people unable to consider an independent school education without substantial financial support and a number of these are made every year in partnership with schools already willing to make a contribution to the fees. Bursaries are also awarded to children, whether at state or independent schools, who have proven abilities, the pursuit of which is putting financial strain on the parents. Grants are also available for travel expenses, school trip expenses, uniform costs, sports training, extra tuition, specialist equipment and instruments for academic subjects (art, music and sports).

Grants, usually between £250 and £1,500, are provided towards the costs of vocational training, apprenticeships and the development of skills and costs associated with university or any other tertiary education course, such as travel expenses. Grants can also be awarded for extra tuition and master classes while engaged in tertiary education. Bursaries and scholarship schemes are also available and in 2018 they ranged between £2,400 and £5,000 a year.

Applications

Application forms can be downloaded from the charity's website. The charity requires details of parental income and a testimonial from a teacher or tutor. Grant applications can be submitted at any time and will be considered at the governors' quarterly meetings held in January, April, July and October, if they are received by the 1st of those months.

The bursary awards have a different application process. The deadline for these applications is the end of November in the year prior to the award. The applications are then reviewed in January and shortlisted applicants will be invited for an interview in February.

Financial information

Year end	31/12/2018
Income	£253,600
Total expenditure	£217,400

Further financial information

The grant total has been estimated from the 2018 accounts.

Other information

The charity also makes grants to organisations, particularly schools.

Sources of information

Accounts; annual report; Charity Commission record; funder's website.

The Hale Trust

 £19,500 (2017/18)

Correspondent: Lady Broughton, Secretary, Rosemary House, Woodhurst Park, Oxted, Surrey RH8 9HA

(tel: 01883 713912; email: schools.funding@surreycc.gov.uk)

CC number: 313214

Eligibility

Young people under the age of 25 who live in Greater London, Kent, Surrey or Sussex .

Types of grant

Grants are awarded to promote the education and training of people at school, university, college and those undertaking apprenticeships. Grants can also be given towards books, clothing and tools for people entering a profession/trade as well as travel abroad to pursue education.

Applications

Apply in writing to the correspondent.

Financial information

Year end	31/03/2018
Income	£57,400
Total expenditure	£56,300

Further financial information

Educational bursaries were given to 23 individuals.

Other information

The trust also supports charitable organisations whose objects focus on helping young people by promoting education and improving life conditions through leisure time activities.

Sources of information

Accounts; annual report; Charity Commission record.

Sarum St Michael Educational Charity
See record on page 250

Berkshire

The Polehampton Charity

 £7,100 (2018)

Correspondent: Caroline White, Clerk to the Trustees, 65 The Hawthorns, Charvil, Reading, Berkshire RG10 9TS (tel: 0118 934 0852; email: polehampton. applications@gmail.com or thepolehamptoncharity@gmail.com)

🌐 www.thepolehamptoncharity.co.uk

CC number: 1072631

Eligibility
Residents of Twyford and Ruscombe who are in need.

Types of grant
Educational grants are made for books and tools required for students and apprentices studying at university, college or other recognised places of education (including apprenticeships.)

Applications
Apply in writing to the Clerk. Alternatively, applications can be made to the Assistant Clerk to the Charity, Miss E Treadwell, by email (polehampton.applications@gmail.com) or by post to 114 Victoria Road, Wargrave, Berkshire, RG10 8AE.

Financial information
Year end	31/12/2018
Income	£118,100
Total expenditure	£106,800

Other information
The charity also makes grants to organisations/groups and to schools for equipment and resources.

Sources of information
Accounts; annual report; Charity Commission record; funder's website.

Reading

The Earley Charity

 £2,400 (2018)

Correspondent: Jane Wittig, Clerk to the Trustees, St Nicolas Centre, Sutcliffe Avenue, Earley, Reading, Berkshire RG6 7JN (tel: 0118 926 1068; email: enquiries@earleycharity.org.uk)

🌐 www.earleycharity.org.uk

CC number: 244823

Eligibility
People in need who have lived in Earley and the surrounding neighbourhood for at least six months. Applicants must be living in permanent accommodation and have UK citizenship or have been granted indefinite leave to remain in the UK. In order to check whether applicants live within the area of benefit, see the map available on the charity's website. If in doubt, contact the correspondent for confirmation.

Types of grant
Grants are awarded to support young people who are learning a trade.

Exclusions
Grants are not given to:
- Fund postgraduate education
- Cover general running/living costs
- Pay off debts
- People who have received three grants already
- People who are moving out of the area

Applications
Application forms can be requested from the correspondent or through using the enquiry form on the charity's website. They can be submitted either directly by the individual or through a social worker, Citizens Advice or other welfare agency. Applications for grants under £500 and applications for grants over £500 are considered at separate meetings around five times each year. The dates of these meetings, along with application submission deadlines, are published on the website.

Financial information
Year end	31/12/2018
Income	£950,500
Total expenditure	£1,820,200

Other information
Grants are also made to organisations and local voluntary and community groups. According to the charity's website, the main focus is currently the relief of poverty but the priorities do change. Check the website for further information.

Sources of information
Accounts; annual report; Charity Commission record; funder's website.

John Sykes Foundation

 £3,900 (2018)

Correspondent: The Trustees, 1st Floor, 23/24 Market Place, Reading, Berkshire RG1 2DE (tel: 0118 903 5909; email: mail@johnsykesfoundation.org)

🌐 johnsykesfoundation.org

CC number: 1156623

Eligibility
Individuals in need who live within a five-mile radius of Reading town centre. A map showing the area of benefit can be found on the foundation's website.

Types of grant
Educational grants are awarded to individuals for purposes relating to arts and culture, education, science and sport, as well as for needs relating to health and disability.

Applications
Application forms can be downloaded from the foundation's website and should be completed and returned to the foundation's office by post or email. When applications are submitted, a notification will be sent to confirm it has been received by the trustees. The application will then be assessed and the applicant informed whether it has been taken forward to the next stage. Applicants who are unsuccessful at this point will also be notified. Those invited to the next stage will then either be invited to the foundation's office or visited at home to discuss the application, financial details, reasons for applying and what the applicant hopes to achieve. Applicants will be informed of the trustees' final decision following this meeting.

Financial information
Year end	31/12/2018
Income	£2,800
Total expenditure	£8,300

Further financial information
Full accounts were not available to view on the Charity Commission's website due to the charity's low income. We have therefore estimated the grant total based on the charity's total expenditure.

Sources of information
Charity Commission record; funder's website.

Windsor and Maidenhead

The Spoore, Merry and Rixman Foundation

 £133,400 (2018)

Correspondent: Clerk to the Trustees, PO Box 4787, Maidenhead, Berkshire SL60 1JA (tel: 020 3286 8300; email: clerk@smrfmaidenhead.org)

🌐 www.smrfmaidenhead.org.uk

CC number: 309040

Eligibility
People under the age of 25 who are in need and live in Maidenhead and the

surrounding areas (postcodes SL6 1–9). There is a helpful map on the foundation's website which shows the area of benefit.

Types of grant

Grants can be given for a range of general educational needs. Support is given to those in further or higher education, which may include funding the cost of a university course for students from low-income families. Grants are available for young people under the age of 25 on low incomes who have been accepted on an apprenticeship; this is up to £1,500 for those living independently and up to £1,000 for those living with parents/ guardians.

Applications

Application forms can be found on the foundation's website. They can be submitted by post or online by the individual or through an educational institution. Parents are required to provide a statement of their income. Applications should not be sent via recorded or registered delivery, as the foundation uses a PO Box address and is unable to sign receipts. The trustees meet four times each year and the dates of upcoming meetings are posted on the foundation's website. Applications must be received two weeks prior to a meeting, or they will be considered at the next meeting instead.

Financial information

Year end	31/12/2018
Income	£483,800
Total expenditure	£1,290,000

Further financial information

The grant total has been estimated from the 2018 accounts.

Other information

Grants are also given to schools for educational facilities not funded by school budgets (e.g. development of school grounds or specialist equipment), as well as to youth clubs and other organisations for wider educational facilities. Every child leaving a local authority maintained primary school in the charity's area receives a dictionary from the trust.

Sources of information

Accounts; annual report; Charity Commission record; funder's website.

Buckinghamshire

Edmund Arnold's Charity (Poors Branch)
See record on page 145

Frogmoor Foundation

 £1,900 (2017/18)

Correspondent: The Trustees, Adult Learning, The Gallery Suite, Buckinghamshire County Council, County Hall, Aylesbury HP20 1UU (tel: 01296 383470; email: albussupport@ buckscc.gov.uk)

https://www.buckscc.gov.uk/ services/education/financial- support-for-students

CC number: 310649

Eligibility

Young people aged between 16 and 24 who are normally resident in Buckinghamshire and have received approved, full-time education up until the age of 16, or part-time education for at least two years after leaving school.

Types of grant

Grants ranging from £300 to £600 are awarded for a maximum of two years for any approved full-time further or higher education course. Bursaries of £30 to £150 are made towards the costs of clothing, tools or books required specifically for entry into a trade or profession. Travelling scholarships of between £150 and £300 are given for approved educational visits/studies abroad for up to three months. Research scholarships ranging from £300 to £600 are awarded towards any post-diploma/ degree course for a maximum period of one year.

Exclusions

Applicants must be under the age of 25 during the period of funding.

Applications

Application forms are available to download from the Buckinghamshire County Council website. Applications must include a detailed statement of the cost of the course proposed, or a list of requirements in the case of a bursary. Applicants will be required to provide evidence of their income (P60, etc.) Photocopies of such documents will suffice. Completed forms should be

returned by post. Applications typically open in March.

Financial information

Year end	31/03/2018
Income	£4,100
Total expenditure	£2,100

Further financial information

Full accounts were not available to view on the Charity Commission's website due to the charity's low income. We have therefore estimated the grant total based on the charity's total expenditure.

Sources of information

Buckinghamshire County Council website; Charity Commission record.

Norman Hawes Memorial Trust

 £2,600 (2017/18)

Correspondent: Sara Butler, Secretary, c/o Leadership and Governance Services, Saxon Court, 502 Avebury Boulevard, Milton Keynes, Buckinghamshire MK9 3HS (tel: 01908 253614; email: sara.butler@milton-keynes.gov.uk)

CC number: 310620

Eligibility

Young people between the ages of 15 and 18 who are in full-time education in Milton Keynes, Buckingham or Winslow (North Bucks).

Types of grant

Financial assistance to students travelling abroad for educational purposes. The trust does not usually provide the full cost of the trip but makes a contribution towards it.

Applications

Application forms are available from the correspondent or from the applicant's school/college/educational institution. A letter must accompany the application outlining costs and a report is required, to be submitted after the trip to inform the trustees how the project achieved the aims: to help young people travel and broaden their minds.

Financial information

Year end	31/03/2018
Income	£6,000
Total expenditure	£5,800

Further financial information

Full accounts were not available to view on the Charity Commission's website due to the charity's low income. We have therefore estimated the grant total based on the charity's total expenditure.

Other information

Grants may also be made to schools and colleges in the area.

Sources of information

Charity Commission record; Milton Keynes Council website.

The Walter Hazell Charitable and Educational Trust Fund

£13,600 (2018/19)

Correspondent: Rodney Dunkley, Trustee, 20 Aviemore Gardens, Northampton, Northamptonshire NN4 9XJ (tel: 01604 765925; email: roddunkley@yahoo.co.uk)

CC number: 1059707

Eligibility

Individuals and further/education students living in Buckinghamshire.

Types of grant

Annual grants towards the cost of further education.

Applications

Apply in writing to the correspondent.

Financial information

Year end	31/03/2019
Income	£11,700
Total expenditure	£30,100

Further financial information

Full accounts were not available to view on the Charity Commission's website due to the charity's low income. We have therefore estimated the grant total based on the charity's total expenditure.

Other information

This fund also awards Christmas payments to ex-employee pensioners of BPC Hazells.

Sources of information

Charity Commission record.

The Marlow Educational Foundation

£2,400 (2017)

Correspondent: P. A. R. Land, Clerk, Cripps & Shone, The Old House, West Street, Marlow, Buckinghamshire SL7 2LX (tel: 01628 472119 or 01628 482115)

CC number: 310650

Eligibility

People under the age of 25 who live, were born or have attended school for at least one year in the parish of Great Marlow or the urban districts of Marlow.

Types of grant

Grants are awarded for scholarships, bursaries and maintenance allowances for further education, including combining travel and study. Grants are also awarded for tools, clothing, etc., for individuals starting work and for training and apprenticeships.

Applications

Application forms are available from the correspondent and should be submitted for consideration over the summer school holidays.

Financial information

Year end	31/12/2017
Income	£6,400
Total expenditure	£2,700

Further financial information

Full accounts were not available to view on the Charity Commission's website due to the charity's low income. We have therefore estimated the grant total based on the charity's total expenditure.

Sources of information

Charity Commission record; Uni Grants website.

The Stoke Mandeville and Other Parishes Charity

£28,200 (2018)

Correspondent: Caroline Dobson, Administrator, 17 Elham Way, Aylesbury, Aylesbury, Buckinghamshire HP21 9XN (tel: 01296 431859; email: smandopc@gmail.com)

 smandopc.org

CC number: 296174

Eligibility

People in need who live in the parishes of Stoke Mandeville, Great Missenden and Great and Little Hampden, Buckinghamshire. Applicants should have been resident in the area of benefit for at least two years.

Types of grant

An annual educational grant is available to assist with the costs of books and equipment for further or higher education courses. University students will receive £500 and college students will receive £300.

Exclusions

Students undertaking GCSEs, AS or A-levels cannot apply for an educational grant. Grants for tuition fees are not available.

Applications

Application forms are available to download from the charity's website.

Financial information

Year end	31/12/2018
Income	£106,900
Total expenditure	£111,300

Other information

The charity also makes grants to local schools, clubs and organisations (including local parish councils).

Sources of information

Accounts; annual report; Charity Commission record; funder's website.

Stoke Poges Hastings Community Fund

£3,000 (2017)

Correspondent: The Trustees, Village Hall, 129 Rogers Lane, Stoke Poges, Slough, Berkshire SL2 4LP (tel: 01753 646323; email: SPHCF11@outlook.com)

 www.stokepogescharities.com/stoke-poges-hastings-community-fund.html

CC number: 206915

Eligibility

People in need and resident in the parish of Stoke Poges are eligible to apply.

Types of grant

Grants are available for the following: white goods and essential furniture; stair lifts, wheelchairs and other independence aids; school uniforms; breaks for carers; and the cost of non-university courses.

Applications

Application forms can either be downloaded from the charity's website and returned by post or completed online.

Financial information

Year end	31/12/2017
Income	£21,800
Total expenditure	£13,400

Further financial information

Full accounts were not available to view on the Charity Commission's website due to the charity's low income. We have therefore estimated the grant total based on the charity's total expenditure.

Other information

Grants are also made to local organisations.

Sources of information

Charity Commission record; funder's website.

Stokenchurch Educational Charity

£ £39,400 (2017/18)

Correspondent: Martin Sheehy, The Fish Partnership, The Mill House, Boundary Road, Loudwater, High Wycombe, Buckinghamshire HP10 9QN (tel: 01628 527956; email: martins@fishpartnership. co.uk)

CC number: 297846

Eligibility

People under the age of 25 who live in the parish of Stokenchurch.

Types of grant

Grants are available for educational expenses and training, including awards for clothing, tools, books, equipment/ instruments and study of music and other arts. Schoolchildren, further/higher education students and people entering a trade/starting work or undertaking apprentices can be supported.

Exclusions

Grants are not normally made for private tuition and where statutory grants are available. Applications from outside the parish cannot be considered.

Applications

Application forms can be requested from the correspondent. Ordinarily the trustees place an advertisement in the local press and two public places in Stokenchurch in August to invite applications. They should be returned by 30 November each year. Grants are paid in or around April. Applications from outside the parish cannot be considered and will not receive a response.

Financial information

Year end	30/09/2018
Income	£74,600
Total expenditure	£67,900

Other information

The charity also awards grants to organisations.

Sources of information

Accounts; annual report; Charity Commission record.

Aylesbury Vale

Cheddington Town Lands Charity

£ £8,000 (2017/18)

Correspondent: The Trustees, 9 Church Hill, Cheddington, Leighton Buzzard, Bedfordshire LU7 0SX (email: berraassociates@aol.com)

CC number: 235076

Eligibility

People in need who live in the parish of Cheddington.

Types of grant

Grants are awarded to students in further and higher education for financial help with costs towards educational materials and equipment.

Applications

Applications can be made in writing to the correspondent, directly by the individual or a family member.

Financial information

Year end	31/03/2018
Income	£29,400
Total expenditure	£27,000

Other information

One-third of the charity's income goes to the maintenance of the parish church. The remainder is divided between village organisations, volunteer hospital drivers, students, and people in need.

Sources of information

Accounts; annual report; Charity Commission record.

William Harding's Charity

£ £125,100 (2018)

Correspondent: John Leggett, Clerk to the Trustees, Parrott & Coales Solicitors, 14 Bourbon Road, Aylesbury, Buckinghamshire HP20 2RS (tel: 01296 318501; email: doudjag@pandcllp.co.uk)

CC number: 310619

Eligibility

People under the age of 25 who live in the town of Aylesbury.

Types of grant

One-off grants are made to young people in further/higher education and vocational training towards, for example, living expenses. Facilities for recreation, social or physical training may be provided to people in further education.

Applications

Application forms are available on request from the correspondent. The trustees meet ten times a year to consider applications.

Financial information

Year end	31/12/2018
Income	£1,174,000
Total expenditure	£928,100

Further financial information

The grant total has been estimated from the 2018 accounts.

Other information

The charity also owns almshouses, provides relief-in-need and supports local educational institutions, youth groups and organisations.

Sources of information

Accounts; annual report; Charity Commission record; Uni Grants website.

Rogers' Educational Trust

£ £1,400 (2018)

Correspondent: The Trustees, 21 Park Road, Winslow, Buckingham, Buckingham MK18 3DL (tel: 01296 714592; email: tbecapstick@yahoo.com)

CC number: 310557

Eligibility

People who live in the parish of Winslow-Cum-Shipton.

Types of grant

Grants are awarded to assist students to attend higher education courses by paying fees, maintenance allowances or travel expenses.

Applications

Apply in writing to the correspondent.

Financial information

Year end	31/12/2018
Income	£2,400
Total expenditure	£3,100

Further financial information

Full accounts were not available to view on the Charity Commission's website due to the charity's low income. We have therefore estimated the grant total based on the charity's total expenditure.

Sources of information

Charity Commission record.

The Saye and Sele Foundation

£ £2,200 (2017)

Correspondent: R. T. Friedlander, Clerk, Parrot & Coales Solicitors, 14 Bourbon Street, Aylesbury, Buckinghamshire HP20 2RS (tel: 01296 318500)

CC number: 310554

Eligibility

People under the age of 25 who live in the parishes of Grendon Underwood and Quainton.

Types of grant

One-off grants to help college and university students with books, equipment and training costs. Grants have been made towards computers for people from low-income families and equipment for people with disabilities.

Applications

Apply in writing to the correspondent, to be considered in January, April, July and October.

Financial information

Year end	31/12/2017
Income	£16,100
Total expenditure	£9,900

Further financial information

Full accounts were not available to view on the Charity Commission's website due to the charity's low income. We have therefore estimated the grant total based on the charity's total expenditure.

Other information

The foundation also provides building space in the community and can support local schools.

Sources of information

Charity Commission record; Uni Grants website.

Milton Keynes

The Ancell Trust

£ £3,300 (2017/18)

Correspondent: Karen Phillips, Secretary, 78 London Road, Stony Stratford, Milton Keynes, Buckinghamshire MK11 1JH (tel: 01908 563350; email: karen.phillips440@gmail. com)

CC number: 233824

Eligibility

People in need in the town of Stony Stratford.

Types of grant

One-off grants according to need for education, training and apprenticeships.

Applications

Apply in writing to the correspondent.

Financial information

Year end	05/04/2018
Income	£15,000
Total expenditure	£14,800

Further financial information

Full accounts were not available to view on the Charity Commission's website due to the charity's low income. We have therefore estimated the grant total based on the charity's total expenditure.

Other information

The trust owns the sports ground in Stony Stratford, which provides cricket, football, bowls, croquet and tennis facilities. Support is also given to organisations.

Sources of information

Charity Commission record; Stony Stratford Town Council website.

The Great Linford Advancement in Life Charity

£ £1,600 (2017)

Correspondent: Michael Williamson, Trustee, 2 Lodge Gate, Great Linford, Milton Keynes, Buckinghamshire MK14 5EW (tel: 01908 605664)

CC number: 310570

Eligibility

People under the age of 25 who live in the civil parish of Great Linford.

Types of grant

Grants are awarded for educational purposes for entry into university or other educational establishment. Grants can be made for clothing, tools, musical instruments, books, and travel in the furtherance of study, or for preparation for entry into a profession, trade or calling. Grants are normally up to £200.

Applications

Apply in writing to the correspondent, either directly by the individual or through their school, college or educational welfare agency. Applications must include details of the purpose for which the request is being made and estimates of the costs involved. They are considered in January, May and September.

Financial information

Year end	31/12/2017
Income	£1,700
Total expenditure	£3,700

Further financial information

Full accounts were not available to view on the Charity Commission's website due to the charity's low income. We have therefore estimated the grant total based on the charity's total expenditure.

Sources of information

Charity Commission record; Uni Grants website.

Wolverton Science and Art Institution Fund

£ £1,900 (2017/18)

Correspondent: Karen Phillips, 78 London Road, Stony Stratford, Milton Keynes, Buckinghamshire MK11 1JH (tel: 01908 563350; email: karen.phillips440@gmail.com)

CC number: 310652

Eligibility

People who live, study or work in the parishes of Wolverton or Stantonbury.

Types of grant

The fund provides financial assistance in the form of scholarships and bursaries.

Applications

Application forms are available from the correspondent.

Financial information

Year end	30/06/2018
Income	£6,400
Total expenditure	£3,700

Further financial information

Full accounts were not available to view on the Charity Commission's website due to the charity's low income. We have therefore estimated the grant total based on the charity's total expenditure.

Other information

The fund allocates up to a third of its income to provide benefits to educational organisations that are not normally provided by local authorities.

Sources of information

Charity Commission record.

East Sussex

The Bedgebury Foundation
See record on page 239

The Blatchington Court Trust (BCT)

£ £74,900 (2018/19)

Correspondent: The Trustees, 6A Hove Park Villas, Hove, East Sussex BN3 6HW (tel: 01273 727222; email: info@ blatchingtoncourt.org.uk)

 www.blatchingtoncourt.org.uk

CC number: 306350

Eligibility

People under the age of 30 who live in the Sussex area and are visually impaired.

Types of grant

One-off and recurrent support to people at any school, university, college or other institution of further education and training, approved by the trustees. The trust provides equipment, mobility aids, books and other necessities (including those for the study of music and other arts) which will assist in the pursuit of education, training and employment, or business development. Assistance will also be given in connection with preparation to enter a school, profession, trade, occupation or service. Most grants awarded are under £3,000.

Exclusions
The trust does not give cash grants or bursaries and will not normally provide funding for wheelchairs, school fees, holidays or travel costs.

Applications
Apply in writing to the correspondent.

Financial information
Year end	31/03/2019
Income	£558,300
Total expenditure	£593,000

Other information
The trust also arranges social activities for beneficiaries and their families. There is also an outreach service, providing one-to-one support for socially isolated clients. The trust also runs various support and advice lines, including life coaching, IT training and support, employment advice, benefits advice, advocacy and information, and counselling.

Sources of information
Accounts; annual report; Charity Commission record; funder's website.

The T. A. K. Turton Charitable Trust

£ £15,400 (2018)

Correspondent: The Trustees, 47 Lynwood Road, London W5 1JQ (tel: 020 8998 1006)

CC number: 268472

Eligibility
Young people with a good academic record (e.g. good GCSE results or equivalent) who are in their final years at school (A-levels or other university entrance qualifications). The trust usually supports three pupils in the UK. Applications are only accepted from schools which have awarded the candidate a bursary of at least 25% of the fees.

Types of grant
Support is given to cover a proportion of school fees for a two-year period, normally leading to A-levels or equivalent university entrance qualifications.

Applications
Applications should be made in writing to the correspondent, through the school where the applicant wishes to study.

Financial information
Year end	31/12/2018
Income	£15,700
Total expenditure	£16,000

Further financial information
Full accounts were not available to view on the Charity Commission's website due to the charity's low income. We have therefore estimated the grant total based on the charity's total expenditure.

Other information
Our research suggests that since grants are normally given for a two-year period, new applications from UK students can only be considered every two years.

Sources of information
Charity Commission record.

Brighton and Hove
Catherine Martin Trust

£ £15,700 (2017/18)

Correspondent: The Trustees, Hove Vicarage, Wilbury Road, Hove, East Sussex BN3 3PB (email: marion197@btinternet.com)

CC number: 258346

Eligibility
Children and young people under the age of 21 who are in full-time education, British-born and have lived in the old borough of Hove and Portslade for at least one year.

Types of grant
One-off and recurrent grants according to need.

Applications
Apply in writing to the correspondent.

Financial information
Year end	31/03/2018
Income	£14,700
Total expenditure	£17,400

Further financial information
Full accounts were not available to view on the Charity Commission's website due to the charity's low income. We have therefore estimated the grant total based on the charity's total expenditure.

Sources of information
Charity Commission record.

Hastings
The Isabel Blackman Foundation

£ £33,200 (2018/19)

Correspondent: John Francis Lamplugh, Secretary, Stonehenge, 13 Laton Road,

Hastings, East Sussex TN34 2ES (tel: 01424 431756; email: ibfoundation@uwclub.net)

CC number: 313577

Eligibility
People who live in Hastings and St Leonards-on-Sea and require financial assistance.

Types of grant
One-off and recurring grants according to need.

Applications
Apply in writing to the correspondent.

Financial information
Year end	05/04/2019
Income	£981,700
Total expenditure	£289,600

Further financial information
The welfare grant total was broken down as follows:

Social services	4	£2,100
Health	1	£2,000
Culture and recreation	1	£1,500

Education grants were awarded to 27 individuals.

Other information
The foundation also makes grants to organisations active in the community.

Sources of information
Accounts; annual report; Charity Commission record.

Magdalen and Lasher Educational Foundation

£ £49,000 (2017/18)

Correspondent: The Trustees, 132 High Street, Hastings, East Sussex TN34 3ET (tel: 01424 452646; email: mlc@oldhastingshouse.co.uk)

 www.magdalenandlasher.co.uk

CC number: 306969

Eligibility
People under the age of 25 who live in the borough of Hastings or who have attended schools in the borough for more than two years.

Types of grant
The types of grants awarded include: scholarships, bursaries or maintenance allowances at any educational institution for any profession, trade or calling, maintenance allowances, and financial assistance to study music or other arts.

Applications
Application forms and guidelines are available to download from the foundation's website.

Financial information

Year end	31/03/2018
Income	£180,700
Total expenditure	£172,300

Other information

The foundation also makes grants to organisations.

Sources of information

Accounts; annual report; Charity Commission record.

Wealdon

The Mayfield Trust

 £850 (2017)

Correspondent: Brenda Hopkin, Clerk, Appletrees, Alexandra Road, Mayfield, East Sussex TN20 6UD (tel: 01435 873279; email: clerk.mayfield.trust@ outlook.com)

https://mayfieldfiveashes.org.uk/ about-us/the-mayfield-trust

CC number: 212996

Eligibility

People in need who live in the parish of Mayfield, which includes Mayfield, Five Ashes and part of Hadlow Down.

Types of grant

One-off grants are awarded towards educational needs.

Exclusions

Grants are not made for religious or political causes.

Applications

Apply in writing to the correspondent.

Financial information

Year end	31/12/2017
Income	£4,800
Total expenditure	£3,800

Further financial information

Full accounts were not available to view on the Charity Commission's website due to the charity's low income. We have therefore estimated the grant total based on the charity's total expenditure.

Other information

The trust also makes grants to organisations.

Sources of information

Charity Commission record; funder's website.

Warbleton Charity

 £830 (2018)

Correspondent: The Trustees, 3 Benhall Mill Place, Benhall Mill Road, Tunbridge Wells, Kent TN2 5EE (tel: 01892 513899; email: leeves@freenetname.co.uk)

CC number: 208130

Eligibility

People living in the parish of Warbleton.

Types of grant

Small vocational training and apprenticeship grants.

Applications

Apply in writing to the correspondent.

Financial information

Year end	31/12/2018
Income	£3,700
Total expenditure	£1,800

Further financial information

Full accounts were not available to view on the Charity Commission's website due to the charity's low income. We have therefore estimated the grant total based on the charity's total expenditure.

Sources of information

Charity Commission record.

Hampshire

The Cliddesden and Farleigh Wallop Educational Trust

 £7,800 (2017)

Correspondent: The Trustees, 11 Southlea, Cliddesden, Basingstoke, Hampshire RG25 2JN

CC number: 307150

Eligibility

People under the age of 25 who are in need of financial assistance and live within the original boundaries of the parishes of Cliddesden and Farleigh Wallop only.

Types of grant

One-off and recurrent grants to assist with academic, physical, and musical education.

Applications

Apply in writing to the correspondent.

Financial information

Year end	31/12/2017
Income	£11,800
Total expenditure	£17,400

Further financial information

Full accounts were not available to view on the Charity Commission's website due to the charity's low income. We have therefore estimated the grant total based on the charity's total expenditure.

Sources of information

Charity Commission record.

Miss Gale's Educational Foundation (The Gale Trust)

 £4,500 (2018)

Correspondent: Martin Boiles, Trustee, 18 Winchester Road, Andover, Hampshire SP10 2EG (tel: 01264 355445 or 07712 695543; email: gales.trust@ yahoo.co.uk)

CC number: 307145

Eligibility

Children and young people who are resident in or near Andover who are in need. Those who attend, or have attended, any school in the area of Andover are also eligible. Preference is given to girls/young women.

Types of grant

The charity awards scholarships, bursaries and maintenance allowances to be used at 'a place of learning', which includes primary schools and secondary or further education. Scholarships and maintenance allowances are also available to enable students to pursue their education abroad. Financial assistance is awarded to young people preparing for entry into a trade or profession.

Applications

Apply in writing to the correspondent.

Financial information

Year end	31/12/2018
Income	£12,700
Total expenditure	£10,100

Further financial information

Full accounts were not available to view on the Charity Commission's website due to the charity's low income. We have therefore estimated the grant total based on the charity's total expenditure.

Other information

The charity also makes grants to organisations, to provide facilities to beneficiaries for educational and recreational purposes, as well as social and physical training. These facilities are not normally provided by the local education authority.

Sources of information

Charity Commission record; Hampshire County Council website.

The Robert Higham Apprenticing Charity

£ £6,800 (2018)

Correspondent: The Trustees, Russell House, Ashford Hill Road, Headley, Thatcham RG19 8AB (tel: 07796 423108; email: kingsclerecharities@iname.com)

CC number: 307083

Eligibility

People aged between 16 and 25 attending sixth forms, colleges and universities who live in the parishes of Kingsclere, Ashford Hill and Headley.

Types of grant

Grants towards books, specialist equipment and clothing or travelling expenses for those preparing for or engaged in any profession, trade, occupation or service, and towards books, study or travel abroad for those studying A-levels.

Applications

Application forms are available from the correspondent. Applications must include a letter outlining the applicant's further educational plans. Applications are not accepted from parents.

Financial information

Year end	31/12/2018
Income	£13,700
Total expenditure	£7,500

Further financial information

Full accounts were not available to view on the Charity Commission's website due to the charity's low income. We have therefore estimated the grant total based on the charity's total expenditure.

Sources of information

Charity Commission record.

Basingstoke and Deane

Ashford Hill Educational Trust

£ £870 (2018)

Correspondent: The Trustees, Minnesota, Ashford Hill Road, Headley, Thatcham, Berkshire RG19 8AB (tel: 01635 269596)

CC number: 1040559

Eligibility

People who live in the parish of Ashford Hill with Headley or the surrounding area. The grants have no age limits.

Types of grant

Grants are awarded for educational purposes.

Applications

Apply in writing to the correspondent.

Financial information

Year end	31/12/2018
Income	£7,400
Total expenditure	£3,900

Further financial information

Full accounts were not available to view on the Charity Commission's website due to the charity's low income. We have therefore estimated the grant total based on the charity's total expenditure.

Sources of information

Charity Commission record.

East Hampshire

Bramshott Educational Trust

£ £3,800 (2017/18)

Correspondent: Clerk, 107 Haslemere Road, Liphook, Hampshire GU30 7BU (tel: 01428 724289; email: clerk.bramshott.trust@hotmail.co.uk)

 www.bramshotteducationaltrust.org.uk

CC number: 277421

Eligibility

Children and young people under the age of 25 who live, or have a parent/guardian who lives, in the ancient parish of Bramshott, which includes Liphook, Bramshott, Passfield, Conford and the parts of Hammer Vale located in Hampshire.

Types of grant

According to the trust's website, grants are made for a variety of purposes such as 'school trips, music and ballet lessons, the purchase of books, specialist tools and other equipment.'

Exclusions

The trust's eligibility guidelines on its website state that 'in order to support as many applicants as possible, the trustees do not fund the whole amount required and do not award grants for expenditure which would reasonably be provided by the local authority'. The trustees will not consider late, incomplete or retrospective applications.

Applications

Application forms can be found on the trust's website or requested from the correspondent. Deadline dates are 15 April and 15 October.

Financial information

Year end	31/08/2018
Income	£7,600
Total expenditure	£6,300

Further financial information

Full accounts were not available to view on the Charity Commission's website due to the charity's low income. We have therefore estimated the grant total based on the charity's total expenditure.

Other information

Up to one third of the yearly income can be allocated to help local schools.

Sources of information

Charity Commission record; funder's website.

Fareham

The William Price Charitable Trust

£ £19,500 (2018/19)

Correspondent: Christopher Thomas, Clerk, 24 Cuckoo Lane, Fareham, Hampshire PO14 3PF (tel: 01329 663685; email: mazchris@tiscali.co.uk)

 www.pricestrust.org.uk

CC number: 307319

Eligibility

Children and young people under the age of 25 who live in the parishes of St Peter and St Paul, Holy Trinity with St Columba and St John the Evangelist (the same area as the original Fareham town parish but not the whole area of the Fareham borough).

Types of grant

Grants are awarded to pupils whose families are in financial need, to take part in educational visits, purchase of school uniforms, tools and equipment.

Applications

Where possible, applications should be made through a school/college; however, individual applications will be considered, particularly from people in further/higher education. Application forms can be downloaded from the trust's website or requested from the correspondent. Bursaries and college/university grants are considered twice a year, normally in March and September, and applications should be received by the first day of these months. Applications for smaller hardship grants can be made at any time and will be paid through a school/college.

Financial information

Year end	31/03/2019
Income	£197,300
Total expenditure	£255,600

Further financial information

During 2018/19 the trustees awarded 61 welfare grants to individuals and 16 grants for educational purposes.

Other information

Grants are also made to churches and schools/colleges, and there is an annual grant to the Fareham Welfare Trust.

Sources of information

Accounts; annual report; Charity Commission record.

Gosport

Thorngate Trust

 £4,700 (2017/18)

Correspondent: The Clerk, 52 Brooklands Road, Bedhampton, Havant, Hampshire PO9 3NT (tel: 07954 411852; email: info@thorngatecharity.co.uk)

🌐 www.thorngatecharity.co.uk

CC number: 210946

Eligibility

People in need who live in Gosport.

Types of grant

Grants are awarded for furniture, bedding, white goods, heating, travel expenses for hospital appointments, appliances to help maintain independence, and tools or equipment for further education and vocational courses. In the past educational grants have been made for contributions to fees for veterinary school, ballet or drama courses, and theological college.

Exclusions

The trustees cannot award grants to pay for rates or taxes.

Applications

Educational grant application forms can be downloaded from the trust's website and should be made directly to the Clerk at the above address.

Financial information

Year end	31/03/2018
Income	£9,200
Total expenditure	£15,600

Further financial information

Full accounts were not available to view on the Charity Commission's website due to the charity's low income. We have therefore estimated the grant total based on the charity's total expenditure.

Other information

Grants are also awarded to local organisations.

Sources of information

Charity Commission record; funder's website.

New Forest

Dibden Allotments Fund

 £3,300 (2017/18)

Correspondent: Valerie Stewart, Clerk to the Trustees, 7 Drummond Court, Prospect Place, Hythe, Southampton, Hampshire SO45 6HD (tel: 023 8084 1305; email: dibdenallotments@ btconnect.com)

🌐 daf-hythe.org.uk

CC number: 255778

Eligibility

People in need who have lived in the parishes of Hythe, Dibden, Marshwood or Fawley in Hampshire for at least 12 months. Priority is given to Hythe and Dibden. Support may also be given to ex-service personnel and their dependants.

Types of grant

One-off grants are awarded towards educational costs, for example educational travel.

Exclusions

The fund will not usually award a grant to someone who has previously received a grant from the fund within the last 12 months.

Applications

Application forms for general educational support can be downloaded from the fund's website. Completed forms should be submitted along with a supporting statement from a professional such as a health or social worker, midwife or teacher. Shoe vouchers provided by the charity are mainly distributed through schools and participating organisations; however, those who don't have access to either may make an application using the application form available on the fund's website. The Garden Support Scheme is designed to assist the elderly and people with disabilities to manage their essential garden work, during the growing season of March to November. Applications can be made at any time either by a letter or phone call; however, the fund encourages applications to be made during January and February. Once the application has been received, the fund will arrange a visit to discuss requirements.

Financial information

Year end	31/03/2018
Income	£339,200
Total expenditure	£398,400

Further financial information

Educational grants were made to four individuals during 2017/18.

Other information

Grants are also made to organisations.

Sources of information

Accounts; annual report; Charity Commission record; funder's website.

Winchester

The Winchester Rural District Welfare Trust

💷 £950 (2018/19)

Correspondent: The Trustees, Nutley, Manor Road, Twyford, Winchester, Hampshire SO21 3JG (tel: 07765 068556; email: winchestervillagestrust@gmail. com)

CC number: 246512

Eligibility

Residents in the Winchester rural district. This includes the parishes of Bighton, Bramdean, Compton, Headbourne Worthy and Abbot's Barton, Hursley, Itchen Valley, King's Worthy, Micheldever, Old Alresford, Owslebury, Sparsholt, Twyford, Wonston, Beauworth, Bishop's Sutton, Cheriton, Chilcomb, Crawley, Itchen Stoke and Ovington, Kilmeston, Littleton, New Alresford, Northington, Oliver's Battery and Tichborne.

Types of grant

Educational grants are awarded to students in the area of benefit for costs associated with study.

Exclusions

Grants are not made for items or services available through public funds.

Applications

Apply in writing to the correspondent.

Financial information

Year end	31/03/2019
Income	£4,600
Total expenditure	£4,200

Further financial information

Full accounts were not available to view on the Charity Commission's website due to the charity's low income. We have therefore estimated the grant total based on the charity's total expenditure.

Other information

This charity also makes grants to organisations.

Sources of information

Charity Commission record.

Kent

The Bedgebury Foundation

 £84,200 (2017/18)

Correspondent: Jane Angell-Payne, Priory Cottage, Romford Road, Pembury, Tunbridge Wells, Kent TN2 4JD (tel: 07872 464195; email: clerk@bedgeburyfoundation.org.uk)

www.thebedgeburyfoundation.org.uk

CC number: 306306

Eligibility

Young people under the age of 25 may only apply if they are resident or have undertaken their secondary education in the counties of Kent or East Sussex. This does not include London boroughs but does include the Medway towns. This geographical requirement does not apply to ex-Bedgebury School pupils and their first generation offspring or dependants (foster or kinships placements).

Types of grant

The foundation awards grants to individuals roughly equally across two programmes: **Additional Educational Needs** – learning support across the ability spectrum, from those with special educational needs to those who are gifted and talented; and **Vocational Educational and Training** – funding to improve the employment opportunities for young adults (16–25) who need a second chance to join training or further education courses that could lead to employment or self-employment. Full details of each programme can be found on the foundation's website.

Exclusions

According to the foundation's website, the trustees are unlikely to award grants for projects that are:

- Covered by the National Curriculum
- Mainstream undergraduate/postgraduate fees
- Simply travel or living expenditures unrelated to a particular need or project
- Courses designed for exam cramming
- To repay debt
- A replacement of statutory obligations
- Hardship funding

- Of no specific educational focus
- Festivals
- Easily funded elsewhere

Applications

To be eligible for a grant, applicants need to complete an online application via a grant management portal on the foundation's website.

The following will need to be provided:

- Relevant background information about yourself
- The potential benefit(s) which a grant award may make
- Referee and assessment details
- Some household information

Financial information

Year end	31/08/2018
Income	£149,300
Total expenditure	£176,200

Further financial information

A total of 61 grants were awarded to individuals during 2017/18.

Other information

The trustees also make around ten special awards each year of between £500 and £1,000 to young people between the ages of 17 and 25 who wish to undertake a voluntary role in a project either in the UK or overseas. Grants are also made to organisations.

Sources of information

Accounts; annual report; Charity Commission record; funder's website.

Dunk's and Springett's Educational Foundation

 £3,400 (2017)

Correspondent: Lisa Panting, Clerk, Fothersby, Rye Road, Hawkhurst, Kent TN18 5DB (tel: 01580 388973; email: contact form on the website)

www.dunkscharities.com

CC number: 307664

Eligibility

Children and young people under the age of 25 who live in the ancient parish of Hawkhurst and are in need.

Types of grant

The foundation's website notes that grants are made to support local young people 'in various ways, especially those of school-leaving age contemplating apprenticeships or further training'.

Applications

Contact the correspondent in the first instance. A contact form is available through the website. Alternatively, applicants can reach the correspondent by telephone, if they leave a message, the

trustees will return your call as soon as possible.

Financial information

Year end	31/12/2017
Income	£16,200
Total expenditure	£7,400

Further financial information

Full accounts were not available to view on the Charity Commission's website due to the charity's low income. We have therefore estimated the grant total based on the charity's total expenditure.

Other information

The Clerk to the trustees is responsible for both Dunk's charities. Should applicants need to contact the correspondent, it is helpful to specify that the query is for the educational foundation not the almshouses charity. The foundation's record on the Charity Commission's website indicates that organisations may also be assisted.

Sources of information

Charity Commission record; funder's website.

The Gibbon and Buckland Charity

 £23,500 (2018)

Correspondent: David Harmsworth, Trustee, Hemsted Oaks, Cranbrook Road, Benenden, Cranbrook, Kent TN17 4ES (tel: 01580 240683; email: daharmsworth@hotmail.com)

www.benendenparishcouncil.org/content/grants-young-persons-aged-16–25

CC number: 307682

Eligibility

People between the ages of 16 and 25 who have lived in Benenden for at least three years.

Types of grant

Grants are awarded to students entering further/higher education, also people starting work and apprenticeships.

Applications

Apply in writing to the correspondent.

Financial information

Year end	31/12/2018
Income	£25,000
Total expenditure	£25,800

Other information

The charity also supports Benenden Primary School and provides bibles to year six pupils in the school.

Sources of information

Accounts; annual report; Charity Commission record.

Headley-Pitt Charitable Trust

£ £16,000 (2017/18)

Correspondent: The Administrator, Old Mill Cottage, Ulley Road, Kennington, Ashford, Kent TN24 9HX (tel: 01233 626189; email: thelma.pitt7@gmail.com)

 https://headleypitt.site123.me

CC number: 252023

Eligibility
People in need who live in East Kent which comprises the district council areas of Ashford, Canterbury, Dover, Folkestone and Hythe, Maidstone, Medway Unitary Authority, Swale and Thanet.

Types of grant
Grants are awarded to assist with the costs of education.

Applications
Apply in writing to the correspondent, either by email or by post. Applications should include the name, address and contact details of the applicant (and of the beneficiary if different) as well as brief details of the amount needed, how the money would be used and any other steps to find funding that have been taken. The name and address in which the cheque should be made out to should be provided. The trustees meet once a month to consider applications will contact the applicant with a decision, although this may take several weeks.

Financial information
Year end	31/01/2018
Income	£77,700
Total expenditure	£96,400

Other information
The trust administers ten bungalows for the benefit of older people. In addition, the trust may support any charitable objects in connection with the town of Ashford in Kent as well as the Religious Society of Friends.

Sources of information
Accounts; annual report; Charity Commission record; funder's website.

Hothfield Educational Foundation

£ £2,800 (2017)

Correspondent: The Trustees, The Granary, Church Lane, Hothfield, Ashford, Kent TN26 1EN (tel: 01233 620880; email: hothfieldeducation@gmail.com)

CC number: 307670

Eligibility
Adults or children of any age who live in the parish of Hothfield.

Types of grant
Grants can be given for educational trips abroad, support for children to go on school trips or residential adventure camps and music lessons.

Applications
Apply in writing to the correspondent. Applications are considered on an ongoing basis.

Financial information
Year end	31/12/2017
Income	£8,200
Total expenditure	£12,500

Further financial information
Full accounts were not available to view on the Charity Commission's website due to the charity's low income. We have therefore estimated the grant total based on the charity's total expenditure.

Other information
Grants are also made to local organisations.

Sources of information
Charity Commission record.

Educational Foundation of James Morris

£ £2,100 (2017/18)

Correspondent: The Trustees, 4 Bybrook Field, Sandgate, Folkestone, Kent CT20 3BQ (tel: 01303 248092; email: robjhudson@ntlworld.com)

CC number: 307559

Eligibility
Young people who live within the boundaries of Sandgate on a permanent basis.

Types of grant
One-off and recurrent grants according to need.

Applications
Apply in writing to the correspondent.

Financial information
Year end	30/06/2018
Income	£3,000
Total expenditure	£2,300

Further financial information
Full accounts were not available to view on the Charity Commission's website due to the charity's low income. We have therefore estimated the grant total based on the charity's total expenditure.

Sources of information
Charity Commission record.

Southland's Educational Charity

£ £3,100 (2017/18)

Correspondent: The Trustees, c/o Town Hall, High Street, New Romney, Kent TN28 8BT (tel: 01797 362348; email: sacclerk@gmail.com)

CC number: 307783

Eligibility
Children under the age of 25 who are continuing into further education, live in the parish of New Romney and are in need.

Types of grant
One-off and recurrent grants according to need.

Applications
Apply in writing to the correspondent.

Financial information
Year end	31/03/2018
Income	£4,000
Total expenditure	£3,400

Further financial information
Full accounts were not available to view on the Charity Commission's website due to the charity's low income. We have therefore estimated the grant total based on the charity's total expenditure.

Sources of information
Charity Commission record.

The Reverend Tatton Brockman

£ £12,200 (2017/18)

Correspondent: Janet Salt, Greatfield House, Ivychurch Road, Brenzett, Romney Marsh, Kent TN29 0EE (tel: 01797 344364; email: bracken@ciarrai364.plus.com)

CC number: 307681

Eligibility
People under the age of 25 who are in full-time education and live in the ancient parishes of Brenzett, Cheriton, and Newington-next-Hythe in the county of Kent.

Types of grant
One-off and recurrent grants according to need.

Applications
Apply in writing to the correspondent.

Financial information
Year end	31/03/2018
Income	£24,300
Total expenditure	£27,100

Further financial information

Full accounts were not available to view on the Charity Commission's website due to the charity's low income. We have therefore estimated the grant total based on the charity's total expenditure.

Other information

The charity also awards payments to voluntary schools in the area to cover costs not provided by the local authority.

Sources of information

Charity Commission record.

Canterbury

The Canterbury United Municipal Charities

£ £2,600 (2018)

Correspondent: The Trustees, c/o Furley Page Solicitors, 39–40 St Margaret's Street, Canterbury, Kent CT1 2TX (tel: 01227 863140; email: aas@ furleypage.co.uk)

CC number: 210992

Eligibility

Residents in the city of Caterbury who are in need.

Types of grant

Educational grants are made to students in higher and further education towards books and equipment.

Applications

Apply in writing to the correspondent.

Financial information

Year end	31/12/2018
Income	£9,300
Total expenditure	£5,900

Further financial information

Full accounts were not available to view on the Charity Commission's website due to the charity's low income. We have therefore estimated the grant total based on the charity's total expenditure.

Sources of information

Charity Commission record.

Fordwich United Charities

£ £4,300 (2018)

Correspondent: Roger Green, Trustee, 17 Brooklands Close, Fordwich, Canterbury, Kent CT2 0BT (tel: 01227 713661 or 07981 491654; email: rogergreen@fordwich.net)

 www.fordwich.net/FUC.htm

CC number: 208258

Eligibility

People in need living in Fordwich. Educational grants are awarded to help young people under the age of 25 with their training and education after leaving school.

Types of grant

One-off and recurring grants according to need.

Applications

Applications may be made in writing to correspondent. The deadline for applications is normally 1 September and a decision should be made within a month.

Financial information

Year end	31/12/2018
Income	£14,300
Total expenditure	£19,400

Further financial information

Full accounts were not available to view on the Charity Commission's website due to the charity's low income. We have therefore estimated the grant total based on the charity's total expenditure.

Other information

The charity is also responsible for the maintenance of the Town Hall.

Sources of information

Charity Commission record; funder's website.

Streynsham's Charity

£ £1,900 (2018)

Correspondent: Clerk to the Trustees, PO Box 970, Canterbury, Kent CT1 9DJ (tel: 0845 094 4769)

CC number: 214436

Eligibility

People who live in the ancient parish of St Dunstan's in Canterbury.

Types of grant

Grants to assist students with further or higher education fees.

Applications

Apply in writing to the correspondent.

Financial information

Year end	31/12/2018
Income	£76,700
Total expenditure	£73,200

Other information

The charity also makes grants to organisations.

Sources of information

Accounts; annual report; Charity Commission record.

Maidstone

Yalding Educational Foundation

£ £4,000 (2017/18)

Correspondent: The Trustees, Hawthorns, Laddingford, Yalding, Maidstone, Kent ME18 6BP (tel: 01622 873140; email: garyejsa@hotmail.com)

CC number: 307646

Eligibility

Children and young people who live in, or are educated in, the parishes of Yalding and Collier Street. Former pupils of local primary schools are also eligible for support.

Types of grant

Grants, awards and prizes are given to young people in schools or further education to support their studies.

Applications

Apply in writing to the correspondent.

Financial information

Year end	28/02/2018
Income	£8,100
Total expenditure	£8,800

Further financial information

Full accounts were not available to view on the Charity Commission's website due to the charity's low income. We have therefore estimated the grant total based on the charity's total expenditure.

Other information

This charity makes grants to organisations, particularly local schools. The charity also sponsors a spoken English competition in local primary schools.

Sources of information

Charity Commission record.

Medway

Arthur Ingram Trust

£ £79,100 (2017/18)

Correspondent: The Trustees, Medway Council, Gun Wharf, Dock Road, Chatham ME4 4TR (tel: 01634 332319; email: robin.baker@medway.gov.uk)

CC number: 212868

Eligibility

Young people in need between the ages of 14 and 20 who are in full-time education, live in the Medway council area and are on a low income/from a low-income family.

Types of grant

The 2017/18 annual report states that educational grants are provided for the following purposes:

- 'To families with young people in further education (or to independent students where they have no family)'
- 'For specialist equipment needed for training in a profession'

Applications

Application forms can be requested from the correspondent.

Financial information

Year end	31/03/2018
Income	£77,800
Total expenditure	£113,700

Further financial information

According to the 2017/18 annual report, educational grants were distributed as follows:

Bursary grants	34	£75,000
Continuing education	10	£4,000

According to the 2017/18 annual report, welfare grants were awarded to parents of schoolchildren for uniforms.

Other information

Grants were awarded to organisations for school field trips and school equipment/books.

Sources of information

Accounts; annual report; Charity Commission record.

Richard Watts and the City of Rochester Almshouse Charities

 £5,500 (2018)

Correspondent: Jane Rose, Clerk and Chief Officer, Administrative Offices, Watts Almshouses, Maidstone Road, Rochester, Kent ME1 1SE (tel: 01634 842194; email: admin@richardwatts.org. uk)

www.richardwatts.org.uk

CC number: 212828

Eligibility

Educational grants are available to support residents within the postcode areas of ME1 and Me2. Trade apprentices under the age of 25 are also eligible for support.

Types of grant

Educational grants are awarded for costs associated with education and training. Apprenticeship grants are made to cover the cost of tools, protective clothing, equipment, travel costs and any additional study costs.

Applications

Application forms are available to download from the funder's website. For full guidelines for each grant scheme, see the charity's website.

Financial information

Year end	31/12/2018
Income	£1,380,000
Total expenditure	£1,310,000

Further financial information

Note: the grant total has been estimated.

Other information

The charity operates and maintains almshouses, which are available to occupants who are aged 65 and over, and who are 'in reasonable health'. The charity also operates a subsidised home help service for older residents in the area of benefit. The service can provide help with general housework, taking out rubbish, shopping, personal paperwork, making telephone calls and so on. A lawn cutting service is also provided by the charity, designed for older people or people with disabilities who are unable to cut their lawn themselves.

Sources of information

Accounts; annual report; Charity Commission record; funder's website.

Swale

The William Barrow's Charity

 £51,000 (2018)

Correspondent: Stuart Mair, Clerk to the Trustees, c/o George Webb Finn, 43 Park Road, Sittingbourne, Kent ME10 1DY (tel: 01795 470556; email: stuart@georgewebbfinn.com)

www.thewilliambarrowscharity.org. uk

CC number: 307574

Eligibility

Students under the age of 25 who live in the parish of Borden, Kent and are in full-time education. Priority is given to students entering tertiary education.

Types of grant

Scholarships and bursaries are given to assist students undertaking further education and can be used towards books, travel, living expenses and so on.

Applications

Applications can be made through the charity's website.

Applications can be made through the charity's website. Those who have previously received a grant from the charity may apply to renew their educational grant. Applicants must

provide their exam results and confirmation of acceptance at a college/ university. Applications should be submitted before the end of August prior to the academic year, consult the website for current deadlines.

Financial information

Year end	31/12/2018
Income	£293,100
Total expenditure	£357,300

Further financial information

In 2018 £70,500 was awarded to individuals for welfare purposes including 13 older people and six people with disabilities. Educational grants were awarded to 34 higher/further education students totalling £51,000.

Other information

The charity also provides grants to local schools and organisations.

Sources of information

Accounts; annual report; Charity Commission record; funder's website.

Oxfordshire

Bakehouse or Shepherd's Charity

 £4,700 (2017/18)

Correspondent: The Trustees, Barn Elms, The Green, Barford St Michael, Banbury, Oxfordshire OX15 0RN (tel: 01869 338937; email: carole. coppin@hotmail.co.uk)

CC number: 309173

Eligibility

Young people under the age of 25 who (or whose parents) have lived in the parish of Barford St John or Barford St Michael for at least three years.

Types of grant

Financial assistance for undertaking apprenticeships; clothes for employment; fees and expenses for advancement of education; and scholarships, grants and maintenance allowances tenable at any secondary school, further education college or university.

Exclusions

Our research indicates that provisions are not made for primary schoolchildren.

Applications

Apply in writing to the correspondent.

Financial information

Year end	30/09/2018
Income	£4,300
Total expenditure	£5,200

Further financial information

Full accounts were not available to view on the Charity Commission's website due to the charity's low income. We have therefore estimated the grant total based on the charity's total expenditure.

Sources of information

Charity Commission record.

Bartholomew Educational Foundation

 £4,300 (2018)

Correspondent: The Trustees, 20 High Street, Eynsham, Witney, Oxfordshire OX29 4HB (tel: 01865 880665; email: eynshamcharities@gmail.com)

eynsham-pc.gov.uk/org.aspx?n=
Bartholomew-Educational-
Foundation

CC number: 309278

Eligibility

People under the age of 25 who live in the parish of Eynsham.

Types of grant

Grants of up to £3,000 are available towards educational travel abroad; study of music and other arts; the cost of tools, equipment/instruments, books and clothing to students, apprentices and trainees; to schoolchildren and university/college students for general educational needs.

Applications

Applications should be made in writing to the correspondents. The trustees meet four times per year in February, May, August/September, and November. To be considered, applications must be received the month before the next meeting.

Financial information

Year end	31/12/2018
Income	£3,700
Total expenditure	£4,800

Further financial information

Grants were awarded to 15 individuals during 2018.

Other information

Local educational bodies can also be supported, after the needs of individuals have been met.

Sources of information

Accounts; annual report; Charity Commission record.

The Exuberant Trust

 £3,900 (2018)

Correspondent: The Trustees, 11 St Margaret's Road, Oxford, Oxfordshire OX2 6RU (tel: 01865 751056; email: admin@exuberant-trust.org.uk)

www.exuberant-trust.org.uk

CC number: 1095911

Eligibility

People up to the age of 30 who are from Oxfordshire and are developing their interest in the arts (music, drama, dance, arts and crafts, jewellery, multimedia and so on). Preference is given for first-time applicants.

Types of grant

One-off grants of up to a maximum of £500 for a specific project or activity. These awards can be made for tools, training, music lessons, general costs, instruments, music events, venue hire and any other associated costs of the project.

Applications

The application form and guidelines can be downloaded from the trust's website. Applicants should give convincing reasons for applying and should include appropriate references and a budget proposal. When fully completed, applications must be sent by post and also by email to the correspondent. Full details are available on the website.

Financial information

Year end	31/12/2018
Income	£4,000
Total expenditure	£4,300

Further financial information

Full accounts were not available to view on the Charity Commission's website due to the charity's low income. We have therefore estimated the grant total based on the charity's total expenditure.

Other information

The trust's website states that it 'raises funds by organising concerts throughout the year and from donations received from its supporters' and notes that 'successful applicants are encouraged to take part in concerts and other activities in support of the trust'.

Sources of information

Charity Commission record; funder's website.

The Hope Ffennell Trust

 £2,700 (2017)

Correspondent: The Trustees, Church End, Wytham Abbey, Wytham, Oxfordshire OX2 8QE (tel: 01865 203475)

CC number: 309212

Eligibility

People under the age of 25 who live in the parishes of Wytham and North Hinksey.

Types of grant

One-off and recurrent grants according to need.

Applications

Apply in writing to the correspondent.

Financial information

Year end	31/12/2017
Income	£7,100
Total expenditure	£5,900

Further financial information

Full accounts were not available to view on the Charity Commission's website due to the charity's low income. We have therefore estimated the grant total based on the charity's total expenditure.

Other information

Grants are also awarded to organisations.

Sources of information

Charity Commission record.

The Kathryn Turner Trust (Whitton's Wishes)

 £10,100 (2018)

Correspondent: The Trustees, Unit 3, Suffolk Way, Abingdon, Oxfordshire OX14 5JX (tel: 01235 527310; email: kathrynturnertrust@hotmail.co.uk)

CC number: 1111250

Eligibility

Children and young people, older people and individuals with disabilities. Members of the Royal Navy, Army, Royal Air Force, and their dependants are also supported.

Types of grant

Grants are awarded to provide support according to need and towards equipment and educational costs.

Applications

Apply in writing to the correspondent. The trustees meet every three months.

Financial information

Year end	31/12/2018
Income	£180,800
Total expenditure	£175,900

Further financial information

We estimate that in 2018, around £20,200 was awarded to individuals with £10,100 awarded to individuals for welfare purposes and £10,100 for educational purposes.

Other information

Grants are also provided to organisations.

Sources of information

Accounts; annual report; Charity Commission record.

Cherwell

Banbury Charities

 £26,700 (2018)

Correspondent: Mr N. Yeadon, Clerk to the Trustees, 36 West Bar, Banbury, Oxfordshire OX16 9RU (tel: 01295 251234)

https://banburycharities.co.uk

CC number: 201418

Eligibility

People living within a five-mile radius of Banbury Cross (or a ten-mile radius in the case of Banbury Poor Trust grant) who are in need.

Types of grant

Educational grants are made for a range of needs, including for books and equipment. Specific grant schemes are available for apprentices and those studying STEM subjects, or subjects involving literature and the arts. For full details, see the funder's website.

Applications

Apply in writing to the correspondent.

Financial information

Year end	31/12/2018
Income	£948,800
Total expenditure	£328,900

Further financial information

The charity awarded grants to 179 individuals for welfare and educational purposes.

Other information

Banbury Charities is a group of eight registered charities, comprised of the following: Bridge Estate Charity; Countess of Arran's Charity; Banbury Arts and Educational Charity; Banbury Almshouses Charity; Banbury Sick Poor Fund; Banbury Welfare Trust; Banbury Poor Trust; and Banbury Recreation Charity. One of the objectives of the

Banbury Charities is to provide and maintain almshouses accommodation for people in financial need.

Sources of information

Accounts; annual report; Charity Commission record; funder's website.

Oxford

The City of Oxford Charity

 £10,100 (2018)

Correspondent: Grants Administrator, The Office, Stones Court, St Clements, Oxford, Oxfordshire OX14 1AP (tel: 01865 247161; email: enquiries@ oxfordcitycharity.org.uk)

https://www.oxfordcitycharity.org. uk

CC number: 1172230–1

Eligibility

Educational grants are available to young residents in the city of Oxford who are under the age of 25. Applicants must have lived in the city for a minimum of three years.

Types of grant

Educational grants are made to students in any level of education, including higher and further education. Grants have been awarded towards the cost of books, material and equipment for college and undergraduate students. Student can also apply for grants to help cover the cost of a bus pass for travel to and from their place of education.

Exclusions

Grants are not given to residents who are in the city solely for the purpose of education (i.e. students at one of Oxford's universities or colleges.) The charity does not normally award funding to those studying beyond a first degree.

Applications

Application forms are available to download from the funder's website. For welfare grants, all applications must include a letter of support from a third party such as a social worker, health visitor or advice agencies/organisations active within the community.

Financial information

Year end	31/12/2018
Income	£404,100
Total expenditure	£303,200

Further financial information

During 2018, the charity awarded 35 educational grants. Note: the grant total for **education** has been estimated.

Other information

The charity is an amalgamation of several ancient charities working for the benefit of the people of Oxford city. The charity owns and operates almshouses at Stone's Court in St Clements, which are available to residents in the city who are in need. Preference is given to older residents.

Sources of information

Accounts; annual report; Charity Commission record; funder's website.

Vale of White Horse

Faringdon United Charities

 £1,800 (2017/18)

Correspondent: Vivienne Checkley, c/o Bunting & Co., Brunel House, Volunteer Way, Faringdon, Oxfordshire SN7 7YR (tel: 01367 243789; email: vivienne. checkley@buntingaccountants.co.uk)

faringdonunitedcharities.co.uk

CC number: 237040

Eligibility

People who are in need and live in the parishes of Great Faringdon, Littleworth or Little Coxwell, in Oxfordshire.

Types of grant

Grants are awarded towards education.

Applications

Applications can be downloaded from the charity's website and can be submitted directly by the individual or by a healthcare professional or third party on behalf of an individual. The charity aims to be in contact within 48 hours.

Financial information

Year end	31/03/2018
Income	£33,700
Total expenditure	£16,200

Other information

The charity also supports organisations and groups.

Sources of information

Accounts; annual report; Charity Commission record; funder's website.

West Oxfordshire

The Bampton Exhibition Foundation

 £2,700 (2017/18)

Correspondent: Bursary Administrator, 2 Castle Mews, Bridge Street, Bampton, Oxfordshire OX18 2HA

https://www.astonoxon.com/bampton-exhibition-foundation.html

CC number: 309238

Eligibility

People under the age of 25 who live in Bampton, Aston, Cote, Weald or Lew and are in need.

Types of grant

Financial support is given for the participation in any academic or sporting course or activity of educational value which would otherwise be beyond means.

Applications

Apply in writing to the correspondent.

Financial information

Year end	31/03/2018
Income	£9,600
Total expenditure	£27,400

Further financial information

Full accounts were not available to view on the Charity Commission's website due to the charity's low income. We have therefore estimated the grant total based on the charity's total expenditure.

Other information

The foundation also spends some of its income on a listed building used as a community library and historical archive.

Sources of information

Charity Commission record; funder's website.

The Burford Relief-in-Need Charity

 £3,400 (2018)

Correspondent: The Trustees, Whitehill Farm, Burford, Oxfordshire OX18 4DT (tel: 01993 822894)

CC number: 1036378

Eligibility

People living within a seven-mile radius of The Tolsey in Burford, who are in need.

Types of grant

One-off and recurring grants according to need.

Applications

Apply in writing to the correspondent.

Financial information

Year end	31/12/2018
Income	£14,200
Total expenditure	£7,500

Further financial information

Full accounts were not available to view on the Charity Commission's website due to the charity's low income. We have therefore estimated the grant total based on the charity's total expenditure.

Sources of information

Charity Commission record.

Charlbury Exhibition Foundation

 £13,600 (2017/18)

Correspondent: The Trustees, Took House, Sheep Street, Charlbury, Chipping Norton OX7 3RR (tel: 01608 810793)

CC number: 309236

Eligibility

Young people aged between 16 and 24, who live in Charlbury and have a guaranteed or continuing place for a University or College course or an apprenticeship.

Types of grant

Recurrent grants for up to three years for costs associated with education.

Applications

According to the foundation's website, applications must be emailed to the correspondent and detail the following:

- Your name and date of birth
- Schools you have attended
- The University or College name (or your employer for apprentices)
- The course and level (e.g. BA) and your year of study (or for apprentices, the type of apprenticeship and level)
- Your home address in Charlbury

Financial information

Year end	30/09/2018
Income	£13,500
Total expenditure	£15,100

Further financial information

Full accounts were not available to view on the Charity Commission's website due to the charity's low income. We have therefore estimated the grant total based on the charity's total expenditure.

Other information

The foundation owns a property and a field in Charlbury, Oxfordshire and uses the rental income from these assets to award grants.

Sources of information

Charity Commission record; funder's website.

Surrey

Humphrey Richardson Taylor Charitable Trust

 £37,900 (2017)

Correspondent: Mrs K. Perry, Administrator, c/o Palmers, 28 Chipstead Station Parade, Chipstead, Coulsdon, Surrey CR5 3TF (tel: 01737 557546; email: hrtaylortrust@btconnect.com)

 www.hrtaylortrust.org.uk

CC number: 1062836

Eligibility

Children and young adults with exceptional musical talent who live in Surrey, or have a strong link to Surrey.

Types of grant

Grants are available towards music-related undergraduate or postgraduate studies, tuition fees and the purchase of instruments.

Exclusions

UK citizens only. The trust will not fund courses at foreign universities.

Applications

Applications can be made by email and should be no longer than four to six A4 pages when printed. Full details of what should be included can be found on the trust's website.

Financial information

Year end	31/12/2017
Income	£558,900
Total expenditure	£510,000

Further financial information

In 2017, grants totalling £22,800 was awarded for scholarships and tuition fees, £15,100 was awarded for the purchase of instruments.

Other information

The trust also supports schools and music societies/organisations.

Sources of information

Accounts; annual report; Charity Commission record; funder's website.

Epsom and Ewell

Epsom Parochial Charities (Epsom Almshouse Charity)

Correspondent: The Trustees, Farm View Suite, 42 Canons lane, Burgh Heath, Tadworth, Surrey KT20 6DP (tel: 01737 361243; email: vanstonewalker@ntlworld.com)

CC number: 200571

Eligibility

People under the age of 25 who live in the ancient parish of Epsom and are undertaking education.

Types of grant

The Advancement in Life Charity provides financial assistance towards education.

Applications

Apply in writing to the correspondent.

Financial information

Year end	31/12/2018
Income	£87,300
Total expenditure	£118,600

Further financial information

We estimate that in 2018 a total of £3,300 was awarded to nine individuals through the Relief in Need Charity. No awards were given through the Advancement in Life Charity in 2018; however, in recent years grants have totalled up to £6,900.

Other information

The charity also manages a number of almshouses.

Sources of information

Accounts; annual report; Charity Commission record.

Guildford

The Archbishop Abbot's Exhibition Foundation

 £5,600 (2017)

Correspondent: The Trustees, 17 Ashdale, Great Bookham, Surrey KT23 4QP (tel: 01483 302345; email: grants@aaef.org.uk)

 aaef.org.uk

CC number: 311890

Eligibility

People aged between 11 and 28 who live, or attend school, in the boroughs of Guildford or Waverley in Surrey.

Types of grant

Grants of £50 to £1,250 are available and can be made on a single or recurrent basis (recurrent grants must be re-applied for).

Applications

First-time applicants or those applying on behalf of another individual must first complete the quick application form available on the foundation's website. The quick application will be assessed, and if the applicant is successful, they will be required to complete the full application and provide a parent/guardian form, both available on the website.

Financial information

Year end	31/12/2017
Income	£6,600
Total expenditure	£6,200

Further financial information

Full accounts were not available to view on the Charity Commission's website due to the charity's low income. We have therefore estimated the grant total based on the charity's total expenditure.

Sources of information

Charity Commission record; funder's website.

Ted Adams Trust Ltd

 £23,000 (2017/18)

Correspondent: Rosie Stables, Administrator, 208 High Street, Guildford, Surrey GU1 3JB (email: tedadamstrust@live.co.uk)

 www.tedadamstrust.org.uk

CC number: 1104538

Eligibility

Students of nursing and midwifery and post-registration nurses and midwives who are working or attending courses in the Guildford area. Nursing service managers are also eligible to apply for funding towards course fees or costs to further their professional education and development. The trust is particularly keen to support individuals whose study outcomes of will enhance patient care in the local area.

Types of grant

Grants are available to fund course fees and other costs to enable nurses and midwives to further their professional education. Scholarships of £3,000 in each year of study are available for mature students who wish to study mental health, children's nursing or midwifery at the University of Surrey. Details of applicable courses and eligibility can be found on the trust's website. Funding can also be given to post-registration nurses to undertake further study and professional development, including in-house training events, lectures, specialist qualifications, conferences and study days.

Exclusions

The trust does not offer support towards living expenses, childcare or debts.

Applications

Application forms for each different type of grant can be downloaded from the trust's website and, once completed, should be returned to the relevant email address, details of which can be found of the website. Funds for scholarships will usually be paid during the first semester. Grants are usually paid through electronic transfer. Consult the website for further guidelines and current deadlines.

Financial information

Year end	31/07/2018
Income	£158,800
Total expenditure	£101,000

Other information

The trust also makes awards to final year undergraduate students at the University of Surrey who have displayed outstanding performance on their Practice Assessment Document and clinical performance. The trust runs an accommodation house for students of nursing and midwifery.

Sources of information

Accounts; annual report; Charity Commission record; funder's website.

Mole Valley

John Bristow and Thomas Mason Trust

 £2,600 (2017/18)

Correspondent: Sam Songhurst, Trust Secretary, Beech Hay, Ifield Road, Charlwood, Surrey RH6 0DR (tel: 01293 862734; email: trust.secretary@jbtmt.org.uk)

 www.jbtmt.org.uk

CC number: 1075971

Eligibility

People in need living in the ancient parish of Charlwood as constituted in 1926. This includes Hookwood and Lowfield Heath. A map of the area of benefit can be found on the trust's website.

Types of grant

Educational grants are awarded to young people to help with costs associated with further education.

Welfare grants are also awarded according to need.

Applications
Applications can be made using an online form featured on the trust's website. Alternatively, applicants may wish to download a copy of the application form which, once completed, can be sent to the Trust Secretary at their postal address. The trustees meet every alternate month to consider grant applications. For dates of upcoming meetings, see the website.

Financial information
Year end	30/09/2018
Income	£93,100
Total expenditure	£127,800

Further financial information
During 2017/18, educational grants were awarded to three individuals. No applications were received for welfare grants.

Other information
The trust also supports schools, churches, and the overall improvement of the area of benefit.

Sources of information
Accounts; annual report; Charity Commission record; funder's website.

Reigate and Banstead

Mary Stephens Foundation

£ £9,200 (2017/18)

Correspondent: John Stephenson, Trustee, Mornington, 11B Holly Hill Drive, Banstead, Surrey SM7 2BD (tel: 01737 556548; email: john.stephenson24@gmail.com or marystephensfoundation@talktalk.net)

CC number: 311999

Eligibility
People under the age of 25 who live, or whose parents live, in the ancient parish of Chipstead, which includes Hooley and Netherne.

Types of grant
One-off and recurrent grants of up to a maximum of £1,200 a year. Assistance can be given towards purposes such as books, equipment, uniforms and school trips. Three-year scholarships may also be awarded to those in higher education, towards the costs of accommodation, study materials and field trips.

Exclusions
The foundation does not award grants to pre-schoolchildren or provide loans.

Applications
Application forms can be requested from the correspondent. They are considered at quarterly meetings and should be made directly by the individual, or by the individual's head of school or church leader.

Financial information
Year end	31/03/2018
Income	£7,600
Total expenditure	£10,200

Further financial information
Full accounts were not available to view on the Charity Commission's website due to the charity's low income. We have therefore estimated the grant total based on the charity's total expenditure.

Sources of information
Charity Commission record.

Waverley

The Archbishop Abbot's Exhibition Foundation
See record on page 246

West Sussex

The Blatchington Court Trust (BCT)
See record on page 234

Betty Martin Charity

£ £2,400 (2017/18)

Correspondent: Madeleine Crisp, Clerk, 46 Guillards Oak, Midhurst, West Sussex GU29 9JZ (tel: 01730 813769)

CC number: 1029337

Eligibility
Young people who live in West Sussex, with a preference for those who live within a 15-mile radius of the parish church in Midhurst. Preference may also be given to young people with disabilities.

Types of grant
Grants are awarded towards a range of educational costs including course fees, travel expenses, maintenance for those undertaking apprenticeships, books, tools and so on.

Applications
Apply in writing to the correspondent either by email or by post.

Financial information
Year end	30/09/2018
Income	£22,400
Total expenditure	£15,600

Further financial information
In 2017/18 a total of £2,400 was awarded to individuals for educational purposes.

Sources of information
Accounts; annual report; Charity Commission record; Disability Grants website.

Arun

William Older's School Charity

£ £7,400 (2018)

Correspondent: The Trustees, Parish Office, Church House, Arundel Road, Angmering, Littlehampton, West Sussex BN16 4JS (tel: 01903 784459)

CC number: 306424

Eligibility
Children and young people who live in the ecclesiastical parish of Angmering.

Types of grant
One-off grants according to need.

Applications
Apply in writing to the correspondent.

Financial information
Year end	31/12/2018
Income	£18,200
Total expenditure	£16,400

Further financial information
Full accounts were not available to view on the Charity Commission's website due to the charity's low income. We have therefore estimated the grant total based on the charity's total expenditure.

Other information
Grants can also be made to organisations.

Sources of information
Charity Commission record.

South West

General

The Christina Aitchison Trust

£ £520 (2017/18)

Correspondent: The Trustees, The Old Post Office, The Street, West Raynham, Fakenham, Norfolk NR21 7AD

CC number: 1041578

Eligibility
Educational grants are made to young people under the age of 25, who live in North East or South West England.

Types of grant
One-off and recurring grants according to need.

Applications
Apply in writing to the correspondent.

Financial information

Year end	05/04/2018
Income	£2,100
Total expenditure	£2,300

Further financial information
Full accounts were not available to view on the Charity Commission's website due to the charity's low income. We have therefore estimated the grant total based on the charity's total expenditure.

Other information
The charity also makes grants to organisations to promote research into ophthalmic diseases and to support the education in and appreciation of the arts, science and music.

Sources of information
Charity Commission record.

The Dairy Crest and National Farmers' Union Scholarship Fund

£ £19,400 (2017/18)

Correspondent: Donna Evans, Administrator, Park Farm, Dunkeswell,

Honiton, Devon EX14 4RN (tel: 01823 680968; email: westcountrydairyawards@gmail.com)

 https://www.afcp.org.uk/node/66

CC number: 306598

Eligibility
Students who, according to the charity's website, can 'demonstrate commitment to the dairy industry and show aptitude to 'add value' to the industry' and are undertaking further education courses related to the diary industry are eligible to apply. This includes sons and daughters of farmers or farm employees. Applicants must live in Cornwall, Devon, Dorset or Somerset.

Types of grant
The fund distributes over £15,000 every year. All qualifying applicants receive 'some' funding and the best four receive between £1,000 and £2,000 each.

Applications
Application forms can be downloaded from the charity's website. A leaflet containing further information about the fund can also be found on the website.

Financial information

Year end	31/03/2018
Income	£19,400
Total expenditure	£21,500

Further financial information
Full accounts were not available to view on the Charity Commission's website due to the charity's low income. We have therefore estimated the grant total based on the charity's total expenditure.

Other information
From time to time funds are available for postgraduate scholarships in dairy science. Contact the administrator for more details.

Sources of information
Charity Commission record; funder's website.

The Elmgrant Trust

£ £4,800 (2018/19)

Correspondent: Mrs A. Critchlow Horning, Secretary, Elmhirst Centre, Dartington Hall, Totnes, Devon TQ9 6EL (tel: 01803 863160; email: info@elmgrant.org.uk)

 www.elmgrant.org.uk

CC number: 313398

Eligibility
People living in south west England.

Types of grant
The trust's website states that it funds 'individuals who are further educating themselves to improve their job prospects with a clear compassionate need'.

Exclusions
The trustees will not provide support towards the following:
- Postgraduate study or related expenses
- Second and subsequent degrees
- Overseas student grants
- Expeditions, travel and study projects overseas
- Training in counselling courses

Grants will not be given to organisations or individuals who have already received a grant from the trust within the previous two years. Research is rarely funded and support cannot be given retrospectively.

Applications
Applications can be made in writing to the correspondent. All applications need to be posted; the trust does not accept emailed applications. Application letters should provide the following details:
- Full contact details (name, address, email address, phone number, etc.)
- For students – evidence of your attendance or course place
- Full list of items required, including costs
- Evidence of your financial status and why funding is needed – receipt of benefits, low income, etc. (all information is confidential)

- Letters of support from a professional person who knows the applicant, for example a tutor, GP, employer or social worker
- If a medical condition is part of the application – evidence from the medical professional

The trust's website states:

We aim to respond to every application we receive with a decision of being short-listed or not within 6 weeks. The Trustees decision is final and we do not usually enter into further correspondence.

All short-listed applicants will be emailed just after the application deadline which is one calendar month before the Trustees Meeting, indicating whether or not their application will go forward to the meeting or not. At this point we will ask applicants to confirm that there are no changes to their application or that full funding has been achieved already.

After the Trustees Meeting we aim to contact all applicants with the outcome of their application, and if successful post a cheque out, within 3 weeks of the Meeting. Grants for courses and fees will normally be paid to the course provider.

The trustees meet three times a year usually on the last Saturday of February, June and October. It is crucial to submit the application at least one month prior to the meeting.

Financial information

Year end	31/03/2019
Income	£281,400
Total expenditure	£119,400

Further financial information

In 2018/19 grants were paid to 20 individuals.

Other information

The trust also supports organisations, groups and educational establishments, with strong preference for those in the south west.

Sources of information

Accounts; annual report; Charity Commission record; funder's website.

The Royal Bath and West of England Society

 £7,000 (2018)

Correspondent: Paul Hooper, Company Secretary, The Bath and West Showground, Shepton Mallett, Somerset BA4 6QN (tel: 01749 822205; email: paul.hooper@bathandwest.co.uk)

www.bathandwestsociety.com

CC number: 1039397

Eligibility

Artists between the ages of 21 and 30 living in the south west area, who are inspired by 'rural life in the UK', and young people under the age of 16. Under-16 applicants must reside in one of the following areas: Somerset, Dorset, Devon, Wiltshire, Gloucestershire or Bristol.

Types of grant

Scholarships and grants are awarded towards courses and projects that promote agriculture and rural economy. Previously support has been given to individuals attending agricultural colleges, veterinary schools, livestock photography courses, forestry courses, undertaking an NVQ and so on. Applications for PhDs and second degrees will be considered.

Applications

Application forms for the art scholarship are available on the society's website. Under-16 applicants should contact the correspondent to apply.

Contact the correspondent for further information and to request an application form. The deadline for scholarship and grant applications falls on 1 June each year. Further information can be found on the society's website.

Financial information

Year end	31/12/2018
Income	£3,680,000
Total expenditure	£3,490,000

Further financial information

We estimate that around £16,000 was awarded to individuals in 2018. Within this, we estimate that £9,000 was awarded to individuals for welfare purposes and a further £7,000 was awarded for educational purposes.

Other information

The society aims to promote agriculture and rural economy through seminars, conferences, open days and so on. In addition, the society administers a range of events and awards for both organisations and individuals. The society sponsors the West Country Dairy Awards which offer support to individuals undertaking further education courses related to the dairy industry.

Sources of information

Accounts; annual report; Charity Commission record; funder's website.

Sarum St Michael Educational Charity

 £82,600 (2017)

Correspondent: Clerk to the Governors, First Floor, 27A Castle Street, Salisbury, Wiltshire SP1 1TT (tel: 01722 422296 (Monday to Thursday mornings); email: clerk@sarumstmichael.org)

 www.sarumstmichael.org

CC number: 309456

Eligibility

People over the age of 16 who live or study in the diocese of Salisbury or adjoining dioceses, including Bath and Wells, Exeter, Oxford and Winchester (for exact geographical area see the map on the charity's website).

Types of grant

Grants are available to those studying for first degrees (including mature students), diplomas, access courses, Open University courses, vocational courses, postgraduate degrees, gap-year activities and projects. Support can be given towards general educational expenses, including fees, necessities, books, equipment, travel, dissertation expenses and so on. The charity also provides teaching bursaries for students who are intending to become teachers of religious education.

Exclusions

The charity will not:
- Make retrospective grants
- Contribute towards maintenance (unless an integral part of a residential course)
- Pay money for buildings, fixtures or fittings

Grants for people attending educational establishments are continued only if the applicant remains at that establishment.

Applications

Application forms can be obtained from the charity's website. Grants are considered 4–5 times a year, normally in January, March, June, August and October. Exact dates of the meetings are available online. Applications can be submitted directly by individuals, preferably by email.

Financial information

Year end	31/12/2017
Income	£218,900
Total expenditure	£223,800

Other information

The charity also makes grants to schools and local parish councils.

Sources of information

Accounts; annual report; Charity Commission record; funder's website.

Bristol

Christ Church Exhibition Fund

(£) £5,700 (2018)

Correspondent: The Trustees, 1 All Saints Court, Bristol BS1 1JN (tel: 0117 929 2709; email: ascl.charity@btconnect.com)

CC number: 325124

Eligibility
Students in higher/further education who have attended school in the city and county borough of Bristol, with a preference for those who have lived in the ecclesiastical parish of Christ Church with St Ewen for at least two years.

Types of grant
Grants are available for students at university or other further education institutions.

Applications
Apply in writing to the correspondent.

Financial information
Year end	31/12/2018
Income	£19,500
Total expenditure	£12,700

Further financial information
Full accounts were not available to view on the Charity Commission's website due to the charity's low income. We have therefore estimated the grant total based on the charity's total expenditure.

Other information
The charity provides funding towards the running of a Sunday school in St Ewen. The fund also supports the education of choristers of the parish church of Christ Church with St Ewen.

Sources of information
Charity Commission record.

Edmonds and Coles Scholarships (Edmonds and Coles Charity)

(£) £2,500 (2018/19)

Correspondent: The Trustees, The Society of Merchant Venturers, Merchants' Hall, The Promenade, Clifton Down, Bristol BS8 3NH (tel: 0117 973 8058; email: treasurer@merchantventurers.com)

 www.merchantventurers.com/what-we-do/charitable-giving

CC number: 311751

Eligibility
People in need who are under the age of 25 and live in the area of benefit, which includes: Aust, Avonmouth, Bishopston, Brentry, Charlton Mead, Coombe Dingle, Cotham, Durdham Down, Hallen, Henbury, Henleaze, Horfield, Kingsweston, Kingsdown, Lawrence Weston, New Passage, Northwick, Pilning, Redland, Redwick, Sea Mills, Severn Beach, Shirehampton, Southmead, Stoke Bishop, Tyndalls Park, Westbury-on-Trym, Westbury Park and Woolcott Park.

Types of grant
Grants towards general educational expenses, including the cost of books, equipment/instruments or travel. Support can be given to people at school, college/university, or those undertaking vocational training.

Exclusions
At primary and secondary school level, grants are not normally given to enable children to enter private education when parents cannot afford the cost. Help may, however, be given in respect of children already in private education.

Applications
Application forms are available from the charity's website or the correspondent. They can be submitted by the individual or, if the applicant is under the age of 16, a third party. Grants are usually considered in February, July and September.

Financial information
Year end	31/08/2019
Income	£12,400
Total expenditure	£5,400

Further financial information
Full accounts were not available to view on the Charity Commission's website due to the charity's low income. We have therefore estimated the grant total based on the charity's total expenditure.

Other information
Our research shows that this charity consults and co-operates with Bristol Municipal Charities in some cases.

Sources of information
Charity Commission record.

Anthony Edmonds Charity

(£) £2,300 (2017/18)

Correspondent: Fran Greenfield, Clerk, 43 Meadowland Road, Bristol BS10 7PW (tel: 0117 909 8308; email: fran.greenfield@blueyonder.co.uk)

 www.edmondscharity.org.uk

CC number: 286709

Eligibility
Young people up to the age of 25 who live in any of the ancient parishes of Henbury, Westbury and Horfield.

Types of grant
Grants to help with activities of a broadly educational nature including apprentices and courses.

Applications
Apply on a form available from the correspondent, to be submitted directly by the individual. Application forms can be downloaded from the charity's website or contact the Clerk for a hard copy. The trustees meet to consider applications in March and September.

Financial information
Year end	30/09/2018
Income	£8,900
Total expenditure	£5,500

Further financial information
Full accounts were not available to view on the Charity Commission's website due to the charity's low income. We have therefore estimated the grant total based on the charity's total expenditure.

Sources of information
Charity Commission record; funder's website.

The Stokes Croft Educational Foundation

(£) £13,700 (2018)

Correspondent: Frances Webster, Secretary, 120 Badger Road, Thornbury, Bristol BS35 1AD (email: scefbristol@live.com)

CC number: 311672

Eligibility
People of any age who reside in Bristol.

Types of grant
Grants are awarded for maintenance allowances, overseas travel, books, clothing, and equipment/instruments for beneficiaries looking to enter a particular profession, trade or calling.

Applications
Apply in writing to the correspondent.

Financial information
Year end	31/12/2018
Income	£61,600
Total expenditure	£56,000

Other information
The foundation's high expenditure in 2018 is due to the purchase of investments.

Sources of information
Accounts; annual report; Charity Commission record.

Cornwall

Blanchminster Trust

 £295,000 (2018)

Correspondent: Jane Bunning, Clerk to the Trustees, Blanchminster Building, 38 Lansdown Road, Bude, Cornwall EX23 8BN (tel: 01288 352851; email: office@blanchminster.plus.com)

https://blanchminster.wordpress.com

CC number: 202118

Eligibility
Educational grants are awarded to people in need who live in, or who have one parent residing in, the beneficial area. The trustees also support current or recent past pupils of Budehaven Community School. Proof of financial need must be shown.

Types of grant
Grants can be used for the provision of books, equipment, instruments, clothing, travel or any other associated study cost.

Applications
For educational grants, applicants that are applying for the first time should contact the Clerk in October after the course has begun. If applying for a second or subsequent grant, download the 'Repeat SSG Form' on the trust's website and return it via email or post.

Financial information

Year end	31/12/2018
Income	£528,800
Total expenditure	£473,700

Other information
Grants are also made for local community projects.

Sources of information
Accounts; annual report; Charity Commission record; funder's website.

Trevilson Educational Foundation

£8,600 (2017)

Correspondent: The Trustees, 8 Wheal Golden Drive, Holywell Bay, Newquay, Cornwall TR8 5PE (tel: 01637 830220; email: clerk@stnewlyneast-pc.org.uk)

CC number: 306555

Eligibility
People under the age of 25 who live in the parish of St Newlyn East and are in need.

Types of grant
Grants are available for costs associated with leaving school or university, entering a profession or trade.

Applications
Apply in writing to the correspondent.

Financial information

Year end	31/12/2017
Income	£18,800
Total expenditure	£19,000

Further financial information
Full accounts were not available to view on the Charity Commission's website due to the charity's low income. We have therefore estimated the grant total based on the charity's total expenditure.

Other information
Some support may be given to local schools and organisations helping people under the age of 25.

Sources of information
Charity Commission record.

Devon

The Andy Gunn Foundation

 £980 (2018)

Correspondent: Wendy Gunn, c/o The Post Office, 50 Fore Street, Teign Street, Bishopsteignton, Devon TQ14 9QZ (tel: 07585 603357; email: enquiries@andygunnfoundation.co.uk)

www.andygunnfoundation.co.uk

CC number: 1162439

Eligibility
Any person who has lived in Devon for at least 12 months, is over the age of 16 and is working or intends to work within the hospitality industry.

Types of grant
Small, one-off grants for training and education in the hospitality industry. Grants can be used towards books, equipment, clothing, travel, etc. Grants of up to £400 are usually awarded and are paid to organisations, suppliers or other charities on behalf of the individual.

Exclusions
Grants will not be made to replace statutory funding or to pay for work that has already commenced, equipment already purchased, deposits paid or goods on order.

Applications
Application forms can be downloaded from the foundation's website.

Financial information

Year end	31/12/2018
Income	£1,100
Total expenditure	£2,300

Further financial information
Full accounts were not available to view on the Charity Commission's website due to the foundation's low income. We have therefore estimated the grant total based on the foundation's total expenditure.

Other information
The foundation was established in memory of Andy Gunn, a young man who was passionate about his role in the hospitality industry. It aims to help others discover their passion and allow them to achieve their goals in the industry.

Sources of information
Charity Commission record; funder's website.

Chaloner's Educational Foundation

£1,600 (2017/18)

Correspondent: The Trustees, c/o Slee Blackwell Solicitors, 10 Cross Street, Barnstaple, Devon EX31 1BA (tel: 01271 349943; email: louise.langabeer@sleeblackwell.co.uk)

CC number: 286580

Eligibility
People under the age of 25 who live in the parish of Braunton and are in need.

Types of grant
Grants are made towards equipment, instruments, tools, books and so on.

Applications
Apply in writing to the correspondent.

Financial information

Year end	31/03/2018
Income	£3,500
Total expenditure	£1,800

Further financial information
Full accounts were not available to view on the Charity Commission's website due to the charity's low income. We have therefore estimated the grant total based on the charity's total expenditure.

Sources of information
Charity Commission record.

The Devon Educational Trust

 £17,300 (2018)

Correspondent: The Clerk to the Trustees, PO Box 86, Teignmouth, Devon TQ14 8ZT (tel: 01626 776653; email: devonedtrust@talktalk.net)

devoneducationaltrust.co.uk

CC number: 1157674

Eligibility

Pupils and students under the age of 25 who live, or whose parents' normal place of residence is, in Devon. Preference is given to applicants from low-income families. Applicants or their parents must be living in Devon on a permanent basis for at least 12 months.

Types of grant

One-off grants are available to:
- Schoolchildren for uniforms/clothing and equipment/instruments
- Young people with specific learning difficulties to help with the cost of one-to-one specialist tuition and, for those who are visually impaired, computer equipment and software
- College students and undergraduates for special clothing, study/travel costs, books, equipment/instruments and maintenance/living expenses
- Vocational students and people starting work for uniforms/clothing, books, equipment/instruments and maintenance/ living expenses

Exclusions

Assistance is not normally given to those embarking on a second or higher degree course. In some cases, however, the trustees may make a small grant to assist with living costs or the purchase of books, equipment, etc. No assistance is available for the payment of university fees and only in exceptional cases will the trustees consider paying school or boarding fees.

Applications

Apply on a form available from the correspondent or to download from the trust's website. Applications must include details of two referees. The completed application form must be returned by post or email. Application deadlines fall on 1 February, 1 June and 1 October each year.

Financial information

Year end	31/12/2018
Income	£43,100
Total expenditure	£52,000

Further financial information

Grant total was estimated from the 2018 accounts. Grants were awarded to 98 individuals for both welfare and educational purposes.

Other information

The charity also provides assistance to organisations for the promotion of education or improvement in conditions of life.

Sources of information

Accounts; annual report; Charity Commission record; funder's website.

The Exeter Advancement in Life Charity

 £7,100 (2017)

Correspondent: Trevor Perkins, Grants Administrator, Exeter Homes Trust, 6 Southernhay West, Exeter, Devon EX1 1JG (tel: 01392 421162; email: info@exeterhomestrust.com)

https://www.exeterhomestrust.com/index.php?page=grants-2

CC number: 1002151

Eligibility

People under the age of 25 who live in the city of Exeter or within 15 miles of the city centre, and are in higher education.

Types of grant

Grants are awarded for educational purposes such as books, equipment, travel or maintenance expenses and help towards fees.

Applications

Application forms are available by contacting the correspondent and will be sent to the applicant either by post or email. Potential candidates may be interviewed by a director, whose decision will be final.

Financial information

Year end	31/12/2017
Income	£8,000
Total expenditure	£7,900

Further financial information

Full accounts were not available to view on the Charity Commission's website due to the charity's low income. We have therefore estimated the grant total based on the charity's total expenditure.

Other information

This charity is part of Exeter Homes Trust (Charity Commission no. 201530). Support for welfare needs is available through The Exeter Relief in Need Charity.

Sources of information

Charity Commission record; funder's website.

A. B. Lucas Memorial Awards

 £2,100 (2017/18)

Correspondent: The Trustees, Green Meadows, Lower Odcombe, Yeovil, Somerset BA22 8TZ (tel: 01935 863522; email: martindare@btinternet.com)

CC number: 282306

Eligibility

Young people who are undertaking the study of dairy agriculture and live in the administrative counties of Cornwall, Devon, Somerset, Dorset and those parts of Avon that were previously part of Somerset.

Types of grant

Provision of scholarships, grants and loans for studies of agriculture, particularly dairy farming.

Applications

Apply in writing to the correspondent.

Financial information

Year end	05/04/2018
Income	£2,500
Total expenditure	£2,300

Further financial information

Full accounts were not available to view on the Charity Commission's website due to the charity's low income. We have therefore estimated the grant total based on the charity's total expenditure.

Sources of information

Charity Commission record.

Dulce Haigh Marshall Trust

 £4,000 (2017/18)

Correspondent: The Secretary, Rosemary Cottage, 38 Fore Street, Budleigh Salterton, Devon EX9 7HB (tel: 01395 568802; email: nicholas.marshall21@btinternet.com)

www.dulcehaighmarshalltrust.com

CC number: 286273

Eligibility

Individuals under the age of 25 who live in Devon, are studying a stringed instrument (violin, viola, cello, double bass), and are in need of financial assistance.

Types of grant

Grants towards tuition fees or the purchase of instruments. Only in exceptional circumstances will the trust consider funding the costs of courses or travelling expenses.

Exclusions

Grants are not given to people who, or whose parents, have sufficient income to meet their needs.

Applications

Application forms can be downloaded from the trust's website. Completed forms can be posted or emailed to the correspondent.

Financial information

Year end	31/03/2018
Income	£180
Total expenditure	£4,400

Further financial information

Full accounts were not available to view on the Charity Commission's website due to the charity's low income. We have therefore estimated the grant total based on the charity's total expenditure.

Sources of information

Charity Commission record; funder's website.

The Maudlyn Lands Charity

 £1,600 (2017/18)

Correspondent: The Trustees, Blue Haze, Down Road, Tavistock, Devon PL19 9AG (tel: 01822 612983; email: avda10@dsl.pipex.com)

CC number: 202577

Eligibility

People undertaking education who live in the Plympton and Sparkwell areas of Devon.

Types of grant

One-off grants are awarded towards education.

Applications

Apply in writing to the correspondent.

Financial information

Year end	31/10/2018
Income	£7,100
Total expenditure	£7,100

Further financial information

Full accounts were not available to view on the Charity Commission's website due to the charity's low income. We have therefore estimated the grant total based on the charity's total expenditure.

Other information

This charity also gives grants to organisations.

Sources of information

Charity Commission record.

The Vivian Moon Foundation

 £23,300 (2017/18)

Correspondent: The Trustees, c/o Simpkins Edwards, 21 Boutport Street, Barnstaple, Devon EX31 1RP (email: info@vivianmoonfoundation.co.uk)

www.vivianmoonfoundation.co.uk

CC number: 298942

Eligibility

People who have links with North Devon and have an offer of a place on a course of further educational, professional or vocational training which will lead to employment or improve individuals' skills and their career opportunities. Preference is given to people who intend to return to North Devon to work and, ideally, have an employment secured there at the end of their training.

Types of grant

One-off and recurrent grants, usually ranging between around £100 and £300 (rarely more than £500), are available to people in further education and training, including college students, vocational students, mature students, people starting work, unemployed people seeking to get into employment or working people who wish to develop their skills. Full-time, part-time and distance-learning courses can be supported, as well as those including a placement year. Most applicants are funded partially and on a course or annual basis.

Exclusions

First degree applicants are unlikely to be supported, unless in extraordinary circumstances.

Applications

The foundation prefers to receive applications online through its website in order to speed up the process. Applicants who are unable to apply in such way can book computer time at a Pathfinder centre (contact details on the foundation's website) or request an application form from the correspondent. Applicants should provide an email address of one referee. Grants are considered in January, May and September.

Financial information

Year end	31/03/2018
Income	£15,400
Total expenditure	£25,900

Further financial information

Full accounts were not available to view on the Charity Commission's website due to the charity's low income. We

have therefore estimated the grant total based on the charity's total expenditure.

Other information

North Devon comprises the area administered by either Torridge or North Devon District Council.

Sources of information

Charity Commission record; funder's website.

The Plymouth and Cornwall Cancer Fund

£8,200 (2017/18)

Correspondent: Peter Harker, Honorary Secretary, 16 Wilderness Road, Mannamead, Plymouth, Devon PL3 4RN (tel: 01752 220587; email: admin@pccf. org.uk)

https://www.plymouthandcornwall cancerfund.org.uk

CC number: 262587

Eligibility

The fund makes grants to healthcare professionals and staff involved in cancer treatment, for support in further education.

Types of grant

Educational grants are awarded to healthcare professionals or staff involved in caring for cancer patients to attend courses, conferences and to access postgraduate training opportunities.

Applications

Apply in writing to the correspondent. Applications must be made by a recognised healthcare professional on the individual's behalf. When applying, the third party must explain the following: why the funding is needed; what the funding is for; a confirmation that a financial assessment has taken place, concluding that the applicant has received all relevant entitlements and that the costs and expenses of the grant request are reasonable. Completed applications should be sent to the correspondent at their postal or email address.

Financial information

Year end	31/10/2018
Income	£260,100
Total expenditure	£135,200

Further financial information

During 2017/18, the charity awarded grants totalling £8,200 towards courses and training.

Other information

The fund operates a charity shop in Hyde Park Village which is run by a team of over 20 volunteers. The shop generates a large portion of the fund's income. The fund also makes grants in support of local research projects related to improving the treatment of cancer, and to Derriford Hospital to help improve its facilities.

Sources of information
Accounts; annual report; Charity Commission record; funder's website.

The Sidmouth Educational Foundation

 £3,000 (2018)

Correspondent: The Administrator, PO Box 99, Sidmouth, Devon EX10 1DH (tel: 01395 516956; email: info@sidmouthconsolidatedcharities.co.uk)

https://sidmouthconsolidated charities.co.uk

CC number: 306892

Eligibility
Children and adults who live in the area covered by the Sidmouth Town Council. This includes Sidmouth, Sidford, Sidbury and Salcombe Regis.

Types of grant
Educational grants are made towards books, computers, travel expenses and course fees.

Applications
Applications can be made online using a form on the funder's website.

Financial information
Year end	31/12/2018
Income	£8,200
Total expenditure	£13,300

Further financial information
Full accounts were not available to view on the Charity Commission's website due to the charity's low income. We have therefore estimated the grant total based on the charity's total expenditure.

Other information
This charity also makes grants to organisations.

Sources of information
Charity Commission record; funder's website.

Mid Devon

The Richards Educational Charity

 £21,400 (2018)

Correspondent: Geoffrey Knowles, Secretary, 5 Tuns Lane, Silverton, Exeter, Devon EX5 4HY (tel: 01392 860464; email: jmthomas1951@yahoo.co.uk)

CC number: 306787

Eligibility
Young people under the age 25 who live in the parish of Silverton.

Types of grant
Grants are made towards the costs associated with pursuing further/higher education, such as books, equipment and general living expenses.

Applications
Application forms are available at the village shop/post office, school or health centre. The trustees meet regularly to consider grant applications.

Financial information
Year end	31/12/2018
Income	£48,600
Total expenditure	£34,700

Further financial information
During 2018, the charity awarded 15 grants to university students and three grants for vocational training.

Other information
The charity also makes grants to children for pre-school classes, after-school classes, school trips and extracurricular classes.

Sources of information
Accounts; annual report; Charity Commission record.

North Devon

George Ley Educational Trust

 £4,000 (2018)

Correspondent: The Trustees, Springside, Rews Close, Combe Martin, Ilfracombe, Devon EX34 0DW (tel: 01271 883880)

CC number: 306788

Eligibility
People who live in Combe Martin.

Types of grant
Scholarships to students to encourage them to stay in further education and to students in higher education.

Applications
Apply in writing to the correspondent.

Financial information
Year end	31/12/2018
Income	£6,000
Total expenditure	£4,500

Further financial information
Full accounts were not available to view on the Charity Commission's website due to the charity's low income. We have therefore estimated the grant total based on the charity's total expenditure.

Sources of information
Charity Commission record.

Plymouth

The Olford Bequest

 £4,100 (2017/18)

Correspondent: John Coates, Clerk to the Trustees, 24 Dolphin House, Sutton Wharf, Plymouth, Devon PL4 0BL (tel: 01752 225724; email: johnbcoates@btinternet.com)

https://olfordbequest.weebly.com

CC number: 306936

Eligibility
Young people from Plymouth who are going to university. To be eligible, students must have completed their A-levels at a school or college in Plymouth.

Types of grant
Allowances are available to five university students each year. Two grants are reserved for students from Devonport School for Boys. The charity provides £250 a year for three years to be spent on anything which will allow the student to 'more fully enjoy their stay at university'. Its website states that 'ability to pass exams or buy books is therefore not a criterion which the Trustees will consider'.

Applications
Applications can be made on a form available to download from the charity's website, which should be submitted the end of June.

Financial information
Year end	31/03/2018
Income	£4,700
Total expenditure	£4,600

Further financial information
Full accounts were not available to view on the Charity Commission's website due to the charity's low income. We have therefore estimated the grant total based on the charity's total expenditure.

Sources of information
Charity Commission record; funder's website.

SOUTH WEST – DEVON

Orphans Aid Educational Foundation (Plymouth)

£ £750 (2017)

Correspondent: Vanessa Steer, 184 Mannamead Road, Plymouth, Devon PL3 5RE (tel: 01752 703280; email: v_steer@yahoo.co.uk)

CC number: 306770

Eligibility
Children and young people living in Plymouth who are in need. Preference is given to children with one parent or families experiencing severe hardship.

Types of grant
Grants are awarded in the form of higher education scholarships. Grants for clothing, tools, books and more general financial assistance required for entry into a trade or profession are also available.

Applications
Apply in writing to the correspondent.

Financial information
Year end	31/12/2017
Income	£2,800
Total expenditure	£1,600

Further financial information
Full accounts were not available to view on the Charity Commission's website due to the charity's low income. We have therefore estimated the grant total based on the charity's total expenditure.

Sources of information
Charity Commission record.

The Plymouth and Cornwall Cancer Fund
See record on page 254

South Hams

Parish Lands (South Brent Feoffees)

£ £23,200 (2018)

Correspondent: J. Blackler, Clerk to the Trustees, c/o Luscombe Maye Ltd, 6 Fore Street, South Brent, Devon TQ10 9BQ (tel: 01364 646180)

 www.sbrentfeoffees.btck.co.uk

CC number: 255283

Eligibility
Educational grants are available to current or former residents of South Brent parish who are in post-18 education.

Types of grant
Educational grants are made to help with costs associated with vocational training and university studies.

Welfare support is also given.

Applications
Application forms for educational grants are available to download from the funder's website. All applications must include written evidence from the applicant's Head of Department or tutor confirming their attendance. Written evidence confirming an *offer* to a place of higher education will not suffice. Applicants should have already started their course before applying for funding. Each individual can apply for funding once a year for three years. For current application deadlines, consult the funder's website.

Applications for welfare grants should be made in writing to the correspondent.

Financial information
Year end	31/12/2018
Income	£60,000
Total expenditure	£55,600

Further financial information
Note: the grant total has been estimated.

Other information
This charity also makes grants to the local parish church for general upkeep.

Sources of information
Accounts; annual report; Charity Commission record; funder's website.

Reverend Duke Yonge Charity

£ £3,200 (2018)

Correspondent: David Farnham, Trustee, 8 Chipple Park, Lutton, Ivybridge, Devon PL21 9TA (tel: 01752 837566; email: davefarnham@btinternet.com)

CC number: 202835

Eligibility
Educational grants are available to younger residents in the parish of Cornwood.

Types of grant
Educational grants are awarded according to need.

Applications
Apply in writing to the correspondent.

Financial information
Year end	31/12/2018
Income	£14,300
Total expenditure	£14,400

Further financial information
Full accounts were not available to view on the Charity Commission's website due to the charity's low income. We have therefore estimated the grant total based on the charity's total expenditure.

Other information
This charity also makes grants to organisations and provides religious materials/literature.

Sources of information
Charity Commission record.

Torridge

The Bridge Trust (Bideford Bridge Trust)

£ £88,700 (2017/18)

Correspondent: P. Sims, The Steward, 24 Bridgeland Street, Bideford, Devon EX39 2QB (tel: 01237 473122; email: info@bidefordbridgetrust.org.uk)

 https://www.bidefordbridgetrust. org.uk

CC number: 204536

Eligibility
Residents of Bideford, and its immediate neighbourhood, who are in need.

Types of grant
Educational grants of up to £600 are available to students who are in any year of their degree course. Grants of up to £300 are awarded to students who are about to start post-A-level training, or are in the second or third year of such course, to purchase any books or equipment required for study. Grants of up to £250 are available to non-residents, but who are studying in the area of benefit, for support with costs incurred as part of post-A-level study.

Exclusions
The charity does not support postgraduate courses/students.

Applications
Application forms are available to download from the funder's website. Completed forms should be sent to the charity by post.

Financial information
Year end	21/12/2018
Income	£830,000
Total expenditure	£765,200

Other information
The charity also makes grants to organisations and to local schools to

help with the cost of funding swimming lessons for pupils.

Sources of information
Accounts; annual report; Charity Commission record; funder's website.

West Devon

Okehampton Educational Foundation

 £87,900 (2018)

Correspondent: Karen Percival, Clerk, 15 Upper Crooked Meadow, Okehampton, Devon EX20 1WW (tel: 01837 55179; email: clerk@ okehamptoncharities.org.uk)

https://www.okehamptoncharities. org.uk

CC number: 306677

Eligibility
People who have lived in Okehampton for over 12 months.

Types of grant
Awards are available for further, higher and vocational courses for young people aged between 16 and 24. Scholarships of £750 per year can be awarded to people attending university or higher education organisations. Bursaries of £450 are available to those attending a further education course and £650 is available to those attending vocational courses to assist with the cost of course fees, equipment, tools, clothing and books. In exceptional circumstances awards might be made for post-25 education.

Applications
Application forms and policy documents are available to download from the charity's website.

Financial information
Year end	31/12/2018
Income	£158,700
Total expenditure	£175,000

Further financial information
A total of 139 students received scholarships and bursaries in 2018.

Other information
The foundation's website refers to both this charity and the Okehampton General Charity (Charity Commission no. 202686), collectively known as Okehampton United Charities. The charities award grants to both individuals and organisations for educational and welfare needs and application forms for different types of support are available on the website.

Sources of information
Accounts; annual report; Charity Commission record; funder's website.

Dorset

The Bridge Educational Trust (1996)

 £38,100 (2017/18)

Correspondent: The Trustees, c/o Piddle Valley First School, Piddletrenthide, Dorchester, Dorset DT2 7QL (tel: 07775 961370; email: bridgeeducationaltrust@ outlook.com)

www.bridgeeducationaltrust.org.uk

CC number: 1068720

Eligibility
People who live, or who were born, in the county of Dorset, primarily in the parishes of Piddletrenthide (with Plush), Piddlehinton and Alton St Pancras. This excludes residents of the South East Dorset conurbation including Bournemouth, Poole and Christchurch. The trust provides grants for people in the following circumstances:

- Students undertaking a first degree or other qualification in order to further their career who are experiencing financial difficulty
- Mature students who are retraining
- Students, whether studying or on a gap-year, who wish to undertake an educational expedition or course
- Individuals working with support agencies looking to improve their life chances
- Students of school age with special educational needs that cannot be met by the local authority
- Single parents, or those with a partner who has a disability, undertaking training to support their children or family members
- Individuals recommended by probation services for training to help rehabilitation

Types of grant
One-off and recurrent grants are offered to people in education at school, college or other educational establishment. Grants are not normally paid to individuals directly unless a prior arrangement has been made. Average grants range from £500 to around £2,000 and are awarded towards fees, accommodation, educational travel, books, equipment, exhibitions, visits and other expenses.

Exclusions
The trust will not provide grants for fees which can be covered by student loans,

retrospective purchases or for master's or second degrees. Those who have a temporary address in Dorset for student accommodation do not meet the Dorset resident criterion.

Applications
Application forms are available to complete on the trust's website or can be requested from the correspondent. Forms should be completed by the applicant or by a parent when the applicant is under the age of 16. Applications should preferably be submitted at least two weeks before one of the regular meetings of the trustees which are normally held in February, June and September. For those on a course of study lasting over 12 months, a new application is required for the second and subsequent years. Three years is normally the maximum period for support to any one person. For applicants who no longer live in Dorset, evidence of place of birth (i.e. birth certificate or passport) should accompany the application.

Financial information
Year end	31/03/2018
Income	£78,400
Total expenditure	£43,600

Further financial information
In 2017/18 grants totalling £40,600 were awarded to 45 people. This is broken down as follows: £11,400 to 11 mature students; £21,500 to 15 young students in higher/further education; £5,200 to 15 school/university students for courses and educational trips; £330 to one school child to assist with independent school fees; £30 to one individual introduced by a support agency for training to improve life chances; £2,100 to two individuals to resolve short-term problems.

Sources of information
Accounts; annual report; Charity Commission record; funder's website.

Corfe Castle Charity

£16,000 (2017/18)

Correspondent: Clerk to the Trustees, 2 Battlemead, Corfe Castle, Wareham, Dorset BH20 5ER (tel: 01929 480873; email: cccharity1602@outlook.com)

CC number: 1055846

Eligibility
People in need who live in the parish of Corfe Castle (including Kingston).

Types of grant
Grants are awarded towards the cost of education and training.

Applications
Apply in writing to the correspondent.

Financial information

Year end	31/03/2018
Income	£243,100
Total expenditure	£238,600

Further financial information

In 2017/18 a total of £40,000 was awarded to individuals. We estimate that around £24,000 was awarded to 48 individuals for welfare purposes, including six grants towards pre-school and after-school club attendance, and £16,000 was awarded to 14 individuals for educational purposes.

Other information

The charity also makes grants to local organisations and administers both almshouse accommodation and affordable housing. The charity also provide interest-free loans to individuals in need.

Sources of information

Accounts; annual report; Charity Commission report; Corfe Castle Community Pre-school website.

Dorset Community Foundation

(£) £30,400 (2018)

Correspondent: Ellie Maguire, Grants Manager, Dorset Community Foundation, The Spire, High Street, Poole, Dorset BH15 1DF (tel: 01202 670815; email: grants@dorsetcf.org)

 https://www.dorsetcommunity foundation.org

CC number: 1122113

Eligibility

The foundation administers four educational funds for young people. Each fund has its own eligibility criteria:

Dorset Community Fund Bursary Scheme
- Applicants must be aged 16 to 25 and attending a vocational course including access courses, traineeships and supported internships
- Applicants must have attended one of the following colleges: Bournemouth and Poole College; Kingston Maurward College; Brockenhurst College; Weymouth College; Yeovil College; or Wiltshire College (Salisbury Campus)
- The scheme is intended to help those who have a disadvantage (for example, care-leavers, those who have care responsibilities for other family members, those who live on a family income of less than £25,000 and people with disabilities or special educational needs)

Superior STEM Bursary Fund
- Applicants must be aged 16 to 25 and living in a specific area of Dorset (see details on the foundation's website)
- Applicants should be planning to attend a course at Brockenhurst or Bournemouth and Poole colleges on a STEM (science, technology, engineering or mathematics) course
- The scheme is intended to help those who have a disadvantage (for example, care-leavers, those who have care responsibilities for other family members, those who live on a family income of less than £21,000 and people with disabilities or special educational needs)

Lord Lieutenant's Fund for Young and Talented
- Applicants must be aged 14 to 21 and living in Dorset
- Applicants must have an exceptional sporting talent which has been recognised or acknowledged by an appropriate national governing body
- Applicants must be unable to achieve their ambitions without help due to financial or personal circumstances

The Dorset Performing Arts Bursary
- Applicants must be aged 14 to 21 and living in the Dorset Council area (excluding the borough council areas of Bournemouth, Poole and Christchurch)
- Applicants must have an exceptional talent in performing arts, which has been recognised, and should be actively performing at a high standard
- Applicants must be unable to achieve their ambitions without help due to financial or personal circumstances

Types of grant

The Dorset Community Fund Bursary Scheme provides grants of up to £1,000 to applicants who are studying for a vocational qualification. Funding is given to assist with the costs of tools, clothing, IT equipment, study trips and so on. The Superior STEM Bursary Fund awards grants of up to £1,500 to young people studying science, technology, engineering or maths, to be used towards course fees, IT equipment, travel costs and clothing. The Lord Lieutenant's Fund for Young and Talented provides grants up to £1,000 towards sports kits/clothing, competition fees, travel costs, accommodation and so on. The Dorset Performing Arts Bursary gives grants of up to £1,000 to assist with the ongoing costs of attending a course such as equipment, short courses, tuition or coaching, travel costs, accommodation and so on.

Applications

Further guidelines and details on how to apply for each fund can be found on the foundation's website, along with current deadlines.

Financial information

Year end	31/12/2018
Income	£839,900
Total expenditure	£598,100

Further financial information

In 2018 a total of £30,400 was awarded to individuals for educational purposes. Within this total, £10,400 was awarded through the Lord Lieutenant's Fund for Young and Talented to 18 individuals, £5,000 was awarded through the Dorset Community Fund Bursary Scheme and £4,600 was awarded through the Superior STEM Bursary Fund.

Other information

Dorset Community Foundation also manages funds which give grants to local community organisations. This is one of the 46 community foundations, which distribute funding for a wide range of purposes. Grant schemes tend to change frequently; therefore, consult the foundation's website for details of current programmes and upcoming deadlines.

Sources of information

Accounts; annual report; Charity Commission record; funder's website.

Gordon Charitable Trust

(£) £14,200 (2017/18)

Correspondent: Gerry Aiken, Trustee, 45 Dunkeld Road, Bournemouth BH3 7EW (tel: 01202 768337; email: gerry_aitken@hotmail.com)

CC number: 200668

Eligibility

Young people between the ages of 15 and 25 living in the county of Dorset who are in further/higher education or undertaking apprenticeships. Preference is given to individuals who have lived, or whose parents have lived, in the borough council areas of Bournemouth, Poole and Christchurch and who are in need of financial assistance.

Types of grant

The trust provides scholarships, bursaries and other financial help 'to a very limited extent'. Support is given towards the cost of books, clothing, equipment/instruments, maintenance/living expenses. People starting work, and students studying music and the arts are also supported.

Applications

Contact the correspondent for further information.

Financial information

Year end	30/06/2018
Income	£6,000
Total expenditure	£14,600

Further financial information

Full accounts were not available to view on the Charity Commission's website due to the charity's low income. We have therefore estimated the grant total based on the charity's total expenditure.

Other information

Our research indicates that grants are targeted at young people with no family support and mainly from single-parent households.

Sources of information

Charity Commission record.

Lockyer's Charity

 £2,300 (2017)

Correspondent: The Trustees, 37 Gorse Lane, Poole, Dorset BH16 5RR (tel: 01202 620239)

CC number: 306246

Eligibility

People who live in Lytchett Minster, Upton and Organford, aged up to 25.

Types of grant

Grants to students going to college or university for the purchase of books or other equipment.

Applications

Apply in writing to the correspondent.

Financial information

Year end	31/12/2017
Income	£2,400
Total expenditure	£2,500

Further financial information

Full accounts were not available to view on the Charity Commission's website due to the charity's low income. We have therefore estimated the grant total based on the charity's total expenditure.

Sources of information

Charity Commission record.

A. B. Lucas Memorial Awards
See record on page 253

Sir Samuel Mico's Charities

 £23,500 (2017)

Correspondent: Howard Jones, c/o Edwards and Keeping Unity Chambers, 34 High East Street, Dorchester, Dorset DT1 1HA (tel: 01305 251333; email: howardjones@edwardsandkeeping.co.uk)

www.weymouthtowncharities.org.uk

CC number: 202629

Eligibility

Young people between the ages of 16 and 24 who reside in the borough of Weymouth and Portland and have been born in the borough, or have resided there for at least ten years. The charity particularly welcomes applications from those on apprenticeships and those wishing to take up professional careers.

Types of grant

Grants to students in further or higher education or those undertaking apprenticeships. Grants are awarded towards educational course fees, living costs for those on educational courses, equipment, books and assisted places on the Tall Ships Youth Trust ships.

Applications

Apply on a form available to download from the charity's website or from the correspondent. Applicants must be able to show that they are in difficult financial circumstances and have a desire to extend their education.

Financial information

Year end	31/12/2017
Income	£47,900
Total expenditure	£28,000

Sources of information

Accounts; annual report; Charity Commission record; funder's website.

The William Williams Charity

 £114,300 (2017)

Correspondent: The Clerk to the Trustees, Burraton House, 5 Burraton Square, Poundbury, Dorchester, Dorset DT1 3GR (tel: 01305 571274; email: enquires@williamwilliams.org.uk)

www.williamwilliams.org.uk

CC number: 202188

Eligibility

People in need who live in the ancient parishes of Blandford Forum, Shaftesbury or Sturminster Newton. Individuals must reside in one of the specific postcodes listed on the charity's website.

Types of grant

Educational grants are made to students, mature students or apprentices embarking on higher education or recognised training schemes.

Applications

Details on how to apply, application forms and guidance can be found on the charity's website.

Financial information

Year end	31/12/2017
Income	£464,600
Total expenditure	£397,400

Further financial information

In 2017 a total of 202 grants were awarded and the average value of each grant was £799.

Other information

Grants are also made to local organisations.

Sources of information

Accounts; annual report; Charity Commission record; funder's website.

Bournemouth, Christchurch and Poole

The Cecil Charity

£15,900 (2017/18)

Correspondent: Lord Rockley, Lytchett Heath House, Lytchett Heath, Poole, Dorset BH16 6AE (email: charity@lytchettheath.co.uk)

https://www.bournemouth.ac.uk/news/2019–05–02/need-help-living-costs-apply-now-cecil-charity

CC number: 306248

Eligibility

Young people under the age of 25 who live within a ten-mile radius of the parish church at Lytchett Matravers.

Types of grant

Grants, scholarships and bursaries at any secondary school, university, college or other place of education. Grants can be awarded for accommodation costs, equipment including books, tools and musical instruments, living costs and travel as part of fieldwork/placements. The charity awards around £900 each year to students.

Applications

Contact the correspondent for further information and to request an application form. The trustees meet in March, July and November to consider applications.

Financial information

Year end	31/03/2018
Income	£26,600
Total expenditure	£19,500

Further financial information

Grants were awarded to 13 individuals.

Other information

The charity commenced a music scholarship programme with Lytchett Minster School providing up to £4,000 each year for at least three years to fund 25 music lessons every year for ten students showing music aptitude (or up to 20 lessons if shared). In 2017/18, 18 students benefited from the programme.

Sources of information

Accounts; annual report; Charity Commission record.

Clingan's Trust

 £21,800 (2018)

Correspondent: David Richardson, Clerk, 4 Bournewood Drive, Bournemouth, Dorset BH4 9JP (tel: 01202 766838; email: davidrichardson652@gmail.com)

www.clinganstrust.co.uk

CC number: 307085

Eligibility

Young people aged under the age of 25 who are attending (or who have at some point attended) a place of education in Christchurch. Applicants must have a parent/guardian resident in the area of benefit. There must be an evident financial need in each case; therefore, parental income will be taken into account.

Types of grant

Grants are made towards expenses incurred when pursuing higher and further education, including apprenticeships and vocational training. Grants have been given towards computers, equipment, books, travel, university costs, etc.

Applications

Application forms are available to download from the trust's website. Completed forms can be returned by post or by email.

Financial information

Year end	31/12/2018
Income	£83,400
Total expenditure	£66,800

Further financial information

Note: the grant total has been estimated.

Other information

The trust also makes grants to organisations.

Sources of information

Accounts; annual report; Charity Commission record; funder's website.

Gloucester-shire

The Macfarlane Walker Trust

 £18,900 (2017/18)

Correspondent: Sophie Walker, 4 Shooters Hill Road, London SE3 7BD (tel: 020 8858 4701; email: sophiewalker@mac.com)

CC number: 227890

Eligibility

Music students in full-time tertiary education (colleges and universities), with a preference for those who live in Cheltenham and Gloucestershire.

Types of grant

Grants are awarded for instrument purchase/upgrades. The rationale for this policy is that all students pay fees and living costs, but instrumental music students have the additional costs of providing their own instruments.

Exclusions

The trust does not provide financial assistance towards tuition fees or gap-year trips. Large charities, animal charities, foreign charities or major building projects are not supported.

Applications

Apply in writing to the correspondent.

Financial information

Year end	05/04/2018
Income	£40,400
Total expenditure	£37,700

Further financial information

The trust's grant total included grants to individuals and organisations. We have estimated how much was given to individuals.

Other information

The charity also supports organisations.

Sources of information

Accounts; annual report; Charity Commission record; further information provided by the funder.

Weston-sub-Edge Educational Charity

 £3,000 (2017/18)

Correspondent: Rachel Hurley, Clerk, Longclose Cottage, Weston-sub-Edge, Chipping Campden, Gloucestershire GL55 6QX (tel: 01386 841808; email: hurleyrac@gmail.com)

www.westonsubedge.com/?page_id=143

CC number: 297226

Eligibility

Children and young people under the age of 25 who or whose parents live in Weston-sub-Edge, or who have at any time attended (or whose parents have attended) Weston-sub-Edge Church of England Primary School.

Types of grant

Grants of between £10 and £500 can be given for costs associated with further and higher education.

Exclusions

Retrospective applications are unlikely to be considered.

Applications

Application forms can be obtained from the correspondent and should be submitted directly by the individual in question, unless they are under the age of 16, in which case a parent or guardian can apply on their behalf. The trustees meet on the fourth Monday in January, March, May, July, September and November, and applications must be received at least ten days in advance of a meeting. Only one application per student per term will be considered.

Financial information

Year end	31/08/2018
Income	£36,200
Total expenditure	£29,500

Other information

The charity's high expenditure in 2017/18 is due to the purchase of investments.

Sources of information

Accounts; annual report; Charity Commission record; funder's website.

Cheltenham

Higgs and Cooper's Educational Charity

£3,300 (2017/18)

Correspondent: Martin Fry, 7 Branch Hill Rise, Charlton Kings, Cheltenham GL53 9HN (tel: 01242 239903; email: martyn.fry@dsl.pipex.com)

www.higgsandcooper.org

CC number: 311570

Eligibility

People under the age of 25 who were born or live in the former Charlton Kings civil parish. Preference is given to people from single-parent families.

Types of grant

Grants are awarded for further/higher education students and people starting work/entering a trade. Support is given for general educational expenditure, including books, equipment/instruments, fees and so on. Grants can also be given for postgraduate degrees and training.

Applications

Application forms can be found on the charity's website and must be forwarded to the clerk by post or hand two weeks before the meeting at which they are to be considered. Two reference letters must be submitted along with the application: one professional reference (school or institution for which the applicant needs support), and one personal reference from someone who has known the applicant for a number of years (references from family are not accepted). An sae should accompany the application. The trustees meet four times a year normally in March, June, September and December.

Financial information

Year end	31/03/2018
Income	£20,800
Total expenditure	£14,500

Further financial information

Full accounts were not available to view on the Charity Commission's website due to the charity's low income. We have therefore estimated the grant total based on the charity's total expenditure.

Other information

The charity also supports local schools and youth organisations in their educational development and pursuits.

Sources of information

Charity Commission record; funder's website.

Lumb's Educational Foundation

£ £6,500 (2018)

Correspondent: The Trustees, 54 Collum End Rise, Leckhampton, Cheltenham GL53 0PB (tel: 01242 515673; email: lumbsfoundation@ virginmedia.com)

CC number: 311683

Eligibility

People between the ages of 16 and 25 who live in the borough of Cheltenham and the surrounding parishes. Students whose home address is in Gloucestershire can be considered.

Types of grant

Support can be given for course fees, books, clothing, equipment and instruments.

Exclusions

People who are permanently resident outside the area of benefit are ineligible. Grants are not made towards trips that are not of an educational nature. Living expenses or school fees are not supported.

Applications

Application forms can be requested from the correspondent. Once completed they should be returned with a supporting letter, including details of income, expenditure, the applicant's parents' financial situation and the purpose of the grant. Candidates are interviewed. Each application is assessed according to need and funds available at the time.

Financial information

Year end	31/12/2018
Income	£13,200
Total expenditure	£14,500

Further financial information

Full accounts were not available to view on the Charity Commission's website due to the charity's low income. We have therefore estimated the grant total based on the charity's total expenditure.

Sources of information

Charity Commission record.

Cotswold

John Edmonds' Charity

£ £5,900 (2017)

Correspondent: The Trustees, 7 Dollar Street, Cirencester, Gloucestershire GL7 2AS (tel: 01285 650000; email: rrm@sml-law.co.uk)

CC number: 311495

Eligibility

People under the age of 25 who were born or are resident in Cirencester and the surrounding area.

Types of grant

Help is given to young people entering or engaged in a trade or profession. Assistance is given towards the cost of education, training or apprenticeships, including fees, equipment/tools, clothing, travel costs or maintenance expenses.

Applications

Apply in writing to the correspondent.

Financial information

Year end	31/12/2017
Income	£6,600
Total expenditure	£6,600

Further financial information

Full accounts were not available to view on the Charity Commission's website due to the charity's low income. We have therefore estimated the grant total based on the charity's total expenditure.

Sources of information

Charity Commission record.

South Gloucestershire

The Chipping Sodbury Town Lands

£ £2,800 (2018)

Correspondent: Nicola Gideon, Clerk to the Trustees, Town Hall, 57–59 Broad Street, Chipping Sodbury, Bristol BS37 6AD (tel: 01454 852223; email: nicola.gideon@chippingsodburytownhall. co.uk)

 www.chippingsodburytown hall.co.uk

CC number: 236364

Eligibility

Residents in the parish of Sodbury who are in need.

Types of grant

Educational grants are made to aid the promotion of education, including further education courses.

Applications

Apply in writing to the correspondent.

Financial information

Year end	31/12/2018
Income	£332,300
Total expenditure	£303,200

Further financial information

Grants were made to ten students on further education courses. Note: the grant total has been estimated.

Other information

The charity also makes grants to local schools and organisations.

Sources of information

Accounts; annual report; Charity Commission record; funder's website.

Stroud

The Stroud and Rodborough Educational Charity

 £14,300 (2017/18)

Correspondent: Shani Baker, Clerk to the Trustees, 14 Green Close, Uley, Dursley, Gloucestershire GL11 5TH (tel: 01453 860379; email: info@ stroudrodboroughed.org)

www.stroudrodboroughec.org

CC number: 309614

Eligibility

Children and young people in need who are under the age of 25 and resident in the parishes comprising the old Stroud rural district (Bisley-with-Lypiatt, Chalford, Cranham, Horsley, Kings Stanley, Leonard Stanley, Minchinhampton, Miserden, Oakridge, Painswick, Pitchcombe, Randwick, Rodborough, Stonehouse, Thrupp, Whiteshill, Woodchester and Nailsworth urban district).

Types of grant

Grants can be given towards general educational needs, including study/travel overseas, equipment, clothing, books, course-related necessities and so on.

Exclusions

Support is not given in the cases where funding should be provided by the local authority.

Applications

Application forms are available on the charity's website or from the correspondent. The trustees meet four times a year, see the website for the next application deadline. Applications should include a reference from a teacher and be submitted in advance to the meetings.

Financial information

Year end	31/03/2018
Income	£90,100
Total expenditure	£95,900

Further financial information

The grant total has been estimated from the 2017/18 accounts.

Other information

The priority of the charity is to assist Marling School, Stroud High School and Archway School, where support is not already provided by the local authority. The charity also gives grants to local charitable organisations working for the benefit of young people and administers a number of prize funds tenable at the local schools.

Sources of information

Accounts; annual report; Charity Commission record; funder's website.

Somerset

Blackford Educational Charity

 £2,300 (2017/18)

Correspondent: The Trustees, Hugh Sexey Middle School, Blackford, Wedmore, Somerset BS28 4ND (tel: 07887 637474; email: simon. kraeter@blomasa.com)

CC number: 277339

Eligibility

Children and young people under the age of 25 who live in the parish of Blackford.

Types of grant

One-off and recurrent grants according to need.

Applications

Apply in writing to the correspondent.

Financial information

Year end	30/09/2018
Income	£5,100
Total expenditure	£5,100

Further financial information

Full accounts were not available to view on the Charity Commission's website due to the charity's low income. We have therefore estimated the grant total based on the charity's total expenditure.

Other information

The charity also assists primary and secondary schools in the parish of Blackford where these are not already supported by the local authority. Grants can also be provided for recreational development.

Sources of information

Charity Commission record.

The Ilminster Educational Foundation

£14,000 (2017/18)

Correspondent: The Trustees, 20 Station Road, Ilminster, Somerset TA19 9BD (tel: 01460 53029; email: e.wells125@ btinternet.com)

CC number: 310265

Eligibility

People under the age of 25 who live or have attended an educational institution for at least two years in the parish of Ilminster.

Types of grant

Grants are available to schoolchildren for educational outings in the UK/overseas.

Applications

Apply in writing to the correspondent.

Financial information

Year end	31/07/2018
Income	£96,200
Total expenditure	£110,000

Other information

The foundation also makes grants to schools and parishes.

Sources of information

Accounts; annual report; Charity Commission record.

John Nowes Exhibition Foundation

£2,100 (2017/18)

Correspondent: Amanda Goddard, Clerk to the Trustees, Battens Solicitors, Mansion House, 54–58 Princes Street, Yeovil, Somerset BA20 1EP (tel: 01935 846000; email: amanda.goddard@battens. co.uk)

https://www.battens.co.uk/news-events/news/john-nowes-exhibition-foundation-applications-2

CC number: 309984

Eligibility

Children and young people between the ages of 16 and 25 living in the borough of Yeovil and surrounding parishes (including Alvington, Barwick, Brympton, Chilthorne Domer, East Coker, Limington, Mudford, Preston Plucknett, Yeovil Without or West Coker), who have a household income of less than £33,000 per annum.

Types of grant

Scholarships, bursaries and maintenance allowances are provided to those in school, university or college. Small grants are awarded towards clothing, equipment or books for those preparing to enter work. There are also grants available towards travel abroad for educational purposes.

Applications

An application form can be downloaded from the foundation's website or requested from the correspondent. It should be submitted along with a parental declaration, evidence of household income and a reference from the head of the student's current educational establishment. Check the website for the closing date, which is usually in June so the grants can be awarded in September.

Financial information

Year end	31/03/2018
Income	£6,300
Total expenditure	£4,600

Further financial information

Full accounts were not available to view on the Charity Commission's website due to the charity's low income. We have therefore estimated the grant total based on the charity's total expenditure.

Sources of information

Charity Commission record; guidelines for applicants; funder's website.

Prowde's Educational Foundation (Prowde's Charity)

£9,600 (2017/18)

Correspondent: Richard Lytle, Clerk, 39 Stanley Street, Southsea, Portsmouth, Hampshire PO5 2DS (tel: 023 9279 9142; email: mbyrne@vwv.co.uk)

CC number: 310255

Eligibility

Boys and young men aged 9 to 25 who live in Somerset or the North or East Ridings of Yorkshire. Preference is given to those who are descendants of the named people in the will of the founder.

Types of grant

One-off and recurrent grants according to need.

Exclusions

Girls and women are not supported.

Applications

Apply in writing to the correspondent.

Financial information

Year end	31/05/2018
Income	£33,000
Total expenditure	£34,400

Further financial information

44 grants totalling £19,200 were awarded for both educational and welfare purposes in 2017/18. We have estimated the grant total for educational purposes.

Sources of information

Accounts; annual report; Charity Commission record.

Bath and North East Somerset

Ralph and Irma Sperring Charity

£56,700 (2017/18)

Correspondent: G. Persson, Company Secretary, c/o Thatcher & Hallam Solicitors, Island House, The Island, Midsomer Norton, Radstock, Somerset BA3 2HJ (tel: 01761 409316; email: info@thesperringcharity.co.uk)

 https://www.thesperringcharity.co.uk

CC number: 1048101

Eligibility

Educational grants are available to children and young people living within a five-mile radius of the church of St John the Baptist in Midsomer Norton, who are attending schools or colleges of further education.

Types of grant

One-off and recurring grants according to need.

Exclusions

The charity can only make one grant per individual over a period of one year.

Applications

Application forms are available to download from the funder's website. Completed forms should be sent by post **only**. All applications should include a supporting letter from a recognised third party (doctor, social worker, health visitor, etc.). Copies of estimates or actual costs should also accompany all applications. The trustees meet on a quarterly basis to consider grant applications. For current application deadlines, see the funder's website.

Financial information

Year end	31/03/2018
Income	£222,200
Total expenditure	£335,400

Further financial information

Note: the grant total has been estimated.

Other information

This charity also makes grants to organisations. Recent examples include contributions towards the cost of a new church roof, school libraries and support for village halls and recreation grounds.

Sources of information

Accounts; annual report; Charity Commission record; funder's website.

Mendip

Keyford Educational Foundation

£1,600 (2018)

Correspondent: The Trustees, The Blue House, The Bridge, Frome, Somerset BA11 1AP (tel: 01373 462577; email: finance@thebluehousefrome.co.uk)

CC number: 309989

Eligibility

Young people aged up to 25 who live around the Frome area.

Types of grant

Students in further and higher education can be helped with clothing, books, equipment, fees and study or travel abroad.

Applications

Apply in writing to the correspondent.

Financial information

Year end	31/12/2018
Income	£1,900
Total expenditure	£1,800

Further financial information

Full accounts were not available to view on the Charity Commission's website due to the charity's low income. We have therefore estimated the grant total based on the charity's total expenditure.

Sources of information

Charity Commission record.

The Wells Clerical Charity

£2,900 (2018)

Correspondent: The Trustees, 6 The Liberty, Wells, Somerset BA5 2SU (tel: 01749 670777; email: general@bathwells.anglican.org)

CC number: 248436

Eligibility

People under the age of 25 who are the children of clergy members of the Church of England, including retired or deceased members who have served in the historic archdeaconry of Wells.

Types of grant

Grants are awarded towards education and for people preparing to enter a trade or profession. Support can be given towards travel costs, maintenance, clothing and so on.

Applications

Apply in writing to the correspondent.

Financial information

Year end	31/12/2018
Income	£10,000
Total expenditure	£6,500

Further financial information

Full accounts were not available to view on the Charity Commission's website due to the charity's low income. We have therefore estimated the grant total based on the charity's total expenditure.

Sources of information

Charity Commission record.

North Somerset

Nailsea Community Trust Ltd

 £4,000 (2018/19)

Correspondent: The Secretary, 1st Nailsea Scouts Training and Activity Centre, Clevedon Road, Nailsea, North Somerset BS48 1EH (email: info@nailseacommunitytrust.org.uk)

https://www.nailseacommunity trust.org.uk

CC number: 900031

Eligibility

Individuals who have lived in Nailsea, Backwell, Chelvey, Tickenham and Wraxall for at least 12 months.

Types of grant

Grants are awarded to assist with education, particularly in the areas of science, the arts, religion, commerce and healthcare.

Applications

Application forms can be downloaded from the trust's website. For further information or to discuss an urgent request, contact the trust via email including your contact details and one of the trust's directors will get in touch.

Financial information

Year end	31/03/2019
Income	£4,100
Total expenditure	£18,000

Further financial information

Full accounts were not available to view on the Charity Commission's website due to the charity's low income. We have therefore estimated the grant total based on the charity's total expenditure.

Other information

Grants are also awarded to organisations.

Sources of information

Charity Commission record; funder's website.

South Somerset

The Ilchester Relief in Need and Educational Charity (IRINEC)

 £8,300 (2018)

Correspondent: Kaye Elston, Clerk to the Trustees, 15 Chilton Grove, Yeovil, Somerset BA21 4AN (tel: 07782 251464)

www.ilchesterparishcouncil.gov.uk

CC number: 235578

Eligibility

People in need who live in the parish of Ilchester.

Types of grant

One-off grants are awarded to help with expenses at schools, universities, colleges or other educational organisations. They can help to provide books, tools, etc. or help with travel expenses.

Exclusions

Grants are not available where support should be received from statutory sources.

Applications

Application forms are available on request from the correspondent. The clerk welcomes initial telephone contact to discuss need and eligibility. Check the charity's website for dates applications should be received by.

Financial information

Year end	31/12/2018
Income	£38,200
Total expenditure	£36,600

Further financial information

The grant total has been estimated from the 2018 accounts.

Other information

Grants are also awarded to organisations for educational purposes.

Sources of information

Accounts; annual report; Charity Commission record; Ilchester Parish Council website.

Wiltshire

The Community Foundation for Wiltshire and Swindon

 £200,100 (2017/18)

Correspondent: Grants Team, Ground Floor, Sandcliff House, 21 Northgate Street, Devizes, Wiltshire SN10 1JT

(tel: 01380 729284; email: info@wiltshirecf.org.uk)

https://www.wiltshirecf.org.uk

CC number: 1123126

Eligibility

Individuals in need living in Wiltshire or Swindon. Visit the foundation's website for additional criteria specific to each grant.

Types of grant

The foundation currently provides the following educational grant schemes:

- **University bursary – one degree more:** Supports individuals between 17 and 24 who are about to begin, or who are already studying for an undergraduate degree at a UK university. Bursaries of £1,500 are awarded each year of the course towards living expenses, travel expenses (not including study abroad), books and course costs. In some cases an additional £500 can be granted for certain courses or situations

- **Vocational grants:** Grants are awarded to young people in need between 14 and 24 to support those at school, college, sixth form and those undertaking vocational courses and apprenticeships. Grants of up to £1,000 can be used towards travel costs, IT equipment course-related field trips, educational resources and so on

Visit the foundation's website for further information and specific criteria for each grant scheme. Welfare support is also available.

Applications

Application packs for educational support grants can be requested via the foundation's website.

Financial information

Year end	31/03/2018
Income	£2,750,000
Total expenditure	£1,620,000

Further financial information

In 2017/18 a total of £288,500 was awarded to individuals. Welfare grants totalled £88,400 including 265 surviving winter grants totalling £77,000 and 19 grants were made to schoolchildren totalling £11,400. Educational grants totalled £200,100 including 39 university grants worth £184,000 and 12 vocational grants totalling £16,100.

Other information

This is one of the 46 community foundations, which distribute funding for a wide range of purposes. Grant schemes tend to change frequently; therefore, consult the foundation's website for details of current programmes and upcoming deadlines.

Sources of information

Accounts; annual report; Charity Commission record; funder's website; Our Community Matters Wiltshire website.

Alice Coombe's Education Charity

£2,600 (2018)

Correspondent: The Trustees, 4 High Street, Tisbury, Wiltshire SP3 6LN (tel: 01747 871258; email: alicecombestrust@gmail.com)

CC number: 309359

Eligibility

Children and young people under the age of 25 who live in the ancient parish of Tisbury and West Tisbury.

Types of grant

One-off grants are available to secondary school students, higher or further education students, people in teacher training college or undertaking vocational training. People starting work can be given help towards books, equipment/instruments, clothing and travel.

Applications

Apply in writing to the correspondent.

Financial information

Year end	31/12/2018
Income	£3,600
Total expenditure	£2,900

Further financial information

Full accounts were not available to view on the Charity Commission's website due to the charity's low income. We have therefore estimated the grant total based on the charity's total expenditure.

Other information

Local schools may also be supported if there is excess income.

Sources of information

Charity Commission record.

The Rose Charity

£1,100 (2017/18)

Correspondent: The Trustees, 94 East Street, Warminster, Wiltshire BA12 9BG (tel: 01985 214444; email: cgoodbody@middletonssolicitors.co.uk)

CC number: 900590

Eligibility

Children in need who live in Warminster and the surrounding villages.

Types of grant

Grants are awarded towards educational costs.

Applications

Apply in writing to the correspondent.

Financial information

Year end	31/07/2018
Income	£1,600
Total expenditure	£2,500

Further financial information

Full accounts were not available to view on the Charity Commission's website due to the charity's low income. We have therefore estimated the grant total based on the charity's total expenditure.

Other information

Grants may also be made to organisations.

Sources of information

Charity Commission record.

Salisbury City Educational and Apprenticing Charity

£600 (2016/17)

Correspondent: Clerk to the Trustees, Trinity Hospital, Trinity Street, Salisbury, Wiltshire SP1 2BD (tel: 01722 325640; email: clerk@almshouses.demon.co.uk)

 www.salisburyalmshouses.co.uk

CC number: 309523

Eligibility

Young people under the age of 25 who live in the district of Salisbury.

Types of grant

Welfare grants are awarded for trips, play schemes, adventure activities, expeditions and voluntary work abroad.

Exclusions

Grants are not given for postgraduate study or for daily subsistence expenses (e.g. while at university). Regular payments towards fees or expenses are rarely made.

Applications

Application forms and full guidelines, stating what should be included, are available on the charity's website. Requests are considered on a monthly basis.

Financial information

Year end	24/12/2017
Income	£2,300
Total expenditure	£2,000

Further financial information

The charity's 2016/17 accounts were the latest available at the time of writing (October 2019). Full accounts were not available to view on the Charity Commission's website due to the charity's low income. We have therefore estimated the grant total based on the charity's total expenditure.

Other information

The charity shares the trustees with Salisbury City Almshouse and Welfare Charities (Charity Commission no. 202110), which maintains almshouses and may also provide emergency welfare support.

Sources of information

Charity Commission record; funder's website.

Yorkshire and the Humber

General

The Hesslewood Children's Trust (Hull Seamen's and General Orphanage)

£ £3,200 (2017/18)

Correspondent: Lynne Bullock, 62 The Meadows, Cherry Burton, East Yorkshire HU17 7RQ (tel: 01964 550882; email: misslynneb@aol.com)

CC number: 529804

Eligibility

People under the age of 25 who live or have a parent that lives in the former county of Humberside, or in the districts of Gainsborough or Caistor in Lincolnshire or who are former residents of the Hull Seamen's and General Orphanage. Preference shall be given to children of seamen.

Types of grant

One-off and recurring grants according to need.

Applications

Apply in writing to the correspondent.

Financial information

Year end	31/03/2018
Income	£112,400
Total expenditure	£110,100

Further financial information

Full accounts were not available to view on the Charity Commission's website due to the charity's low income. We have therefore estimated the grant total based on the charity's total expenditure.

Other information

The trust also awards grants to organisations active in the local communities.

Sources of information

Charity Commission record.

Split Infinitive Trust
See record on page 29

East Riding of Yorkshire

Christopher Eden Educational Foundation

£ £7,600 (2017/18)

Correspondent: Judy Dickinson, Trustee, 85 East Street, Leven, Beverley HU17 5NG (tel: 01964 542593; email: judydickinson@mac.com)

 beverley.gov.uk/news/609/creating-opportunities-for-everyone

CC number: 529794

Eligibility

Young people under the age of 25 who live in the town of Beverley and surrounding areas, or have attended school in the area.

Types of grant

Financial support is available for any educational need. This includes, apprenticeship equipment, further and higher education expenses, books, clothing, educational trips and sport, music and art studies.

Applications

Application forms can be obtained from the following: Beverley Library, East Riding Council Customer Information office and local schools. Forms can also be requested from the correspondent.

Financial information

Year end	31/03/2018
Income	£11,800
Total expenditure	£8,500

Further financial information

Full accounts were not available to view on the Charity Commission's website due to the charity's low income. We have therefore estimated the grant total based on the charity's total expenditure.

Sources of information

Charity Commission record; funder's website.

Hook and Goole Charity

£ £11,300 (2018)

Correspondent: The Secretary, c/o Castaway Music Theatre, Estcourt Street, Goole, East Riding of Yorkshire DN14 5AS (tel: 07539 269813)

 www.hookandgoolecharity.org.uk

CC number: 513948

Eligibility

Students and apprentices aged between 17 and 25 who live (or have parents living) in either the former borough of Goole or the parish of Hook, or who have attended a school in this area for at least two years. Applicants must be taking a course or an apprenticeship of two years or longer and must have already completed at least one year (first-year students should apply next year).

Types of grant

The charity provides bursaries to support students in higher education. Grants are awarded to support all areas of education including things such as equipment, clothing, transport or special needs. The charity will also consider applications from apprentices to assist with the cost of tools, books and other items needed during their training. The amount of money available for grants may vary from year to year depending on the number of applicants.

Applications

Application forms can be downloaded from the charity's website or requested in writing from the correspondent. Once completed, the form should be submitted by post. The application deadline is usually towards the end of September; however, refer to the website for specific dates.

Financial information

Year end	31/12/2018
Income	£16,900
Total expenditure	£12,500

Further financial information

Full accounts were not available to view on the Charity Commission's website due to the charity's low income. We have therefore estimated the grant total based on the charity's total expenditure.

Other information

This charity may also give grants to local schools and for charitable purposes that benefit the residents of the area.

Sources of information

Charity Commission record; funder's website.

James Graves

£ £590 (2017/18)

Correspondent: The Trustees, 10 West Close, Beverley, East Riding of Yorkshire HU17 7JJ (tel: 01482 867958; email: ian_merryweather@hotmail.co.uk)

CC number: 529796

Eligibility

Children and young people who live in the parishes of St Martin and St John, Beverley.

Types of grant

Grants are awarded towards the costs of education and training.

Applications

Apply in writing to the correspondent.

Financial information

Year end	31/03/2018
Income	£1,200
Total expenditure	£1,300

Further financial information

Full accounts were not available to view on the Charity Commission's website due to the charity's low income. We have therefore estimated the grant total based on the charity's total expenditure.

Other information

The charity also supports local organisations.

Sources of information

Charity Commission record.

The Nafferton Feoffees Charities Trust

£ £16,900 (2018)

Correspondent: The Secretary, c/o South Cattleholmes, Wansford, Driffield, East Yorkshire YO25 8NW (tel: 01377 254293; email: secretary@feoffeetrust.co.uk)

 www.feoffeetrust.co.uk

CC number: 232796

Eligibility

Individuals living in the parish of All Saints Nafferton with St Mary's Wansford who are intending to undertake a first degree at a UK university or college.

Types of grant

Bursaries are available to local students who are undertaking a first degree. Up to £2,100 per year for each year of the course can be awarded towards books, course materials, study visits and other educational expenses. The trust will also provide support to mature students.

Applications

Application forms for the scholarship scheme can be downloaded from the trust's website or requested from the correspondent. Applicants may be invited for an interview. Consult the website for current deadlines.

Financial information

Year end	31/12/2018
Income	£32,000
Total expenditure	£36,000

Further financial information

In 2018 scholarships totalled £16,900 and £1,300 was awarded for welfare purposes.

Other information

Grants are also made to local organisations.

Sources of information

Accounts; annual report; Charity Commission record; funder's website.

Charity of Peter Nevill

£ £1,100 (2017/18)

Correspondent: The Trustees, Marleigh, Arnold Lane West, Arnold, Hull, East Yorkshire HU11 5HP (tel: 01964 562872)

CC number: 506325

Eligibility

Young people under the age of 25 who live, or who have a parent living, in the parish of Long Riston and Arnold.

Types of grant

Grants are awarded towards educational needs including social and physical training.

Applications

Apply in writing to the correspondent.

Financial information

Year end	31/03/2018
Income	£2,700
Total expenditure	£2,600

Further financial information

Full accounts were not available to view on the Charity Commission's website due to the charity's low income. We have therefore estimated the grant total based on the charity's total expenditure.

Other information

Grants are also given to organisations.

Sources of information

Charity Commission record.

Prowde's Educational Foundation (Prowde's Charity)

See record on page 263

The Rawcliffe Educational Charity

£ £3,800 (2016/17)

Correspondent: The Trustees, 26 Station Road, Rawcliffe, Goole, East Yorkshire DN14 8QR (tel: 01405 839637)

CC number: 509656

Eligibility

People under the age of 25 who (or whose parents) live in the parish of Rawcliffe and who have attended one of the local schools, particularly those over 18 who are starting university.

Types of grant

Grants are awarded to assist students going into higher/further education towards the cost of study.

Applications

Apply in writing to the correspondent.

Financial information

Year end	31/08/2017
Income	£9,600
Total expenditure	£8,500

Further financial information

The 2016/17 accounts were the latest available at the time of writing (December 2019). Full accounts were not available to view on the Charity Commission's website due to the charity's low income. We have therefore estimated the grant total based on the charity's total expenditure.

Other information

The charity also provides scientific calculators to each child in the parish who is leaving primary school and going into secondary education.

Sources of information

Accounts; annual report; Charity Commission record.

Nancie Reckitt Charity

£8,700 (2017/18)

Correspondent: The Trustees, 19 Northside, Patrington, Hull, East Yorkshire HU12 0PA (tel: 01964 630960; email: maureenstansfield838@btinternet.com)

CC number: 509380

Eligibility

People under the age of 25 who (or whose parents) have lived in the parishes of Patrington, Rimswell and Winestead for at least five years.

Types of grant

Grants are awarded to individuals to be used towards the cost of education.

Applications

Apply in writing to the correspondent.

Financial information

Year end	28/02/2018
Income	£7,000
Total expenditure	£9,700

Further financial information

Full accounts were not available to view on the Charity Commission's website due to the charity's low income. We have therefore estimated the grant total based on the charity's total expenditure.

Sources of information

Charity Commission record.

Henry Samman's Hull Chamber of Commerce Endowment Fund

£7,700 (2017)

Correspondent: The Secretary, Hull and Humber Chamber of Commerce, Industry and Shipping, 34–38 Beverley Road, Hull, East Yorkshire HU3 1YE (tel: 01482 324976; email: i.kelly@hull-humber-chamber.co.uk)

 https://www.hull-humber-chamber.co.uk/pages/henry-samman-fund

CC number: 228837

Eligibility

British citizens who are over the age of 18 and are studying either business methods (business studies) or a foreign language. Preference is given to young people from Hull and East Riding or Northern Lincolnshire. Candidates should be studying or planning to study at degree level.

Types of grant

Bursaries to enable individuals to spend a period of three to twelve months abroad in connection to their studies of business methods and/or foreign languages. The award is generally of around £100 a month. Longer periods of travel may be funded at the trustees' discretion.

Applications

Apply in writing to the correspondent. Applications should be sent before the proposed date of departure. Successful applicants will be required to write a report to the trustees halfway through their period abroad highlighting how they have benefited in the 'study of business methods and/or languages', while they have been away.

Financial information

Year end	31/12/2017
Income	£10,800
Total expenditure	£8,500

Further financial information

Full accounts were not available to view on the Charity Commission's website due to the charity's low income. We have therefore estimated the grant total based on the charity's total expenditure.

Other information

The fund was set up in 1917 originally to encourage the study of Russian, in a commercial context, but has since widened its remit.

Sources of information

Charity Commission record; funder's website.

The Town Trust or Lords Estate

£52,200 (2018)

Correspondent: Cheryl Walker, Clerk to the Trustees, Manor House, 64 High St, Bridlington, East Riding of Yorkshire YO16 4PZ (tel: 01262 674308; email: office@lordsfeoffees.com)

 https://www.lordsfeoffees.co.uk/about-the-lords

CC number: 252207

Eligibility

Students living in Bridlington who are undertaking an undergraduate degree at university or college.

Types of grant

Grants of up to £1,200 for three years towards the costs of studying.

Applications

Application forms will become available when submissions open, usually in spring each year. Check the charity's website for current dates. Applicants are considered on the basis of academic ability, commitment to work and financial need. Candidates may be required to attend an interview.

Financial information

Year end	31/12/2018
Income	£737,200
Total expenditure	£545,000

Other information

Grants are also given to organisations including local schools and sports clubs.

Sources of information

Accounts; annual report; Charity Commission record; funder's website.

Robert Towrie's Charity

£3,000 (2017/18)

Correspondent: The Trustees, Stud Farm, Hull Road, Aldbrough, Hull, East Yorkshire HU11 4RE (tel: 01964 527580; email: roberttowerytrust@googlemail.com)

CC number: 222568

Eligibility

Educational grants are available to residents in the parishes of Aldbrough and Burton Constable.

Types of grant

One-off and recurring grants according to need.

Applications

Apply in writing to the correspondent.

Financial information

Year end	01/04/2018
Income	£11,500
Total expenditure	£13,100

Further financial information

Full accounts were not available to view on the Charity Commission's website due to the charity's low income. We have therefore estimated the grant total based on the charity's total expenditure.

Other information

The charity makes grants to individuals and organisations for both educational and welfare needs.

Wray Educational Trust

 £1,400 (2016/17)

Correspondent: Judy Dickinson, Trustee, 85 East Street, Leven, Beverley, East Yorkshire HU17 5NG (tel: 01964 542593; email: judydickinson@mac.com)

https://levencofe.eschools.co.uk/ website/home/413032

CC number: 508468

Eligibility
People under the age of 25 who have lived in the parish of Leven for at least three years.

Types of grant
Grants are awarded to students in further or higher education and people starting work. Support is available towards general educational costs, including books, equipment/instruments, fees, educational outings, study or travel abroad and musical or sports activities.

Applications
Application forms can be downloaded from the Leven CE Primary School website. Alternatively, forms can be obtained directly from the school or from the Leven Post Office. Applications should be submitted by early January, April, July and October for consideration during that month.

Financial information
Year end	31/10/2017
Income	£7,500
Total expenditure	£6,200

Further financial information
The 2016/17 accounts were the latest available at the time of writing (November 2019). Full accounts were not available to view on the Charity Commission's website due to the charity s low income. We have therefore estimated the grant total based on the charity s total expenditure.

Other information
The trust also makes grants to local organisations that work with young people.

Sources of information
Accounts; annual report; Charity Commission record; funder's website.

Kingston

Alderman Ferries Charity (Hull United Charities)

 £22,000 (2017/18)

Correspondent: Janine Lambert, Secretary, Hull United Charities, Northumberland Court, Northumberland Avenue, Hull, East Yorkshire HU2 0LR (tel: 01482 323965; email: info@hullunitedcharities.org.uk)

www.hullunitedcharities.org.uk/ alderman-ferries.html

CC number: 529821

Eligibility
People under the age of 25 who are entering further/higher education or apprenticeships and who live in the city of Kingston upon Hull or have attended a primary/secondary school in the area for at least two years prior to applying. Candidates must be willing to provide the trustees with any such information they require, including proof of identity and address.

Types of grant
Grants are awarded for fees, clothing, travel costs, maintenance expenses and any other purpose that enables the advancement of education.

Applications
Application forms and detailed guidelines are available on the charity's website or can be requested from the correspondent. The trustees consider grants every December and applications should be submitted by the middle of November. Applicants may be required to attend an interview if the trustees see fit.

Financial information
Year end	31/03/2018
Income	£15,300
Total expenditure	£24,400

Further financial information
Full accounts were not available to view on the Charity Commission's website due to the charity's low income. We have therefore estimated the grant total based on the charity's total expenditure.

Sources of information
Charity Commission record; funder's website.

Dr A. E. Hart Trust

 £20,500 (2017/18)

Correspondent: The Secretary, Williamsons Solicitors, 45 Lowgate, Hull, East Yorkshire HU1 1EN (tel: 01482 323697; email: jane.cousins@williamsons. co.uk)

 www.williamsons-solicitors.co.uk/ dr-hart-trust

CC number: 529780

Eligibility
Eligible candidates must: be at least 18 years old; be studying for their first degree (or equivalent), PGCE, Legal Practice Course (LPC) or Bar Professional Training Course (BPTC); reside within the boundary of the city and county of Kingston upon Hull; agree to permit the trustees to verify information provided in any manner they wish.

Types of grant
Small grants are awarded at the discretion of the trustees who will consider the following in order to determine the amount that will be offered to the individual: the proposed programme of study, income and any forms of support available to the individual, costs of the programme and any special circumstances.

Exclusions
Surrounding villages are not included (e.g. Willerby, Hessle, Anlaby and Hedon). Applications from students who are resident in Hull only because they are attending an educational institution there will not be considered.

Applications
Application forms are available to download from the trust's website. Applications must be filled out in block capitals and black ink. Applications cannot be considered unless all supporting documentation is attached. Eight copies of the application must be submitted before December (i.e. the original plus seven photocopies). Applications received after the deadline will not be considered unless exceptional circumstances are outlined in the application.

Financial information
Year end	30/09/2018
Income	£21,800
Total expenditure	£22,700

Further financial information
Full accounts were not available to view on the Charity Commission's website due to the charity's low income. We have therefore estimated the grant total based on the charity's total expenditure.

Other information
The funder's website states: 'Grants available from the Trust are relatively modest and are most unlikely to have any significant bearing on an applicant's decision to embark on any given course.'

Sources of information
Charity Commission record; funder's website.

The Jvenn Foundation

 £66,900 (2018/19)

Correspondent: John Cliff, Trustee, c/o HEY Smile Foundation, The Loft, Dock Street, Hull, Surrey HU1 3AE (tel: 07856 751176; email: info@jvennfoundation.org)

www.jvennfoundation.org

CC number: 1160632

Eligibility
Young people under the age of 23, who are currently resident in the city of Hull, and are going to begin studying for a first degree at a British university or for an alternative tertiary qualification. According to the foundation's website, applicants must fall into one or more of the following categories of eligibility:

- Financial – a combined parent/guardian income of less than £20,000 per year
- Disability – the student has a disability and is in receipt of appropriate disability benefit
- In care – students currently in care, care-leavers or those who have been in care for more than six months over the last three years
- Carers and parents – students who are carers or parents
- Ethnic minority – including refugees and those from traveller families

Types of grant
The foundation provides bursaries of £5,000 per year for students studying for a first degree at a British university, or pursuing another tertiary educational qualification.

Applications
Application forms are available to download from the foundation's website and should be submitted either by post or email or through the head of the applicant's school or college. A statement from a sponsor (a lecturer or teacher) should also be included – further guidance is given on the website. Up-to-date deadlines for applications are stated on the website – applicants are usually shortlisted in May and interviews are arranged soon afterwards.

Financial information
Year end	28/02/2019
Income	£127,800
Total expenditure	£82,900

Further financial information
Bursaries totalling £66,700 were awarded to 17 individuals. Gift vouchers totalling £200 were awarded to unsuccessful applicants.

Other information
The foundation also awards grants to secondary schools in Hull to support extracurricular activities and activities related to reading and writing.

Sources of information
Accounts; annual report; Charity Commission record; funder's website.

Kingston upon Hull Education Foundation

 £1,000 (2017/18)

Correspondent: The Trustees, Corporate Finance, City Treasury, Hull City Council, Guildhall Road, Hull, East Yorkshire HU1 2AB (tel: 01482 615010; email: corpfinanceplanning@hullcc.gov.uk)

www.hull.gov.uk/benefits-support-and-welfare-advice/welfare-advice/educational-trust-funds

CC number: 514427

Eligibility
People over 13 who live, or whose parents live, in the city of Kingston upon Hull and either attend, or have attended, a school in the city.

Types of grant
Grants are awarded to assist young people preparing to enter a trade, occupation, profession or service and can be used towards clothing, tools or instruments.

Applications
Apply in writing to the correspondent. Alternatively, application forms are available to download from the Hull City Council website. Deadlines for applications are usually the last week in October and the middle of February, applications are considered in November and February.

Financial information
Year end	31/03/2018
Income	£4,900
Total expenditure	£1,200

Further financial information
Full accounts were not available to view on the Charity Commission's website due to the charity's low income. We have therefore estimated the grant total based on the charity's total expenditure.

Sources of information
Charity Commission record; funder's website.

Lincolnshire (formerly part of Humberside)

Freshtime Futures Trust

Correspondent: John Stokes, Secretary, Glen Fairways, Reservoir Road, Spalding PE11 4DH (tel: 01205 312010; email: brittany.jarman@greencore.com)

 https://freshtimefuturestrust.org

CC number: 1171984

Eligibility
Children and young people aged 11 to 25 who live in Lincolnshire and are in need.

Types of grant
The charity can make grants for a range of educational purposes, including for specialist training/apprenticeship schemes (and other academic pursuits), travel expenses and course materials.

Applications
Applications can be made on the funder's website using an online form. Alternatively, applicants may wish to download a copy of the application form and, once completed, send it by post to the charity.

Financial information
Year end	31/03/2019
Income	£131,900
Total expenditure	£103,000

Further financial information
During 2018/19, no grants were given for educational purposes.

Sources of information
Accounts; annual report; Charity Commission record; funder's website.

The Kochan Trust

£24,200 (2017/18)

Correspondent: Revd Roger Massingberd-Mundy, Honorary Secretary, The Old Post Office, The Street, West Raynham, Fakenham, Norfolk NR21 7AD (tel: 01328 838611; email: revmassingberd@gmail.com)

CC number: 1052976

Eligibility

People living in Lincolnshire who study creative arts, music or veterinary science and are in need of financial assistance.

Types of grant

One-off grants are awarded towards the costs of study, veterinary research, course expenses, the purchase of instruments and so on.

Applications

Apply in writing to the correspondent including details about the candidate and what the grant is needed for. Applications can be made by individuals directly or through a third party, such as a school/college or educational welfare agency.

Financial information

Year end	31/03/2018
Income	£40,200
Total expenditure	£32,400

Further financial information

In 2017/18 a total of £24,200 was awarded to individuals and is broken down as follows:

Veterinary grants	8	£14,400
Music and arts grants	14	£9,800

Other information

Grants are also awarded to local churches.

Sources of information

Accounts; annual report; Charity Commission record; Uni Grants website.

North Lincolnshire

Henry Samman's Hull Chamber of Commerce Endowment Fund

See record on page 269

Withington Education Trust

£ £5,400 (2017/18)

Correspondent: The Trustees, Frederick Gough School, Grange Lane South, Bottesford, Scunthorpe, Lincolnshire DN16 3NG (tel: 01724 860151; email: escatola@frederickgoughschool.co.uk)

CC number: 507975

Eligibility

People under the age of 21 who live in the North Lincolnshire Council area. This area is comprised of Scunthorpe, Glanford and Boothferry, excluding the parishes of East Halton, North Killingholme and South Killingholme,

and the part of the district of Boothferry that lies north of the river Ouse.

Types of grant

Grants that enable individuals to continue or begin educational courses or to undertake ventures that the trustees consider fall within the objects of the trust.

Applications

Apply in writing to the correspondent.

Financial information

Year end	31/08/2018
Income	£4,000
Total expenditure	£6,000

Further financial information

Full accounts were not available to view on the Charity Commission's website due to the charity's low income. We have therefore estimated the grant total based on the charity's total expenditure.

Sources of information

Charity Commission record.

North Yorkshire

The Beckwith Bequest

£ £3,500 (2017/18)

Correspondent: The Clerk, 2 Station Court, Tollerton, York, North Yorkshire YO61 1RH (tel: 07929 372352; email: beckwithbequest@outlook.com)

 www.husthwaite.n-yorks.sch.uk/ useful-links/partnerships

CC number: 532360

Eligibility

People who live or were educated in the parishes of Easingwold and Husthwaite.

Types of grant

Grants are available to assist with the furtherance of education and can help towards the cost of books, equipment, instruments, etc.

Applications

Applications can be found on the Husthwaite Church of England Primary School's website or can be requested from the correspondent.

Financial information

Year end	31/03/2018
Income	£11,900
Total expenditure	£5,200

Further financial information

Full accounts were not available to view on the Charity Commission's website due to the charity's low income. We

have therefore estimated the grant total based on the charity's total expenditure.

Other information

Grants may also be awarded to organisations and local schools.

Sources of information

Charity Commission record; funder's website.

The Gargrave Poor's Land Charity

£ £16,800 (2017/18)

Correspondent: Mr D. H. Turner, Secretary, Kirk Syke, High Street, Gargrave, Skipton, North Yorkshire BD23 3RA (tel: 01756 748117)

CC number: 225067

Eligibility

People who are in need and are permanently resident in Gargrave, Banknewton, Coniston Cold, Flasby, Eshton or Winterburn.

Types of grant

Grants to students towards the costs of maintenance, books and tuition fees. The 2018 annual report states that the trustees want to extend the support to students taking vocational further educational courses and other vocational training.

Applications

Applications can be made on a form, which is available from the correspondent, and can be submitted at any time.

Financial information

Year end	05/04/2018
Income	£26,855
Total expenditure	£55,392

Other information

The charity also makes grants to organisations.

Sources of information

Accounts; annual report; Charity Commission record.

Reverend Matthew Hutchinson Charity (Gilling and Richmond)

£ £2,500 (2018)

Correspondent: The Trustees, Oak Tree View, Hutton Magna, Richmond, North Yorkshire DL11 7HQ (tel: 01833 627997; email: gilling.matthewhutchinsontrust@ gmail.com (for Gilling branch) richmond.matthewhutchinsontrust@ gmail.com (for Richmond branch))

CC number: 220870/220779

Eligibility

Residents in the parishes of Gilling and Richmond who are in need.

Types of grant

Educational grants have been made previously for equipment, travel and books required for training as well as academic study.

Applications

Apply in writing to the correspondent.

Financial information

Year end	31/12/2018
Income	£24,600
Total expenditure	£11,300

Further financial information

Full accounts were not available to view on the Charity Commission's website due to the charity's low income. We have therefore estimated the grant total based on the charity's total expenditure.

Other information

This charity also makes grants to organisations.

Sources of information

Charity Commission record.

Knowles Educational Foundation (Acaster Malbis Knowles Education Foundation)

£1,400 (2018)

Correspondent: Julia Campbell, Secretary, 39 Mill Lane, Acaster Malbis, York, North Yorkshire YO23 2UJ (tel: 01904 705527; email: julia.campbell13@icloud.com)

 https://www.naburnvillage.org/knowles-educational-foundation

CC number: 529183

Eligibility

Children and young people in need living in the villages of Acaster Malbis and Naburn.

College/university students and apprentices living in the villages of Acaster Malbis and Naburn.

Types of grant

Grants are awarded towards a range of educational purposes including extracurricular lessons and exams, school trips, equipment and any other costs that may arise from an educational course.

Student grants are awarded towards educational trips, books for coursework, equipment required for courses (including computers), travel and any other costs relating to a course or apprenticeship. In some cases the foundation may provide funding towards accommodation.

Applications

Apply in writing to the correspondent. The trustees meet three times a year, in March, June and October, to consider applications.

Financial information

Year end	31/12/2018
Income	£3,500
Total expenditure	£6,100

Further financial information

Full accounts were not available to view on the Charity Commission's website due to the charity's low income. We have therefore estimated the grant total based on the charity's total expenditure.

Other information

Grants may also be awarded to organisations.

Sources of information

Charity Commission record; funder's website.

Raygill Trust

£2,300 (2017/18)

Correspondent: The Trustees, 6 The Fold, Lothersdale, Keighley, West Yorkshire BD20 8HD (tel: 01535 636682; email: stephen.z.brown@btinternet.com)

CC number: 249199

Eligibility

Educational grants are available to full-time students on a first degree, or an equivalent course at a university or college, who live in the ecclesiastical parish of Lothersdale. Grants are made to applicants in their first three years of further education.

Types of grant

One-off and recurring grants according to need.

Applications

Apply in writing to the correspondent.

Financial information

Year end	18/07/2018
Income	£11,900
Total expenditure	£10,300

Further financial information

Full accounts were not available to view on the Charity Commission's website due to the charity's low income. We have therefore estimated the grant total based on the charity's total expenditure.

Other information

This charity also makes grants to organisations.

Sources of information

Charity Commission record.

John Stockton Educational Foundation

£1,500 (2018/19)

Correspondent: Mary Kendall, Clerk, Park Garth, School Lane, Nawton, York, North Yorkshire YO62 7SF (tel: 01439 771575; email: marykendall@hotmail.co.uk)

CC number: 529642

Eligibility

Higher education students and apprentices aged 25 and under who live in Kirkbymoorside or other specified parishes in the area.

Types of grant

Grants for higher education and apprenticeships to be used towards books, fees, equipment and tools.

Applications

Apply in writing to the correspondent.

Financial information

Year end	28/02/2019
Income	£1,400
Total expenditure	£1,700

Further financial information

Full accounts were not available to view on the Charity Commission's website due to the charity's low income. We have therefore estimated the grant total based on the charity's total expenditure.

Sources of information

Charity Commission record.

Scarborough United Scholarships Foundation

£3,400 (2018/19)

Correspondent: Anne Marr, Secretary, 11A Lightfoots Close, Scarborough, North Yorkshire YO12 5NR (tel: 01723 375908; email: a.j.marr3@outlook.com)

CC number: 529678

Eligibility

People under the age of 25 who live in the borough of Scarborough. Previous research suggests applicants should have attended school in the area for at least three years.

Types of grant

Grants are awarded to assist with the cost of education. In the past the foundation has awarded grants towards specific items with an educational benefit, such as computers, travel expenses, projects or equipment as well as supporting study of music and the arts, vocational studies, educational visits, work experience opportunities and support for children with special needs.

Applications

Apply in writing to the correspondent.

Financial information

Year end	31/03/2019
Income	£9,600
Total expenditure	£7,500

Further financial information

Full accounts were not available to view on the Charity Commission's website due to the charity's low income. We have therefore estimated the grant total based on the charity's total expenditure.

Sources of information

Charity Commission record.

Madeleine Mary Walker Foundation

 £600 (2017/18)

Correspondent: The Trustees, 1 Levington Wynd, Nunthorpe, Middlesbrough, North Yorkshire TS7 0QD (email: m100pfb@yahoo.co.uk)

https://mmwf2003.org

CC number: 1062657

Eligibility

People in need of support towards their education. Priority is given to those living within a 30-mile radius of Stokesley, North Yorkshire and those working towards their first degree or equivalent.

Types of grant

Support can be given towards the cost of education including books, tuition fees, tools, equipment, instruments, travel, projects abroad and field studies.

Applications

Applications can be submitted electronically using the form available on the foundation's website. Alternatively, forms can be downloaded can from the website and returned by email to the correspondent. Applicants will undergo a telephone interview before grants are awarded. If the foundation has not responded within two months, it should be assumed the application was unsuccessful.

Financial information

Year end	31/03/2018
Income	£44,300
Total expenditure	£14,400

Other information

The foundation also makes grants to organisations, particularly local colleges.

Sources of information

Accounts; annual report; Charity Commission record; funder's website.

Yorebridge Educational Foundation

£3,600 (2017/18)

Correspondent: The Trustees, The Marshes, Moor Road, Bellerby, Leyburn, North Yorkshire DL8 3RA (tel: 01969 622300; email: bobtunstall@hotmail.co.uk)

CC number: 518826

Eligibility

People under the age of 25 who live or have a parent living in the area of benefit which includes the parishes of Askrigg, Aysgarth, Bainbridge, Bellerby, Bishopdale, Burton-cum-Walden, Caldbergh with East Scrafton, Carlton Highdale, Carlton Town, Carperby-cum-Thoresby, Castle Bolton with East and West Bolton, Coverham with Agglethorpe, East Witton Out, Harmby, Hawes, High Abbotside, Leyburn, Low Abbotside, Melmerby, Middleham, Newbiggin, Preston under Scar, Redmire, Spennithorne, Thoralby, Thornton Rust, Wensley, West Scrafton and West Witton.

Preference is given to those who either live or have a parent living in the parishes of Askrigg, Bainbridge, Hawes, High Abbotside or Low Abbotside.

Types of grant

Small grants are awarded for educational purposes, including towards the cost of higher education.

Applications

Apply in writing to the correspondent.

Financial information

Year end	31/03/2018
Income	£18,700
Total expenditure	£8,000

Further financial information

Full accounts were not available to view on the Charity Commission's website due to the charity's low income. We have therefore estimated the grant total based on the charity's total expenditure.

Other information

Grants are also available to organisations.

Sources of information

Charity Commission record.

Harrogate
The Haywra Crescent Educational Trust Fund

 £1,300 (2017/18)

Correspondent: Post-16 Team, Jesmond House, 31/33 Victoria Avenue, Harrogate, North Yorkshire HG1 5QE (tel: 01609 780780; email: post16@northyorks.gov.uk)

https://www.northyorks.gov.uk/news/article/grants-offer-help-students

CC number: 1042141

Eligibility

Students who live in the Harrogate Borough Council area and are undertaking any form of post-16 education.

Types of grant

Grants are available towards books, equipment and educational travel for people studying at college, university or other institution of further education.

Applications

Application forms and further guidelines can be requested from the correspondent.

Financial information

Year end	31/03/2018
Income	£7,000
Total expenditure	£1,400

Further financial information

Full accounts were not available to view on the Charity Commission's website due to the charity's low income. We have therefore estimated the grant total based on the charity's total expenditure.

Sources of information

Charity Commission record; funder's website; Harrogate Informer website.

Ryedale
Christopher Wharton Educational Foundation

£1,400 (2017/18)

Correspondent: The Trustees, 12 Hudson Close, Stamford Bridge, York, North Yorkshire YO41 1QR (tel: 01759 373842)

CC number: 506958

Eligibility

Young people between the ages of 18 and 25 who are in need of financial assistance and who live, or have parents living, in the areas of Stamford Bridge, Gate Helmsley and Kexby.

Types of grant
Grants are awarded to promote education and training.

Applications
Apply in writing to the correspondent.

Financial information

Year end	20/12/2018
Income	£1,900
Total expenditure	£1,500

Further financial information
Full accounts were not available to view on the Charity Commission's website due to the charity's low income. We have therefore estimated the grant total based on the charity's total expenditure.

Sources of information
Charity Commission record.

York

The Company of Merchant Taylors of the City of York (Merchant Taylors – York)

£8,900 (2017/18)

Correspondent: Clerk, UHY Calvert Smith Accountants, 31 St Saviourgate, York, North Yorkshire YO1 8NQ (tel: 01904 557570; email: clerk@ merchant-taylors-york.org)

www.merchant-taylors-york.org

CC number: 229067

Eligibility
Young people in education or training in the fields of arts, music and craftsmanship who live in York and the surrounding area.

Types of grant
Bursaries, prizes and other grants are available for a wide range of activities under the headings of arts, music and craftsmanship to develop applicants' skills and enhance their career prospects. Typically grants are of up to £1,000.

Applications
Application forms can be downloaded from the charity's website or requested from the correspondent. Applications can be submitted at any time and should be sent by email to the correspondent.

Financial information

Year end	24/06/2018
Income	£91,600
Total expenditure	£70,500

Other information
The charity also maintains the company's hall and premises, almshouses and documents; runs the guild; pays pensions to tailors in the area of benefit; and supports individuals and organisations for welfare causes. The amount awarded to individuals for educational purposes includes the annual David Cramb Memorial Prizes for the best performing students on the York College BA Fashion Design Programme, and bursaries awarded to students in the fashion, music, drama and craft departments at York College.

Sources of information
Accounts; annual report; Charity Commission record; funder's website.

South Yorkshire

The Elmhirst Trust

£3,500 (2018/19)

Correspondent: The Trustees, 2 Paddock Close, Staincross, Barnsley, South Yorkshire S75 6LH (tel: 01226 384563)

CC number: 701369

Eligibility
People living in Barnsley, Doncaster and Rotherham who are seeking personal or professional development, usually after a life change, but are in need of financial assistance.

Types of grant
Grants are awarded to assist with the costs of education, training, workshops and work experience to enable applicants to obtain vocational skills and gain employment.

Applications
Apply in writing to the correspondent.

Financial information

Year end	31/03/2019
Income	£5,000
Total expenditure	£3,900

Further financial information
Full accounts were not available to view on the Charity Commission's website due to the charity's low income. We have therefore estimated the grant total based on the charity's total expenditure.

Sources of information
Charity Commission record.

The Swann-Morton Foundation

£14,000 (2017/18)

Correspondent: Michael Hirst, Swann-Morton Ltd, Owlerton Green, Sheffield, South Yorkshire S6 2BJ (tel: 0114 234 4231)

CC number: 271925

Eligibility
People studying or working in the fields of surgery and medicine.

Types of grant
Grants according to need to students of medicine and surgery for electives, general educational expenses and research projects.

Applications
Apply in writing to the correspondent. The foundation's annual report for 2017/18 states that it:

> Invites applications for funding of projects from hospitals, charities and students. Applicants are invited to submit a summary of their proposals in a specific format. The applications are reviewed against specific criteria and research objectives which are set by the trustees.

Financial information

Year end	30/06/2018
Income	£75,000
Total expenditure	£75,300

Other information
The foundation welcomes applications from individual students, charities and hospitals. Support can also be given to current or former employees of W. R. Swann and Co. Ltd.

Sources of information
Accounts; annual report; Charity Commission record.

Doncaster

Robert Woods Exhibition Foundation

£950 (2017/18)

Correspondent: The Trustees, 15 Woodford Road, Barnby Dun, Doncaster, South Yorkshire DN3 1BN (tel: 01302 883496)

CC number: 529415

Eligibility
Students in higher education who live in the parish of Kirk Sandall.

Types of grant
Grants are available for young people undertaking higher/further education and training.

Applications

Apply in writing to the correspondent.

Financial information

Year end	31/03/2018
Income	£1,100
Total expenditure	£1,400

Further financial information

Full accounts were not available to view on the Charity Commission's website due to the charity's low income. We have therefore estimated the grant total based on the charity's total expenditure.

Other information

The charity also supports a local library.

Sources of information

Charity Commission record.

Sheffield

Bolsterstone Educational Charity

£ £3,700 (2017/18)

Correspondent: Cliff North, 5 Pennine View, Stocksbridge, Sheffield, South Yorkshire S36 1ER (tel: 0114 288 2757; email: cliff.north39@icloud.com)

CC number: 529371

Eligibility

People between the ages of 16 and 25 who live in the parishes of St Mary, Bolsterstone and St Matthias, Stocksbridge.

Types of grant

Grants are awarded for general educational purposes such as books and equipment as well as towards the costs of university or other higher education courses and apprenticeships.

Exclusions

Grants are not given to A-level students.

Applications

Apply in writing to the correspondent.

Financial information

Year end	31/03/2018
Income	£10,600
Total expenditure	£8,100

Further financial information

Full accounts were not available to view on the Charity Commission's website due to the charity's low income. We have therefore estimated the grant total based on the charity's total expenditure.

Other information

The charity also supports a number of local schools.

Sources of information

Charity Commission record.

The Sheffield Bluecoat and Mount Pleasant Educational Foundation

£ £5,500 (2017/18)

Correspondent: Ms S. M. Greaves, Secretary, Wrigleys Solicitors, 3rd Floor, Fountain Precinct, Balm Green, Sheffield, South Yorkshire S1 2JA (tel: 01426 75588; email: sue.greaves@wrigleys.co.uk)

CC number: 529351

Eligibility

Young people under the age of 25 who live within a 20-mile radius of Sheffield city centre and are in need.

Types of grant

Grants can assist with a wide range of educational purposes including course fees, maintenance allowances, educational travel, the study of music and the arts and so forth.

Welfare support is also available.

Applications

Application forms can be requested from the correspondent both in hard copy and by email. Application forms should be submitted along with supporting documents and evidence of financial need. The trustees usually meet twice a year to consider applications.

Financial information

Year end	31/03/2018
Income	£63,100
Total expenditure	£64,800

Further financial information

In 2017/18 a total of £11,000 was awarded to 15 individuals. We estimate that around £5,500 was awarded for welfare purposes and £5,500 for education.

Other information

The foundation also supports local organisations.

Sources of information

Accounts; annual report; Charity Commission record.

Sheffield Grammar School Exhibition Foundation

£ £14,000 (2017/18)

Correspondent: Gillian Mills, Charity Administrator, c/o Wrigleys Solicitors LLP, 3rd Floor, Fountain Precinct, Balm Green, Sheffield, South Yorkshire S1 2JA (tel: 0114 267 5596; email: sheffieldgrammarschool@wrigleys.co.uk)

 www.sgsef.org.uk/index.htm

CC number: 529372

Eligibility

People who have lived in the city of Sheffield for at least three years, with a preference for those who are attending/have attended King Edward VII School for at least two years. A map of eligible areas can be found on the foundation's website.

Types of grant

Grants can be used for a number of educational purposes such as costs associated with courses (e.g. bachelor's, master's and PhD degrees), studying overseas and travel to pursue education.

Exclusions

The foundation does not award grants to individuals outside Sheffield or for non-educational purposes.

Applications

Application forms can be downloaded from the foundation's website or can be requested from the correspondent. Completed applications must be returned as a hard copy by post. The trustees meet four times a year to consider applications, usually in March, June, September and December. Check the website for current deadlines.

Financial information

Year end	31/03/2018
Income	£194,000
Total expenditure	£178,500

Further financial information

In 2017/18, grants were awarded to 52 individuals. We estimated that around £14,000 was awarded for educational purposes.

Other information

Grants are also awarded to local schools, academies and community groups.

Sources of information

Accounts; annual report; Charity Commission record; funder's website.

West Yorkshire

Brooksbank Educational Charity

£ £550 (2017/18)

Correspondent: John Batchelor, Trustee, 4 Shaw Close, Holywell Green, Halifax, West Yorkshire HX4 9DS (tel: 07940 503423; email: jk.batchelor@outlook.com)

CC number: 529146

Eligibility

Children and young people under the age of 25 who live in the area of the former urban district of Elland (as constituted on 31 March 1974).

Types of grant

Assistance may be available to students entering university.

Applications

Apply in writing to the correspondent.

Financial information

Year end	31/03/2018
Income	£1,700
Total expenditure	£1,200

Further financial information

Full accounts were not available to view on the Charity Commission's website due to the charity's low income. We have therefore estimated the grant total based on the charity's total expenditure.

Sources of information

Charity Commission record.

Haworth Exhibition Endowment

 £700 (2017/18)

Correspondent: The Trustees, 38 Gledhow Drive, Oxenhope, Keighley, West Yorkshire BD22 9SA (tel: 01535 644447; email: hawexhibtrust@btinternet.com)

 haworthexhibitionendowment. weebly.com

CC number: 507050

Eligibility

People who live, or whose parents lived, in the ancient township of Haworth. Candidates must have attended one of the schools in the Haworth district for at least three years. The Haworth district includes Oakbank, Oxenhope and Stanbury but excludes Lees and Crossroads. Candidates must have completed their A-levels and intend to enter higher education.

Types of grant

One-off grants ranging from £25 to £75 for books and equipment to be used in higher education.

Applications

The grant will first be advertised in the local newspaper, after this an application form will become available from Haworth Town Hall. Application forms can be completed either by the applicant or a parent/guardian. The closing date for applications is usually the end of August; however, consult the charity's website for current guidelines. The

trustees meet once a year, in October, to consider applications.

Financial information

Year end	31/03/2018
Income	£900
Total expenditure	£800

Further financial information

Full accounts were not available to view on the Charity Commission's website due to the charity's low income. We have therefore estimated the grant total based on the charity's total expenditure.

Other information

The charity may also take into account exam results and academic progress.

Sources of information

Charity Commission record; funder's website.

Calderdale

Bearder Charity

 £37,200 (2017/18)

Correspondent: Richard Smithies, Trustee, 5 King Street, Brighouse, West Yorkshire HD6 1NX (tel: 01484 710571; email: bearders@btinternet.com)

 www.bearder-charity.org.uk

CC number: 1010529

Eligibility

People in need who live in Calderdale, West Yorkshire.

Types of grant

Grants to individuals are awarded under the categories: welfare, education and the arts.

Applications

All applicants are asked to apply in writing to the secretary. Applications may be made directly by the applicant or through a local third-party organisation. State what is needed and how much it will cost. The trustees meet six times a year to assess grant applications.

Financial information

Year end	05/04/2018
Income	£112,600
Total expenditure	£232,800

Further financial information

In 2017/18 grants to individuals were awarded under the following categories: general welfare grants (£99,200); education grants (£37,200); and grants for the arts and artists (£1,100). Grants to organisations totalled £71,900.

Sources of information

Accounts; annual report; Charity Commission record.

Community Foundation for Calderdale

Correspondent: Grants Team, The 1855 Building (first floor), Discovery Road, Halifax, West Yorkshire HX1 2NG (tel: 01422 349700; email: grants@cffc.co.uk)

www.cffc.co.uk

CC number: 1002722

Eligibility

People in need who live in Calderdale.

Types of grant

The foundation also awards bursaries to students through the Calderdale College Education Fund although none were awarded in 2017/18. Bursaries can be used for travel assistance, educational materials or can be awarded as scholarships.

Applications

Applications should be made in writing through a third party such as Citizens Advice.

Financial information

Year end	30/06/2018
Income	£1,140,000
Total expenditure	£1,480,000

Further financial information

In 2017/18 a total of 137 grants were awarded through the Individual Fund. The foundation administers grants awarded by the Henry Smith Charity in Calderdale – these totalled £60,400 in 2017/18.

Other information

This is one of the 46 community foundations, which distribute funding for a wide range of purposes. Grant schemes tend to change frequently; therefore, consult the foundation's website for details of current programmes and upcoming deadlines.

Sources of information

Accounts; annual report; Charity Commission record; funder's website.

Kirklees

Mirfield Educational Charity

 £1,000 (2017/18)

Correspondent: Clerk, 6 Rectory View, Thornhill, Dewsbury, West Yorkshire WF12 0NN (tel: 01924 456780; email: parkinson922@btinternet.com)

CC number: 529334

Eligibility

People under the age of 25 who or whose parents live in the former urban district of Mirfield.

Types of grant

Grants are awarded for a range of educational purposes. Previous examples include course fees, travel, accommodation costs and equipment.

Applications

Apply in writing to the correspondent. The trustees usually meet in February, May and October each year to consider applications.

Financial information

Year end	31/03/2018
Income	£54,900
Total expenditure	£37,700

Further financial information

Grants were awarded to two individuals.

Other information

The charity also supports schools, groups and other organisations. The annual report (for 2017/18) states: 'The charity has also launched the Dr H. G. Grason Scholarship as a new initiative to provide significant financial assistance to a hard working student from a family of modest means who might otherwise not go on to higher education.'

Sources of information

Accounts; annual report; Charity Commission record.

Leeds

Kirke's Charity

£ £2,300 (2017/18)

Correspondent: Bruce Buchan, Trustee, 8 St Helens Croft, Leeds, West Yorkshire LS16 8JY (tel: 0113 267 9780)

CC number: 246102

Eligibility

People in need who live in the ancient parishes of Adel, Arthington or Cookridge.

Types of grant

One-off and recurring grants according to need.

Applications

Applications can be submitted directly by the individual or through a social worker, Citizens Advice or other welfare agency.

Financial information

Year end	31/10/2018
Income	£9,500
Total expenditure	£10,300

Further financial information

Full accounts were not available to view on the Charity Commission's website due to the charity's low income. We have therefore estimated the grant total based on the charity's total expenditure.

Other information

Grants are also awarded to local organisations.

Sources of information

Charity Commission record.

The Rawdon and Laneshaw Bridge School Trust

£ £720 (2017/18)

Correspondent: Anthea Hargreaves, Trustee, Park Dale, Layton Drive, Rawdon, Leeds, West Yorkshire LS19 6QY (tel: 0113 250 4061)

 https://democracy.leeds.gov.uk/ mgOutsideBodyDetails.aspx?ID= 358

CC number: 529197

Eligibility

People under the age of 21 who live in Rawdon and are in full-time education at school, college or university.

Types of grant

Grants are available towards the maintenance and advancement of people in education or training at secondary school, college or university, including vocational and teacher training.

Applications

Apply in writing to the correspondent.

Financial information

Year end	31/03/2018
Income	£1,600
Total expenditure	£800

Further financial information

Full accounts were not available to view on the Charity Commission's website due to the charity's low income. We have therefore estimated the grant total based on the charity's total expenditure.

Sources of information

Charity Commission record; funder's website.

The T. A. K. Turton Charitable Trust
See record on page 235

Wakefield

Lady Bolles Foundation

£ £4,000 (2017)

Correspondent: The Trustees, 6 Lynwood Drive, Wakefield, West Yorkshire WF2 7EF (tel: 01924 250473; email: neil.holland@wakefield-cathedral. org.uk)

CC number: 529344

Eligibility

People under the age of 21 who live in the county borough of Wakefield. At the trustees' discretion support may be continued up to the age of 24.

Types of grant

Grants are provided to support those undertaking apprenticeships.

Applications

Apply in writing to the correspondent.

Financial information

Year end	31/12/2017
Income	£8,700
Total expenditure	£8,900

Further financial information

Full accounts were not available to view on the Charity Commission's website due to the charity's low income. We have therefore estimated the grant total based on the charity's total expenditure.

Sources of information

Charity Commission record.

Daniel Gaskell Foundation

£ £17,000 (2017)

Correspondent: Martin Milner, Clerk, Meadow View, Haigh Moor Road, Tingley, Wakefield, West Yorkshire WF3 1EJ (tel: 07550 085465)

 https://www.horburyacademy.com/ News/Daniel-Gaskell- Foundation-Form

CC number: 529262

Eligibility

People under the age of 25 who are living, or who have a parent living, in the former urban district of Horbury.

Types of grant

Grants towards the cost of essential clothing, books, tools, instruments and travel associated with the pursuance of educational or vocational training in preparation for entry to a profession or trade occupation on leaving school, university or other educational establishment (not including sixth form college). Financial assistance is also available towards the cost of university courses or similar.

Applications

Application forms may be collected from Handyman Supplies, Black Olive Delicatessen, Rickaro Books, Mr K's Newsagents and the post office. Alternatively, forms can be downloaded from the Horbury Academy website. Completed forms must be returned directly to the correspondent by post. Application deadlines are usually the end of September; however, consult the website for current deadlines.

Financial information

Year end	31/12/2017
Income	£23,200
Total expenditure	£26,500

Further financial information

In 2017 a total of £17,000 was awarded to 41 students to assist with educational costs.

Other information

The foundation also provides grants to local schools for prizes and assists with the cost of training at Outward Bound for pupils at Horbury academy.

Sources of information

Accounts; annual report; Charity Commission record; funder's website.

279

Statutory grants and student support

A complete overview of benefits is beyond the scope of this book. There are a number of organisations which provide comprehensive guides, information and advice to students wishing to study in the UK and overseas. Contact details for these organisations can be found in the 'Contacts and sources of further information' section on page 293.

Statutory provision of both educational and welfare support is extremely complex and continuously changing. The following is intended to act as a signpost to helpful sources of information.

This chapter includes information on:
- Schoolchildren (aged 16 and over)
- Further education
- Student support

Schoolchildren (aged 16 and over)

The following benefits are all administered separately by individual local education authorities (LEAs) which set their own rules of eligibility and set the level of grants. The following information covers the basic general criteria for benefits, but you should contact your LEA directly for further information and advice.

Free school meals

Children may be eligible for free school meals if their parent(s) or guardian(s) are receiving certain benefits. For more information on eligibility visit: www.gov.uk/apply-free-school-meals.

School clothing grants

In England and Wales, children who attend maintained schools (those funded and run by the LEA), further education colleges and sixth form colleges may be able to receive help with the costs of their school clothing, including PE kits. However, this is at the discretion of their LEA and the policies on who can receive help and what items help can be given for vary widely from area to area. Check with your LEA to find out what policies apply in your area.

As it is not a legal requirement for schoolchildren to wear a uniform, some local authorities do not provide financial assistance to help with the purchase of school clothing. Citizens Advice is campaigning to encourage more parents to challenge local authorities that have policies of not providing financial assistance with school uniforms. More information on this is available from www. citizensadvice.org.uk.

More information on school clothing grants across the UK is available from:
- **England and Wales**: www.gov.uk/ help-school-clothing-costs (contains a local authority postcode search)
- **Northern Ireland**: www.nidirect. gov.uk/articles/school-uniform-and-uniform-grants
- **Scotland**: www.citizensadvice.org. uk/scotland/family/education/school-and-pre-school-education-s/help-with-school-costs-s
- **Wales**: www.gov.wales/topics/ educationandskills/schoolshome/ parents/uniform

School transport

Generally, children aged 16 may qualify for free school transport if they go to their nearest suitable school and live at least three miles from the school. Children who have no safe walking route to school are entitled to free transport, however far from the school they live. There are different requirements for families on low incomes and some LEAs may provide free transport for other reasons. Check with your local LEA for more information.

Young people who are over 16 years old and in further education may qualify for help with transport costs, although this varies for each LEA.

Local authorities also have to consider any disability or special educational needs when deciding whether transport is necessary for a child. If a child has a statement of special educational needs and disability (known as a SEND) and has transport requirements written into their statement, the local authorities must meet them. Discretionary grants may also be available from LEAs to cover travel expenses for parents visiting children at special schools.

Pupils living in London can also qualify for free transport on London buses and trams if they are in full-time education or work-based learning. For more information, a helpline is available on 0343 222 1234, or information can be found online at www.tfl.gov.uk.

Further education

Depending on their circumstances and the subject being studied, individuals who are in further education may qualify to receive help with the costs of their course, day-to-day living expenses and childcare. More information on the types of funding available can be found at www.gov.uk/further-education-courses/overview.

Student support

Information on financial support available for students can be found at www.gov.uk/browse/education/student-finance.

Advice is also available from your LEA. However, note that the busiest time for LEAs is the period between mid-August (when A-level results come out) and about mid-November (by which time most awards have been given). It is probably best not to contact your LEA for detailed advice at this time, unless absolutely necessary. Students should also check with their university or college for other funds that may be available within the institution.

Supplementary grants

Some students are entitled to extra statutory help; this is currently available through the following forms of support:
- Childcare Grant
- Parents' Learning Allowance
- Adult Dependants' Grant
- Disabled Students' Allowance (DSA)
- 16 to 19 Bursary Fund

Refer to the Gov.uk site referenced at the beginning of the 'Student support' section on this page, for current information on the types of grant available.

Further useful contacts include:
- **Student Finance England**: PO Box 210, Darlington DL1 9HJ (tel: 0300 100 0607; website: www.gov.uk/student-finance)
- **Student Finance Wales**: PO Box 211, Llandudno Junction LL30 9FU (tel: 0300 200 4050; website: www.studentfinancewales.co.uk)
- **Student Finance Northern Ireland**: (tel: 0300 100 0077; website: www.studentfinanceni.co.uk)
- **Student Awards Agency for Scotland**: Saughton House, Broomhouse Drive, Edinburgh EH11 3UT (tel: 0300 555 0505; website: www.saas.gov.uk)
- **For students from other EU countries**: Student Finance Services Non-UK Team, PO Box 89, Darlington DL1 9AZ (tel: 0141 243 3570; website: www.gov.uk/student-finance)

NHS bursaries

Subject to certain criteria, full-time or part-time NHS students can apply for a bursary from the NHS. Students who started on or after 1 August 2018 should be enrolled on a course that will lead to registering as a doctor or dentist.

Please visit www.gov.uk/nhs-bursaries for further current information.

NHS Learning Support Fund

Healthcare students who started a course on or after 1 August 2017 may be entitled to support under the Learning Support Fund. Students should be registered on one of the following courses:
- Dietetics
- Midwifery
- Nursing (adult, child, mental health, learning disability, joint nursing/social work)
- Occupational therapy
- Operating department practice
- Orthoptics
- Orthotics and prosthetics
- Physiotherapy
- Podiatry/chiropody
- Radiography (diagnostic and therapeutic)
- Speech and language therapy

Social Work Bursaries

Social Work Bursaries can help with living costs and tuition fees.

For students in England: NHS Business Services Authority, Stella House Goldcrest Way, Newburn Riverside, Newcastle upon Tyne NE15 8NY (tel: 0191 232 5371; website: www.nhsbsa.nhs.uk/social-work-students)

For students in Wales: Social Care Wales, South Gate House, Wood Street, Cardiff CF10 1EW (tel: 0300 30 33 444; email: info@socialcare.wales; website: www.socialcare.wales)

For students in Scotland: Scottish Social Services Council, Compass House, 11 Riverside Drive, Dundee DD1 4NY (tel: 0345 60 30 891; website: www.sssc.uk.com)

Teacher training funding

Funding is available for full-time or part-time students on Initial Teacher Training (ITT), Postgraduate Certificate in Education (PGCE) and School-Centred Initial Teacher Training (SCITT) courses through the main student finance avenue. For more details, visit: www.gov.uk/teacher-training-funding.

Department for Education: (tel: 0800 389 2500; website: http://getintoteaching.education.gov.uk)

Loans

The government's Professional and Career Development Loan scheme has now ended. The scheme has been replaced by a number of new loans including the Master's Loan scheme and the Advanced Learner Loan. Visit www.gov.uk/browse/education for further information.

Types of school in the UK and their funding

This section contains information about the types of school that exist in the UK, how they are funded and how funding can be obtained to attend them.

Maintained schools

These schools are funded by the local education authority and include foundation schools, community schools, voluntary-controlled schools, voluntary-aided schools, nursery schools and some special schools. They all follow the national curriculum and are inspected by Ofsted.

The Gov.uk website supplies some information about the different types of school, how to find one and apply for a place. See www.gov.uk/types-of-school for more information.

Academies

Academies are independently managed schools which are funded directly by the Education Funding Agency and operate outside the control of the local authority. They are set up by sponsors from business, faith or voluntary groups in partnership with the Department for Education and the local authority. In 2018 over 70% of secondary schools were academies. Many factors have caused academies to be a source of controversy – because of this, there exists a wide range of information available about academies from all perspectives. The Department for Education supplies some details (see www.gov.uk/types-of-school/academies).

Free schools

These schools are non-profit, independent, state-funded schools which are not controlled by the local authority. They are similar to academies but are usually new schools, set up as a response to a demand that is not being met by existing schools.

The New Schools Network provides advice about free schools, including how to set one up. See www. newschoolsnetwork.org or call 020 7952 8558 for more information.

Independent schools

Independent schools are independent in their finances and governance, and are funded by charging parents fees (on average over £17,000 a year, or £33,000 for boarders). They set their own curriculum and admission policies and are inspected by Ofsted or other approved inspectorates. According to the Independent Schools Council, around 6.5% of schoolchildren in the UK are educated in independent schools, with the figure rising to 15% of pupils for those over the age of 16.

Most independent schools offer scholarships and bursaries to some applicants, ranging from 10% of fees to (very occasionally) the full amount of fees being paid. They are subject to fierce competition and are usually awarded on the basis of academic merit, as well as individual need.

A number of independent schools also offer music scholarships, varying from 10% of fees to the full amount of fees being paid (including free musical tuition). Candidates are usually expected to offer two instruments at grades 6 to 8 at least. Contact the director of music at the school you are interested in for more details.

The Independent Schools Directory

This searchable directory lists all the UK independent schools, has an interactive map and offers further details on each school.

Tel: 020 8906 0911

Website: www.indschools.co.uk

The Independent Schools Council

The Independent Schools Council is the main source of information on independent schools. It has a website containing detailed information to help families select the right school and find possible sources of funding.

Website: www.isc.co.uk

The Independent Schools Yearbook

The Independent Schools Yearbook contains details of schools with a membership of one or more of the Constituent Associations of the Independent Schools Council. It is published by A&C Black and can be bought online.

Email: isyb@acblack.com

Website: www.isyb.co.uk

The Independent Association of Prep Schools

The Independent Association of Prep Schools is the professional association for headteachers of the leading 600 independent prep schools in the UK and worldwide.

Tel: 01926 887833

Email: iaps@iaps.uk

Website: http://iaps.uk

The Council of British International Schools

The Council of British International Schools is a membership organisation of British schools of quality, providing British education in Europe and worldwide.

Tel: 020 3826 7190

Website: www.cobis.org.uk

Boarding schools

Boarding Schools' Association

The Boarding Schools' Association serves and represents boarding schools and promotes boarding education in the UK, including both state and private boarding schools.

Very occasionally the local authority may pay for a child's boarding fees if they have a particularly difficult home situation. Contact the Director of Education or the Chief Education Officer for the area in which you live (if you live outside the UK, approach the area with which you have the closest connection).

Tel: 020 7798 1580

Website: www.boarding.org.uk

Maintained boarding schools

These are state schools that take boarders as well as day pupils; they only charge for the cost of boarding, not for tuition. Boarding costs are generally between £8,000 and £13,000 a year. According to the State Boarding Schools' Association, there are 37 state boarding schools in England. They are a mix of all-ability comprehensive schools, academies and grammar schools. They all follow the national curriculum and take the same examinations as pupils in day state schools.

State Boarding Schools' Association

Tel: 020 7798 1580

Email: info@sbsa.org.uk

Website: www.sbsa.org.uk

Music, dance and stage schools

Choir schools

Choir Schools' Association

The Choir Schools' Association is a group of 44 schools which are attached to cathedrals, churches and college chapels around the country. The majority are fee-paying, with nine out of ten choristers qualifying for financial help with fees through the schools.

Tel: 01359 221333

Email: info@choirschools.org.uk

Website: www.choirschools.org.uk

Music schools

There are various specialist music schools in the UK, with no single umbrella body. Contact the school directly for information about fees and funding.

Music Teachers Association

The Music Teachers Association is the national association for music teaching professionals. It annually publishes the *Music Directory*, a comprehensive guide to music departments and music scholarships in the UK, which can be purchased on its website.

Tel: 01223 312655

Email: membership@musicteachers.org

Website: www.musicteachers.org

Music and dance

Music and Dance Scheme

This government scheme is designed to help exceptionally talented young musicians between the ages of 8 and 19, and dancers between the ages of 11 and 19. Means-tested fee support and grants are distributed through specialist centres of education and training, and conservatoires. Applications should be made directly to the school or centre you wish to attend. A full list of schools is available on the scheme's website.

Website: www.gov.uk/music-dance-scheme

Foundations for Excellence

The Foundations for Excellence website provides information, guidance and signposting in the areas of health and well-being for young musicians and dancers.

Website: www.foundations-for-excellence.org

Dance schools

Council for Dance and Education Training

Information on dance education and training can be obtained from the Council for Dance and Education Training. It is a quality-assurance body of the dance and musical theatre industries and provides information on its recognised schools and teachers.

Tel: 020 7240 5703

Email: info@cdet.org.uk

Website: www.cdet.org.uk

Dance Schools UK

Dance Schools UK provides a directory of dance schools and teachers across the UK and Ireland.

Website: www.danceschools-uk.co.uk

Stage schools

Federation of Drama Schools

The Federation of Drama Schools was established in 2017 following the closure of Drama UK. It is a group of organisations that provide conservatoire-style vocational training for people who want to be professional performers, theatre makers and technical theatre practitioners.

Email: Contact form on the website

Website: www. federationofdramaschools.co.uk

FreeIndex

Using the FreeIndex directory you can browse a list of stage schools in the UK.

Website: www.freeindex.co.uk

Other possible sources of help with fees

Allowances for armed forces personnel

The Children's Education Advisory Service (CEAS) provides expert and impartial advice about the education of children of armed forces personnel.

Children whose parents are members of Her Majesty's Forces are eligible for an allowance towards boarding education, whether their parent is (or parents are) serving at home or abroad. This is the Continuity of Education Allowance which is available for children who are eight years old and older. Families are expected to contribute a minimum of 10% towards the fees. Further information on the support available can be found at www.gov.uk/ guidance/childrens-education-advisory-service.

Multinational companies

Some multinational companies and organisations help with school fees if parents have to work overseas. A few firms make grants, run scholarship schemes or provide low-interest loans for employees who reside in the UK. Consult your employer for further information.

Alternative routes to employment: apprenticeships

In this section, you will find information on apprenticeships and how to apply for one.

What is an apprenticeship?

Briefly, an apprenticeship is a job that also provides rigorous skills training in order to equip a school leaver with enough experience to work in their chosen field and improve their career prospects. Apprentices are awarded a nationally recognised qualification at the end of their apprenticeship.

Types of apprenticeship

Apprenticeship sectors include: agriculture, horticulture and animal care; higher education institutions; arts, media and publishing; business, administration and law; construction, planning and the built environment; education and training; engineering and manufacturing; health, public services and care; information and communication technology; leisure, travel and tourism; postgraduate teaching; financial services; public relations; retail and commercial enterprise; and traffic office.

Training duration

Generally, an apprenticeship takes between one and four years to complete. The duration varies depending on the level of existing skills of the apprentice, the qualification being obtained and the chosen industry sector.

Main benefits

The main benefits of becoming an apprentice are the following:
- You earn a wage during your entire apprenticeship
- There is a guaranteed, nationally recognised qualification awarded to you as you complete each stage of your training
- You gain skills and knowledge which can be used across a range of jobs and industries
- Once the apprenticeship has finished there is an opportunity to carry on working, potentially get promoted or go on to higher education in a college or university
- You can learn at your own pace and get support as and when you need it

Entry requirements

Different apprenticeships have different entry requirements depending on the type of work you will do. However, the most important requirements are the following:
- You must be living in England and not taking part in full-time education
- You must be aged 16 or over
- If you took your GCSEs more than five years ago and did not gain a top grade (A or A*), or you do not have good GCSE grades in Maths and English, you will need to take a literacy and numeracy test

Are there any costs involved?

The National Apprenticeship Service supports, funds and co-ordinates the delivery of apprenticeships throughout England. It may also pay the costs of your training in certain circumstances.

How to apply

To apply for an apprenticeship or a traineeship, visit the apprenticeship vacancies' website (www.findapprenticeship.service.gov.uk/apprenticeshipsearch).

Application support

If you would like some help on registering, searching and applying for your chosen apprenticeship, please read the 'How to write a winning apprenticeship application' guide at: www.gov.uk/guidance/apprenticeships-resources-for-teachers-and-advisers.

Company sponsorships

Company sponsorships particularly apply to people in their last year at school who are intending to study a business-related, engineering, or science-based subject at university.

Sponsorship of degree courses

A number of companies sponsor students who are taking degree courses at universities, usually in business, engineering, technology or other science subjects. Such sponsorships are generally for students who are UK residents and are taking their first degree course (or a comparable course).

Sponsorship generally takes the form of cash support (such as a bursary or scholarship) while at university, with a salary being paid during pre-university and holiday employment, or during periods of industrial training at the company concerned. If, for example, the sponsorship is for a sandwich course, the placements will be for longer than the holiday period and will form an integral part of the course. Sponsorships are highly competitive but can be of great value to students who, for any reason, do not receive the full grant. They may also help students avoid having to take out a loan.

Each company has its own sponsorship policy. Some sponsorships are tied to a particular course or institution, whereas others are only given for specific subjects. It is worth noting that the value of the sponsorship also varies. Additional help can be available in the form of discretionary educational gifts or degree prizes.

Sponsorships do not necessarily offer a permanent job at the end of the course (unless the student is classed as an employee). Equally, the student does not usually have to take up a job if offered by the company, although there may be at least a moral obligation to consider the offer.

Students should not decide on a course simply because there may be sponsorship available, they should choose the course first and seek sponsorship afterwards if appropriate.

In most sponsorships it is the student, not the company, who has to make arrangements to get on the course. Indeed some companies will only sponsor students who have already been accepted on a course. However, most university departments have well-established links with the industry and actively encourage students who are seeking sponsorship.

Students should apply for sponsorships as early as possible in the autumn term of their final year at school or college before moving to university.

Further information

Individuals are advised to identify major institutions working in the industry they intend to follow and see what schemes are available. An example of such an institution is The Engineering Development Trust (www.etrust.org.uk), which runs a number of schemes for individuals who wish to pursue a career in STEM (Science, Technology, Engineering, Mathematics) subjects.

Funding for gap-years and overseas voluntary work

Gap-years have traditionally been a popular choice with school leavers looking to travel, volunteer, work or broaden their horizons in some other way before embarking on university life. With increasingly high costs of education, many feel the need to be extra careful in choosing a career path. A short pause between leaving school and continuing education may be a smart, rather than just an adventurous, decision. A 'mini-gap', for example, during the summer holidays can equally add valuable experience and skills to a CV and is seen by many universities and potential employers as an advantage in what is a very competitive job market.

There are some opportunities to participate in voluntary work, expeditions and other activities which can be funded or partly funded through charities, bursaries and schemes. Generally, most grant-making charities have quite specific criteria which will not apply to all eligible applicants; it is important to keep this in mind and not assume that you can apply just because you wish to travel to a particular area or place. Likewise, some grant-makers have a particular preference for a certain type of project, for example conservation or one that involves working for the benefit of the local community. They may also give within a specific catchment area, so it can be useful to look at local grant-

makers first. Many of the local charities in this guide will give grants under terms such as 'travel overseas' or 'personal development activities'. This allows them to give broadly to a number of different activities which may fall into these categories, such as gap-year projects and voluntary work overseas.

It cannot be over-emphasised enough that it is your responsibility to check your eligibility for funding from any charity to which you intend to apply. Please do not apply if you are in doubt of your eligibility. Where appropriate, contact the organisation for further clarification.

If you succeed in gaining financial support, remember that it is always good practice to keep charities informed of the progress of your project and what you have achieved with the funding. This might even be a requirement of accepting the funding. You may also be asked to act as an ambassador to the charity back in the UK by giving talks or presentations on your experiences. This might be something to think about when making your application, particularly if the organisation is keen to involve past participants in promoting its scheme.

It may help your cause if you raise some of the funds yourself. By doing this, it might give you an edge over other applicants and prove how dedicated and determined you are to

succeed. You may also find it useful to break down the total costs of your project and apply to several different grant-makers for smaller amounts of money, as this could increase your chances of securing the right amount of funding.

There are other alternatives to funding gap-year projects and voluntary work overseas. Many large volunteer organisations provide funded or partly funded volunteering and exchange schemes that will allow you to take part in voluntary work at a minimum cost. Some can offer bursaries to cover specific costs, such as the project fee or flight fare, and others may ask you to fundraise a block amount of money but will pay for all your necessary costs in return.

Below are a few fully or partly funded voluntary schemes available to young people living in the UK.

Lattitude Global Volunteering

Lattitude Global Volunteering is a UK-based volunteering organisation and registered charity (Charity Commission no. 272761) that organises volunteer placements in financially developing countries for young people aged 17 to 25, as well as offering bursaries and funded projects for applicants in need of financial help. Volunteers can take part in a number of different projects, such as camps and outdoor education, as well as environmental, medical and community projects. More information about the opportunities that Lattitude Global Volunteering can offer is available from the charity's website (www.lattitude.org.uk).

The Jack Petchey Foundation

The foundation supports young people aged 11 to 25 who live in Essex or London who are raising money in order to be involved in a voluntary project or participate in events that will benefit others in society. Grants are given to cover up to 50% of the cost of the project (but no more than £400 per person). Full details of eligibility criteria and how to apply can be found on the foundation's website (www.jackpetcheyfoundation.org.uk).

Project Trust

Project Trust is an educational charity which specialises in overseas volunteering placements for school-leavers. Young people aged between 17 and 19 are given training and support to undertake voluntary teaching and social care projects abroad lasting around eight to twelve months. Living allowances are provided by the trust or by the overseas host. More details on the opportunities available can be found on the trust's website (www.projecttrust.org.uk).

Other helpful contacts

www.igapyear.com

iGapyear.com provides advice on how to put together a proposal for a funding application as well as offering other information on gap-year and volunteering opportunities.

www.gapyear.com

An online community where backpackers and gap-year travellers can meet, chat and share experiences.

www.idealist.org

Idealist.org is an independent online network of non-profit and voluntary organisations that provide information on voluntary opportunities worldwide.

www.eurodesk.eu

The website holds information on European policies and opportunities for young people.

www.yearoutgroup.org

Year Out Group is an association of organisations running gap-year and volunteering projects. The website provides general information for people planning to take a year out and offers the details of member organisations.

Volunteer organisations

www.vsointernational.org

www.frontier.ac.uk

www.raleighinternational.org

Contacts and sources of further information

Many people in education and training need financial advice and help from time to time. It is usually best to contact somebody at one of the following organisations as a starting point:

- The educational institution you are studying at
- Your local education authority
- Your local Citizens Advice or other welfare agencies

These organisations will be in the best position to point you in the right direction for further or more specialist advice if necessary. For resources that offer information and advice in specific areas, readers should also see the details listed in the preceding sections:

- Statutory grants and student support (page 281)
- Types of school in the UK and their funding (page 283)
- Alternative routes to employment: apprenticeships (page 287)
- Company sponsorships (page 289)
- Funding for gap-years and overseas voluntary work (page 291)

We have put together the following list of organisations that provide information and guidance on a broad range of issues.

General

Citizens Advice

Provides free, independent, confidential and impartial advice to everyone on their rights and responsibilities. Find your local bureau or get advice online at www.citizensadvice.org.uk.

England: 03444 111 444 (national phone line)

Wales: 03444 77 20 20 (national phone line)

There is no national phone line for Scotland and Northern Ireland, although details for local offices in all areas of the UK can be found on the website.

Department for Education

Piccadilly Gate, Store Street, Manchester M1 2WD (tel: 03700 002288; website: www.gov.uk/dfe).

Department of Education for Northern Ireland

Rathgael House, Balloo Road, Rathgill, Bangor, County Down BT19 7PR (tel: 028 9127 9279; email: de.dewebmail@education-ni.gov.uk; website: www.education-ni.gov.uk).

Education Scotland

Denholm House, Almondvale Business Park, Almondvale Way, Livingston EH54 6GA (tel: 0131 244 4330; email: enquiries@educationscotland.gsi.gov.uk; website: www.education.gov.scot).

Gov.uk

General advice and information on government services (website: www.gov.uk).

The Money Advice Service

The Money Advice Service helps people to manage their money, providing a free and impartial advice service. It also works in partnership with other organisations to help people to make the most of their money. It is an independent service set up by the government.

Holborn Centre, 120 Holborn, London EC1N 2TD (tel: 0800 138 7777 (English), 0800 138 0555 (Welsh); Mon to Fri 8am to 8pm, Sat 9am to 1pm; email: enquiries@moneyadviceservice.org.uk; website: www.moneyadviceservice.org.uk; an online chat facility is also available).

The Prince's Trust

The Prince's Trust helps people aged between 13 and 30 who are unemployed or struggling at school to transform their lives.

Prince's Trust House, 9 Eldon Street, London EC2M 7SL (tel: 0800 842842; website: www.princes-trust.org.uk).

Welsh Assembly Education and Skills

Cathays Park, Cardiff CF10 3NQ (tel: 03000 604400 (English and Welsh); email: customerhelp@gov.wales; website: www.gov.wales/education-skills).

Children

Child Poverty Action Group (CPAG)

CPAG publishes a number of guides which include information on state benefits and entitlements for both schoolchildren and students.

Child Poverty Action Group, 30 Micawber Street, London N1 7TB (tel: 020 7837 7979; email: info@cpag.org.uk; website: www.cpag.org.uk).

CPAG in Scotland, Unit 9, Ladywell, 94 Duke Street, Glasgow G4 0UW (tel: 0141 552 3303; email: staff@cpagscotland.org.uk; website: www.cpag.org.uk/scotland).

National Youth Advocacy Service

Tower House, 1 Tower Road, Birkenhead, Wirral CH41 1FF (tel: 0151 649 8700; helpline: 0808 808 1001 (Mon to Fri 8am to 8pm, Sat 10am to 4pm); email: main@nyas.net or help@nyas.net; website: www.nyas.net).

Youth Access

1–2 Taylors Yard, 67 Alderbrook Road, London SW12 8AD (tel: 020 8772 9900; email: admin@youthaccess.org.uk; website: www.youthaccess.org.uk – an online directory of information, advice and support services for young people).

Further and continuing education

City and Guilds

City and Guilds provides support to learners and training providers.

5–6 Giltspur Street, London EC1A 9DE (tel: 0844 543 0033; email: learnersupport@cityandguilds.com; website: www.cityandguilds.com).

Learning and Work Institute

National Learning and Work Institute, 4th Floor, Arnhem House, 31 Waterloo Way, Leicester LE1 6LP (tel: 0116 204 4200; email: enquiries@learningandwork.org.uk; website: www.learningandwork.org.uk).

Higher Education

The National Union of Students (NUS)

NUS UK, Ian King House, Snape Road, Macclesfield SK10 2NZ (tel: 0300 303 8602; email: use online contact form; website: www.nus.org.uk).

NUS Scotland

1 Papermill Wynd, McDonald Road, Edinburgh EH7 4QL (email: mail@nus-scotland.org.uk; website: www.nus-scotland.org.uk).

NUS-USI

42 Dublin Road, Belfast BT2 7HN (email: info@nistudents.org; website: www.nus-usi.org).

NUS Wales

2nd Floor, Cambrian Buildings, Mount Stuart Square, Cardiff CF10 5FL (email: office@nus-wales.org.uk).

The Open University (OU)

The Open University, PO Box 197, Milton Keynes MK7 6BJ (tel: 0300 303 5303; email: use online contact form; website: www.open.ac.uk).

Scholarship Search

Search scholarships in the UK for pre-university, undergraduate and postgraduate learning.

Website: www.scholarship-search.org.uk

Student Awards Agency for Scotland (SAAS)

Saughton House, Broomhouse Drive, Edinburgh EH11 3UT (tel: 0300 555 0505; email: please use online contact form; website: www.saas.gov.uk).

University and Colleges Admissions Service (UCAS)

Rosehill, New Barn Lane, Gloucestershire GL5 3LZ (tel: 0371 468 0468; website: www.ucas.com).

UCAS can also be contacted via social media.

Applications for full-time university degree courses must be made through UCAS (part-time degree courses and the Open University are not covered by UCAS – apply directly to the university).

Careers

National Careers Service

The National Careers Service provides information, advice and guidance to help people make decisions on learning, training and work opportunities. The service offers confidential and impartial advice, supported by qualified careers advisers.

National Careers Service, PO Box 1331, Newcastle upon Tyne NE99 5EB (tel: 0800 100900; website: www.nationalcareers.service.gov.uk; an online chat service is also available).

Not Going to Uni

Opportunities for people leaving school or college that are outside the traditional university route, including apprenticeships, sponsored degrees, diplomas, gap-years, distance learning and jobs.

Mountcharm House, Ground Floor 102–104, Queen's Road, Buckhurst Hill IG9 5BS (tel: 020 3691 2800; email: info@notgoingtouni.co.uk; website: www.notgoingtouni.co.uk).

Prospects

Graduate careers website for jobs, postgraduate courses, work experience and careers advice.

Prospects, Booth Street East, Manchester M13 9EP (tel: 0161 277 5200; website: www.prospects.ac.uk).

Students with disabilities

Disability Rights UK

National pan-disability organisation led by people with disabilities that provides advice to students with disabilities.

Plexal, 14 East Bay Lane, Here East, Queen Elizabeth Olympic Park, Stratford, London E20 3BS (tel: 0330 995 0400; email: enquiries@ disabilityrightsuk.org; website: www. disabilityrightsuk.org).

Lead Scotland

Lead Scotland aims to widen access to learning for young people and adults with disabilities and carers across Scotland.

525 Ferry Road, Edinburgh EH5 2FF (tel: 0131 228 9441; email: enquiries@ lead.org.uk; website: www.lead.org. uk).

Study overseas

The British Council

Advice and publications on educational trips overseas.

British Council Customer Service UK, Bridgewater House, 58 Whitworth Street, Manchester M1 6BB (tel: 0161 957 7755; email: use online contact form; website: www.britishcouncil. org).

Erasmus

Erasmus enables higher education students, teachers and institutions in 32 European countries to study for part of their degree in another country. At the time of writing (January 2020) the negotiations with the EU on the continuity of Erasmus after Brexit had yet to commence. Funding is still available for the 2020/21 programme and students are being encouraged to apply as usual. See the website for the latest information.

Tel: 0161 957 7755; email: erasmus@ britishcouncil.org; website: www. erasmusplus.org.uk.

Overseas students

United Kingdom Council for International Students' Affairs (UKCISA)

UKCISA provides information for overseas students on entering the UK, as well as general advice.

9–17 St Alban's Place, London N1 0NX (advice line: 020 7288 4330; website: www.ukcisa.org.uk).

Other funding or sources of help

Community foundations

These local organisations sometimes have a pot of money available for individuals to apply for. Use the website to identify your local community foundation.

Unit 1.04 Piano House, 9 Brighton Terrace, London SW9 8DJ (tel: 020 7713 9326; website: www. ukcommunityfoundations.org).

Money Saving Expert

A British consumer finance information and discussion website providing information and journalistic articles to help people save money.

Website: www.moneysavingexpert. com

Index

Abbot's: The Archbishop Abbot's Exhibition Foundation 246

Aberdeenshire: Aberdeenshire Educational Trust 120

Acton: Acton (Middlesex) Educational Charity 199
The Tom Acton Memorial Trust 175

Actors': The Actors' Children's Trust (ACT) 79

Actuaries: The Company of Actuaries Charitable Trust Fund 34

Adams: Ted Adams Trust Ltd 246

Air: The Air Pilots Benevolent Fund 106
Air Pilots Trust 106

Aisling: Aisling Bursaries 114

Aitchison: The Christina Aitchison Trust 249

Aitken: The John Maurice Aitken Trust 15

AJA-UJS: AJA-UJS Student Welfare Fund 72

Aldgate: The Aldgate and Allhallows Foundation 193

Alenson: The Alenson and Erskine Educational Foundation 140

Alfrick: Alfrick Educational Charity 167

All: All Ireland Scholarships 113
The All Saints Educational Trust 35

Allen: Elizabeth Allen Trust 196

Allen's: Allen's Charity (Apprenticing Branch) 143

Allendale: Allendale Exhibition Endowment 212

Alsager: Alsager Educational Foundation 216

Alvechurch: Alvechurch Grammar School Endowment 167

Alzheimer's: Alzheimer's Society 44

Ameobi: Ameobi Hardship Fund for International Students (AHFIS) 6

Amiel: The Barry Amiel and Norman Melburn Trust 51

Amos: Tom Amos Charity 176

Ancell: The Ancell Trust 234

Anglo: The Anglo Jewish Association 72

Anguish's: Anguish's Educational Foundation 185

Angus: Angus Educational Trust 125

Apothecaries: The Worshipful Society of Apothecaries General Charity Ltd 45

Arlidge's: Arlidge's Charity 160

Armenian: Armenian General Benevolent Union London Trust 59
The Armenian Relief Society of Great Britain Trust 59

Arnold: Arnold Educational Foundation 149

Arnold's: Edmund Arnold's Charity 145

Artistic: The Artistic Endeavours Trust 25

Ashford: Ashford Hill Educational Trust 237

Ashton: Ashton Schools Foundation 172

Ataxia: Ataxia UK 65

Athletics: Athletics for the Young 104

Audlem: Audlem Educational Foundation 216

Australian: The Australian Music Foundation in London 14

Aviva: Aviva Scholarships 59

Ayrshire: Ayrshire Educational Trust 116

Aziz: The Aziz Foundation 71

Babington's: Babington's Charity 138

Bader: The Douglas Bader Foundation 65

Baines's: Baines's Charity 223

Bakehouse: Bakehouse or Shepherd's Charity 242

Baker: The June Baker Trust 80

Bampton: The Bampton Exhibition Foundation 245

Banbury: Banbury Charities 244

Banffshire: Banffshire Educational Trust 121

Bankers: The Bankers Benevolent Fund (The Bank Workers Charity) 86

Barbers': The Barbers' Company General Charities 45

Barford: Barford Relief-in-Need Charity 160

Barnard: The Michael Barnard Charitable Trust 9

Barnes: The Barnes Workhouse Fund 204

Barrack: The Barrack Hill Educational Charity (Barrack Hill Trust) 222

Barrow's: The William Barrow's Charity 242

Barry: The William Barry Trust 42

Bart: The Lionel Bart Foundation 25

Bartholomew: Bartholomew Educational Foundation 243

Bates: The Philip Bates Trust 25

Battersea: Battersea United Charities 208

Baylies': Baylies' Educational Foundation 164

Bearder: Bearder Charity 277

Beaumont's: Ann Beaumont's Educational Foundation 190

Beckett's: Beckett's and Sergeant's Educational Foundation 147

Beckwith: The Beckwith Bequest 272

Bedgebury: The Bedgebury Foundation 239

Belfast: Belfast Association for the Blind 113

Belfield: Felicity Belfield Scholarship 26

Benham: The Hervey Benham Charitable Trust 178

Benney: Benney Arts Foundation 25

Berwickshire: Berwickshire Education Trust 125

Bestway: The Bestway Foundation 60

Bewdley: The Bewdley Old Grammar School Foundation 168

Bilton: The Bilton Poors' Land and Other Charities 159

Bingham: The Bingham Trust 136

Birmingham: The Birmingham and Three Counties Trust for Nurses 162

Bishop: The Bishop Sheppard Tenth Anniversary Trust 215

Black: The Black Watch Association 75

Blackford: Blackford Educational Charity 262

Blackman: The Isabel Blackman Foundation 235

Blanchminster: Blanchminster Trust 252

Blatchington: The Blatchington Court Trust (BCT) 234

Blue: Blue Coat Educational Charity 147

BMA: BMA Charities Trust Fund 45

Boas: The Nicholas Boas Charitable Trust 80

Bold: Charity of William Bold 129

Bolles: Lady Bolles Foundation 278

Bolsterstone: Bolsterstone Educational Charity 276

Bomford: The Douglas Bomford Trust 38

Book: The Book Trade Charity 9

Boreman's: Sir William Boreman's Foundation 200

Botanical: Botanical Society of Britain and Ireland 32

Bowdler's: Bowdler's Educational Foundation 154

Brackley: Brackley United Feoffee Charity 148

Bramshott: Bramshott Educational Trust 237

Brancaster: The Brancaster Educational and Almshouse Charity 184

Brenley: The Brenley Trust 10

Brentnall: The Alan Brentnall Charitable Trust 10

Bridge: The Bridge Educational Trust (1996) 257

The Bridge Trust (Bideford Bridge Trust) 256

Bristow: John Bristow and Thomas Mason Trust 246

British: British Association for Irish Studies 53

The British Computer Society (BCS) 23

The British Council 10

The British Institute of Archaeology at Ankara (British Institute at Ankara) 24

The British Jewellery, Giftware and Finishing Federation Benevolent Society 50

The British Ornithologists' Union 32

British Pharmacological Society 46

British Veterinary Nursing Association 92

Broadlands: Broadlands Home Trust 62

Bromfield's: Bromfield's Educational Foundation 197

Broncel: The Broncel Trust 24

Brooksbank: Brooksbank Educational Charity 276

BTMA: The BTMA Trust 88

Buchanan: The Buchanan Society 68

Building: Building Birmingham Scholarship 162

Bunting's: The Bunting's Fund 182

Burford: The Burford Relief-in-Need Charity 245

Burton: The Burton Latimer United Educational Foundation 147

Consolidated Charity of Burton upon Trent 156

Burton-in-Kendal: Burton-in-Kendal Educational Foundation 217

Busenhart: The Busenhart Morgan-Evans Foundation 26

Butler: The Butler Educational Foundation 178

Butterworth: Ann Butterworth and Daniel Bayley Charity 220

Buttle: Buttle UK 56

Calderdale: Community Foundation for Calderdale 277

Calthorpe: Calthorpe and Edwards Educational Foundation 187

Cambrian: Cambrian Educational Foundation for Deaf Children in Wales 65

Cameron: The Cameron Fund 93

Campden: The Campden Charities 202

Canadian: Canadian Centennial Scholarship Fund (UK) 60

Canewdon: The Canewdon Educational Foundation 179

Canterbury: The Canterbury United Municipal Charities 241

Capstone: The Capstone Care Leavers' Trust 73

Cardiff: Cardiff Further Education Trust Fund 131

Careswell: The Careswell Foundation 154

Carlisle: Carlisle Educational Charity 219

Carnegie: The Carnegie Trust for the Universities of Scotland 6

Carpenter: The Thomas Carpenter Educational and Apprenticing Foundation (Thomas Carpenter's Trust) 197

Cartmel: Cartmel Old Grammar School Foundation 219

Casson: The Elizabeth Casson Trust 93

Cass's: Sir John Cass's Foundation 193

Castle: The Castle Baynard Educational Foundation 194

Caunt: The Francis Bernard Caunt Education Trust 148

Cecil: The Cecil Charity 259

Chadacre: Chadacre Agricultural Trust 39

Chaloner's: Chaloner's Educational Foundation 252

Charlbury: Charlbury Exhibition Foundation 245

Chartered: The Chartered Institute of Management Accountants Benevolent Fund 87

The Chartered Society of Physiotherapy Charitable Trust 93

Chauntry: The Chauntry Estate 147

Cheddington: Cheddington Town Lands Charity 233

Chelmsford: Chelmsford Educational Foundation (CEF) 178

Chester: Chester Municipal Charities 216

Chipping: The Chipping Sodbury Town Lands 261

Chizel: The Chizel Educational Trust 57

Christ: Christ Church Exhibition Fund 251

Churches: Churches International Student Network Hardship Fund 60

Churchill: The Winston Churchill Memorial Trust 19

Churchill University Scholarships Trust for Scotland 10

Circolo: Il Circolo Italian Cultural Association Ltd 53

City: The City and Guilds of London Institute 20

Clark: The Clark Foundation for Legal Education 31

Clergy: Clergy Support Trust 99

Clerkson's: Faith Clerkson's Exhibition Foundation 148

Cliddesden: The Cliddesden and Farleigh Wallop Educational Trust 236

Clingan's: Clingan's Trust 260

Coachmakers: The Coachmakers and Coach Harness Makers Charitable Trust 1977 35

Coal: The Coal Industry Social Welfare Organisation 96

Coates: Coates Educational Foundation 213

Coats: The Coats Foundation Trust 88

Community: The Community Foundation for Wiltshire and Swindon 264

The Community Foundation in Wales 10

Company: The Company of Arts Scholars Charitable Trust 26

Coombe's: Alice Coombe's Education Charity 265

Corfe: Corfe Castle Charity 257

Corporation: The Corporation of Trinity House of Deptford Strond 89

CoScan: CoScan Trust Fund 19

Cotton: The Cotton Industry War Memorial Trust 80

County: County Durham Community Foundation 210

Courtney: The Educational Foundation of Francis Courtney 199

Cowell: Cowell and Porrill 142

Cranfield: The Cranfield Charitable Trust 176

Creative: Creative Scotland 15

Crewe's: Lord Crewe's Charity 209

Crisis: Crisis 64

Cross: The Cross Trust 115

Culham: Culham St Gabriel's Trust (The Culham Institute) 48

Cumbria: Cumbria Community Foundation 217

Cutler: The Cutler Trust 194

Cutlers: The Worshipful Company of Cutlers General Charitable Fund – Captain F. G. Boot Scholarships 19

Cystic: Cystic Fibrosis Trust 66

Dairy: The Dairy Crest and National Farmers' Union Scholarship Fund 249

Dancers': Dancers' Career Development 81

Deacon: Deacon and Fairfax Educational Foundation 140

Deeping: Deeping St James United Charities 144

Denning: The Frank Denning Memorial Charity 199

Dennington: The Dennington Consolidated Charities 190

Derbyshire: Derbyshire Community Foundation 135

Design: Design History Society 33

Devon: The Devon Educational Trust 253

Dewhurst's: Robert Dewhurst's School Foundation 179

Diamond: Diamond Education Grant (DEG) 106

Dibden: Dibden Allotments Fund 238

Digby: Educational Foundation of Simon Lord Digby and Others 159

Dixie: The Dixie Educational Foundation 139

Dorset: Dorset Community Foundation 258

Downham: The Downham Feoffee Charity 174

Drexler: The George Drexler Foundation 101

Duffy: The Marie Duffy Foundation 68

Dumfriesshire: The Dumfriesshire Educational Trust 118

Dunchurch: Dunchurch and Thurlaston Educational Foundation 159

Duncraig: Duncraig Educational Trust Scheme 122

Dundee: City of Dundee Educational Trust Scheme 125

Dunk's: Dunk's and Springett's Educational Foundation 239

Dunn: The W. E. Dunn Trust 151

Earley: The Earley Charity 230

Earls: Earls Colne and Halstead Educational Charity 176

East: East Lothian Educational Trust 124

Economic: Economic History Society 52

Eden: Christopher Eden Educational Foundation 267

Eden's: James Eden's Foundation 220

Edinburgh: Edinburgh Association of University Women – President's Fund 62

Edmonds: Edmonds and Coles Scholarships (Edmonds and Coles Charity) 251
Anthony Edmonds Charity 251

Edmonds': John Edmonds' Charity 261

Educational: The Educational Charity of John Matthews 128

Edwards: Dr Edwards and Bishop King's Fulham Charity 201
Austin Edwards Charity 160
William Edwards Educational Charity 157

Ekins: The Charity of Hervey and Elizabeth Ekins 148

Elizabeth: Queen Elizabeth Scholarship Trust Ltd 103

Elmgrant: The Elmgrant Trust 249

Elmhirst: The Elmhirst Trust 275

Elmley: The Elmley Foundation 153

Emmott: The Emmott Foundation Ltd 57

Engineers: The Worshipful Company of Engineers Charitable Trust Fund 84

England: England Golf Trust 15

Epsom: Epsom Parochial Charities (Epsom Almshouse Charity) 246

Equity: Equity Charitable Trust 81

Ercall: Ercall Magna Education Endowment 155

Esdaile: Esdaile Trust Scheme 1968 99

Essex: Essex Community Foundation 176

Ewelme: Ewelme Exhibition Endowment 229

Exeter: The Exeter Advancement in Life Charity 253

Exhall: Exhall Educational Foundation 159

Exuberant: The Exuberant Trust 243

Family: Family Action 3

Faringdon: Faringdon United Charities 244

Farmer: Farmer Educational Foundation 144

Farmington: Farmington Institute Scholarships 83

Farnsfield: The Farnsfield Trust 149

Farrington: Educational Foundation of John Farrington 225

Fashion: The Fashion and Textile Children's Trust 104

Fawbert: Fawbert and Barnard School's Foundation 180
The Fawbert and Barnard's Educational Foundation 179

Feckenham: The Feckenham Educational Foundation 168

Feltmakers: The Feltmakers Charitable Foundation 97

Fentham: The George Fentham Birmingham Charity 162

Fermanagh: The Fermanagh Trust 114

Ferries: Alderman Ferries Charity (Hull United Charities) 270

FfWG: FfWG (Funds for Women Graduates) 62

Finnart: Finnart House School Trust 72

Finzi: The Gerald Finzi Trust 81

Fire: The Fire Service Research and Training Trust 3

Fishley: The Fishley Educational and Apprenticing Foundation 166

Fitzmaurice: The Caroline Fitzmaurice Trust 115

Flitwick: Flitwick Combined Charities 173

Follett: The Follett Trust 180

Fordath: The Fordath Foundation 165

Fordwich: Fordwich United Charities 241

Forest: Forest Industries Education and Provident Fund 85

Fort: The Fort Foundation 11

Founders: Charities Administered by the Worshipful Company of Founders 50

Fowler: The Dawson and Fowler Foundation 138

Framework: The Worshipful Company of Framework Knitters Education Charity 50

Frampton: Frampton Educational Foundation 142

French: The French Huguenot Church of London Charitable Trust 71

Freshtime: Freshtime Futures Trust 271

Fresson: The Fresson Trust 122

Frogmoor: Frogmoor Foundation 231

Frosterley: Frosterley Exhibition Foundation 210

Fulbright: Fulbright Postgraduate Scholarships 16

Gainsborough: Gainsborough Educational Charity 140

Gale's: Miss Gale's Educational Foundation (The Gale Trust) 236

Gamekeepers: Gamekeepers Welfare Trust 85

Gane: The Gane Charitable Trust 82

Garboldisham: The Garboldisham Parish Charities 184

Gardeners': Gardeners' Royal Benevolent Society (Perennial) 86

Gardiner: Gardiner Hill Foundation 140

Gardner's: Gardner's Trust for the Blind 66

Gargrave: The Gargrave Poor's Land Charity 272

Garnett: The Zibby Garnett Travelling Fellowship 41

Gaskell: Daniel Gaskell Foundation 278

General: General Charity (Coventry) 163

Genetics: The Genetics Society 33

George: The Ruby and Will George Trust 101

Gibbon: The Gibbon and Buckland Charity 239

Gibbs: The William Gibbs Trust 57

Gilchrist: Gilchrist Educational Trust 6

Gillan's: James Gillan's Trust 121

Girls: The Girls of the Realm Guild (Women's Careers Foundation) 63
Girls Welfare Fund 225

Girton: Girton Town Charity 175

Gislingham: Gislingham United Charity 190

Glamorgan: Glamorgan Further Education Trust Fund 133

Glasgow: Glasgow Educational and Marshall Trust 120
The Glasgow Highland Society 120

Go: Go Make it Happen: a Project in Memory of Sam Harding 106

Goldie: The Grace Wyndham Goldie (BBC) Trust Fund 91

Google: Google Scholarship for Students with Disabilities 23

Gordon: Gordon Charitable Trust 258

Gorsuch: The Gorsuch, Langley and Prynce Charity 155

Goward: George Goward and John Evans 191

GPM: The GPM Charitable Trust 91

Grantham: Grantham Yorke Trust 162

Gray's: Gray's Inn Scholarships 31

Great: The Great Britain-China Educational Trust 17
Great Bursthead Exhibition Foundation (Billericay Educational Trust) 177
The Great Linford Advancement in Life Charity 234

Green: Henry Green Scholarships in Conection with Council Schools 207

Greenwich: Greenwich Blue Coat Foundation 200
Greenwich Hospital 75

Grey's: Lady Dorothy Grey's Foundation 156

Guildry: Guildry Incorporation of Perth 126

Gunmakers': The Gunmakers' Company Charitable Trust 51

Gunn: The Andy Gunn Foundation 252

Gurney: The Gurney Fund 98

Hale: The Hale Trust 229

Hallam: The Ephraim Hallam Charity 222

Hall's: Hall's Exhibition Foundation 184

Halsall: Halsall Educational Foundation 226

Hampton: The Hampton Wick United Charity 205

Harding's: William Harding's Charity 233

Hardman: The Hardman Trust 69

Harpur: The Harpur Trust 172

Harris: The Harris Charity 223

Harrison: Audrey Harrison Heron Memorial Fund 149
The Dick Harrison Trust 39

Hart: Dr A. E. Hart Trust 270

Hartwell: The Hartwell Educational Foundation 211

Hatton: Hatton Consolidated Fund (Hatton Charities) 161

Hawes: Norman Hawes Memorial Trust 231

Haworth: Haworth Exhibition Endowment 277

Hayes: The Hayes (Kent) Trust 196
The Carol Hayes Foundation 11

Hayman: Ruth Hayman Trust 55

Haywra: The Haywra Crescent Educational Trust Fund 274

Hazell: The Walter Hazell Charitable and Educational Trust Fund 232

Headley-Pitt: Headley-Pitt Charitable Trust 240

Heim: George Heim Memorial Trust 11

Hellenic: The Hellenic Foundation 41

Help: Help for Heroes 76

Hereford: Hereford Municipal Charities 153
The Hereford Society for Aiding the Industrious 153

Heron: The Eleemosynary Charity of Giles Heron 212

Hertfordshire: Hertfordshire Community Nurses' Charity 180
The Hertfordshire Educational Foundation 180

Hesslewood: The Hesslewood Children's Trust (Hull Seamen's and General Orphanage) 267

Hewley's: Lady Hewley's Charity 100

Heywood: The Heywood Educational Trust 220

Hickman: The Hickman Education Foundation 35

Hidden: Hidden Pearls Bursaries 71

Higgs: Higgs and Cooper's Educational Charity 260

Higham: The Robert Higham Apprenticing Charity 237

Highland: Highland Children's Trust 123

Highlands: Highlands and Islands Educational Trust Scheme 122

Hilgay: Hilgay United Charities (Non-Ecclesiastical Branch) 184

Hill: The Derek Hill Foundation 82

Hilton: Hilton Educational Foundation 136

HIT: HIT Scotland 42

Hitcham's: Sir Robert Hitcham's Exhibition Foundation 177

Hockerill: Hockerill Educational Foundation 48

Holywood: The Holywood Trust 118

Hook: Hook and Goole Charity 267

Hope: The Hope Ffennell Trust 243
Hope House and Gippeswyk Educational Trust 190

Horne: Horne Foundation 145

Hornsey: The Hornsey Parochial Charities (Educational and Vocational Foundation) 194

Hothfield: Hothfield Educational Foundation 240

Hughes: The Robert David Hughes Scholarship Foundation 129

Hundon: Hundon Educational Foundation 191

Huntingdon: Huntingdon Freemen's Trust 175

Huntly: Huntly Educational Trust 1997 121

Hutchinson: Reverend Matthew Hutchinson Charity (Gilling and Richmond) 272

Hyde: The Hyde Foundation 196

ICE: ICE Benevolent Fund 36

Ilchester: The Ilchester Relief in Need and Educational Charity (IRINEC) 264

Ilminster: The Ilminster Educational Foundation 262

Ingram: Arthur Ingram Trust 241

Institute: The Institute of Chartered Foresters 39

Institution: The Institution of Engineering and Technology (IET) 84

The Institution of Mechanical Engineers (IMechE) 36

The Benevolent Fund of the Institution of Mechanical Engineers (IMechE) (known as Support Network) 84

Insurance: The Insurance Charities 87

Interdoceo: Interdoceo 30

James: James Graves 268

Jarvis: The Jarvis Educational Foundation 154

Jeffreys: The Educational Foundation of Dame Dorothy Jeffreys 130

Jewish: The Jewish Widows and Students Aid Trust 73

Jobson's: George Jobson's Trust 142

Johnson: The Dorothy Johnson Charitable Trust 145

Johnson's: Ann Johnson's Educational Foundation 178

Johnston: Johnston Educational Foundation 211

The Brian Johnston Memorial Trust 16

Jones: The Charity of Doctor Jones 127

Geoffrey Jones (Penreithin) Scholarship Fund 133

Owen Jones Charity 130

Thomas John Jones Memorial Fund for Scholarships and Exhibitions 128

Jones': Elizabeth Jones' Scholarships for Boys and Girls of Aberavon and Margam (Elizabeth Jones' Trust) 133

Jones': Edmund Jones' Charity 128

Journalism: The Journalism Diversity Fund 43

Jvenn: The Jvenn Foundation 271

Kathleen: The Kathleen Trust 26

Kay: Sheila Kay Fund 226

Kelsick's: Kelsick's Educational Foundation 218

Kennedy: Helena Kennedy Foundation 4

The Kennedy Memorial Trust 19

Kentish's: Kentish's Educational Foundation 171

Keyford: Keyford Educational Foundation 263

Kidney: Kidney Care UK 66

Killingley: S. Y. Killingley Memorial Trust 209

Kincardineshire: Kincardineshire Educational Trust 121

King: Joseph King Trust 179

King's: The King's Norton United Charities 163

Kingston: Kingston upon Hull Education Foundation 271

Kirke's: Kirke's Charity 278

Kirkley: Kirkley Poor's Land Estate 187

Kirton-in-Lindsey: Kirton-in-Lindsey Exhibition Foundation 141

Kitchings: Kitchings Educational Charity 144

Knowles: Knowles Educational Foundation (Acaster Malbis Knowles Education Foundation) 273

Knox: Frank Knox Fellowships 20

Kochan: The Kochan Trust 271

Koning: Koning Willem Fonds – The Netherlands Benevolent Society 61

Lancashire: Community Foundations for Lancashire and Merseyside 215

Laney's: Bishop Laney's Charity 174

Latham's: Parson Latham's Educational Foundation 146

Lathom's: Peter Lathom's Charity (including the Lathom Educational Foundation) 225

Launderers: The Worshipful Company of Launderers Benevolent Trust Fund 103

Learner: Learner Support Fund 164

Leathersellers': The Leathersellers' Company Charitable Fund 36

Lee: The Lee Education Charity of William Hatcliffe 204

Leeke: Leeke Church Schools and Educational Foundation 143

Leigh: The Leigh Educational Endowment 223

The Leigh Educational Foundation 157

Lester: The Henry Lester Trust 61

Letchworth: The Letchworth Civic Trust 182

Leukaemia: The Leukaemia Care Society 66

Leverhulme: Leverhulme Trade Charities Trust 101

The Leverhulme Trust 17

Levy: The Joseph Levy Memorial Fund 67

Lewisham: Lewisham Educational Charity 204

Ley: George Ley Educational Trust 255

Lillingstone: The Lillingstone Trust 146

Lincolnshire: Lincolnshire Community Foundation 141

Liverpool: The Liverpool Council of Education (Incorporated) 227

Lloyd: The Doctor Dorothy Jordan Lloyd Memorial Fund 104

The W. M. and B. W. Lloyd Trust 224

Lloyds: Lloyds Scholars 7

Lloyd's: Lloyd's Tercentenary Research Foundation 7

Lockyer's: Lockyer's Charity 259

London: The City of London Corporation Combined Education Charity 197

The London Institute of Banking and Finance 34

Longford: The Longford Trust 70

Longwill: John Longwill Education Trust 117

Lowestoft: Lowestoft Church and Town Educational Foundation 188

Lucas: A. B. Lucas Memorial Awards 253

Lumb's: Lumb's Educational Foundation 261

Macfarlane: The Macfarlane Walker Trust 260

Mackichan: Catherine Mackichan Trust 24

Magdalen: Magdalen and Lasher Educational Foundation 235

Mallinson: Sir William Mallinson Scholarship Trust 207

Manchester: The Manchester Publicity Association Educational Trust 91

Manse: Manse Bairns Network 71

Mapletoft: Mapletoft Scholarship Foundation 141

Marine: The Marine Society and Sea Cadets 89

Marlow: The Marlow Educational Foundation 232

Marr: The C. K. Marr Educational Trust Scheme 117

Marshall: The James Marshall Foundation 182
Dulce Haigh Marshall Trust 253
Martin: Betty Martin Charity 247
Catherine Martin Trust 235
Martin's: John Martin's Charity 168
Martindale: The Hilda Martindale Educational Trust 63
Mary: The Mary Grave Trust 218
Mason: Sir Josiah Mason Trust 151
Masonic: Masonic Charitable Foundation 69
Master: The Honourable Company of Master Mariners and Howard Leopold Davis Charity 89
Mathew: Mathew Trust 116
Matthey: Johnson Matthey Public Ltd Company Educational Trust 11
Maudlyn: The Maudlyn Lands Charity 254
Maxell: Maxell Educational Trust 156
Mayfield: The Mayfield Trust 236
Maynard's: Lord Maynard's Charity 177
McAlpine: The McAlpine Educational Endowments Ltd 58
McCosh: The Alice McCosh Trust 30
McGlashan: McGlashan Charitable Trust 18
Mellon: Paul Mellon Centre 27
Mendlesham: The Mendlesham Education Foundation 188
Meningitis: Meningitis Now (formerly known as Meningitis Trust) 67
Merchant: The Company of Merchant Taylors of the City of York (Merchant Taylors – York) 275
Mico's: Sir Samuel Mico's Charities 259
Middlecott's: Sir Thomas Middlecott's Exhibition Foundation 141
Middleton: Middleton Educational Trust (The Emerson Educational Trust for Middleton) 221
Millington's: Millington's Charity (Millington's Hospital) 155
Mills: The Mills Educational Foundation 188
Milton: The Sir Simon Milton Foundation 198
Miners': Miners' Welfare National Educational Fund (MWNEF) 96
Mining: Mining Institute of Scotland Trust 96
Mirfield: Mirfield Educational Charity 277
Mitchell: The Mitchell City of London Educational Foundation 198
Mitchells: The Mitchells and Butlers Charitable Trusts 42
Monmouth: Monmouth Charity 131

Monmouthshire: The Monmouthshire County Council Welsh Church Act Fund 131
The Monmouthshire Farm School Endowment 132
The Monmouthshire Further Education Trust Fund 132
Monoux: Sir George Monoux Exhibition Foundation 207
Moon: The Vivian Moon Foundation 254
Moray: Moray and Nairn Educational Trust 122
Morgan's: Minnie Morgan's Scholarship 130
Morris: Educational Foundation of James Morris 240
Moulson: The Sir Thomas Moulson Trust 217
Moulton: The Moulton Harrox Educational Foundation 144
Moundeford: Sir Edmund Moundeford Charity 185
Mount: The Mount Everest Foundation 53
Mountsorrel: Mountsorrel Educational Fund 137
Muirhead: The Muirhead Trust 63
Murray: Gilbert Murray Trust – International Studies Committee 52
Musicians: Worshipful Company of Musicians Charitable Fund 82
Mynshull's: Mynshull's Educational Foundation 220
Nafferton: The Nafferton Feoffees Charities Trust 268
Nailsea: Nailsea Community Trust Ltd 264
Narberth: Narberth Educational Charity 127
National: National Trainers' Federation (NTF) Charitable Trust 105
National Youth Arts Trust (NYAT) 27
Navenby: The Navenby Town's Farm Trust 143
Neave: The Airey Neave Trust 51
Nevill: Charity of Peter Nevill 268
Newcomen: Newcomen Collett Foundation 206
Newfield: Newfield Charitable Trust 158
Newton: Newton Exhibition Foundation 181
Newton's: Alderman Newton's Educational Foundation 137
NFL: The NFL Trust 5
Nightingale: The Florence Nightingale Foundation 94
The Nightingale Fund 93

Norcross: Herbert Norcross Scholarship Fund 221
Norfolk: Norfolk Community Foundation 183
Norman: Educational Foundation of Alderman John Norman 186
Norton: The Norton Foundation 151
Norton: The Norton, Salisbury and Brailsford Educational Foundation 139
Norwich: Norwich French Church Charity 183
Norwich Town Close Estate Charity 186
Nottingham: Nottingham Gordon Memorial Trust for Boys and Girls 150
The Nottingham Roosevelt Memorial Travelling Scholarship Fund 148
Nowes: John Nowes Exhibition Foundation 262
Nurses': The Nurses' Memorial to King Edward VII Edinburgh Scottish Committee 94
Oadby: The Oadby Educational Foundation 137
Oakley: Oakley Educational Foundation 172
Officers': Officers' Association Scotland 76
Okehampton: Okehampton Educational Foundation 257
Old: The Old Enfield Charitable Trust 200
Old School Fund 188
Older's: William Older's School Charity 247
Oldfield: Dr Robert Oldfield Charity 217
Olford: The Olford Bequest 255
One: One Me 58
Orphans: Orphans Aid Educational Foundation (Plymouth) 256
Owen: The Richard Owen Scholarships and Exhibitions Foundation 129
Oxford: The City of Oxford Charity 244
Paddington: Paddington Charitable Estates Educational Fund 198
Pakenham: Pakenham Educational Trust 188
Palmer: The Palmer and Seabright Charity 164
Palmer Educational Charity (The Palmer Trust) 165
Pantyfedwen: The James Pantyfedwen Foundation (Ymddiriedolaeth James Pantyfedwen) 18
Paradigm: Paradigm Foundation 12

Parish: Parish Lands (South Brent Feoffees) 256

Parkinson: John Parkinson (Goosnargh and Whittingham United Charity) 224

Parsons: Daniel Parsons Educational Charity 165

Pathological: Pathological Society 46

Perkins's: Perkins's Educational Foundation 158

Perry: Perry Foundation 40
The Sidney Perry Foundation 8

Perth: Perth and Kinross Educational Trust 126

Petersham: The Petersham United Charities 205

Philological: Philological Foundation 196

Physics: The Institute of Physics 33

Picto: The Charity of Sir John Picto and Others 183

Pike: The Pike and Eure Educational Foundation 143

Plaisterers: The Worshipful Company of Plaisterers Charitable Trust 82

Plowden: Anna Plowden Trust 41

Plumb: The Henry Plumb Foundation 40

Plumbers': The Worshipful Company of Plumbers' Charitable and Educational Trust 104

Plymouth: The Plymouth and Cornwall Cancer Fund 254

Pocklington: The Pocklington and the Thomas Huggett Apprenticeship Aid Fund Trust 203

Polehampton: The Polehampton Charity 230

Police: Police Care UK 98

Poors: The Poors Allotment 146

Poppyscotland: Poppyscotland 76

Potton: Potton Consolidated Charity 173

Powis: Powis Exhibition Fund 100

Praebendo: The Praebendo Charitable Foundation 4

Presbyterian: The Presbyterian Children's Society 113

Preston: The Preston Simpson and Sterndale Young Musicians Trust 212

Price: The William Price Charitable Trust 237
The Lucy Price Relief-in-Need Charity 161

Primrose: John Primrose Trust 118

Prince's: The Prince's Trust 58

Printing: The Printing Charity 92

Prisoners: The Prisoners of Conscience Appeal Fund 55

Prisoners': Prisoners' Education Trust 70

Professional: The Professional Footballers' Association Charity 105

Professionals: Professionals Aid Council 12

Prowde's: Prowde's Educational Foundation (Prowde's Charity) 263

Queen's: The Queen's Nursing Institute 94

Randall: David Randall Foundation 177

Rand's: Rand's Educational Foundation 171

Rawcliffe: The Rawcliffe Educational Charity 268

Rawdon: The Rawdon and Laneshaw Bridge School Trust 278

Rawlet: The Rawlet Trust 157

Raygill: Raygill Trust 273

RCN: The RCN Foundation 95

Read's: Read's Exhibition Foundation 149

Reardon: Reardon Smith Nautical Trust 90

Reckitt: Nancie Reckitt Charity 269

Red: Red House Home Trust 124

Reeve's: William James Reeve's Charity 167

Reid: Rhona Reid Charitable Trust 46

Retail: Retail Trust 102

Reuben: Reuben Foundation 8

RFL: The RFL Benevolent Fund (Try Assist) 105

Rhymney: The Rhymney Trust 131

Richards: The Richards Educational Charity 255

Richmond: Richmond Parish Lands Charity (RPLC) 205

Rifles: The Rifles Benevolent Trust 77

Risley: Risley Educational Foundation 135

Robinson: The Gus Robinson Foundation 210

Robinson's: Robinson's Educational Foundation 218

Rochdale: Rochdale Ancient Parish Educational Trusts 221

Roe: Foundation of Thomas Roe 146

Roger: The Roger Edwards Educational Trust (formerly the Monmouthshire Further Education Trust Fund) 132

Rogers': Rogers' Educational Trust 233

Rose: The Rose Charity 265

Ross: Ross and Cromarty Educational Trust 123
Ross Educational Foundation 154

Rotary: The Rotary Foundation Scholarships 12

Rothbury: Rothbury Educational Trust 212

Rowe's: John James Rowe's Foundation for Girls 226

Royal: The Royal Academy of Engineering 37
The Royal Air Force Benevolent Fund 77
The Royal Bath and West of England Society 250
The Royal British Legion 77
The Royal Caledonian Education Trust 78
Royal Commission for the Exhibition of 1851 37
Royal Geographical Society (with the Institute of British Geographers) 53
The Royal Horticultural Society (RHS) 86
The Royal Liverpool Seamen's Orphan Institution (RLSOI) 90
The Royal Medical Foundation 95
Royal Merchant Navy Education Foundation 90
The Royal Naval Benevolent Trust 78
The Royal Navy and Royal Marines Children's Fund 79
The Royal Navy Officers' Charity 79
The Royal Pinner School Foundation 102
The Royal Scottish Academy (RSA) 28
The Royal Society of Chemistry – Chemists' Community Fund 102
Royal Television Society 43

Rushworth: The Rushworth Trust 226

RVW: The RVW Trust 28

Salford: The Salford Foundation Trust 222

Salisbury: Salisbury City Educational and Apprenticing Charity 265

Salter: George and Thomas Henry Salter Trust 166

Samman's: Henry Samman's Hull Chamber of Commerce Endowment Fund 269

Sandra: Sandra Charitable Trust 47

Sarum: Sarum St Michael Educational Charity 250

Savoy: The Savoy Educational Trust 88

Saye: The Saye and Sele Foundation 233

Scaldwell: The Scaldwell Charity 147

Scarborough: Scarborough United Scholarships Foundation 273

Scargill's: Scargill's Educational Foundation 136

Scarr-Hall: Scarr-Hall Memorial Trust 13

Schilizzi: Schilizzi Foundation in Memory of Eleutherios and

Helena Veniselos (The Schilizzi Foundation) 61

School: The School Fees Charitable Trust 13

Schoolmasters: The National Association of Schoolmasters Union of Women Teachers (NASUWT) Benevolent Funds 83

Schwab: The Walter and Liesel Schwab Charitable Trust (also known as Schwab and Westheimer Trust) 56

Scientific: The Worshipful Company of Scientific Instrument Makers 103

Scott: The Foundation of Joanna Scott and Others 186

James Scott Law Charitable Fund 123

Scottish: Scottish Borders Council Charitable Trusts 125

Scottish Building Federation Edinburgh and District Charitable Trust 83

Scottish Chartered Accountants' Benevolent Association 87

Scottish International Education Trust 116

Scottish Power Foundation 5

ScreenSkills: ScreenSkills 92

Seaman's: Sir Peter Seaman's Charity 187

Sebrights: Sebrights Educational Foundation 152

Seckford: The Seckford Foundation 189

Sedgefield: The Sedgefield District Relief in Need Charity (The Sedgefield Charities) 211

The Sedgefield Educational Foundation 211

Sedgley: The Sedgley Educational Trust 165

Sedley: The Sir John Sedley Educational Foundation 150

Shaftoe: Shaftoe Educational Foundation 213

Sharma: Dr Meena Sharma Memorial Foundation 64

Sheffield: The Sheffield Bluecoat and Mount Pleasant Educational Foundation 276

Sheffield Grammar School Exhibition Foundation 276

Shepherd: The Shepherd Street Trust 225

Sheriffs': The Sheriffs' and Recorders' Fund 195

Shipston-on-Stour: The Shipston-on-Stour Educational Charity 160

Sidmouth: The Sidmouth Educational Foundation 255

Silecroft: Silecroft School Educational Charity 219

Smith: The Marc Smith Educational Charity 138

The Mary Smith Scholarship Fund 139

Snowdon: Snowdon Trust 68

Social: Social Workers' Educational Trust 48

Society: Society for Assistance of Medical Families 95

Society for the Benefit of Sons and Daughters of the Clergy of the Church of Scotland 100

Society of Antiquaries of London 24

Sola: Sola Trust 100

Soothern: Soothern and Craner Educational Foundation 164

South: The South Square Trust 29

South Wales Institute of Engineers Educational Trust 38

South Yorkshire Community Foundation 13

Southland's: Southland's Educational Charity 240

Southwark: Southwark Scholarship Scheme 206

Spalding: The Spalding Trusts 49

Spark: The Spark Foundation 73

Speak: John Speak Foundation Foreign Languages Scholarships Trust Fund (John Speak Trust) 31

Sperring: Ralph and Irma Sperring Charity 263

Spier's: The Spier's Trust 117

Split: Split Infinitive Trust 29

Spondon: Spondon Relief-in-Need Charity 135

Spooner: W. W. Spooner Charitable Trust 88

Spoore: The Spoore, Merry and Rixman Foundation 230

SPRET: SPRET (The Sir Philip Reckitt Educational Trust Fund) 171

Saint: St Andrew Holborn and Stafford's Charity 195

The St Chad's and St Alkmund's Charity 128

St George's Police Children Trust 98

The Foundation of St Matthias 49

St Olave, St Thomas and St John United Charity 206

St Olave's and St Saviour's Schools Foundation CIO 206

Stafford: Stafford Educational Endowment Charity 157

Stanford: The Educational Foundation of Philip and Sarah Stanford 142

Stapley: The Sir Richard Stapley Educational Trust 8

Stationers': The Stationers' Foundation 97

Stein: The Stanley Stein Deceased Charitable Trust 59

Stephens: Mary Stephens Foundation 247

Stirlingshire: Stirlingshire Educational Trust 117

Stocks-Massey: Edward Stocks-Massey Bequest Fund 224

Stockton: John Stockton Educational Foundation 273

Stoke: Stoke Golding Boys' Charity 139

The Stoke Mandeville and Other Parishes Charity 232

Stoke Poges Hastings Community Fund 232

Stokenchurch: Stokenchurch Educational Charity 233

Stokes: The Stokes Croft Educational Foundation 251

Stowmarket: The Stowmarket Educational Foundation 191

Streynsham's: Streynsham's Charity 241

Stroud: The Stroud and Rodborough Educational Charity 262

Studley: Studley College Trust 40

Sunderland: The Sunderland Orphanage and Educational Foundation 214

Sutton: The Sutton St James United Charities 144

Swallowdale: Swallowdale Children's Trust 224

Swann-Morton: The Swann-Morton Foundation 275

Sykes: John Sykes Foundation 230

Talbot: The Talbot House Trust 29

Talisman: The Talisman Charitable Trust 13

Tasker: Tasker Milward and Picton Charity 127

Tatton: The Reverend Tatton Brockman 240

Taylor: Humphrey Richardson Taylor Charitable Trust 245

Ursula Taylor Charity 173

Tees: Tees Valley Community Foundation 210

Thorngate: Thorngate Trust 238

Thornley: Felix Thornley Cobbold Agricultural Trust 189

Thornton-Smith: Thornton-Smith and Plevins Trust 5

Tottenham: The Tottenham Grammar School Foundation 201

Town: The Town Estate Educational Foundation (Hempnall) 187

Town Lands Educational Foundation (Outwell Town Lands Educational Foundation) 185

Town Lands Educational
Foundation 174
The Town Moor Money Charity 213
The Town Trust or Lords Estate 269
Towrie's: Robert Towrie's Charity 269
Trades: The Trades House of
Glasgow 120
Trades Union Congress Educational
Trust 97
Trevelyan: Mary Trevelyan Fund 195
Trevilson: Trevilson Educational
Foundation 252
Truro: Truro Fund 195
Turath: Turath Scholarship Fund 50
Turner: The Kathryn Turner Trust
(Whitton's Wishes) 243
Turton: The T. A. K. Turton
Charitable Trust 235
Tyler: Tyler Educational
Foundation 145
Tyre: Charles and Barbara Tyre
Trust 119
UK: UK Business School Bursary 34
UK Electronics Skills Foundation 9
Unite: The Unite Foundation 73
Universal: Universal Music UK Sound
Foundation 29
Uxbridge: Uxbridge United Welfare
Trust 202
Vegetarian: The Vegetarian Charity 69
Victoria: The Victoria Foundation 47
Viner: George Viner Memorial Fund
Trust 44
Virgin: Virgin Atlantic Be the Change
Volunteer Trip Scholarship 16
Walcot: Walcot Educational
Foundation 203
Walker: Charity of Charles Clement
Walker (The Walker Trust) 155
C. C. Walker Charity 166
Madeleine Mary Walker
Foundation 274
Wall: The Thomas Wall Trust 21
Wallace: The Charles Wallace India
Trust 14
John Wallace Trust Scheme 118
Walwyn's: Walwyn's Educational
Foundation 154
Warbleton: Warbleton Charity 236
Ware: The Ware Charities 181
Warwick: Warwick Apprenticing
Charities 161
Watts: Richard Watts and the City of
Rochester Almshouse
Charities 242
Wellbeing: Wellbeing of Women 47
Wells: The Wells Clerical Charity 263
Wessex: The Wessex Young Musicians
Trust 152
West: West Lothian Educational
Trust 124

West Norfolk and King's Lynn Girls'
School Trust 185
Westoe: Westoe Educational
Charity 213
Weston-sub-Edge: Weston-sub-Edge
Educational Charity 260
Westwood: Margaret Westwood
Memorial Charity 153
Wharton: Christopher Wharton
Educational Foundation 274
White: Charity of Sir Thomas White,
Warwick 161
Whittlesey: The Whittlesey
Charity 174
Wigtownshire: Wigtownshire
Educational Trust 119
William's: Dr Daniel William's
Educational Fund 130
Williams: The William Williams
Charity 259
Wilson: Thomas Wilson Educational
Trust 205
Winchester: The Winchester Rural
District Welfare Trust 238
Wing: W. Wing Yip and Brothers
Foundation 62
Winwick: The Winwick Educational
Foundation 215
Withington: Withington Education
Trust 272
Wolverton: Wolverton Science and
Art Institution Fund 234
Women's: Women's Engineering
Society 38
Woods: Robert Woods Exhibition
Foundation 275
Worcester: Worcester Municipal
Charities (CIO) 166
World: World Friendship 227
Wormley: Wormley Parochial
Charity 181
Worrall: Worrall and Fuller Exhibition
Fund 202
Wray: Wray Educational Trust 270
Wrenbury: The Consolidated Charity
of the Parish of Wrenbury 216
Wrexham: The Wrexham (Parochial)
Educational Foundation 131
Wright's: Elizabeth Wright's
Charity 174
Wrightson's: Miss E. B. Wrightson's
Charitable Settlement 16
WRNS: WRNS Benevolent Trust 79
WRVS: WRVS Benevolent Trust 107
Wymeswold: Wymeswold Parochial
Charities 138
Yalding: Yalding Educational
Foundation 241
Yardley: Yardley Educational
Foundation 163

Ymddiriedolaeth: Yr Ymddiriedolaeth
Ddarlledu Gymreig (The Welsh
Broadcasting Trust) 44
Yonge: Reverend Duke Yonge
Charity 256
Yorebridge: Yorebridge Educational
Foundation 274
Yorkshire: Yorkshire Ladies' Council
of Education (Incorporated) 64

What else can DSC do for you?

Let us help you to be the best you possibly can be. DSC equips individuals and organisations with expert skills and information to help them provide better services and outcomes for their beneficiaries. With the latest techniques, best practice and funding resources all brought to you by our team of experts, you will not only boost your income but also exceed your expectations.

Publications

We produce fundraising directories and research reports, as well as accessible 'how to' guides and best practice handbooks, all to help you help others.

Training

The voluntary sector's best-selling training, with courses covering every type of voluntary sector training.

In-house training

All DSC courses are available on your premises, delivered by expert trainers and facilitators. We also offer coaching, consultancy, mentoring and support.

Conferences and fairs

DSC conferences are a fantastic way to network with voluntary sector professionals while taking part in intensive, practical training workshops.

Funds Online

Funds Online contains information on over 8,000 funders giving a combined total of £8 billion. Find out more and subscribe now at:

www.**fundsonline**.org.uk

@DSC_Charity
For top tips and special offers

Visit our website today and see what we can do for you:

www.**dsc**.org.uk

Or contact us directly:
publications@dsc.org.uk